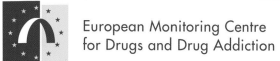

European Monitoring Centre
for Drugs and Drug Addiction

EMCDDA

MONOGRAPHS

Harm reduction:
evidence, impacts and challenges

Editors

Tim Rhodes and Dagmar Hedrich

Legal notice

A great deal of additional information on the European Union is available on the Internet. It can be accessed through the Europa server (**http://europa.eu**).

Europe Direct is a service to help you find answers to your questions about the European Union

Freephone number (*):
00 800 6 7 8 9 10 11

(*) Certain mobile telephone operators do not allow access to 00 800 numbers or these calls may be billed.

Cataloguing data can be found at the end of this publication.

Luxembourg: Publications Office of the European Union, 2010

ISBN 978-92-9168-419-9

doi: 10.2810/29497

European Monitoring Centre
for Drugs and Drug Addiction

Cais do Sodré, 1249-289 Lisbon, Portugal
Tel. (351) 211 21 02 00 • Fax (351) 218 13 17 11
info@emcdda.europa.eu • www.emcdda.europa.eu

Contents

Conclusions

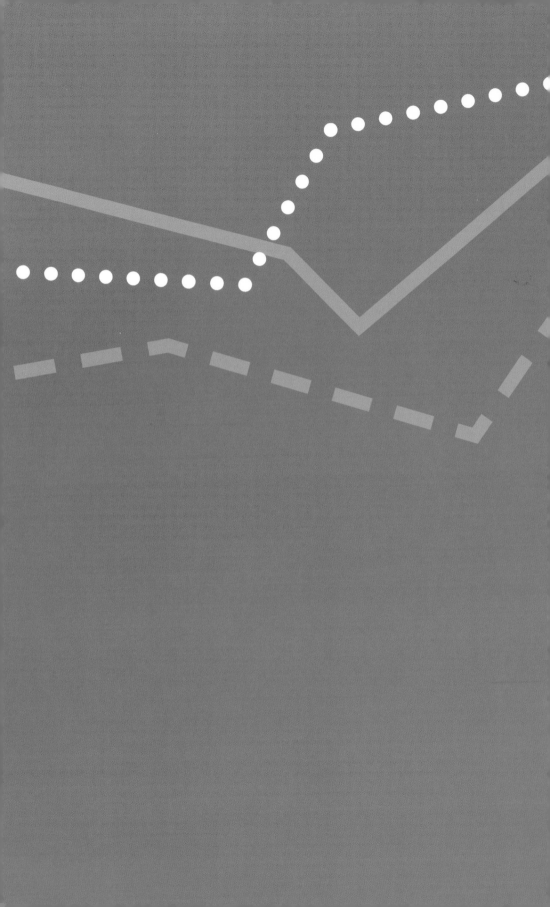

Foreword

It is with great pleasure that I introduce the EMCDDA's latest Scientific monograph, which provides a state-of-the-art review of the role of harm reduction strategies and interventions. Harm reduction has become an integral part of the European policy debate on drugs, but this was not always the case. Although harm reduction approaches have a long history in the addictions field and in general medicine, our modern concept of harm reduction has its roots in the challenges posed by the rapid spread of HIV infection among drug injectors in the mid-1980s. Initially, there was considerable controversy surrounding the notion that preventing the spread of HIV was of paramount importance and required immediate and effective action, even if this meant that abstinence as a therapeutic goal had to take second place.

In Europe today, that controversy has to a large extent been replaced by consensus. This reflects not only a general agreement on the value of the approach but also recognition that national differences in interpretation and emphasis exist. Harm reduction as a concept is now accepted as part of a *balanced approach,* an integral element of a comprehensive strategy that includes prevention, treatment, social rehabilitation and supply reduction measures. This, I would argue, is a strong endorsement of the pragmatic and evidence-based approach that European drug policies have come to embrace.

It would be wrong to overstate this position; the drug debate remains an ideological as well as a scientific one. Nonetheless, the evidence that needle exchange and substitution treatment can be effective elements in a strategy to reduce HIV infection among injectors, and importantly that these interventions do not lead to greater harms in the wider community, has had a significant impact on European drug policies and actions. Although it would be wrong to minimise the continuing problem that we face, when comparing Europe to many other parts of the world it is clear that overall our pragmatic approach has borne fruit. Arguments may still exist about the relative role played by different types of interventions, but most informed commentators would now agree that harm reduction approaches have been influential in addressing the risks posed by drug injecting in Europe over the last 20 years.

This is, then, an appropriate moment to take stock of existing scientific evidence on harm reduction and consider the issues that we will need to tackle in the future. The evidence for some harm reduction interventions is relatively robust. For others, methodological difficulties make generating a solid evidence base difficult, and the current scientific bases for guiding policymaking need to be strengthened.

The assertion that the concept of harm reduction is an accepted part of the European drug policy landscape does not mean that all interventions that fall under this heading are either widely supported or endorsed. Many areas of controversy remain, and one purpose of this monograph is to chart where the current fault lines now lie, with the hope that future studies will provide a sounder basis for informed actions. Moreover, and perhaps more importantly, the drug problems and issues we face in Europe today are very different to those we struggled with in the past. HIV remains an important issue, but it is no longer the predominant one. From a quantitative public health point of view, drug overdose, HCV infection, and other psychiatric and physical co-morbidities are becoming of equal or even greater importance. In addition, drug injecting levels appear to be falling and patterns of drug taking are become more complex and are increasingly characterised by the consumption of multiple substances, both licit and illicit.

What role will harm reduction have within this new landscape? This monograph begins to explore that question, as we consider how harm reduction strategies may be a useful component of our approach to the challenges that drug use in twenty-first century Europe will bring. I strongly believe that in taking drug policy forward we have a duty to learn from the past, and that ideological positions should not stand in the way of a cool-headed analysis of the evidence. In the future this is likely to become imperative both to those who instinctively support harm reduction approaches, and to those who instinctively oppose them. This monograph makes an important contribution to the debate by highlighting where we are now, and considering how we have got here. It also draws our attention to some of the challenges that lie ahead, if we are to understand the role and possible limits of harm reduction approaches to future European drug policies.

Wolfgang Götz
Director, EMCDDA

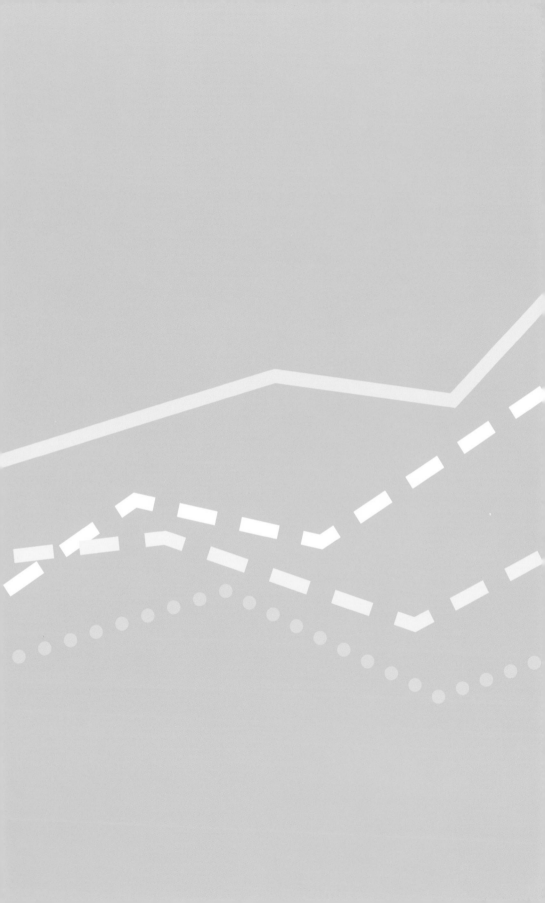

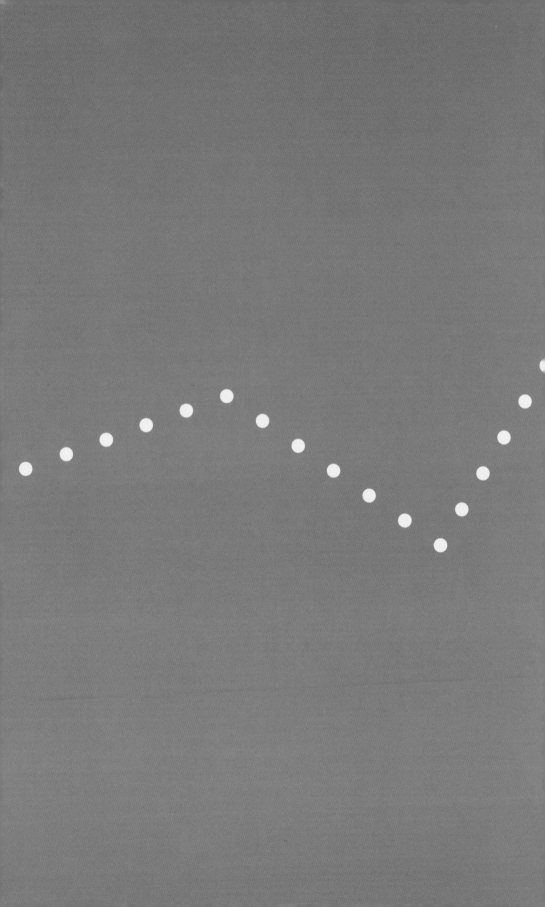

Acknowledgements

The EMCDDA would like to thank all authors, editors and reviewers who have worked on this publication. In particular, the monograph benefited from overall editorial input by Tim Rhodes and Dagmar Hedrich. A special mention goes to the members of the internal coordination group who accompanied the project from inception to publication — namely to Alessandro Pirona and Anna Gyarmathy; as well as to the planning group: Roland Simon, Rosemary de Sousa, Paul Griffiths, Julian Vicente and Lucas Wiessing. The EMCDDA gratefully acknowledges the contributions from many unknown external reviewers and from the reviewers drawn from the EMCDDA's Scientific Committee. Furthermore, valuable review comments and input were received from EMCDDA staff members Marica Ferri, Brendan Hughes, André Noor, Cécile Martel, Luis Prieto and Frank Zobel. Vaughan Birbeck provided much appreciated help with bibliographic references, and Alison Elks of Magenta Publishing edited the final publication.

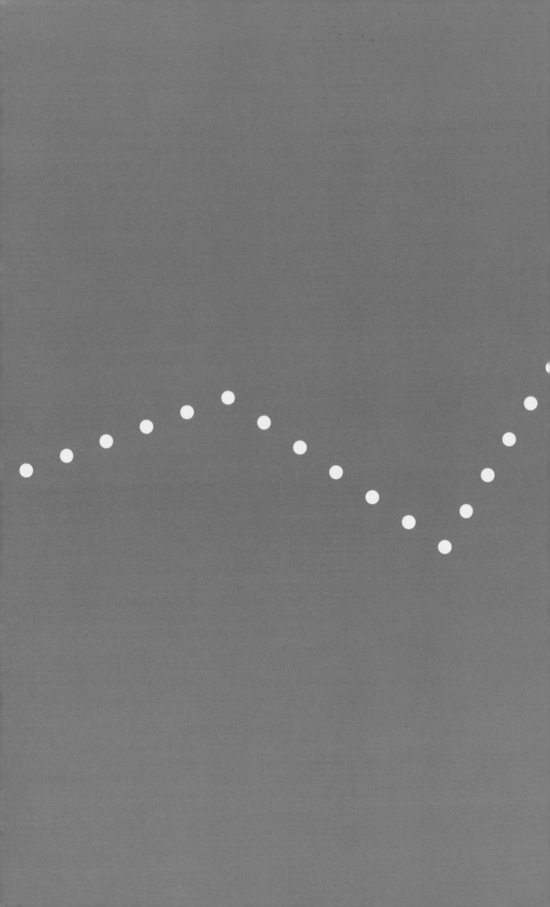

Preface

Harm reduction is now positioned as part of the mainstream policy response to drug use in Europe. However, this has not always been the case, and in reflecting on this fact we felt that the time was right to take stock of how we had arrived at this position, ask what it means for both policies and action, and begin to consider how harm reduction is likely to develop in the future.

This monograph builds on other titles in the EMCDDA's Scientific monographs series, where we have taken an important and topical subject, assembled some of the best experts in the field, and allowed them to develop their ideas constrained only by the need to demonstrate scientific rigour and sound argument. Our Scientific monographs are intended to be both technically challenging and thought provoking. Unlike our other publications we take more of an editorial 'back seat' and we do not seek consensus or necessarily to produce a balanced view. Good science is best done when unconstrained, and best read with a critical eye.

This volume includes a variety of perspectives on harm reduction approaches, together with an analysis of the concept's role within drug policies, both in Europe and beyond. Readers may not necessarily agree with all of the arguments made or the conclusion drawn, but we hope it is perceived as a valuable contribution to the ongoing debate on how to respond to contemporary drug problems in Europe.

A number of contributors explore what harm reduction means and what policies it can encompass, as well as charting how the concept evolved. They reflect on the point we have now reached in terms of both harm reduction practice and the evidence base for its effectiveness. A major issue that many contributors touch on is the difficulty of assessing how complex interventions occurring in real world settings can be evaluated, and why conclusive evidence in such settings can be so elusive.

With an eye to the future, we also asked our contributors to wrestle with the difficult issue of how harm reduction might be extended into new areas that are of particular relevance to the evolving European drug situation. Here the empirical base for grounding discussions is far less developed, and a more exploratory approach is necessary.

As a European agency, the EMCDDA has a somewhat unique perspective on the development of the drugs debate within the European Union. It is therefore appropriate for us to make our own introductory remarks about the mainstreaming of the concept of harm reduction at the European level, as opposed to the national one. This development, we would argue, is sometimes misunderstood, as there is a tendency by some commentators to polarise the position and focus exclusively on either the differences, or alternatively the commonalities, that exist between Member States in their drug policies. Europe is closer now than it once was in terms of how it responds to and views drug use, but differences still exist, reflecting national policy perspectives, cultural differences and, to some extent, simply a different experience of the drug problem.

Despite these differences in opinion and experience, there is a general consensus that abstinence-orientated drug policies need to be supplemented by measures that can demonstrably reduce the harms that drug users are exposed to. This consensus is strongest in the area of reducing HIV infection among injectors — although even here there is disagreement on the appropriateness of which interventions might fall under this general heading. It is also the case that the range and intensity of harm reduction services available in EU Member States varies considerably. Therefore, the observation that harm reduction has played an important part in achieving the relatively positive position that the EU has achieved with respect to HIV infection among injectors has to be tempered with the comment that some countries have maintained low rates of infections among injecting drug users where the availability of harm reduction services has been limited.

In summary, considerable debate still exists at European level on the appropriateness of different approaches, and some interventions, such as drug consumption rooms, are still highly contentious. However, Europe's policy debate in this area appears now to be a more pragmatic one in which harm reduction policies are not automatically considered to conflict with measures intended to deter drug use or promote abstinence. Rather, the consensus is increasingly moving towards a comprehensive, balanced and evidence-based approach that seamlessly includes harm reduction alongside prevention, treatment and supply reduction measures.

This monograph is comprehensive in its scope. It covers interventions that are still controversial and ones that have become so mainstream that many might now find it hard to believe that this has not always been the case. We have included voices from the user community, as activism has historically been an important element in the development of this perspective. The monograph also addresses new challenges for a harm reduction approach, such as alcohol and tobacco use and Europe's growing appetite for stimulant drugs.

The EMCDDA is grateful that so many experts were prepared to assist us with this work, often tackling new and demanding topics. This task would have been infinitely more difficult if we had not benefited from having a first-class editorial team working on this project. We are indebted to our editors, Tim Rhodes and Dagmar Hedrich, who both played a major role in conceptualising, planning and implementing this project and without whose input this document would have been a far less comprehensive and impressive achievement.

It is important to note that the voices presented here are not those of the EMCDDA or the European institutions. As with other Scientific monographs, the intention is to provide a forum for stimulating debate and collecting high-quality scientific opinion and informed comment on a topic of contemporary relevance. The monographs are intended to be of particular interest to a specialist audience and therefore some of the papers in this collection are highly technical in nature. All papers presented here have been peer-reviewed to ensure an appropriate degree of scientific rigour, but the views expressed by the authors remain their own.

The EMCDDA's role is as a central reference point on drug information within the European Union. We are policy neutral; our task is to document and report, and never to advocate or lobby. This neutrality is important when we address any drug use issue, as this is an area where so many have passionate and deeply held views. However, it is particularly important when we address a topic like harm reduction, where perspectives are sometimes polarised and there are those on all sides of the drugs debate that see a linkage between this subject and broader issues about how societies control drug consumption. The rationale for our work is that, over time, better policy comes from debate informed by a cool-headed and neutral assessment of the information available. Many of the contributors to this report are passionate and committed in their views; they also provide a wealth of data, analysis and argumentation. They do not speak with a common voice, and we do not necessarily endorse all the conclusions drawn, but taken collectively we believe they make a valuable contribution to a better understanding of a topic that has become an important element in contemporary drug policies.

Paul Griffiths and Roland Simon
EMCDDA

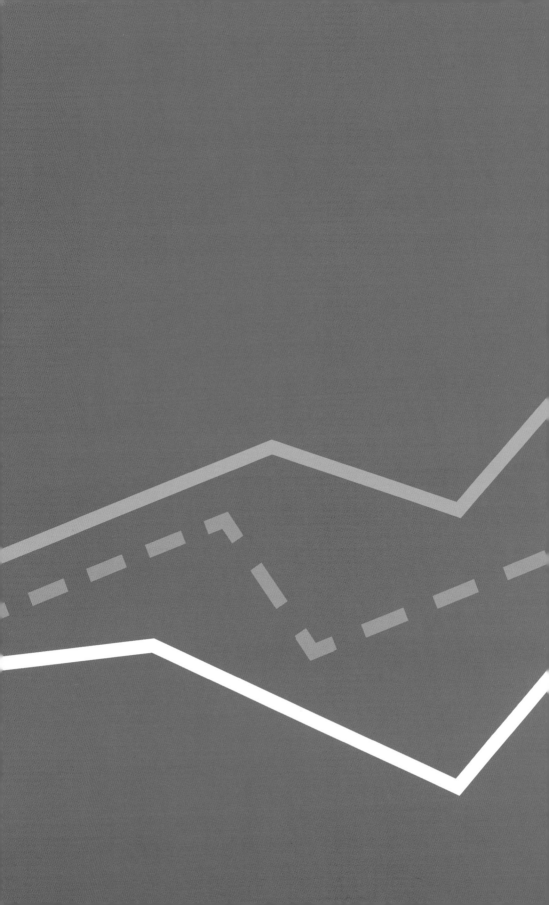

Introduction

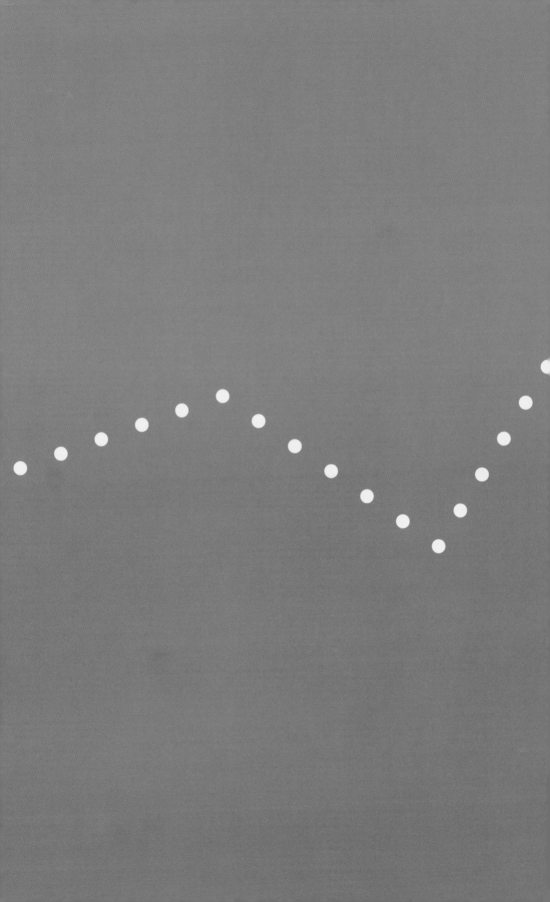

Chapter 1
Harm reduction and the mainstream

Tim Rhodes and Dagmar Hedrich

Abstract

Harm reduction encompasses interventions, programmes and policies that seek to reduce the health, social and economic harms of drug use to individuals, communities and societies. We envisage harm reduction as a *'combination intervention'*, made up of a package of interventions tailored to local setting and need, which give primary emphasis to reducing the harms of drug use. We note the enhanced impact potential derived from delivering multiple harm reduction interventions in combination, and at sufficient scale, especially needle and syringe distribution in combination with opioid substitution treatment programmes. We note that harm reduction is a manifestation of mainstream public health approaches endorsed globally by the United Nations, and in the EU drugs strategy and action plans, and features as an integral element of drug policy in most of the European region. However, we note evidence that links drug harms to policies that emphasise strict law enforcement against drug users; an unintended consequence of international drug control conventions. The continuum of 'combination interventions' available to harm reduction thus extends from drug treatment through to policy or legal reform and the removal of structural barriers to protecting the rights of all to health. We end by introducing this monograph, which seeks to reflect upon two decades of scientific evidence concerning harm reduction approaches in Europe and beyond.

Introduction

Harm reduction encompasses interventions, programmes and policies that seek to reduce the health, social and economic harms of drug use to individuals, communities and societies. A core principle of harm reduction is the development of pragmatic responses to dealing with drug use through a hierarchy of intervention goals that place primary emphasis on reducing the health-related harms of continued drug use (Des Jarlais, 1995; Lenton and Single, 2004). Harm reduction approaches neither exclude nor presume a treatment goal of abstinence, and this means that abstinence-oriented interventions can also fall within the hierarchy of harm reduction goals. We therefore envisage harm reduction as a *'combination intervention'*, made up of a package of interventions tailored to local setting and need that give primary emphasis to reducing the harms of drug use. In relation to reducing the harms of injecting drug use, for example, this combination of interventions may draw upon needle and syringe programmes (NSPs), opioid substitution treatment (OST), counselling services, the provision of drug consumption rooms (DCRs), peer education and outreach, and the promotion of public policies conducive to protecting the health of populations at risk (WHO, 2009).

Harm reduction as mainstream public health

Harm reduction in the drugs field has a long history, variably traced back to the prescription of heroin and morphine to people dependent on opioids in the United Kingdom in the 1920s (Spear, 1994), the articulation of public health concerns of legal drugs, alcohol and tobacco, and the introduction of methadone maintenance in the United States in the 1960s (Bellis, 1981; Erickson, 1999). By the 1970s, the World Health Organization (WHO) recommended policies of harm reduction to 'prevent or reduce the severity of problems associated with the non-medical use of dependence-producing drugs', noting that this goal is at once 'broader, more specific' as well as 'more realistic' than the prevention of non-medical use per se in many countries (WHO, 1974; Ball, 2007).

The concepts of risk and harm reduction are closely aligned to that of health promotion and public health more generally. Yet in relation to illicit drugs, debates about developing public health approaches to reducing drug-related harms are often clouded by harm reduction positioned as a symbol of radical liberalisation or attack upon traditional drug control. Public health has at its core the idea of protecting individual and population health through the surveillance, identification and management of risk to health (Ashton and Seymour, 1988; Peterson and Lupton, 1996). It is essentially a model of risk and harm reduction. The new public health movement of the mid-1980s coincided with the emergence of human immunodeficiency virus (HIV) epidemics in many countries. This new vision of public health was heralded as a shift beyond narrowly defined biomedical understandings towards one that envisaged health and harm as also products of the social and policy environment, and which gave greater emphasis to community-based and 'low-threshold' interventions (WHO, 1986). Contemporary public health thus characterises risk and health decision-making as a responsibility of health conscious individuals whilst also emphasising the significance of the social environment in producing harm and in shaping the capacity of individuals and communities to avoid risk (Peterson and Lupton, 1996; Rhodes, 2002). Consequently, mainstream public health approaches recognise the need to create 'enabling environments' for risk reduction and behaviour change, including through the strengthening of community actions and the creation of public policies supportive of health (WHO, 1986). Harm reduction is an exemplar of mainstream public health intervention.

Harm reduction as mainstream drug policy in Europe

European intergovernmental collaboration and information exchange in the drugs field dates back to the early 1970s. While drug policy in the European Union (EU) remains primarily the responsibility of the Member States, cooperation in matters of drug policy between EU countries increased over the 1990s, resulting in the adoption of a joint EU drugs strategy as well as the elaboration of detailed action plans (MacGregor and Whiting, 2010).

The EU drugs strategy aims at making 'a contribution to the attainment of a high level of health protection, well-being and social cohesion by complementing the Member States' action in preventing and reducing drug use, dependence and drug-related harm to health and society' and at 'ensuring a high level of security for the general public' (Council of the European Union, 2004, p. 5). For over a decade, EU drug action plans have given priority to preventing the transmission of infectious disease and reducing drug-related deaths among drug using populations. In a Recommendation adopted by the European Council of 18 June 2003 on the 'prevention and reduction of health-related harm associated with drug dependence' (Council of the European Union, 2003), a framework for action is outlined to assist Member States to develop strategies to reduce and prevent drug-related harm through the implementation of harm reduction services for problem drug users. The Recommendation seeks to reduce the number of drug-related deaths and extent of health damage, including that related to HIV, hepatitis B (HBV), hepatitis C (HCV) and tuberculosis (TB). These aims are reiterated in the priorities of the current EU drugs strategy 2005–12 related to demand reduction, aiming at the 'measurable reduction' of drug use, dependence and drug-related health and social risk through a package of interventions combining harm reduction, treatment and rehabilitation, and which emphasise the need to enhance both the 'quality' and 'effectiveness' of services.

Under the responsibility of the EU Commission, progress reviews of the implementation of the EU drugs action plans are carried out with the Member States and additional studies are commissioned to assess broader policy aspects. Such studies suggest a growing emphasis placed upon demand and harm reduction in national drug policies in the EU (van der Gouwe et al., 2006; European Commission, 2002, 2006, 2008, 2009). The reduction of drug harms thus features as a public health objective of all EU Member States (van der Gouwe et al., 2006; Cook et al., 2010; MacGregor and Whiting, 2010), with a trend in Europe towards the 'growth and consolidation of harm reduction measures' (EMCDDA, 2009a, p. 31). The European Commission has noted 'a process of convergence' in the drug policy adopted by Member States and, as a consequence, increased evidence of 'policy consistency' across the region (European Commission, 2008, p. 67). This convergence towards harm reduction in drug policy in Europe has been described as the 'common position' (Hedrich et al., 2008, p. 513).

The 'mainstreaming' of harm reduction is also evidenced by its transference across substances, including those causing the greatest burden of global health harm at a population level, such as alcohol and tobacco (Rehm et al., 2009; Mathers and Loncar, 2006; Rehm and Fischer, 2010; Room, 2010). While the adoption of harm reduction measures in relation to tobacco is relatively developmental (Sweanor et al., 2007; Gartner et al., 2010), alcohol harm reduction has a long tradition and is a core feature of alcohol policy in many countries (Robson and Marlatt, 2006; Herring et al., 2010). Harm reduction may also feature as a stratagem of public health intervention in relation to cannabis, recreational and stimulant drug use (Hall and Fischer, 2010; Fletcher et al., 2010; Grund et al., 2010).

Global drug control and harm reduction

A recent EU Commission study on global illicit drug markets found no evidence that the global drug problem had been reduced in the past decade, but judged that the enforcement of drug prohibition had caused substantial unintended harms (European Commission, 2009). This latter finding was shared by the United Nations Office on Drugs and Crime (UNODC) in an evaluation of a century of international drug control efforts 1909–2009 (UNODC, 2009). The report clarifies that public health was the driving concern behind drug control, the fundamental objective of the international drug control conventions being to limit the licit trade in narcotic drugs to medical requirements. It states: 'Public health, the first principle of drug control, has receded from that position, over-shadowed by the concern with public security', and that 'looking back over the last century, one can see that the control system and its applications have had several unintended consequences' (UNODC, 2009, pp. 92–3), among them the emergence or growth of illicit drug markets, and a 'policy displacement' to investing in law enforcement responses, with a corresponding lack of investment in tackling the public health harms of drug use. International drug control is framed by three major UN drug treaties (of 1961, 1971 and 1988), which encourage UN Member States to develop national policies based on strict law enforcement (Bewley-Taylor, 2004; Wood et al., 2009). There is an increased momentum, contextualised by a 'preponderance of evidence', in support of recognising that the current international drug control framework is associated with multiple health and social harms, and that these iatrogenic effects can include the exacerbation of HIV epidemics among injecting drug users (IDUs) (Wood et al., 2009, p. 990).

Agencies within the UN system have recently re-focused their attention on the primacy of public health, embracing harm reduction interventions as part of a balanced approach with complementarity to prevention and treatment interventions. In December 2005, the United Nations (UN) General Assembly adopted a resolution encouraging global actions towards 'scaling-up HIV prevention, treatment, care and support with the aim of coming as close as possible to the goal of universal access to treatment by 2010 for all those who need it' (United Nations General Assembly, 2006). This led to the development of the WHO, UNODC and United Nations Joint Programme on HIV/AIDS (UNAIDS) joint technical guide for countries on target setting for universal access to HIV prevention, treatment and care for injecting drug users, and focused advocacy efforts on the need for greater coverage towards 'universal access' (Donoghoe et al., 2008; WHO et al., 2009; ECOSOC, 2009). Scaling-up access to, and achieving adequate coverage of, a 'comprehensive package' of harm reduction for problem drug users is a major driver of current global drug policy initiatives (WHO, 2009; Ball, 2010; Atun and Kazatchkine, 2010).

Harm reduction as a 'combination intervention'

As a 'combination intervention', harm reduction comprises a package of interventions tailored to local setting and need, including access to drug treatment. In reducing the harms of drug injecting, for example, a harm reduction package may combine OST, NSPs, DCRs and counselling services with peer interventions as well as actions to lobby for policy change.

Envisaging harm reduction as a combination intervention is not merely pragmatic and borne out of need, but is also evidence-based. Evidence points towards the enhanced impact of harm reduction services when they work in combination. Cohort and modelling studies have shown that the impact of NSP and OST on reduced incidence of infectious disease among IDUs can be minimal if delivered as 'stand-alone' interventions but are markedly more effective when delivered in combination, with sufficient engagement among participants to both (Van Den Berg et al., 2007). This may be especially the case in reducing the incidence of HCV among IDUs (Hickman, 2010). While epidemiological studies associate NSP and OST with reduced HIV risk and transmission (Gibson et al., 2001; Wodak and Cooney, 2005; Farrell et al., 2005; Institute of Medicine, 2007; Palmateer et al., 2010; Kimber et al., 2010), the evidence for these interventions impacting on HCV risk and transmission is more modest (Muga et al., 2006; Wright and Tompkins, 2006; Hallinan et al., 2004; Goldberg et al., 2001; Palmateer et al., 2010; Kimber et al., 2010). To date, there is only one European study showing that 'full participation' across combined harm reduction interventions (NSP and OST) can reduce HIV incidence (by 57 %) *and* HCV incidence (by 64 %) (van den Berg et al., 2007). A recent cohort study in the United Kingdom also links OST with statistically significant reductions in the incidence of HCV (Craine et al., 2009). Findings noting the enhanced effect of OST in combination with NSP on reduced HIV and HCV incidence among IDUs have particular relevance for countries experiencing explosive outbreaks of infectious disease.

Just as the effectiveness of NSP and OST services may be enhanced when combined, there is an 'enhanced impact' relationship between participation in OST and adherence to HIV treatment and care among IDUs (Malta et al., 2008; Palepu et al., 2006; Lert and Kazatchkine, 2007). There is a potential HIV prevention effect derived from maximising access to HIV treatment (Ball, 2010; Montaner et al., 2006). Similarly, low-threshold access to HIV testing is an important combinative component of harm reduction. In the EU, there is a considerable level of homogeneity in policy priorities regarding measures to limit the spread of infectious diseases among drug users, with NSP being offered either in combination with voluntary testing and counselling for infectious disease, or in combination with the dissemination of information, education and communication materials (EMCDDA, 2009a, p. 83; EMCDDA, 2009c). Evidence also suggests an enhanced impact relationship between hepatitis C treatment and access to drug treatment and social support services (Grebely et al., 2007; Birkhead et al., 2007). Additionally, the integration of HIV treatment services with TB treatment and prevention services is a critical feature in determining health outcomes in people living with HIV (Sylla et al., 2007), especially in transitional Europe, which is 'especially severely affected' by TB drug resistance among drug using populations (WHO et al., 2008). Moreover, in HIV prevention there may be combined intervention effects resulting from sexual risk reduction being delivered alongside harm reduction (Lindenburg et al., 2006; Copenhaver et al., 2006). Harm reduction integrates with treatment and care in a combined intervention approach (Ball, 2010).

Harm reduction and 'enabling environments' for health

A fundamental tenet of public health intervention is to create environments conducive to individual and community risk avoidance, including through the creation and maintenance of public policies supportive of health (WHO, 1986). The continuum of 'combination interventions' available to harm reduction extends from drug prevention and treatment through to policy reform and the removal of structural barriers to protecting the rights of all to health. WHO makes specific recommendation for 'laws that do not compromise access to HIV services for drug users through criminalisation and marginalisation' (Ball, 2007). If public policies or laws generate harm then these too fall within the scope of the combination of interventions that make up harm reduction. Structural interventions for public health seek to remove contextual or environmental barriers to risk and harm reduction while enabling social and environmental conditions that protect against risk and vulnerability (Blankenship et al., 2006). The delineation of the 'risk environment' surrounding the production of drug harms in different settings has led to the identification of structural interventions with the potential for encouraging community-level change (Rhodes, 2002, 2009).

Of critical concern — as evidenced by multiple studies in multiple settings — is how the legal environment can constrain risk avoidance and promote harm among problem drug users, especially among people who inject drugs (Small et al., 2006; Rhodes, 2009; Kerr et al., 2005). In some settings, intense street-level police surveillance and contact can be associated with reluctance among IDUs to carry sterile needles and syringes for fear of arrest, caution, fine or detention (Rhodes et al., 2003; Cooper et al., 2005; Miller et al., 2008). Evidence associates elevated odds of syringe sharing with increased police contact (Rhodes et al., 2004), confiscation of injecting equipment (Werb et al., 2008), and rates of arrest (Pollini et al., 2008), yet rates of arrest can show no deterrent effect on levels of injecting (Friedman et al., 2010). High-visibility policing, and police 'crackdowns', have been linked to the interruption of safer injecting routines, leading to safety 'short-cuts' or hasty injections, exacerbating the risk of viral and bacterial infections as well as overdose (Blankenship and Koester, 2002; Bluthenthal et al., 1999; Small et al., 2006). Such policing practices may displace drug users geographically, disrupt social networks of support, contribute to the stigmatisation of drug use, and limit the feasibility, coverage and impact of public health responses (Burris et al., 2004; Davis et al., 2005; Friedman et al., 2006; Broadhead et al., 1999). In turn, prison and incarceration are linked to elevated odds of HIV transmission among people who use drugs (Dolan et al., 2007; Jürgens et al., 2009; Stevens et al., 2010).

Harm reduction may therefore include interventions that seek to reduce the harms generated by drug and other public policies, including through policy reform and legal change. For instance, as Room (2010, p. 110) notes: 'If the harm arises from heavy use per se, reducing or eliminating use or changing the mode of use are the logical first choices for reducing the harm. But if the harm results from the criminalisation per se, decriminalising is a logical way of reducing the harm.' WHO also notes that 'the alignment of drug control measures with public health goals [is] a priority' (Ball, 2007, p. 687). It is therefore important to note the potential public health gains of engaging policing and criminal justice agencies as part of local public health partnerships, including in the delivery of harm reduction interventions in community and closed settings (see Stevens et al., 2010).

Coverage and scale-up

2010 is the year for achieving the UN General Assembly target of 'near universal access' to HIV prevention, treatment and care for populations affected by HIV. In Europe, considerable progress has been made towards achieving greater coverage of harm reduction services for IDUs (see Cook et al., 2010). Every EU Member State has one or more needle and syringe programmes (EMCDDA, 2009a). Pharmacy-based NSPs operate in at least 12 Member States. All Member States provide opioid substitution treatment for those with opioid dependence (EMCDDA, 2009a). An estimated 650,000 people were receiving OST in Europe in 2007, though large national variations in coverage exist (EMCDDA, 2009a).

Evidence suggests coverage is an important determinant of drug-related risk and harm. In a recent comparison of the incidence of diagnosed HIV among IDUs and the coverage of OST and NSP in the EU and five other middle- and high-income countries, those countries with greatest provision of both OST and NSP in 2000 to 2004 had lower HIV incidence in 2005 and 2006 (Wiessing et al., 2009). In this study, the availability and coverage of harm reduction measures was considerably lower in Russia and Ukraine where the incidence of HIV was considerably higher when compared to Western European countries. Whereas HIV transmission rates are stabilising or decreasing in most of Western and Central Europe, they are increasing in the Eastern part of the continent, outside the EU, where harm reduction services are 'insufficient and need to be reinforced' (Wiessing et al., 2008).

Coverage of harm reduction interventions is variable within the EU. While recent estimates of the total number of OST clients represent around 40 % of the estimated total number of problem opiate users in the EU, the level of provision is far from uniform across the region. Estimates of coverage from 10 countries where such data are available range from below 5 % to over 50 % of opioid users covered by OST (EMCDDA, 2009e).

European trends in the provision of NSP between 2003 and 2007 show a 33 % increase in the number of syringes distributed through specialised programmes, with steady increases in most countries, except several countries in northern and central Europe (EMCDDA, 2009d). Although country-specific coverage estimates of NSP are scarce, the number of syringes distributed by specialist NSPs per estimated IDU per year seems to vary widely between countries (EMCDDA, 2010). European-level estimates suggest that on average some 50 syringes are distributed per estimated IDU per year across the EU (Wiessing et al., 2009). Overall availability of sterile syringes is also dependent upon pharmacy provision, in turn influenced by legislation, regulations, and pricing, as well as by the attitudes of pharmacists.

In its evaluation of the EU drug action plan, the European Commission emphasised that the 'availability and accessibility of [harm reduction] programmes are still variable among the Member States' and that 'further improvements are still needed in [the] accessibility, availability and coverage' of services (European Commission, 2008, p. 66). In the European region more generally, scaling up comprehensive service provision is a priority, with strengthening health systems, engaging civil society, and securing political commitment for harm reduction considered key determinants to effective scale-up (Atun and Kazatchkine, 2010). There is then considerable variability in how harm reduction is enacted in policy and even more so in practice, as well as resistance to the mainstreaming of harm reduction in some settings. Understanding the failure to implement evidence-based programmes and policies has been identified as a major topic for future research (Des Jarlais and Semaan, 2009). In countries where heroin epidemics are recent and rates of HIV infection among drug users low, implementation of harm reduction measures such as NSP or OST may be perceived by some as difficult to justify. This may be especially so in the context of finite and retracting economic resources in the health sector. Evidence, however, indicates the cost-effectiveness of the introduction and scale-up of harm reduction (Zaric et al., 2000; National Centre in HIV Epidemiology and Clinical Research UNSW, 2009).

Voices of resistance to the mainstreaming of harm reduction in drug policy can be found within the EU (see MacGregor and Whiting, 2010), but are most vociferous within the broader European region, and especially Russia, which today has one of the largest epidemics of HIV associated with drug injecting in the world, has a policy that places strong emphasis on law enforcement, prohibits the introduction of OST and limits the development of NSP and other harm reduction interventions to adequate scale (Sarang et al., 2007; Human Rights Watch, 2007; Elovich and Drucker, 2008).

Evidence, impacts and challenges

An effective harm reduction policy, programme or intervention is one that 'can be demonstrated, to a reasonable and informed audience, by direct measurement or otherwise, that on balance of probabilities has, or is likely to result in, a net reduction in drug-related harm' (Lenton and Single, 2004, p. 217). This monograph aims to reflect upon over two decades of harm reduction research, evidence and impact in Europe and beyond.

There are now multiple systematic and other reviews of the scientific evidence in support of different harm reduction interventions, especially in the context of HIV, hepatitis C and injecting drug use (Wodak and Cooney, 2005; Farrell et al., 2005; Institute of Medicine, 2007; Palmateer et al., 2010). Chapters in this monograph take stock of such evidence in European perspective, including regarding the effectiveness of interventions to prevent HIV and HCV among injecting drug users (Chapter 5 — Kimber et al., 2010), the role of DCRs (Chapter 11 — Hedrich et al., 2010), the effect of epidemiological setting on intervention impact (Chapter 6 — Vickerman and Hickman, 2010) and the implications that variations in drug use patterns have on harm reduction interventions (Chapter 15 — Hartnoll et al., 2010). While diffusing throughout Europe primarily in response to health harms linked to injecting drug use (Chapter 2 — Cook et al., 2010; Chapter 3 — MacGregor and Whiting, 2010), harm reduction approaches have mainstream applicability. Chapters consider the specific challenges of harm reduction interventions and policies regarding alcohol (Chapter 10 — Herring et al., 2010), tobacco (Chapter 9 — Gartner et al., 2010), cannabis (Chapter 8 — Hall and Fischer, 2010), recreational drug use among young people (Chapter 13 — Fletcher et al., 2010), and stimulants (Chapter 7 — Grund et al., 2010). The potential role — often unrealised — of drug user engagement and criminal justice interventions are also discussed (Chapter 12 — Hunt et al., 2010; Chapter 14 — Stevens et al., 2010). Taken together, this monograph seeks to synthesise, as well as critically appraise, evidence of the impacts and challenges of harm reduction interventions and policies in Europe and beyond.

Harm reduction, like any public policy, is inevitably linked to political debate, and it is naive to assume otherwise, but it is precisely because of this that it is imperative that interventions are also developed upon evidence-based argument and critique. Europe is experiencing significant political change, which in 2004 enabled the most extensive wave of European Union enlargement ever seen. Following the ratification of the Lisbon Treaty by all 27 Member States in 2009, the importance of the Union as a major political player in the region will grow. Among the new challenges to be faced is maintaining a strong public health position in controlling and preventing HIV and HCV epidemics linked to drug use. This may be in a context of harsher economic conditions as well as increased migration, including from countries with large HIV epidemics driven by drug injecting and where evidence-based harm reduction measures are not always met with political commitment. The relative success of harm reduction strategies adopted in many European countries over the past two decades, and the evidence gathered in their support, provides a framework for the development, expansion and evaluation of harm reduction across multiple forms of substance use.

References

Note: publications with three or more authors are listed chronologically, to facilitate the location of 'et al.' references.

Ashton, J. and Seymour, H. (1988), *The new public health*, Open University Press, Milton Keynes.

Atun, R. and Kazathckine, M. (2010), 'Translating evidence into action: challenges to scaling up harm reduction in Europe and Central Asia', in Chapter 4, 'Perspectives on harm reduction: what experts have to say', in European Monitoring Centre for Drugs and Drug Addiction (EMCDDA), *Harm reduction: evidence, impacts and challenges*, Rhodes, T. and Hedrich, D. (eds), Scientific Monograph Series No. 10, Publications Office of the European Union, Luxembourg.

Ball, A. (2007), 'HIV, injecting drug use and harm reduction: a public health response', *Addiction* 102, pp. 684–90.

Ball, A. (2010), 'Broadening the scope and impact of harm reduction for HIV prevention, treatment and care among injecting drug users', in Chapter 4, 'Perspectives on harm reduction: what experts have to say', in European Monitoring Centre for Drugs and Drug Addiction (EMCDDA), *Harm reduction: evidence, impacts and challenges*, Rhodes, T. and Hedrich, D. (eds), Scientific Monograph Series No. 10, Publications Office of the European Union, Luxembourg.

Bellis, D. J. (1981), *Heroin and politicians: the failure of public policy to control addiction in America*, Greenwood Press, Westport, CT.

Bewley-Taylor, D. (2004), 'Harm reduction and the global drug control regime: contemporary problems and future prospects', *Drug and Alcohol Review* 23, pp. 483–9.

Birkhead, G. S., Klein, S. J., Candelas, A. R., et al. (2007), 'Integrating multiple programme and policy approaches to hepatitis C prevention and care for injection drug users: a comprehensive approach', *International Journal of Drug Policy* 18, pp. 417–25.

Blankenship, K. M. and Koester, S. (2002), 'Criminal law, policing policy, and HIV risk in female street sex workers and injection drug users', *Journal of Law and Medical Ethics* 30, pp. 548–59.

Blankenship, K. M., Friedman, S. R., Dworkin, S. and Mantell, J. E. (2006), 'Structural interventions: concepts, challenges and opportunities for research', *Journal of Urban Health* 83, pp. 59–72.

Bluthenthal, R. N., Lorvick J., Kral A. H., Erringer, E. A. and Kahn, J. G. (1999), 'Collateral damage in the war on drugs: HIV risk behaviors among injection drug users', *International Journal of Drug Policy* 10, pp. 25–38.

Broadhead, R. S., Van Hulst, Y. and Heckathorn, D. D. (1999), 'Termination of an established syringe-exchange: a study of claims and their impact', *Social Problems* 46, pp. 48–66.

Burris, S., Donoghoe, M., Blankenship, K., et al. (2004), 'Addressing the "risk environment" for injection drug users: the mysterious case of the missing cop', *Milbank Quarterly* 82, pp. 125–56.

Cooper, H., Moore, L., Gruskin, S. and Krieger, N. (2005), 'The impact of a police drug crackdown on drug injectors' ability to practice harm reduction', *Social Science and Medicine* 61, pp. 673–84.

Cook, C., Bridge, J. and Stimson, G. V. (2010), 'The diffusion of harm reduction in Europe and beyond', in European Monitoring Centre for Drugs and Drug Addiction (EMCDDA), *Harm reduction: evidence, impacts and challenges*, Rhodes, T. and Hedrich, D. (eds), Scientific Monograph Series No. 10, Publications Office of the European Union, Luxembourg.

Copenhaver, M., Johnson, B., Lee, I-C., et al. (2006), 'Behavioral HIV risk reduction among people who inject drugs: meta-analytic evidence of efficacy', *Journal of Substance Abuse Treatment* 31, pp. 163–71.

Council of the European Union (2003), 'Council Recommendation of 18 June 2003 on the prevention and reduction of health-related harm associated with drug dependence (2003/488/EC)'. Available at http://eur-lex. europa.eu/LexUriServ/LexUriServ.do?uri=CELEX:32003H0488:EN:HTML.

Council of the European Union (2004), *EU drugs strategy (2005–2012)*, CORDROGUE 77, 22 November 2004. Available at http://ec.europa.eu/justice_home/doc_centre/drugs/strategy/doc_drugs_strategy_en.htm.

Craine, N., Hickman, M., Parry, J. V., et al. (2009), 'Incidence of hepatitis C in drug injectors: the role of homelessness, opiate substitution treatment, equipment sharing, and community size', *Epidemiology and Infection* 137, pp. 1255–65.

Davis, C., Burris, S., Metzger, D., Becjer, J. and Lunch, K. (2005), 'Effects of an intensive street-level police intervention on syringe exchange program utilization', *American Journal of Public Health* 95, pp. 223–36.

Des Jarlais, D. C. (1995), 'Harm reduction: a framework for incorporating science into drug policy', *American Journal of Public Health* 85, pp. 10–12.

Des Jarlais, D. C. and Semaan, S. (2009), 'HIV prevention and psychoactive drug use: a research agenda', *Journal of Epidemiology and Community Health* 63, pp. 191–6.

Des Jarlais, D. C., Perlis, T., Arasteh, K., et al. (2005), 'Reductions in hepatitis C virus and HIV infections among injecting drug users in New York City', *AIDS* 19 (Supplement 3), pp. S20–5.

Dolan, K., Kite, B., Aceijas, C., and Stimson, G. V. (2007), 'HIV in prison in low income and middle income countries', *Lancet Infectious Diseases 7*, pp. 32–43.

Donoghoe, M., Verster, A., Pervilhac, C. and Williams, P. (2008), 'Setting targets for universal access to HIV prevention, treatment and care for injecting drug users (IDUs): towards consensus and improved guidance', *International Journal of Drug Policy* 19 (Supplement 1), pp. S5–14.

ECOSOC (UN Economic and Social Council) (2009), 'Economic and Social Council resolution E/2009/L.23 adopted by the Council on 24 July 2009: Joint United Nations Programme on Human Immunodeficiency Virus/ Acquired Immunodeficiency Syndrome (UNAIDS)'. Available at http://www.un.org/Docs/journal/asp/ws. asp?m=E/2009/L.23.

Elovich, R. and Drucker, E. (2008), 'On drug treatment and social control: Russian narcology's great leap backwards', *Harm Reduction Journal* 5, p. 23. DOI: 10.1186/1477-7517-5-23.

EMCDDA (2009a), *Annual report 2009: the state of the drugs problem in Europe*, European Monitoring Centre for Drugs and Drug Addiction, Lisbon.

EMCDDA (2009b), *Drug offences: sentencing and other outcomes*, European Monitoring Centre for Drugs and Drug Addiction, Lisbon.

EMCDDA (2009c), Statistical bulletin, Table HSR-6, European Monitoring Centre for Drugs and Drug Addiction, Lisbon. Available at http://www.emcdda.europa.eu/stats09/hsrtab6.

EMCDDA (2009d), Statistical bulletin, Table HSR-5, European Monitoring Centre for Drugs and Drug Addiction, Lisbon. Available at http://www.emcdda.europa.eu/stats09/hsrtab5.

EMCDDA (2009e), Statistical bulletin, Figure HSR-1, European Monitoring Centre for Drugs and Drug Addiction, Lisbon. Available at http://www.emcdda.europa.eu/stats09/hsrfig1.

EMCDDA (2010), *Injecting drug use in Europe*, European Monitoring Centre for Drugs and Drug Addiction, Lisbon.

Erickson, P. (1999), 'Introduction: the three phases of harm reduction. An examination of emerging concepts, methodologies, and critiques', *Substance Use and Misuse* 34 (1), pp. 1–7.

European Commission (2002), *Implementation of EU-action plan on drugs 2000–2004: progress review for the Member States*. Available at http://ec.europa.eu/justice_home/doc_centre/drugs/studies/doc/review_actplan_02_04_en.pdf.

European Commission (2006), *2006 progress review on the implementation of the EU drugs action plan (2005–2008)*, Commission Staff Working Document SEC (2006) 1803. Available at http://ec.europa.eu/justice_home/doc_centre/drugs/strategy/doc/sec_2006_1803_en.pdf.

European Commission (2008), *The report of the final evaluation of the EU drugs action plan 2005–2008*, Commission Staff Working Document (accompanying document to the Communication from the Commission to the Council and the European Parliament on an EU drugs action plan 2009–2012) COM (2008) 567, SEC(2008) 2456. Available at http://ec.europa.eu/health/ph_determinants/life_style/drug/documents/COM2008_0567_a1_en.pdf.

European Commission (2009), *Report on global illicit drug markets, 2009*. Available at http://ec.europa.eu/justice_home/doc_centre/drugs/studies/doc_drugs_studies_en.htm.

Farrell, M., Gowing, L., Marsden, J., Ling, W. and Ali, R. (2005), 'Effectiveness of drug dependence treatment in HIV prevention', *International Journal of Drug Policy* 16 (Supplement 1), pp. S67–75.

Fletcher, A., Calafat, A., Pirona, A. and Olszewski, D. (2010), 'Young people, recreational drug use and harm reduction', in European Monitoring Centre for Drugs and Drug Addiction (EMCDDA), *Harm reduction: evidence, impacts and challenges*, Rhodes, T. and Hedrich, D. (eds), Scientific Monograph Series No. 10, Publications Office of the European Union, Luxembourg.

Friedman, S. R., Cooper, H. L. F., Tempalski, B., et al. (2006), 'Relationships between deterrence and law enforcement and drug-related harm among drug injectors in U.S. metropolitan cities', *AIDS* 20, pp. 93–9.

Friedman, S. R., Pouget, E. R., Chatterjee, S., et al. (2010), 'Do drug arrests deter injection drug use?' (in press).

Gartner, C., Hall, W. and NcNeill, A. (2010), 'Harm reduction policies for tobacco', in European Monitoring Centre for Drugs and Drug Addiction (EMCDDA), *Harm reduction: evidence, impacts and challenges*, Rhodes, T. and Hedrich, D. (eds), Scientific Monograph Series No. 10, Publications Office of the European Union, Luxembourg.

Gibson, D. R., Flynn, N. and Perales, D. (2001), 'Effectiveness of syringe exchange programs in reducing HIV risk behavior and HIV seroconversion among injecting drug users', *AIDS* 15, pp. 1329–41.

Goldberg, D., Burns, S., Taylor, A., et al. (2001), 'Trends in HCV prevalence among injecting drug users in Glasgow and Edinburgh during the era of needle/syringe exchange', *Scandinavian Journal of Infectious Diseases* 33, pp. 457–61.

Grebely, J., Genoway, K., Khara, M., et al. (2007), 'Treatment uptake and outcomes among current and former injection drug users receiving directly observed therapy within a multidisciplinary group model for the treatment of hepatitis C virus infection', *International Journal of Drug Policy* 18: 437–43.

Grund, J-P., Coffin, P., Jauffret-Roustide, M., et al. (2010), 'The fast and furious: cocaine, amphetamines and harm reduction', in European Monitoring Centre for Drugs and Drug Addiction (EMCDDA), *Harm reduction: evidence, impacts and challenges*, Rhodes, T. and Hedrich, D. (eds), Scientific Monograph Series No. 10, Publications Office of the European Union, Luxembourg.

Hall, W. and Fischer, B. (2010), 'Harm reduction policies for cannabis', in European Monitoring Centre for Drugs and Drug Addiction (EMCDDA), *Harm reduction: evidence, impacts and challenges*, Rhodes, T. and Hedrich, D. (eds), Scientific Monograph Series No. 10, Publications Office of the European Union, Luxembourg.

Hallinan, R., Byrne, A., Amin, J. and Dore, G. J. (2004), 'Hepatitis C virus incidence among injecting drug users on opioid replacement therapy', *Australian and New Zealand Journal of Public Health* 28, pp. 576–8.

Hartnoll, R., Gyarmarthy, A. and Zabransky, T. (2010), 'Variations in problem drug use patterns and their implications for harm reduction', in European Monitoring Centre for Drugs and Drug Addiction (EMCDDA), *Harm reduction: evidence, impacts and challenges*, Rhodes, T. and Hedrich, D. (eds), Scientific Monograph Series No. 10, Publications Office of the European Union, Luxembourg.

Hedrich, D., Pirona, A. and Wiessing, L. (2008), 'From margins to mainstream: the evolution of harm reduction responses to problem drug use in Europe', *Drugs: education, prevention and policy* 15, pp. 503–17.

Hedrich, D., Kerr, T. and Dubois-Arber, F. (2010), 'Drug consumption facilities in Europe and beyond', in European Monitoring Centre for Drugs and Drug Addiction (EMCDDA), *Harm reduction: evidence, impacts and challenges*, Rhodes, T. and Hedrich, D. (eds), Scientific Monograph Series No. 10, Publications Office of the European Union, Luxembourg.

Herring, R., Thom, B., Beccaria, F., Kolind, T. and Moskalewicz, J. (2010), 'Alcohol harm reduction in Europe', in European Monitoring Centre for Drugs and Drug Addiction (EMCDDA), *Harm reduction: evidence, impacts and challenges*, Rhodes, T. and Hedrich, D. (eds), Scientific Monograph Series No. 10, Publications Office of the European Union, Luxembourg.

Hickman, M. (2010), 'HCV prevention: a challenge for evidence-based harm reduction', in Chapter 4, 'Perspectives on harm reduction: what experts have to say', in European Monitoring Centre for Drugs and Drug Addiction (EMCDDA), *Harm reduction: evidence, impacts and challenges*, Rhodes, T. and Hedrich, D. (eds), Scientific Monograph Series No. 10, Publications Office of the European Union, Luxembourg.

Human Rights Watch (2007), *Rehabilitation required: Russia's human rights obligation to provide evidence-based drug dependence treatment*, Human Rights Watch, New York.

Hunt, N., Albert, E. and Montañés Sánchez, V. (2010), 'User involvement and user organising in harm reduction', in European Monitoring Centre for Drugs and Drug Addiction (EMCDDA), *Harm reduction: evidence, impacts and challenges*, Rhodes, T. and Hedrich, D. (eds), Scientific Monograph Series No. 10, Publications Office of the European Union, Luxembourg.

Institute of Medicine (2007), *Preventing HIV infection among injecting drug users in high-risk countries: an assessment of the evidence*, National Academy of Sciences, Washington, DC.

International Drug Policy Consortium (2009), *The 2009 Commission on Narcotic Drugs and its high level segment: report of proceedings*, Briefing Paper, IDPC, London.

Jürgens, R., Ball, A. and Verster, A. (2009), 'Interventions to reduce HIV transmission related to injecting drug use in prison', *Lancet Infectious Diseases* 9, pp. 57–66.

Kerr, T., Small, W. and Wood, E. (2005), 'The public health and social impacts of drug market enforcement: a review of the evidence', *International Journal of Drug Policy* 16, pp. 210–20.

Kimber, J., Palmateer, N., Hutchinson, S., et al. (2010), 'Harm reduction among injecting drug users: evidence of effectiveness', in European Monitoring Centre for Drugs and Drug Addiction (EMCDDA), *Harm reduction: evidence, impacts and challenges*, Rhodes, T. and Hedrich, D. (eds), Scientific Monograph Series No. 10, Publications Office of the European Union, Luxembourg.

Lancet (2009), 'The future of harm reduction programmes in Russia', *Lancet* 374, p. 1213.

Lenton, S. and Single, E. (2004), 'The definition of harm reduction', *Drug and Alcohol Review* 17, pp. 213–20.

Lert, F. And Kazatchkine, M. (2007), 'Antiretroviral HIV treatment and care for injecting drug users: an evidence-based overview', *International Journal of Drug Policy* 18, 255–61.

Lindenburg, C. E. A., Krol, A., Smit, C., et al. (2006), 'Decline in HIV incidence and injecting, but not in sexual risk behaviour, seen in drug users in Amsterdam', *AIDS* 20, pp. 1771–5.

MacGregor, S. and Whiting, M. (2010), 'The development of European drug policy and the place of harm reduction within this', in European Monitoring Centre for Drugs and Drug Addiction (EMCDDA), *Harm reduction: evidence, impacts and challenges*, Rhodes, T. and Hedrich, D. (eds), Scientific Monograph Series No. 10, Publications Office of the European Union, Luxembourg.

Malta, M., Strathdee, S., Magnanini, M., et al. (2008), 'Adherence to antiretroviral therapy for HIV among drug users: a systematic review', *Addiction* 103, pp. 1242–57.

Mathers, C. D. and Loncar, D. (2006), 'Projections of global mortality and burden of disease from 2002 to 2030', *PLoS Medicine* 3, pp. 2011–30.

Miller, C., Firestone, M., Ramos, R., et al. (2008), 'Injecting drug users' experiences of policing practices in two Mexican–U.S. border cities', *International Journal of Drug Policy* 19, pp. 324–31.

Montaner, J. S., Hogg, R., Wood, E., et al. (2006), 'The case for expanding access to highly active antiretroviral therapy to curb the growth of the HIV epidemic', *Lancet* 368, 531–6.

Muga, R., Sanvisens, A., Bolao, F., et al. (2006), 'Significant reductions of HIV prevalence but not of hepatitis C virus infections in injection drug users from metropolitan Barcelona: 1987–2001', *Drug and Alcohol Dependence* 82, Supplement 1, pp. S29–33.

National Centre in HIV Epidemiology and Clinical Research UNSW (2009), *Return on investment 2: evaluating the cost-effectiveness of needle and syringe programs in Australia 2009*, Australian Government Department for Health and Ageing. Available at http://www.health.gov.au/internet/main/publishing.nsf/Content/needle-return-2.

Palepu, A., Tyndall, M. W., Joy, R., et al. (2006), 'Antiretroviral adherence and HIV treatment outcomes among HIV/HCV co-infected injection drug users: the role of methadone maintenance therapy', *Drug and Alcohol Dependence* 84, pp. 188–94.

Palmateer, N., Kimber, J., Hickman, M., et al. (2010), 'Preventing hepatitis C and HIV transmission among injecting drug users: a review of reviews', *Addiction*, in press.

Peterson, A. and Lupton, D. (1996), *The new public health: health and self in the age of risk*, Sage Publications, Newbury Park, CA.

Pollini, R. A., Brouwer, K. C., Lozada, R. M., et al. (2008), 'Syringe possession arrests are associated with receptive syringe sharing in two Mexico–U.S. border cities', *Addiction* 103, pp. 101–08.

Rehm, J., Mathers, C., Popova, S., et al. (2009), 'Global burden of disease and injury and economic cost attributable to alcohol and alcohol-use disorders', *Lancet* 373, pp. 2223–32.

Rehm, J., Fischer, B., Hickman, M., et al. (2010), 'Perspectives on harm reduction: what experts have to say', in European Monitoring Centre for Drugs and Drug Addiction (EMCDDA), *Harm reduction: evidence, impacts and challenges*, Rhodes, T. and Hedrich, D. (eds), Scientific Monograph Series No. 10, Publications Office of the European Union, Luxembourg.

Rhodes, T. (2002), 'The "risk environment": a framework for understanding and reducing drug-related harm', *International Journal of Drug Policy* 13, pp. 85–94.

Rhodes, T. (2009), 'Risk environments and drug harms: a social science for harm reduction approach', *International Journal of Drug Policy* 20, pp. 193–201.

Rhodes, T., Mikhailova, L., Sarang, A., et al. (2003), 'Situational factors influencing drug injecting, risk reduction and syringe exchange in Togliatti City, Russian Federation: a qualitative study of micro risk environment', *Social Science and Medicine* 57, pp. 39–54.

Rhodes, T., Judd, A., Mikhailova, L., et al. (2004), 'Injecting equipment sharing among injecting drug users in Togliatti City, Russian Federation: maximising the protective effects of syringe distribution', *Journal of Acquired Immune Deficiency Syndromes* 35, pp. 293–300.

Robson, G. and Marlatt, G. (2006), 'Harm reduction and alcohol policy', *International Journal of Drug Policy* 17, pp. 255–7.

Room, R. (2010), 'The ambiguity of harm reduction: goal or means, and what constitutes harm?', in Chapter 4, 'Perspectives on harm reduction: what experts have to say', in European Monitoring Centre for Drugs and Drug Addiction (EMCDDA), *Harm reduction: evidence, impacts and challenges*, Rhodes, T. and Hedrich, D. (eds), Scientific Monograph Series No. 10, Publications Office of the European Union, Luxembourg.

Sarang, A., Rhodes, T., Platt, L., et al. (2006), 'Drug injecting and syringe use in the HIV risk environment of Russian penitentiary institutions', *Addiction* 101, pp. 1787–96.

Sarang, A., Stuikyte, R. and Bykov, R. (2007), 'Implementation of harm reduction in Central and Eastern Europe and Central Asia', *International Journal of Drug Policy* 18, pp. 129–35.

Sarang, A., Rhodes, T. and Platt, L. (2008), 'Access to syringes in three Russian cities: implications for syringe distribution and coverage', *International Journal of Drug Policy* 19, pp. S25–S36.

Small, W., Kerr, T., Charette, J., Schechter, M. T. and Spittal, P. M. (2006), 'Impacts of intensified police activity on injection drug users: evidence from an ethnographic investigation', *International Journal of Drug Policy* 17, pp. 85–95.

Spear, B. (1994), 'The early years of the "British System" in practice', in Strang, J. and Gossop, M. (eds) *Heroin addiction and drug policy*, Oxford University Press, Oxford, pp. 3–28.

Stevens, A., Stöver, H. and Brentari, C. (2010), 'Criminal justice approaches to harm reduction in Europe', in European Monitoring Centre for Drugs and Drug Addiction (EMCDDA), *Harm reduction: evidence, impacts and challenges*, Rhodes, T. and Hedrich, D. (eds), Scientific Monograph Series No. 10, Publications Office of the European Union, Luxembourg.

Sweanor, D., Alcabes, P. and Drucker, E. (2007), 'Tobacco harm reduction: how rational public policy could transform a pandemic', *International Journal of Drug Policy*, 18, pp. 70–4.

Sylla, L., Douglas Bruce, R., Kamarulzaman, A. and Altice, F. L. (2007), 'Integration and co-location of HIV/AIDS, tuberculosis and drug treatment services', *International Journal of Drug Policy* 18, pp. 306–12.

United Nations Development Program (2008), *Living with HIV in Eastern Europe and the CIS*, UNDP, Bratislava.

United Nations General Assembly Sixtieth Special Session (2006), *Political declaration on HIV/AIDS*. Resolution 60/262 adopted by the United Nations General Assembly, United Nations, New York.

UNODC (United Nations Office on Drugs and Crime) (2009), *A century of international drug control*, UNODC, Vienna. Available at http://www.unodc.org/documents/data-and-analysis/Studies/100_Years_of_Drug_Control.pdf.

van den Berg, C., Smit, C., Van Brussel, G., Coutinho, R. A. and Prins, M. (2007), 'Full participation in harm reduction programmes is associated with decreased risk for human immunodeficiency virus and hepatitis C virus: evidence from the Amsterdam cohort studies among drug users', *Addiction* 102, pp. 1454–62.

van der Gouwe, D., Gallà, M., Van Gageldonk, A., Croes, E., Engelhardt, J., Van Laar, M. and Buster, M. (2006), *Prevention and reduction of health-related harm associated with drug dependence: an inventory of policies, evidence and practices in the EU relevant to the implementation of the Council Recommendation of 18 June 2003. Synthesis report. Contract nr. SI2.397049*, Trimbos Instituut, Utrecht. Available at http://ec.europa.eu/health/ph_determinants/life_style/drug/documents/drug_report_en.pdf.

Vickerman, P. and Hickman, M. (2010), 'The effect of epidemiological setting on the impact of harm reduction targeting injecting drug users', in European Monitoring Centre for Drugs and Drug Addiction (EMCDDA), *Harm reduction: evidence, impacts and challenges*, Rhodes, T. and Hedrich, D. (eds), Scientific Monograph Series No. 10, Publications Office of the European Union, Luxembourg.

Werb, D., Wood, E., Small, W., et al. (2008), 'Effects of police confiscation of illicit drugs and syringes among injection drug users in Vancouver', *International Journal of Drug Policy* 19, pp. 332–8.

WHO (World Health Organization) (1974), *Expert committee on drug dependence: twentieth report*, Technical Report Series 551, WHO, Geneva.

WHO (1986), *Ottawa Charter for Health Promotion*, WHO, Geneva, WHO/HPR/HEP/95.1.

WHO (2009), *HIV/AIDS: comprehensive harm reduction package*, WHO, Geneva. Available at http://www.who.int/hiv/topics/idu/harm_reduction/en/index.html.

WHO, UNODC and UNAIDS (Joint United Nations Programme on HIV/AIDS) (2008), *Policy guidelines for collaborative HIV and TB services for injecting and other drug users*, WHO, Geneva. Available at http://www.who.int/tb/publications/2008/en/index.html.

WHO, UNODC and UNAIDS (2009), 'Technical guide for countries to set targets for universal access to HIV prevention, treatment and care for injecting drug users. Available at http://www.who.int/hiv/pub/idu/targetsetting/en/index.html.

Wiessing, L., Van de Laar, M.J., Donoghoe, M.C., et al. (2008), 'HIV among injecting drug users in Europe: increasing trends in the East', *Eurosurveillance* 3 (50). Available at http://www.eurosurveillance.org/ViewArticle.aspx?ArticleId=19067.

Wiessing, L., Likatavičius, G., Klempová, D., et al. (2009), 'Associations between availability and coverage of HIV-prevention measures and subsequent incidence of diagnosed HIV infection among injection drug users', *American Journal of Public Health* 99 (6), pp. 1049–52.

Wodak, A. and Cooney, A. (2005), 'Effectiveness of sterile needle and syringe programmes', *International Journal of Drug Policy* 16, Supplement 1, pp. S31–44.

Wolfe, D. and Malinowska-Sempruch, K. (2004), *Illicit drug policies and the global HIV epidemic*, Open Society Institute, New York.

Wood, E., Spittal, P. M., Li, K., et al. (2004), 'Inability to access addiction treatment and risk of HIV-infection among injection drug users', *Journal of Acquired Immune Deficiency Syndromes* 36, pp. 750–4.

Wood, E., Werb, D., Marshall, B., Montaner, J. S. G. and Kerr, T. (2009), 'The war on drugs: a devastating public-policy disaster', *Lancet* 373, pp. 989–90.

Wright, N. M. and Tompkins, C. N. (2006), 'A review of the evidence for the effectiveness of primary prevention interventions for hepatitis C among injecting drug users', *Harm Reduction Journal* 6 (3), p. 27.

Zaric, G. S., Barnett, P. G. and Brandeau, M. L. (2000), 'HIV transmission and the cost-effectiveness of methadone maintenance', *American Journal of Public Health* 90 (7), pp.1100–11.

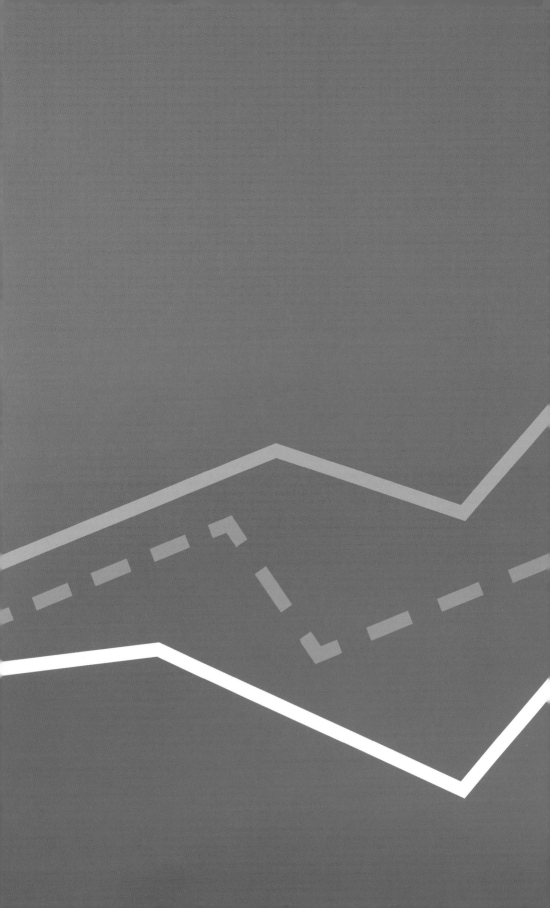

Background

PART I

Chapter 2
The diffusion of harm reduction in Europe and beyond

Catherine Cook, Jamie Bridge and Gerry V. Stimson

Abstract

This chapter traces the diffusion of harm reduction in Europe and around the world. The term 'harm reduction' became prominent in the mid-1980s as a response to newly discovered HIV epidemics amongst people who inject drugs in some cities. At this time, many European cities played a key role in the development of innovative interventions such as needle and syringe programmes. The harm reduction approach increased in global coverage and acceptance throughout the 1990s and became an integral part of drug policy guidance from the European Union at the turn of the century. By 2009, some 31 European countries supported harm reduction in policy or practice — all of which provided needle and syringe programmes and opioid substitution therapy. Six countries also provided prison needle and syringe programmes, 23 provided opioid substitution therapy in prisons, and all but two of the drug consumption rooms in the world were in Europe. However, models and coverage vary across the European region. Harm reduction is now an official policy of the United Nations, and Europe has played a key role in this development and continues to be a strong voice for harm reduction at the international level.

Keywords: history, harm reduction, global diffusion, international policy, Europe.

Introduction

The term 'harm reduction' refers to 'policies, programmes and practices that aim to reduce the adverse health, social and economic consequences of the use of legal and illegal psychoactive drugs', and are 'based on a strong commitment to public health and human rights' (IHRA, 2009a, p. 1). The term came to prominence after the emergence of HIV in Europe and elsewhere in the mid-1980s (Stimson, 2007). However, the underlying principles of this approach can be traced back much further (see box on p. 38). This chapter seeks to explore the emergence and diffusion of harm reduction from a localised, community-based response to international best practice. Since space restricts an exhaustive history transcending all aspects of harm reduction, we will focus primarily on the development and acceptance of approaches to prevent HIV transmission amongst people who inject drugs. It is these interventions that have come to epitomise the essence of harm reduction. For the purposes of this chapter, Europe is defined as comprising 33 countries — the 27 Member States of the European Union (EU), the candidate countries (Croatia, the Former Yugoslav Republic of Macedonia and Turkey), and Norway, Switzerland and Iceland.

Early examples of 'harm reduction' principles and practice

1912 to 1923	Narcotic maintenance clinics in the United States.
1926	Report of the United Kingdom Departmental Committee on Morphine and Heroin Addiction (the Rolleston Committee) concluded in support of opiate prescription to help maintain normality for heroin-dependent patients.
1960s	Emergence of 'controlled drinking' as an alternative to abstinence-based treatments for some alcohol users.
1960s on	Grass-roots work on reducing harms connected to the use of LSD, cannabis, amphetamines, and to glue sniffing.

The diffusion of harm reduction in Europe

In 1985 HIV antibody tests were introduced, leading to the discovery of high rates of infection in numerous European cities among people who inject drugs — including Edinburgh (51 %) (Robertson et al., 1986), Milan (60 %), Bari (76 %), Bilbao (50 %), Paris (64 %), Toulouse (64 %), Geneva (52 %) and Innsbruck (44 %) (Stimson, 1995). These localised epidemics occurred in a short space of time, with 40 % or more prevalence of infection reached within two years of the introduction of the virus into drug-injecting communities (Stimson, 1994). Analysis of stored blood samples indicated that HIV was first present in Amsterdam in 1981, and in Edinburgh one or two years later (Stimson, 1991). Heroin use and drug injecting in European countries had been on the increase since the 1960s (Hartnoll et al., 1989) and research indicated that the sharing of needles and syringes was common amongst people who injected drugs (Stimson, 1991).

It soon became evident that parts of Europe faced a public health emergency (see box below). Across Europe, the response was driven at a city level by local health authorities and civil society (sometimes in spite of interference from government) (O'Hare, 2007a). In 1984 (one year before the introduction of HIV testing), drug user organisations in the Netherlands started to distribute sterile injecting equipment to their peers to counter hepatitis B transmission (Buning et al., 1990; Stimson, 2007). This is widely acknowledged as the first formal needle and syringe programme (NSP), although informal or ad hoc NSPs existed around the world before 1984. Soon after, the Netherlands integrated NSPs within low-threshold centres nationwide (Buning et al., 1990).

The transformation brought by HIV and harm reduction

HIV and AIDS provide the greatest challenges yet to drug policies and services. Policy-makers and practitioners ... have been forced to reassess their ways of dealing with drug problems; this includes clarifying their aims, identifying their objectives and priorities for their work, their styles of working and relationships with clients, and the location of the work. Within the space of about three years, mainly between 1986 and 1988, there have been major debates about HIV, AIDS and injecting drug use. In years to come, it is likely that the late 1980s will be identified as a key period of crisis and transformation in the history of drugs policy.

(Stimson, 1990b)

In 1986, parts of the United Kingdom introduced NSPs (Stimson, 1995; O'Hare, 2007b). By 1987, similar programmes had also been adopted in Denmark, Malta, Spain and Sweden (Hedrich et al., 2008). By 1990, NSPs operated in 14 European countries, and were publicly funded in 12. This had increased to 28 countries by the turn of the century, with public funds supporting programmes in all but one of these (EMCDDA, 2009a, Table HSR-4). Some countries were also experimenting with alternative models of distribution, including syringe vending machines and pharmacy-based schemes (Stimson, 1989). By the early 1990s, there was growing evidence of the feasibility of NSPs and in support of the interventions' ability to attract into services otherwise-hidden populations of people who inject drugs, and reduce levels of syringe sharing (Stimson, 1991).

Figure 2.1: Year of introduction of opioid substitution treatment (OST) and official introduction of needle and syringe programmes (NSPs) in EU countries

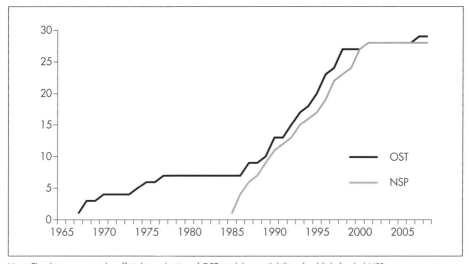

Note: The data represent the official introduction of OST, and the availability of publicly funded NSPs.
Source: Reitox national focal points.

The spread of NSPs in Europe in the late 1980s and throughout the 1990s was the result of broader policy shifts away from the treatment of dependence and towards the management of the health of people who used drugs (Stimson and Lart, 1990). A focus on health and its risk management increased the emphasis on low-threshold access to services and community-based interventions. Outreach, and especially peer-driven outreach, epitomised these shifts (Rhodes and Hartnoll, 1991; Rhodes, 1993). No longer were services solely reliant upon drug users seeking help for treatment, but instead they reached out to those most hidden and vulnerable as a means of reducing population-wide drug-related risk. In many instances, harm reduction was coordinated at the community or city level (Huber, 1995; Hartnoll and Hedrich, 1996).

These shifts enabled the reshaping of prescribing and drug treatment services towards a more 'user friendly' and collaborative model. The practice of prescribing opiates to people dependent on them had been widely adopted as early as the 1920s in the United Kingdom (Department Committee on Morphine and Heroin Addiction, 1926; Stimson and

Oppenheimer, 1982). Methadone maintenance treatment (MMT) was introduced in Europe in the 1960s; first in Sweden, then in the Netherlands, the United Kingdom, and Denmark (Hedrich et al., 2008), albeit with limited provision and often in the context of abstinence-orientated programmes. The emergence of HIV in the mid-1980s served to reinvigorate this intervention, combining it with outreach-based models, such as the 'methadone by bus' project in Amsterdam (Buning et al., 1990). The number of European countries with MMT rapidly increased throughout the 1990s (see Figure 2.1).

By the 1990s, harm reduction was becoming endorsed as part of national drug policies in many European countries, although some were slower to follow suit (including Germany, Greece and France, which maintained abstinence-based policies) (Michels et al., 2007; Stimson, 1995; Bergeron and Kopp, 2002). It took over a decade, however, for the EU to agree, for the first time, a 'Drugs strategy' (European Union, 2000a) with an associated 'Action plan' (European Union, 2000b), for the period 2000–04, containing a number of concrete targets. National drug policies across Europe have always been the individual responsibility of Member States, and as such the EU's role is a 'co-ordinating, complementary and supporting one' (Hedrich et al., 2008), creating frameworks rather than legally binding instruments. This first EU drugs strategy presented six recommended targets, one of which was 'to reduce substantially over five years the incidence of drug-related health damage (including HIV and hepatitis) and the number of drug-related deaths' (European Union, 2000a). Although the document did not explicitly use the term harm reduction, this target represents an important milestone in European drug policy.

The next milestone came in 2003, when the Council of the European Union adopted a recommendation on the prevention and reduction of health-related harm associated with drug dependence. This stated that Member States should set the reduction of drug-related risks as a public health objective and listed some of the key harm reduction measures to 'reduce substantially the incidence of drug-related health damage' (see box below). In 2004 a new eight-year EU drugs strategy (2005–12) was adopted, which explicitly aimed for a 'Measurable reduction of ... drug-related health and social risks' through a comprehensive system 'including prevention, early intervention, treatment, harm reduction, rehabilitation and social reintegration measures within the EU Member States' (European Union, 2004).

Council Recommendation of 18 June 2003 on the prevention and reduction of health-related harm associated with drug dependence (COM 2003/488/EC)

Member States should, in order to reduce substantially the incidence of drug-related health damage (such as HIV, hepatitis B and C and tuberculosis) and the number of drug-related deaths, make available, as an integral part of their overall drug prevention and treatment policies, a range of different services and facilities, particularly aiming at risk reduction; to this end, bearing in mind the general objective, in the first place, to prevent drug abuse, Member States should:

1. provide information and counselling to drug users to promote risk reduction and to facilitate their access to appropriate services;

2. inform communities and families and enable them to be involved in the prevention and reduction of health risks associated with drug dependence;

3. include outreach work methodologies within the national health and social drug policies, and support appropriate outreach work training and the development of working standards and methods; outreach work is defined as a community-oriented activity undertaken in order to contact individuals or groups from particular target populations, who are not effectively contacted or reached by existing services or through traditional health education channels;

4. encourage, when appropriate, the involvement of, and promote training for, peers and volunteers in outreach work, including measures to reduce drug-related deaths, first aid and early involvement of the emergency services;

5. promote networking and cooperation between agencies involved in outreach work, to permit continuity of services and better users' accessibility;

6. provide, in accordance with the individual needs of the drug abuser, drug-free treatment as well as appropriate substitution treatment supported by adequate psychosocial care and rehabilitation, taking into account the fact that a wide variety of different treatment options should be provided for the drug-abuser;

7. establish measures to prevent diversion of substitution substances while ensuring appropriate access to treatment;

8. consider making available to drug abusers in prison access to services similar to those provided to drug abusers not in prison, in a way that does not compromise the continuous and overall efforts of keeping drugs out of prison;

9. promote adequate hepatitis B vaccination coverage and prophylactic measures against HIV, hepatitis B and C, tuberculosis and sexually transmitted diseases, as well as screening for all the aforementioned diseases among injection drug users and their immediate social networks, and take the appropriate medical actions;

10. provide where appropriate, access to distribution of condoms and injection materials, and also to programmes and points for their exchange;

11. ensure that emergency services are trained and equipped to deal with overdoses;

12. promote appropriate integration between health, including mental health, and social care, and specialised approaches in risk reduction;

13. support training leading to a recognised qualification for professionals responsible for the prevention and reduction of health-related risks associated with drug dependence.

(Council of the European Union, 2003)

During this time, the European Monitoring Centre for Drugs and Drug Addiction (EMCDDA) established itself as a core instrument for the monitoring of evidence related to patterns of drug use and policy in the EU. Founded in 1993, and building upon work by the Pompidou Group of the Council of Europe, the EMCDDA generated the first EU-wide overviews of harm reduction activity at the turn of the century (for example, EMCDDA, 2000). As the EU grew, newer Member States began to develop national drug monitoring systems to feed into this process. In addition, it has been argued that 'there is clear evidence that "EU drugs guidance" was a model for national policies' for newer Member States (Commission of the European Communities, 2007; Hedrich et al., 2008, p. 513). By 2009, there was explicit support for harm reduction in national policy documents in all 27 EU Member States, as well as in Croatia, the Former Yugoslav Republic of Macedonia, Norway and Switzerland (Cook, 2009). This convergence towards a 'common position' (Hedrich et al., 2008, p. 513) has allowed the EU to be a strong advocate for harm reduction at international fora (see also MacGregor and Whiting, 2010).

The diffusion of harm reduction beyond Europe

In Australia, medical experts learned of NSPs in the Netherlands through a letter in the medical journal *The Lancet*, and in 1985 'harm minimisation' was universally adopted as a national policy (Wellbourne-Wood, 1999). In 1987, the Canadian Government adopted harm reduction as the framework for the National Drug Strategy (Canadian AIDS Society, 2000), and in the United States the first NSPs appeared before 1988 despite long-standing federal opposition to policies of harm reduction (Sherman and Purchase, 2001; Lane, 1993; Watters, 1996). In many US states, in the absence of legally endorsed needle and syringe distribution, some activist groups also began distributing bleach for cleaning syringes (Watters, 1996; Moss, 1990). The first harm reduction project in Latin America started in Brazil in 1989 (Bueno, 2007). Three years later, the HIV/AIDS Prevention Program for Drug Users was established in Buenes Aires. Touze et al. (1999) attributes 'the increasing amount of information on international harm reduction experiences in the mass media' as one of five contributory factors to the adoption of harm reduction in Argentina.

Much international attention was focused on selected European cities, especially Amsterdam (where a city official was hired to manage the demand for visits), and Liverpool, which hosted the first 'International Conference on the Reduction of Drug Related Harm' in 1990 (O'Hare, 2007b). In the same year, Frankfurt also hosted the first 'Conference of European Cities in the Centre of the Drug Trade'. New networks and alliances of cities and experts were emerging within and beyond Europe (including, in 1996, the International Harm Reduction Association). Bilateral funding and support from European governments also began to focus on harm reduction in the developing world (for example, the Asian Harm Reduction Network was founded in 1996 with support from the Dutch Government).

At a global level, the World Health Organization (WHO) was one of the first multilateral bodies to endorse the underlying principles of harm reduction in a meeting in Stockholm in 1986 (WHO, 1986). As early as 1974, the WHO Expert Committee on Drug Dependence had made reference to 'concern for preventing and reducing problems rather than just drug use' (Wodak, 2004). Other agencies of the United Nations system — including UNAIDS (the Joint United Nations Programme on HIV/AIDS, established in 1996) — showed greater reticence or ambiguity. Since the turn of the century, however, harm reduction appears firmly entrenched in the international policy dialogue (United Nations General Assembly, 2001; International Harm Reduction Association, 2009b).

In 2001, a meeting of the United Nations (UN) General Assembly (the chief policy-making body of the United Nations) adopted a 'Declaration of Commitment', which explicitly stated that 'harm reduction efforts related to drug use' should be implemented by Member States (United Nations General Assembly, 2001). Two years later, the WHO commissioned a review of scientific evidence on the effectiveness of harm reduction interventions targeting people who inject drugs, which was published in 2005 (WHO, 2005a; Wodak and Cooney, 2005; Farrell et al., 2005; Needle et al., 2005). That same year, methadone and buprenorphine were added to the WHO list of 'essential medicines' (WHO, 2005b), and UNAIDS released a position paper entitled 'Intensifying HIV Prevention' that listed a core package of harm reduction interventions (UNAIDS, 2005a) — later expanded to become the 'comprehensive harm reduction package' (WHO, 2009).

In December 2005, the UN General Assembly adopted a resolution requesting that UNAIDS assist in 'scaling-up HIV prevention, treatment, care and support with the aim of coming as close as possible to the goal of universal access to treatment by 2010 for all those who need it' (United Nations General Assembly, 2006). This led to the development of WHO, UNAIDS and UNODC guidelines on national target setting and programming on HIV prevention, treatment and care for injecting drug users, and focused advocacy efforts on the need for greater coverage towards 'universal access' (Donoghoe et al., 2008).

In contrast to the United Nations' HIV/AIDS response, there has been notably less support for harm reduction from the various UN drug control agencies. Within the UNAIDS programme, UNODC is the lead agency on the 'Prevention of transmission of HIV among injecting drug users and in prisons' (UNAIDS, 2005b) but this role remains overshadowed by its parallel remit to control the production and supply of illicit drugs. In addition, UNODC's governing body — the Commission on Narcotic Drugs (CND) — has seen ongoing resistance to harm reduction from some countries (including Japan, Russia and the United States), creating incoherence on a global policy position for harm reduction across the UN system (Hunt, 2008). The International Narcotics Control Board (the expert advisory body monitoring compliance with the UN Drug Conventions) has also regularly questioned the legality of some harm reduction interventions (Csete and Wolfe, 2007). Most recently, in 2009, CND adopted a draft ten-year 'Political Declaration' on drug control that (after months of negotiation and despite advocacy efforts from civil society, the UNAIDS Executive Director, and two UN Special Rapporteurs) resisted requests to include the term harm reduction (United Nations Commission on Narcotic Drugs, 2009; see also MacGregor and Whiting, 2010). Despite this, however, there were 84 countries around the world supporting harm reduction in either policy or practice by 2009, spanning every continent and including 31 European countries (Cook, 2009).

Current harm reduction practice in Europe

Europe remains one of the regions most supportive of harm reduction policy and practice, including through bilateral support from European governments to programmes in low- and middle-income countries. Yet there is still considerable variation within Europe in the extent and nature of harm reduction, and the coverage these interventions achieve among targeted populations (see Table 2.1, Figure 2.2 and Figure 2.3). We synthesise here current harm reduction practices in Europe, focusing on access to sterile injecting equipment, opioid substitution treatment and drug consumption rooms (DCRs) (see also Donoghoe et al., 2008; Aceijas et al., 2007; Kimber et al., 2010; Hedrich et al., 2010).

Access to sterile injecting equipment in Europe

By 2009, there were 77 countries and territories worldwide with at least one operational NSP, and 31 of these countries were European (Cook, 2009). With the exception of Iceland and Turkey, every European country where injecting drug use had been reported had one or more NSP (see Table 2.1). The most recent EU Member to begin providing sterile injecting equipment to people who inject drugs was Cyprus in 2007. Across the region, sterile injecting equipment is delivered through community-based specialist drugs services, pharmacies and outreach (including peer outreach), although not all service delivery models are employed in all countries. For example, access to free injecting equipment is only available through pharmacies in Northern Ireland, and two hospital-based outlets in Sweden (EMCDDA, 2009a, Table HSR-4). Syringe sales are legal in all countries, except in Sweden.

In 2007, subsidised pharmacy-based syringe distribution was available in 12 countries: Austria, Belgium, Croatia, Czech Republic, Denmark, France, Greece, the Netherlands, Portugal, Slovenia, Spain and the United Kingdom. Seven countries also used syringe vending machines (Austria, Denmark, France, Germany, Hungary, Italy and Luxembourg) and several had mobile service provision (EMCDDA, 2009a, Table HSR-4).

Table 2.1: Harm reduction practice in Europe

Country	Needle and syringe programmes	Opioid substitution therapy	Drug consumption rooms	Prison needle and syringe programmes	Prison opioid substitution therapy
Austria	✓	✓			✓
Belgium	✓	✓			✓
Bulgaria	✓	✓			
Croatia	✓	✓			✓
Cyprus	✓	✓			
Czech Republic	✓	✓			✓
Denmark	✓	✓			✓
Estonia	✓	✓			
Finland	✓	✓			✓
France	✓	✓			✓

Table 2.1 (continued)

Country	Needle and syringe programmes	Opioid substitution therapy	Drug consumption rooms	Prison needle and syringe programmes	Prison opioid substitution therapy
Germany	✓	✓	✓	✓	✓
Greece	✓	✓			
Hungary	✓	✓			
Iceland					
Ireland	✓	✓			✓
Italy	✓	✓			✓
Latvia	✓	✓			
Lithuania	✓	✓			
Luxembourg	✓	✓	✓	✓	✓
Former Yugoslav Republic of Macedonia	✓	✓			✓
Malta	✓	✓			✓
Netherlands	✓	✓	✓		✓
Norway	✓	✓	✓		✓
Poland	✓	✓			✓
Portugal	✓	✓		✓	✓
Romania	✓	✓		✓	✓
Slovakia	✓	✓			
Slovenia	✓	✓			✓
Spain	✓	✓	✓	✓	✓
Sweden	✓	✓			✓
Switzerland	✓	✓	✓	✓	✓
Turkey					
United Kingdom	✓	✓			✓

Source: Adapted from Cook, 2009.

Cross-country comparisons of coverage require robust reporting systems and harmonised indicators. While more robust than the data estimates available in other regions of the world, information remains unavailable for some European countries and patchy in others (EMCDDA, 2009a, Table HSR-5). In addition, estimating intervention 'coverage' — the proportion of target populations reached by harm reduction interventions, ideally with sufficient intensity to have probable impact — requires estimates of target population prevalence and intervention dose that are often unavailable or of dubious reliability (Heimer, 2008; Aceijas et al., 2007; Sharma et al., 2008). While most European countries have estimates of the prevalence of problem drug use, far fewer have specific estimates of the prevalence of drug injecting (EMCDDA, 2009a, Table PDU-1).

Available data indicates substantial variation in NSP coverage across the region (Figure 2.2). Even when comparing the number of NSP sites nationwide, an indicator that does not take into account the size of injecting populations, or factors impeding service access, they vary from several thousand (France), several hundred (United Kingdom, Portugal, Spain) to fewer than five (Cyprus, Greece, Romania and Sweden) (Cook and Kanaef, 2008). A number of European countries are providing over 150 syringes per injector per year through specialist NSPs (for example, the Czech Republic, Portugal, Norway and Luxembourg) (EMCDDA, 2010) — levels of coverage that may contribute to the aversion or reduction of HIV epidemics (Vickerman et al., 2006). However, this is by no means consistent throughout Europe, and coverage is almost negligible in some countries (Figure 2.2). In Sweden (one of the first countries to establish NSPs in Europe), there are only two NSP sites, and the intervention reaches approximately 1 200 people; just 5 % of the estimated total number of people who inject drugs in the country (Svenska Brukarföreningen et al., 2007; Olsson et al., 2001).

In addition, national NSP coverage estimates often hide dramatic geographical coverage variations, with provision in many cities, towns and rural areas woefully inadequate. In France, for example, there are no specialist drugs facilities with NSPs in some cities with a population over 100 000 and with known injecting drug use (ASUD, 2008).

Figure 2.2: Syringes distributed through specialised programmes, per estimated IDU per year (2002–07)

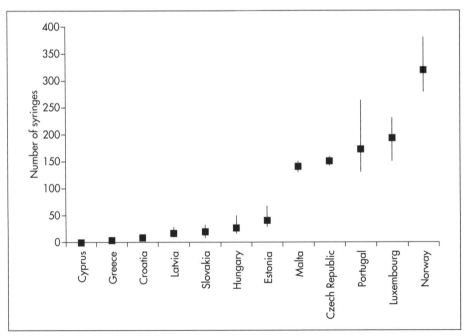

Source: EMCDDA, 2010.

Figure 2.2 illustrates that many people injecting drugs in Europe have inadequate access to subsidised or free syringes from NSPs. In several countries, current coverage levels are not high enough to avert or reverse an HIV epidemic in the IDU population (Vickerman et al., 2006; Heimer et al., 2008). It should be noted, however, that pharmacy sales of injecting equipment are not captured in Figure 2.2 and may be a common source of syringes for some people using drugs in the region.

Several countries have larger numbers of non-specialist pharmacy-based NSPs than specialist agencies (EMCDDA, 2006, Table NSP-1), and some (for example, Northern Ireland and Sweden) rely only on one type of outlet. Specialist NSPs, however, may provide more than needles and syringes alone, including a greater intensity of harm reduction advice and education, referrals into drug and HIV treatment, and a wider range of injecting equipment (including 'spoons' or 'cookers', water, filters, alcohol pads, tourniquets, condoms, acidic powders for dissolving drugs, and aluminium foil or inhalation pipes to assist 'route transitions' from injecting to smoking). Among the common developments in Europe is a diversification of outlets for needle and syringe exchange, which also provides a basis for scaling up syringe provision. In most countries several types of legal syringe sources, including NSPs, pharmacies and mobile units, are available to meet the needs of people who inject drugs.

Access to sterile injecting equipment in European prisons

Despite evidence-based reviews of effectiveness and recommendations for implementation (WHO, 2005a; Kimber et al., 2010), only 10 countries worldwide have introduced needle and syringe programmes (NSPs) in prisons. Six of these countries are European: Germany, Luxembourg, Portugal, Romania, Spain and Switzerland. The first prison NSP was introduced in Switzerland in 1992, followed four years later by Germany, and then Spain in 1997. Service models vary between prisons and include 'one-to-one' exchanges implemented by medical staff, exchanges operated by external NGOs or by peer workers, and the use of automated syringe vending machines.

The number of prisoners with access to this intervention varies across the region, but only in Spain have syringe programmes been made available across a national prison system. In recent years, Spain has scaled-up the availability, while in Germany a change in government led to the closure of six prison-based syringe programmes, leaving only one (WHO, 2005c). In 2009, Belgium and Scotland were in the process of developing pilot programmes. Researchers on this issue have concluded that the poor availability of this intervention in Europe 'cannot be based on logic' (Stöver et al., 2008a, p. 94).

Drug consumption rooms in Europe

With the exception of one Canadian and one Australian facility, all DCRs are operating in European countries (see Hedrich et al., 2010). Germany, Luxembourg, the Netherlands, Norway, Spain and Switzerland have an estimated 90 DCRs collectively, spanning 59 European cities (with the majority in the Netherlands and Germany). These facilities, which are usually integrated into low-threshold drugs agencies, allow the smoking and/or injecting of drugs under supervision by trained staff and without fear of arrest. In 2007, there were an estimated 13 727 supervised consumptions in Luxembourg's sole DCR and 11 600 in Norway's single facility. In Germany, large numbers of supervised consumptions occurred in Frankfurt (171 235 in 2007), Berlin (12 000 in 2006) and Hannover (29 332 in 2006). Despite positive evaluations, these facilities remain controversial both within Europe and elsewhere (Hedrich et al., 2010).

Access to opioid substitution treatment in Europe

By 2009, there were 65 countries and territories worldwide that provided opioid substitution treatment (OST) for drug dependence, almost half of which were in Europe (Cook, 2009). All European countries where injecting drug use is reported, with the exception of Iceland and Turkey, prescribe methadone and/or buprenorphine as treatment for opioid dependence (see Table 2.1).

In 2007, more than 650 000 opioid users were estimated to have received OST in Europe, with huge national variations in coverage (EMCDDA, 2009b). England and Wales, Italy and France were each prescribing the treatment to more than 100 000 people. Methadone is the most commonly prescribed OST medicine across the region, with the exceptions of Croatia, the Czech Republic, Cyprus, France, Finland, Latvia and Sweden, where high-dosage buprenorphine is used and Austria, where slow-release morphine is used more often (EMCDDA, 2009a, Table HSR-3). In general, the volume of OST prescribing increased between 2003 and 2007, with the most dramatic increases in Bulgaria, the Czech Republic, Estonia, Finland, Latvia and Norway. Decreases have been reported in Spain and a stabilisation of the demand for OST seemed also to take place in France, Luxembourg and the Netherlands (see EMCDDA, 2009a, HSR Tables).

Figure 2.3: Opioid maintenance treatment clients as a percentage of the estimated number of problem opioid users, 2007 or most recent year available

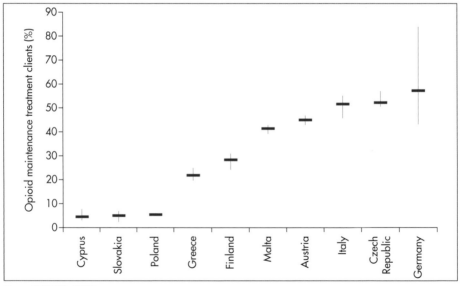

Source: EMCDDA, 2009b.

The coverage of OST provision varies greatly across the region. While countries such as Spain and the United Kingdom have large numbers of OST sites (2 229 and 1 030 respectively; EMCDDA, 2009c; United Kingdom National Treatment Agency, 2007), at least 10 European countries have fewer than 20 sites providing OST (EMCDDA, 2009c). Where estimates of the prevalence of problem drug use and data on clients in substitution treatment are available, the coverage of OST can be calculated (see Figure 2.3). While these estimates must be interpreted with caution due to uncertainties in both values, the results indicate significant variations in coverage across the EU — from 5 % in Cyprus and Slovakia to around 50 % in the Czech Republic, Germany and Italy. In a recent UN target-setting guide, reaching 40 % or more of people using opioids problematically with OST is cited as 'good coverage' (WHO et al., 2009).

Even where OST is available, several factors influence the effective utilisation of services. Long waiting lists, limited treatment slots, strict adherence policies, and an unwillingness of general practitioners to prescribe OST are all reported to impact upon accessibility in European countries. The costs attached to OST, the lack of 'take-home' doses and, in some cases, the need for medical insurance also act as barriers (Cook and Kanaef, 2008).

A number of European countries have remained at the forefront of innovation with regards to OST and drug dependence therapies. For those who cannot or do not wish to stop injecting, a small number of European countries prescribe injectable OST medicines (including the Netherlands, Switzerland and the United Kingdom) (Cook and Kanaef, 2008). The prescription of pharmaceutical heroin (diacetylmorphine) remains limited to a few European countries (Fischer et al., 2007; EMCDDA, 2009a, Table HSR-1). Despite positive findings from randomised controlled trials in several countries (indicating that diacetylmorphine is effective, safe, and cost-effective, and can reduce drug-related crime and improve patient health), only Denmark, Germany, the Netherlands, Switzerland and the United Kingdom include this intervention as part of the national response to drugs. Pilot programmes are currently underway in Belgium and Luxembourg (EMCDDA, 2009a, Table HSR-1).

Access to opioid substitution treatment in European prisons

European countries make up a large proportion of those worldwide that offer OST to prisoners; 23 countries in Europe out of 33 globally (Table 2.1). However, there are 'heterogeneous and inconsistent regulations and treatment modalities throughout Europe', and practice varies within countries and from prison to prison (Stöver et al., 2006). OST is available in the majority of prisons in Austria, Belgium, Croatia, Denmark, Luxembourg, Malta, Portugal, Slovenia and Spain (EMCDDA, 2009a, Figure HSR-2). It remains limited to specific geographical areas or a small proportion of prisons elsewhere in the region. In France, buprenorphine is more widely available in prisons than methadone (as is the case in the community), but this is still restricted to certain prisons (van der Gouwe et al., 2006). Latest estimates show that the national prison system of Spain provided OST to 19 010 prisoners, the highest number reported in Europe. Far fewer prisoners were receiving OST in other countries, including Ireland (1 295), Portugal (707), Belgium (300), Luxembourg (191), Finland (40), Serbia (10) and Montenegro (5) (Cook and Kanaef, 2008). Switzerland is the only country globally providing heroin (diacetylmorphine) maintenance to prisoners, although this is limited to two facilities (Stöver et al., 2008b).

The availability and provision of OST in European prisons has increased in recent years, but the regulations and practices surrounding prison OST vary greatly, leading to gaps between treatment need and provision. For example, prison OST is often subject to overly strict inclusion criteria, resulting in relatively few prisoners being able to access it (BISDRO and WIAD, 2008). Medical risks associated with disruption of long-term maintenance treatment when serving prison sentences remain an issue where OST is not available to prisoners (BISDRO and WIAD, 2008). The difference compared to the availability of OST in the community is particularly striking (EMCDDA, 2009a, Figure HSR-2). Four decades after the introduction of community OST in Europe and following the considerable scale-up in the past two decades, the gap between treatment provision inside and outside prison walls has further increased.

Conclusion

Key messages

- Harm reduction became widely established as a response to HIV/AIDS in the 1980s.
- Early policy and practice was pioneered by a number of European cities.
- By 2009, some 31 countries in Europe had needle and syringe programmes, and 31 had opioid substitution treatment.
- Of the European countries reporting injecting drug use, only Iceland and Turkey have not implemented harm reduction measures.
- Europe had a significant impact on the diffusion of harm reduction globally, and in 2009 there were 84 countries around the world that endorsed harm reduction in policy or practice.
- The European Union has played a crucial role in promoting and supporting harm reduction at the United Nations.

Since the mid-1980s, harm reduction has transformed from a peer-driven, grass-roots approach to an official policy of the United Nations, with Europe playing a leading role. European countries were among the 'earlier adopters' of harm reduction, facilitating its diffusion throughout Europe and beyond. Countries in Europe remain among the forerunners of innovations in harm reduction practice and technology — for example, developing new NSP products (such as coloured syringes to reduce sharing; Exchange Supplies, n.d.) and interventions to encourage transitions away from injecting (Pizzey and Hunt, 2008), delivering NSP and OST in prisons, and establishing DCRs. At the same time, definitions of harm reduction are expanding to embrace the need to protect the rights to health and access to services of people who use drugs, and to protect them from harmful drug policies, and Europe remains central to this dialogue and advocacy. There are now two decades of research and evaluation exploring the feasibility and impact of harm reduction interventions, especially among people who inject drugs (Kimber et al., 2010; Palmateer et al., 2010; Wiessing et al., 2009; Wodak and Cooney, 2005; Farrell et al., 2005; Institute of Medicine, 2007).

Yet harm reduction practice and policy varies across Europe (see also MacGregor and Whiting, 2010). Where national harm reduction responses are well established, these may be threatened by governmental changes. The global politics of drug use continue to be polarised. One recent instance of this was the non-inclusion of the term 'harm reduction' in the 'Political Declaration' of the 2009 Commission on Narcotic Drugs, prompting a coalition of twenty-five UN Member States (the majority being EU countries) to announce that they would interpret sections of the Declaration to nonetheless mean harm reduction (International Drug Policy Consortium, 2009). The need for networking, exchange and coordination within Europe remains if policies of harm reduction in Europe and beyond are to be defended, strengthened and properly evaluated.

Acknowledgements

The authors would like to thank Dagmar Hedrich and Lucas Wiessing from EMCDDA for their feedback and comments. In addition, we would also like to thank Cinzia Bentari, Esther Croes, Pat O'Hare, Tuukka Tammi, Daan van der Gouwe, Annette Verster and Alex Wodak.

References

Aceijas, C., Stimson, G. V., Hickman, M. and Rhodes, T., United Nations Reference Group on HIV/AIDS Prevention and Care among IDU in Developing and Transitional Countries (2004), 'Global overview of injecting drug use and HIV infection among injecting drug users', *AIDS* 18 (17), Nov. 19, pp. 2295–303.

Aceijas, C., Hickman, M., Donoghoe, M. C., Burrows, D. and Stuikyte, R. (2007), 'Access and coverage of needle and syringe programmes (NSP) in Central and Eastern Europe and Central Asia', *Addiction* 102 (8), pp. 1244–50.

ASUD (French National Association for the Safety of Drug Users) (2008), 'Global state of harm reduction qualitative data response', in Cook, C. and Kanaef, N., *Global state of harm reduction: mapping the response to drug-related HIV and hepatitis C epidemics*, International Harm Reduction Association, London.

Bergeron, H., and Kopp, P. (2002), 'Policy paradigms, ideas, and interests: the case of the French public health policy toward drug abuse', *The Annals of the American Academy of Political and Social Science* 582 (1), pp. 37–48.

Bueno, R. (2007), 'The Latin American harm reduction network (RELARD): successes and challenges', *International Journal of Drug Policy* 18, pp. 145–7.

Buning, E. C., Van Brussel, G. H. and Van Santen, G. (1990), 'The "methadone by bus" project in Amsterdam', *British Journal of Addiction* 85, pp. 1247–50.

Canadian AIDS Society (2000), *Position statement: harm reduction and substance use.* Available at www.cdnaids.ca/web/setup.nsf/(ActiveFiles)/PS_Harm_Reduction_and_Substance_Use/$file/Harm_Reduction_and_Substance_Use_En_Red.pdf.

Cook, C. (2009), *Harm reduction policies and practices worldwide: an overview of national support for harm reduction in policy and practice,* International Harm Reduction Association, London.

Cook, C. and Kanaef, N. (2008), *Global state of harm reduction: mapping the response to drug-related HIV and hepatitis C epidemics*, International Harm Reduction Association, London.

Council of the European Union (2003), 'Council Recommendation of 18 June 2003 on the prevention and reduction of health-related harm associated with drug dependence', *Official Journal of the European Union* 3 Jul, L165 (46). Available at http://eur-lex.europa.eu/JOHtml.do?uri=OJ:L:2003:165:SOM:EN:HTML.

Csete, J. and Wolfe, D. (2007), *Closed to reason: the International Narcotics Control Board and HIV/AIDS*, Canadian HIV/AIDS Legal Network and the International Harm Reduction Development Program of the Open Society Institute, Toronto/New York, p. 3.

Department Committee on Morphine and Heroin Addiction (1926) *Report*. Available at www.drugtext.org/index.php/en/reports/220.

Donoghoe, M., Verster, A., Pervilhac, C. and Williams, P. (2008), 'Setting targets for universal access to HIV prevention, treatment and care for injecting drug users (IDUs): towards consensus and improved guidance', *International Journal of Drug Policy* 19 (Supplement 1), pp. S5–S14.

EMCDDA (European Monitoring Centre for Drugs and Drug Addiction) (2000), *Reviewing current practice in substitution treatment*, Office for Official Publications of the European Communities, Luxembourg.

EMCDDA (2006), Table NSP-1: Number of syringe provision outlets and number of syringes (in thousands) exchanged, distributed or sold 2003, Statistical bulletin 2006. Available at http://stats06.emcdda.europa.eu/en/elements/nsptab02-en.html.

EMCDDA (2008), *National drug related research in Europe*, Selected issue, EMCDDA, Lisbon.

EMCDDA (2009a), Statistical bulletin 2009, Available at http://www.emcdda.europa.eu/stats09. Tables HSR 'Health and social responses'. Available at http://www.emcdda.europa.eu/stats09/hsr. Tables PDU 'Problematic drug use population'. Available at http://www.emcdda.europa.eu/stats09/pdu.

EMCDDA (2009b), *Annual report 2009: the state of the drugs problem in Europe*, EMCDDA, Lisbon.

EMCDDA (2009c), Drug treatment overviews. Available at www.emcdda.europa.eu/responses/treatment-overviews.

EMCDDA (2010), *Trends in injecting drug use in Europe*, Selected issue, European Monitoring Centre for Drugs and Drug Addiction, Lisbon.

European Commission (2007), 'Report from the Commission to the European Parliament and the Council on the implementation of the Council Recommendation of 18 June 2003 on the prevention and reduction of health-related harm associated with drug dependence', COM (2007) 199 final (eur-lex.europa.eu/LexUriServ/site/en/com/2007/com2007_0199en01.pdf).

European Union (2000a), *European Union Drug Strategy 2000–2004*. Available at http://www.emcdda.europa.eu/html.cfm/index2005EN.html.

European Union (2000b), *The European Union Action Plan on Drugs 2000–2004*. Available at http://www.emcdda.europa.eu/html.cfm/index1338EN.html.

European Union (2004), *European Union Drugs Strategy 2005–2012*. Available at http://www.emcdda.europa.eu/html.cfm/index6790EN.html.

Exchange Supplies (n.d.), *Nevershare syringe*. Available at http://www.exchangesupplies.org/needle_exchange_supplies/never_share_syringe/never_share_syringe_intro.html.

Farrell, M., Gowing, L., Marsden, J., Ling, W. and Ali, R. (2005), 'Effectiveness of drug dependence treatment in HIV prevention', *International Journal of Drug Policy* 16 (Supplement 1), pp. S67–S75.

Fischer, B., Oviedo-Joekes, E., Blanken, P., et al.. (2007), 'Heroin-assisted treatment (HAT) a decade later: a brief update on science and politics', *Journal of Urban Health* 84, 552–62.

Greenwald, G. (2009), *Drug decriminalization in Portugal: lessons for creating fair and successful drug policies*, Cato Institute, USA.

Hartnoll, R. and Hedrich, D. (1996), 'AIDS prevention and drug policy: dilemmas in the local environment', in Rhodes, T. and Hartnoll, R. (eds) *AIDS, drugs and prevention: perspectives on individual and community action*, Routledge, London, pp. 42–65.

Hartnoll, R., Avico, U., Ingold, F. R., et al. (1989), 'A multi-city study of drug misuse in Europe', *Bulletin on Narcotics* 41, pp. 3–27.

Hedrich, D., Pirona, A. and Wiessing, L. (2008), 'From margins to mainstream: the evolution of harm reduction responses to problem drug use in Europe', *Drugs: education, prevention and policy* 15, pp. 503–17.

Hedrich, D., Kerr, T. and Dubois-Arber, F. (2010), 'Drug consumption facilities in Europe and beyond', in European Monitoring Centre for Drugs and Drug Addiction (EMCDDA), *Harm reduction: evidence, impacts and challenges*, Rhodes, T. and Hedrich, D. (eds), Scientific Monograph Series No. 10, Publications Office of the European Union, Luxembourg.

Heimer, R. (2008), 'Community coverage and HIV prevention: assessing metrics for estimating HIV incidence through syringe exchange', *International Journal of Drug Policy* 19 (Supplement 1), pp. S65–S73.

Huber, C. (1995), 'Needle park: what can we learn from the Zürich experience?' *Addiction* 90, pp. 291–2.

Hunt, P. (2008), *Human rights, health and harm reduction: states' amnesia and parallel universes: an address by Professor Paul Hunt, UN Special Rapporteur on the right to the highest attainable standard of health*, Harm Reduction 2008: IHRA's 19th International Conference, Barcelona — 11 May 2008, International Harm Reduction Association, London.

IHRA (International Harm Reduction Association) (2009a), *What is harm reduction? A position statement from the International Harm Reduction Association*, International Harm Reduction Association, London.

IHRA (2009b), *Building consensus: a reference guide to human rights and drug policy*, International Harm Reduction Association, London.

IHRA (2009c), *German parliament votes in favour of heroin assisted treatment*. Available at www.ihra.net/June200 9#GermanParliamentVotesinFavourofHeroinAssistedTreatment.

IHRA and Human Rights Watch (2009), *Building consensus: a reference guide to human rights and drug policy*, International Harm Reduction Association, London, pp. 18–19.

Institute of Medicine (2007), *Preventing HIV infection among injecting drug users in high risk countries: an assessment of the evidence*, Committee on the Prevention of HIV Infection Among Injecting Drug Users in High-Risk Countries, National Academies Press, Washington.

International Drug Policy Consortium (2009), 'The 2009 Commission on Narcotic Drugs and its high level segment: report of proceedings', *IDPC Briefing Paper*, April.

Kazatchkine, M. and McClure, C. (2009), *From evidence to action: reflections on the global politics of harm reduction and HIV*, International Harm Reduction Association, London.

Kimber, J., Palmateer, N., Hutchinson, S., et al. (2010), 'Harm reduction among injecting drug users: evidence of effectiveness', in European Monitoring Centre for Drugs and Drug Addiction (EMCDDA), *Harm reduction:*

evidence, impacts and challenges, Rhodes, T. and Hedrich, D. (eds), Scientific Monograph Series No. 10, Publications Office of the European Union, Luxembourg.

Lane, S. D. (1993), *Needle exchange: a brief history.* Available at www.aegis.com/law/journals/1993/HKFNE009.html.

MacGregor, S. and Whiting, M. (2010), 'The development of European drug policy and the place of harm reduction within this', in European Monitoring Centre for Drugs and Drug Addiction (EMCDDA), *Harm reduction: evidence, impacts and challenges*, Rhodes, T. and Hedrich, D. (eds), Scientific Monograph Series No. 10, Publications Office of the European Union, Luxembourg.

Michels, I. I., Stöver, H. and Gerlach, R. (2007), 'Substitution treatment for opiate addicts in Germany', *Harm Reduction Journal* 4 (5). Available at http://www.harmreductionjournal.com/content/4/1/5.

Moss, A. (1990), 'Control of HIV infection in injecting drug users in San Francisco', in Strang, J. and Stimson, G. V., *AIDS and drug misuse: the challenge for policy and practice in the 1990s*, Routledge, London.

Needle, R. H., Burrows, D., Friedman, S. R., et al. (2005), 'Effectiveness of community-based outreach in preventing HIV/AIDS among injecting drug users', *International Journal of Drug Policy* 16 (Supplement 1), pp. 45–57.

O'Hare, P. (2007a), 'Harm reduction in the Mersey region', *International Journal of Drug Policy* 18, p. 152.

O'Hare, P. (2007b), 'Merseyside: the first harm reduction conferences and the early history of harm reduction', *International Journal of Drug Policy* 18, pp. 141–4.

Olsson, B., Adamsson Wahren, C. and Byqvist, S. (2001), *Det tunga narkotikamissbrukets omfattning I Sverige 1998*, CAN, Stockholm.

Palmateer, N., Kimber, J., Hickman, M., et al. (2010), 'Preventing hepatitis C and HIV transmission among injecting drug users: a review of reviews', *Addiction*, in press.

Pizzey, R. and Hunt, N. (2008), 'Distributing foil from needle and syringe programmes (NSPs) to promote transitions from heroin injecting to chasing: an evaluation', *Harm Reduction Journal* 5, p. 24.

Rhodes, T. (1993), 'Time for community change: what has outreach to offer?', *Addiction* 88, pp. 1317–20.

Rhodes, T. and Hartnoll, R. (1991), 'Reaching the hard to reach: models of HIV outreach health education', in Aggleton, P., Davies, P. and Hart, G. (eds), *AIDS: responses, interventions and care*, Falmer Press, London.

Robertson, J. R., Bucknall, A. B. V., Welsby, P. D., et al. (1986), 'Epidemic of AIDS-related virus (HTLV-III/LAV) infection among intravenous drug abusers', *British Medical Journal* 292, p. 527.

Sharma, M., Burrows, D. and Bluthenthal, R. (2008), 'Improving coverage and scale-up of HIV prevention, treatment and care for injecting drug users: moving the agenda forward', *International Journal of Drug Policy* 19 (Supplement 1), pp. 1–4.

Sherman, S. G. and Purchase, D. (2001) 'Point defiance: a case study of the United States' first public needle exchange in Tacoma, Washington', *International Journal of Drug Policy* 12, pp. 45–57.

Stimson, G. V. (1989), 'Syringe exchange programmes for injecting drug users', *AIDS* 3, pp. 253–60.

Stimson, G. V. (1990a), 'AIDS and HIV: the challenge for British drug services', *British Journal of Addiction* 85 (3), pp. 329–39.

Stimson, G. V. (1990b), 'Revising policy and practice: new ideas about the drugs problem', in Strang, J. and Stimson, G., *AIDS and drug misuse: the challenge for policy and practice in the 1990s*, London, Routledge.

Stimson, G. V. (1991), 'Risk reduction by drug users with regard to HIV infection', *International Review of Psychiatry* 3, pp. 401–15.

Stimson, G. V. (1994), 'Reconstruction of sub-regional diffusion of HIV infection among injecting drug users in South East Asia: implications for early intervention', *AIDS* 8, pp. 1630–2.

Stimson, G. V. (1995), 'AIDS and injecting drug use in the United Kingdom, 1987–1993: the policy response and the prevention of the epidemic', *Social Science and Medicine* 41 (5), pp. 699–716.

Stimson, G. V. (2007), 'Harm reduction — coming of age: a local movement with global impact', *International Journal of Drug Policy* 18, pp. 67–9.

Stimson, G. V. and Lart, R. (1990), 'HIV, drugs and public health in England: new words, old tunes', *International Journal of the Addictions* 26, pp. 1263–77.

Stimson, G. V. and Oppenheimer, E. (1982), *Heroin addiction: treatment and control in Britain*, Tavistock, London.

Stöver, H., Casselman, J. and Hennebel, L. (2006), 'Substitution treatment in European prisons: a study of policies and practices in 18 European countries', *International Journal of Prisoner Health* March, 2 (1), pp. 3–12.

Stöver, H., Weilandt, C., Zurhold, H., Hartwig, C. and Thane, K. (2008a), *Final report on prevention, treatment, and harm reduction services in prison, on reintegration services on release from prison and methods to monitor/analyse drug use among prisoners*, European Commission Directorate — General for Health and Consumers, Drug Policy and Harm Reduction, SANCO/2006/C4/02.

Stöver, H., Weilandt, C., Huisman, A., et al. (2008b), *Reduction of drug-related crime in prison: the impact of opioid substitution treatment on the manageability of opioid dependent prisoners*, BISDRO, University of Bremen, Bremen.

Svenska Brukarföreningen/Swedish Drug Users Union and International Harm Reduction Association (2007), *Briefing to the Committee on Economic, Social and Cultural Rights on the fifth report of Sweden on the implementation of the International Covenant on Economic, Social and Cultural Rights,* International Harm Reduction Association, London.

Touze, G., Rossi, D., Goltzman, P., et al. (1999), 'Harm reduction in Argentina: a challenge to non-governmental organisations', *International Journal of Drug Policy* 10, pp. 47–51.

van der Gouwe, D., Gallà, M., van Gageldonk, A., et al. (2006), *Prevention and reduction of health-related harm associated with drug dependence: an inventory of policies, evidence and practices in the EU relevant to the implementation of the Council Recommendation of 18 June 2003,* Trimbos Instituut, Utrecht.

UNAIDS (Joint United Nations Programme on HIV/AIDS) (2005a), *Intensifying HIV prevention: UNAIDS Policy Position Paper*, UNAIDS, Geneva. Available at http://data.unaids.org/publications/irc-pub06/jc1165-intensif_hiv-newstyle_en.pdf.

UNAIDS (2005b), *UNAIDS Technical Support Division of Labour: summary & rationale*, UNAIDS, Geneva. Available at data.unaids.org/una-docs/JC1146-Division_of_labour.pdf

United Kingdom National Treatment Agency (2007), *Global state — data collection response*. Cited in Cook, C. and Kanaef, N. (2008), *Global state of harm reduction 2008: mapping the response to drug-related HIV and hepatitis C epidemics*, International Harm Reduction Association, London.

United Nations Commission on Narcotic Drugs (2009), *Report on the fifty-second session (14 March 2008 and 11–20 March 2009) Economic and Social Council Official Records, 2009: supplement no. 8 — political declaration and plan of action on international cooperation towards an integrated and balanced strategy to counter the world drug problem,* United Nations Commission on Narcotic Drugs, Vienna.

United Nations General Assembly Sixtieth Special Session (2006), 'Agenda item 45: resolution adopted by the General Assembly. 60/262', *Political declaration on HIV/AIDS,* New York.

United Nations General Assembly Twenty-Sixth Special Session (2001), 'Agenda item 8: resolution adopted by the General Assembly. S-26/2', *Declaration of Commitment on HIV/AIDS,* New York.

Vickerman, P., Hickman, M., Rhodes, T. and Watts, C. (2006), 'Model projections on the required coverage of syringe distribution to prevent HIV epidemics among injecting drug users', *Journal of Acquired Immune Deficiency Syndromes* 42, pp. 355–61.

Watters, J. (1996), 'Americans and syringe exchange: roots of resistance', in Rhodes, T. and Hartnoll, R. (eds), *AIDS, drugs and prevention: perspectives on individual and community action,* Routledge, London, pp. 22–41.

Wellbourne-Wood, D. (1999), 'Harm reduction in Australia: some problems putting policy into practice', *International Journal of Drug Policy* 10, pp. 403–13.

Wiessing, L., van de Laar, M. J., Donoghoe, M. C., et al. (2008), 'HIV among injecting drug users in Europe: increasing trends in the east', *Eurosurveillance* 13 (50). Available at http://www.eurosurveillance.org/ViewArticle. aspx?ArticleId=19067.

Wiessing, L., Likatavičius, G., Klempová, D., et al. (2009), 'Associations between availability and coverage of HIV-prevention measures and subsequent incidence of diagnosed HIV infection among injection drug users', *American Journal of Public Health* 99 (6), pp.1049–52.

Wodak, A. (2004), 'Letter from Dr Alex Wodak to Dr Zerhouni at the US National Institute of Health NIH'. Available at www.drugpolicy.org/library/05_07_04wodaknih.cfm.

Wodak, A. and Cooney, A. (2005), 'Effectiveness of sterile needle and syringe programmes', *International Journal of Drug Policy* 16, S1, pp. S31–S44.

WHO (World Health Organization) (1986), *Consultation on AIDS among drug abusers,* 7–9 October 1986, Stockholm, ICP/ADA535(S).

WHO (2005a), *Evidence for action series.* Available at www.who.int/hiv/pub/idu/idupolicybriefs/en/index.html and http://whqlibdoc.who.int/publications/2007/9789241595780_eng.pdf.

WHO (2005b), *Essential medicines: WHO model list* (14th edition). Available at http://whqlibdoc.who.int/ hq/2005/a87017_eng.pdf.

WHO (2005c), *Status paper on prisons, drugs and harm reduction,* World Health Organization, Copenhagen. Available at http://www.euro.who.int/document/e85877.pdf.

WHO (2009), *HIV/AIDS: comprehensive harm reduction package.* Available at http://www.who.int/hiv/topics/ idu/harm_reduction/en/index.html.

WHO, UNODC (United Nations Office on Drugs and Crime) and UNAIDS (2009), *Technical guide for countries to set targets for universal access to HIV prevention, treatment and care for injecting drug users,* WHO, UNODC/ UNAIDS.

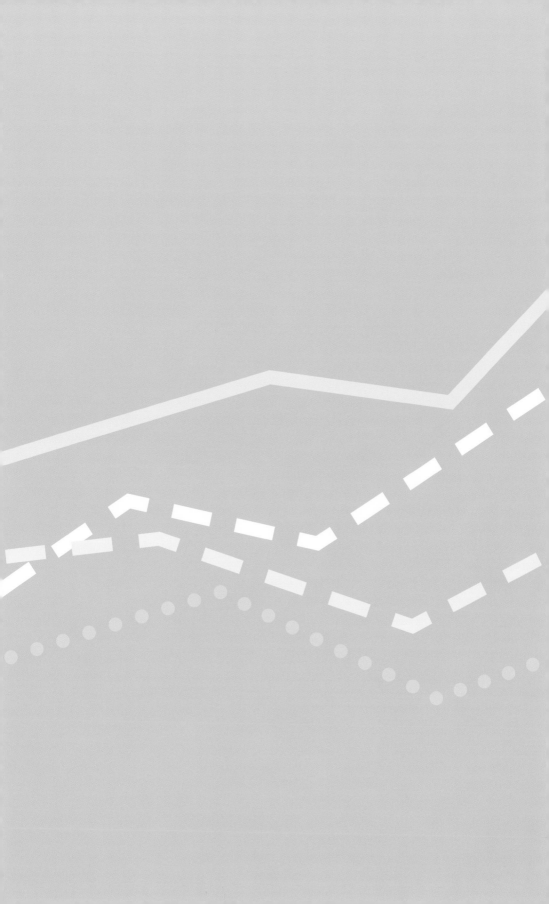

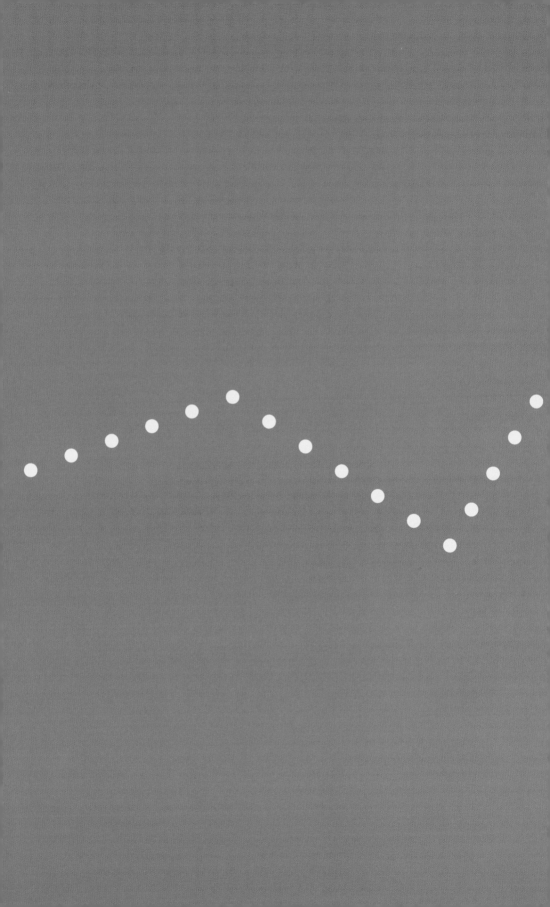

Chapter 3
The development of European drug policy and the place of harm reduction within this

Susanne MacGregor and Marcus Whiting

Abstract

This chapter gives a necessarily brief overview of the development of drug policy at the European Union level in recent decades. These developments are set within the wider context of moves towards European integration. The chapter considers how far a process of convergence has occurred, within which harm reduction may have a central place; and how far this gives a distinctive character to European policy internationally. It draws mainly on documentary evidence and scholarly accounts of policy development. Key processes identified include: the achievement of agreed policy statements at intergovernmental level; the influence of guidance, action plans and target setting; the role of the European Monitoring Centre for Drugs and Drug Addiction (EMCDDA); the spread of information; networking, training and collaborative activities among researchers and practitioners; the size and shape of the drug problem; and the impact of HIV/AIDS. While common agreements have been forged at the supra-national level, differences remain between and within different Member States, reflecting their social and political institutions, differing public attitudes, religious and cultural values, and varying financial and human resources.

Keywords: European drug policy, harm reduction, convergence, cultural and institutional differences, political influences.

Introduction

A steady, progressive evolution of drugs policy, towards a more rational, evidence-based approach, has been the ambition of medical humanists and technocrats involved in policy and practice networks in the EU. Advocates like the International Harm Reduction Association and the Open Society Institute also hope to see harm reduction principles entrenched within policy. In the light of this, the aim of this chapter is to explore how policies have developed over time and what forces have been influential, considering in particular what has been achieved in terms of policy convergence and the introduction of harm reduction. To do this, we draw largely upon an analysis of the content of EU policy documents and key published books and articles.

We define 'Europe' here as primarily referring to the European Union, and 'drug policy' as statements in EU policy documents. However, we recognise that Europe is a larger geographical and cultural entity than the European Union itself, and that the national policies of European countries also form part of 'European drug policy'. In addition, we are aware that policies cannot be judged solely on the basis of statements in documents or the rhetoric of politicians and other players on the policy field. 'Policy' more broadly defined refers to the way a society meets needs, maintains control and manages risks. To describe and assess this would require analysis of what actually happens and with what impacts. Policy judged by functions or effects may result from forces other than the overt goals in formal policy statements. In a short chapter such as this, it is not possible to analyse or account for all these forces. We have chosen instead to look mainly at the formal development of EU drug policy, but attempt to set this within its context and to indicate that the process of development has not been inevitable and has at times been contentious.

Methods

This paper draws on research towards a social history of the development of the drugs problem and responses to it over a 30-year period. Here the focus is on European drug policy and specifically its links to public health and discussions of the role of harm reduction approaches. Methods used have included reviews of secondary literature in books and journals and of documentary evidence, especially that available through European institutions like the European Commission and the EMCDDA. Observation of discussions at conferences and networking meetings has also played a part, along with interviews with some of the key players in the development of policy over this period. A detailed narrative history is not possible in a short chapter so the approach adopted here is to present an interpretative account of developments.

The context for policy development

Development of the European Union

The European Union (EU) is a political and economic union in which sovereign countries agree to share or give up some attributions and powers. A simple description of the process of policy development would note that in any given field it starts with open intergovernmental discussions then moves into areas where the union's institutions obtain some power of proposition, action or decision. The EU is thus a policy actor in itself and one that is progressively trying to create convergence, while limited in its influence on actions at national level.

The EU has expanded rapidly to its current 27 Member States in a period of economic liberalisation involving free movement of both labour and capital and a reduction in border controls. The size and shape of the drugs problem and responses to it within Europe have been influenced by these larger trends and the series of treaties that marked this trajectory: the Single European Act 1986; Maastricht Treaty 1993; Amsterdam Treaty 1997; and the most recent Lisbon Treaty. These Acts were important contextual features and, together with the collapse of the Soviet Union and reductions in border controls, influenced the supply of illicit drugs and the responses of criminal justice agencies. A number of key principles are important features of the European Project, especially human rights, electoral democracy and free trade.

Throughout this period there have been two different visions of the European Union — characterised as the 'widening' or 'deepening' scenarios — with enlargement paralleling the dominance of the widening, free market approach. This approach emphasises economic cooperation alongside the retention of national sovereignty and national differences with regard to social and political institutions. The deepening agenda would hope to see agreement on social policies.

While drug policy does not fit neatly into conventional models of social policy, attitudes to drugs and social responses to problems do reflect the historical development of institutions (constraining and shaping options for policy change) and cultural norms relating to rights and responsibilities. Moves towards a shared EU approach to drugs have been in this sense part of the European Project. The development of a drug policy could indicate some success for moves to deepen integration, with the development of shared practices related to social and criminal justice policies. The widening agenda — with enlargement increasing the number of EU Member States — clearly presents problems for integrationist ambitions as it increases the range of difference to be potentially coordinated in any shared strategy — differences of culture, language, path dependency in the development of institutions, human and financial resources: these and more influence the potential for acceptance and implementation of policy proposals.

National policies

We begin with a brief overview of the current state of play, considering what has been achieved in terms of policy coordination and recognition of a role for harm reduction. In 2008, there were 14 national strategies, 15 action plans, six programmes, two policy notes/ documents, one white paper, one governmental plan, one implementation decree, and numerous provincial, regional, local or devolved administration documents relating to drug policy within the countries of the EU. A general trend can be discerned towards the production of explicit strategies and related action plans, increasingly linked to an overall EU drugs strategy. Within these statements, the term 'harm reduction' is often present and in some countries is specifically identified as a major policy goal (see Table 3.1).

Table 3.1: **Overview of national drug strategies and references to harm reduction within them**

Country	Policy	References to harm reduction
Belgium	Drug policy note 2001; covers both licit and illicit drugs	Harm reduction (plus assistance and reintegration) one of three pillars of policy
Bulgaria	National anti-drug strategy 2003–08 plus action plan	Programme for the development of methadone maintenance adopted 2006
Czech Republic	National Drug Policy Strategy 2005–09 plus action plan	Harm reduction one of seven policy fields in action plan
Denmark	Action plan 'The fight against drugs' 2003	Harm reduction as a goal 'paradoxical' but should be an integrated element — some of these initiatives may be 'pragmatic and reasonable'

Table 3.1 (continued)

Country	Policy	References to harm reduction
Germany	Action plan on drugs and drug addiction 2003 — focus on all psychotropic substances	Harm reduction (with survival aid) one of four pillars of policy
Estonia	National strategy on the prevention of drug dependency 2005 plus triennial action plans	Harm reduction one of six pillars of policy
Ireland	National drug strategy 2001	Need for continued efforts to enhance harm reduction measures, such as needle and syringe programmes (NSPs)
Greece	National strategy on drugs 2006 — focus on illicit drugs and alcohol	
Spain	National drug strategy 1999 plus action plan 2005	Harm reduction a specific section in the strategy, with objective to ensure access to harm reduction programmes for drug dependent people with targets, especially NSPs and vaccinations
France	Governmental plan to fight drugs and drug addiction 2008; covers both alcohol and illicit drugs	Harm reduction (with social reintegration) one of five axes of the plan
Italy	New action plan 2008	
Cyprus	National drug strategy 2004 plus two action plans — focus on licit and illicit substances	Harm reduction objectives listed, including NSPs and opioid substitution treatment (OST)
Latvia	State programme for the reduction of addiction to narcotic and psychotropic substances 2005–08	
Lithuania	National strategy on drug addiction prevention and control, and related national programme for implementation	
Luxembourg	National strategy and action plan on drugs and drug addiction 2005–09	Treatment is preferred to harm reduction, but integrated and complementary approach required; reduction of risks, harms and nuisance one of four axes of policy
Hungary	National strategy on drugs 2000–09, plus action plan 2007	Specific section on harm reduction, with reference to outreach, OST and NSPs as priority goals in context of development of treatment services
Malta	Drugs policy document adopted 2008	

Table 3.1 (continued)

Country	Policy	References to harm reduction
Netherlands	White Paper 1995 Drugs Policy: continuity and change — distinguishes soft and hard drugs	To reduce harm to users, one of four major objectives of policy
Austria	No federal strategy or action plan — objectives devolved by the nine provinces	
Poland	National programme for counteracting drug addiction 2006	Harm reduction (with treatment, rehabilitation and social reintegration) one of five pillars of policy
Portugal	National strategy for the fight against drugs 1999, plus strategic plan for implementation	Specific sections on risk and harm reduction. Aim to constantly improve risk and harm reduction interventions. The boundaries between prevention, treatment, risk and harm reduction, reintegration and dissuasion are 'artificial'
Romania	Anti-drug strategy 2005 plus action plan	Specific section on harm reduction in action plan
Slovenia	Resolution on the national programme on drugs 2004	Specific discussion of harm reduction programmes but in the context of noting that there are too few — aim to set up network of harm reduction programmes and increase access
Slovakia	National programme for the fight against drugs 2005 plus action plans	
Finland	1997 national drug strategy and 2007 resolution	Harm reduction (together with treatment) one of seven policy areas
Sweden	Separate plans for alcohol and drugs but adopted together: national alcohol and drug action plans 2006	
United Kingdom	Drugs: protecting families and communities 2008 — ten-year strategy plus three-year action plan	Reference to harm minimisation through NSE and relevant treatments

Note: The full text versions of the national drug strategies are available at http://www.emcdda.europa.eu/policy-and-law/national/strategies.

At the present time, EMCDDA states, 'the prevention and reduction of drug-related harm is a public health objective in all Member States and in the EU drug strategy and action plan ... The general European trend is one of growth and consolidation of harm reduction measures' (EMCDDA, 2009, p. 31). But a closer look at the current situation gives a more qualified picture. EU Member States do employ a combination of some of the main harm reduction measures, which 'are reported to be available in all countries except Turkey [but] considerable differences exist in the range and levels of service provision' (EMCDDA, 2009, p. 31).

Thus, harm reduction occupies a clear place within European policies but its influence should not be overstated. However, while differences between countries remain, these are not as great as in earlier times. The move to a shared position has involved compromises and a shift to the centre. Shared features of policy are also evident in the stress on research and information exchange and use of managerialist approaches, involving action plans, logframes, strategies, targets and benchmarks.

How, then, do we explain continuing differences at national level? Do drug policies follow the shape of the drug problem in a country, and is this in itself a reflection of attitudes to drug use? Or can the policy environment influence attitudes and thus the size and nature of drug taking and associated problems?

Since 1998, the year of the UNGASS Twentieth Session Declarations (United Nations, 1998), 'most European countries have moved towards an approach that distinguishes between the drug trafficker, who is viewed as a criminal, and the drug user, who is seen more as a sick person in need of treatment' (EMCDDA, 2008, p. 22). Differences remain, however, for example on whether or not to set threshold quantities for personal possession. There are differences also regarding maximum or probable sentences and whether or not these are becoming more punitive or lenient. Encouragement into treatment (increasingly as an alternative to a criminal charge or sentence) is developing across countries, but differences remain with regard to the stage when referral to treatment occurs. In the majority of Member States, substitution treatment combined with psychosocial care is the predominant option for opioid users. Shared concerns about public nuisance are visible, as are concerns around driving under the influence or use in the workplace.

In general, public attitudes to drug taking appear to remain primarily restrictive. For example, a Eurobarometer survey in 2006 conducted in 29 countries found only 26 % supporting legalisation of the possession of cannabis for personal use (ranging from 8 % in Finland to 49 % in the Netherlands) (Eurobarometer, 2006, pp. 36, 49–50). A review of attitudes to drug policy in three countries with relatively restrictive policies (Bulgaria, Poland and Sweden) and three countries with relatively liberal ones (Czech Republic, the Netherlands and Denmark) found that for most people the most important factor influencing them not to use illicit drugs was concern about health consequences (ranging from 73 % in Bulgaria to 27 % in Holland). Fewer were primarily influenced by the fact of illegality (ranging from 3 % in Denmark to 19 % in Poland). Most saw prevention and education as the most important policy area (ranging from 17 % in Poland to 57 % in Sweden). Needle and syringe programmes (NSPs) were supported by some respondents (ranging between 22 % in Sweden and 54 % in Denmark) but opposed by others (ranging from 7 % in Denmark to 29 % in Bulgaria).

This survey found a correlation between public attitudes on drug use and a country's drug policies (Hungarian Civil Liberties Union, 2009). Countries were deeply divided in their views on the decriminalisation of cannabis. The majority considered drug use to be a public health issue and there was wide acceptance of NSPs as a response to HIV. However, the majority believed that prescribing heroin for addicts would do more harm than good. It is worth noting that some of the countries described above as relatively liberal have seen legislative and administrative moves to more repressive responses in recent years. So there is movement in a number of directions, away from harm reduction and public health principles in some cases, while in others there is a move towards agreement around a core of the more moderate and less contentious issues.

European Union drug policy

EU Member States are the main actors in the drug field, and drug legislation is a matter of national competence. However, the Treaties explicitly acknowledge the need to deal with drug issues at EU level, in particular in the fields of justice and home affairs, and public health. The tension between ideas of law enforcement and ideas of public health is built into this policy area. Drug trafficking has been a key area for developing cooperation between police and judiciaries. A multidisciplinary group has been working on organised crime and increased cooperation has developed between police, customs and Europol groups. The main technical and policy forum to facilitate joint efforts of Member States and the Commission is the EU Council's Horizontal Drugs Group (HDG). This meets about once a month, bringing together representatives of Member States and the Commission. The HDG is playing a key role in the drafting of European drug policy documents. One of them is the current EU drugs strategy (2005–12) endorsed by the Council of the European Union in December 2004, which sets out two general aims:

1. The EU aims at a contribution to the attainment of a high level of health protection, well being and social cohesion by complementing Member States' action in preventing and reducing drug use, dependence and drug related harms to health and society; and

2. the EU and its Member States aim to ensure a high level of security for the general public by taking action against drug production, cross border trafficking in drugs and diversion of precursors and by intensifying preventive action against drug related crime through effective cooperation embedded in a joint approach.

(European Commission, 2008, p. 7)

Overall, responsibility for drugs continues to be diffused across all pillars ([1]), leading to some confusion, and a constant struggle to improve coordination, which has developed in some

[1]   Between 1993 and 2009, the European Union (EU) legally comprised three pillars: economic, social and environmental policies; foreign policy and military matters; and one concerning cooperation in the fight against crime. This structure was introduced with the Treaty of Maastricht in 1993, and was eventually abandoned on 1 December 2009 with the entry into force of the Treaty of Lisbon, when the EU obtained a consolidated legal personality.

areas more than others. The strategy also stresses the value of consultation with a broad group of partners, principally scientific centres, drug professionals, representative non-government organisations (NGOs), civil society and local communities. The current EU drugs action plan focuses on five priorities: improving coordination, cooperation and raising public awareness; reducing the demand for drugs; reducing the supply of drugs; improving international cooperation; and improving understanding of the problem.

Moves toward harm reduction

Under the heading of demand reduction, objective 10 of the current 2009–12 EU drugs action plan refers specifically to harm reduction. The objective here is to 'ensure access to harm reduction services in order to reduce the spread of HIV/AIDS, hepatitis C and other drug-related blood borne infectious diseases and to reduce the number of drug-related deaths in the EU' (OJ C 326, 20.12.2008, p. 14).

Before that, on 18 June 2003, the Council of the EU had already adopted a recommendation on the prevention and reduction of health-related harm associated with drug dependence. This referred to the following aims:

> Member States should, in order to provide for a high level of health protection, set as a public health objective the prevention of drug dependence and the reduction of related risks, and develop and implement comprehensive strategies accordingly … Member States should, in order to reduce substantially the incidence of drug-related health damage (such as HIV, hepatitis B and C and tuberculosis) and the number of drug related deaths, make available, as an integral part of their overall drug prevention and treatment policies, a range of different services and facilities, particularly aiming at risk reduction.
>
> (Council of the European Union, 2003/488/EC)

This recommendation called upon Member States to provide a number of harm reduction interventions, including: information and counselling; outreach; drug-free and substitution treatment; hepatitis B vaccination; prevention interventions for HIV, hepatitis B and C, tuberculosis and sexually transmitted diseases; the distribution of condoms; and the distribution and exchange of injecting equipment (see also Cook et al., 2010).

Drawing upon numerous EU policy documents, Figure 3.1 summarises some key events in the development of EU drug policy, noting the place of harm reduction within this. It suggests that until the mid-1980s, the idea of a European drug policy had not even been debated. Since this time, attention to drug issues has increased, and policy has developed in scope and detail. In the 1992 Maastricht Treaty, drug dependence was included in the field of public health. This was the first example of an EU treaty that specifically mentioned drugs and opened the possibility for setting up EU action and funding programmes in this field, although under the principle of 'subsidiarity'. Subsidiarity means that in policy areas that do not come within the exclusive competence of the Community, action would be taken at EU level only if the objectives of the proposed action could not be sufficiently achieved by Member States acting alone and could be better achieved by the Community.

Table 3.2 Some key events in the development of European drug policy

Event	Date	Notes
Co-operation Group to combat drug abuse and illicit trafficking in drugs (Pompidou Group) set up at Council of Europe, Strasbourg	1971	First multidisciplinary cooperation group in drugs field in Europe
Trevi working groups to counter terrorism and to coordinate policing	1976	Agreed by EC Interior Ministers
Schengen Agreement	1985	Removed border controls between Belgium, the Netherlands, Luxembourg, Germany and France
EC countries redefine task of Trevi 3 working group		To focus on international drug trafficking
Single European Act	1986	Signed by EC Member States
Stewart-Clark Inquiry into the Drugs Problem in the Member States of the Community		Commissioned by European Parliament
UN Convention against the Illicit Traffic in Narcotic Drugs and Psychotropic Substances	1988	Adopted at United Nations Conference
CELAD established (European Committee to Combat Drugs)	1989	Members are coordinators of national drug policy — existed until 1993
First European action plan to combat drugs	1990	Adopted by European Council in Rome (December 1990)
Frankfurt Resolution established ECDP (European Cities on Drug Policy)		At First Conference: European Cities at the Centre of Illegal Trade in Drugs, Frankfurt
Revision of European plan to combat drugs	1992	Adopted by European Council in Edinburgh (December)
First European Drug Prevention Week, London		Funded by the European Commission
Cooney Inquiry on Drug Trafficking and Organised Crime		Commissioned by the European Parliament
Maastricht Treaty Europol Drugs Unit agreed EMCDDA agreed	1993	CELAD became K4 Committee — existed until 1997
ECAD (European Cities Against Drugs) set up via Stockholm resolution	1994	At First Major Conference, in Stockholm
EMCDDA established in Lisbon	1995	
European Union action plan to combat drugs (1996–2000)		Adopted at Cannes European Council, June

Table 3.2 (continued)

Event	Date	Notes
Community Programme for the prevention of drug dependence (1996–2000)	1996	Funding programme decided by European Parliament and Council, implemented by European Commission
Dublin European Council		Agreed need for strategy against organised crime
Europol Drugs Unit established in The Hague		
Amsterdam Treaty	1997	Agreement on draft reached (entered into force in 1999)
Horizontal Drugs Group set up		To report back to Coreper — replaced K4 committee
EC Drug Unit placed under Task Force for Justice and Home Affairs	1998	
Agreement between EU and Andes countries on money laundering and precursors	1999	Later agreements also with Chile and Mexico and with West and South Africa and Caribbean
Europol Drug Unit is replaced by Europol		Focus on serious international organised crime
EU drugs strategy (2000–04)	1999	Endorsed by European Council in Helsinki
EU action plan on drugs (2000–04)	2000	Endorsed at European Council in Sta. Maria da Feira
Council of Ministers passes Recommendation on the prevention and reduction of health-related harm associated with drug dependence	2003	Seen as major step towards a progressive public health approach
Pompidou Group platforms for Prevention, Treatment and Research established	2004	
Council Framework Decision on drug trafficking		Also stress on dealing with new synthetic drugs and chemical precursors and money laundering
EU drugs strategy (2005–12) EU drugs action plan (2005–08)	2005	Endorsed by European Council
HIV/AIDS protocols on treatment and care for the European region		Published by WHO/Europe
Green Paper 'The role of civil society in drugs policy in the European Union'	2006	Presented by the European Commission

Table 3.2 (continued)		
Event	Date	Notes
Drug Prevention and Information Programme (2007–13)	2007	Funding programme decided by European Parliament and Council, implemented by European Commission
EU drugs action plan (2009–12)	2008	Endorsed by European Council

The 1997 Treaty of Amsterdam put even more stress on public health and made explicit reference to drugs. It was agreed that 'the Community shall complement the Member States' actions in reducing drugs-related health damage, including information and prevention'.

Specific interventions are now detailed in two action plans (2005–08 and 2009–12) which *inter alia* aim to significantly reduce the prevalence of drug use among the population and the social harm and health damage caused by the use of and trade in illicit drugs. Actions at EU level must be targeted and offer clear added value, and results must be realistic and measurable. Actions must also be cost-effective and contribute directly to the achievement of at least one of the goals or priorities set out in the EU drug strategy. Evaluation of the impact of the first action plan (2005–08) in the area of demand reduction concluded that: 'There remains a lack of reliable and consistent information to describe the existence of or evaluate the impact of prevention programmes; that further improvements are still needed in accessibility, availability and coverage of treatment programmes; and that the majority of Member States offer drug-free treatment, psychosocial treatment and substitution treatment' (European Commission, 2008, p. 66).

The European Commission concluded that:

> In the field of harm reduction, major progress has been achieved in recent years. In all EU Member States the prevention and reduction of drug related harm is a defined public health objective at national level. Among the most prevalent interventions are needle and syringe exchange programmes, outreach workers and opioid substitution treatment combined with psychosocial assistance. However availability and accessibility of these programmes are variable among the Member States and in some countries with low coverage, there are signs of higher levels of risk taking among new, younger generations of — in particular — heroin injectors who have not been reached by prevention and harm reduction messages.
>
> (European Commission, 2008, p. 66 [6.1.2.3: 4])

The continuing lack of provision of services in relation to drug users in prison and released prisoners was also noted, while 'treatment and harm reduction programmes are often not tailored to address the specific needs and problems of different groups of problem or dependent drug users, for example, women, under-aged young people, migrants, specific ethnic groups and vulnerable groups' (European Commission, 2008, p. 66 [6.1.2.3:7]). The Commission also noted that 'the evaluation shows that the action plan supports a process of convergence between Member States' drug policies and helps to achieve policy consistency between countries' (European Commission, 2008, p. 67 [6.1.3:2]).

Factors influencing the development of EU drugs policy

On the occasion of the launch of the EMCDDA's Annual report on the state of the drug problem in Europe in 2008, the Director, Mr Götz, said, 'there is a stronger agreement on the direction to follow and a clearer understanding of the challenges ahead', indicating his opinion that within Europe a convergence of views on policy is developing. If this is so, it is a remarkable change in just over 20 years.

A number of factors appear to have been influential in shaping developments in European drug policy:

- the evolution within the European Union of competencies in the field of drugs;
- the rising political priority of drugs across the areas of public health, public security (justice and home affairs) and external relations;
- a clear demand from various European institutions as well as Member States for information and evidence for policymaking and decisions;
- the creation of institutions such as the Pompidou Group and then EMCDDA and its national counterparts to meet those information needs;
- the existence alongside the institutional developments of longstanding and interlinked human networks of drug researchers and the possibilities to channel that scientific knowledge into the institutional process;
- the wider influence of international connections and the exchange of knowledge and experience.

(Hartnoll, 2003, p. 67)

Additional factors are: the growing similarities between countries in the nature and extent of their drug problems; the influence of evidence-based reason winning over ideology; and the effects of involvement in the practice of data collection and analysis, and a related development of norms, values and institutions (Bergeron and Griffiths, 2006, p. 123). In general terms, trends in drug use have affected many EU countries in roughly the same way and at roughly the same time (Bergeron and Griffiths, 2006). These have led to fairly radical changes in many countries, especially in the light of HIV/AIDS (see also Cook et al., 2010). In most EU countries, HIV and AIDS became a problem in the 1980s, levelling off after the 1990s, but with high levels of hepatitis C (EMCDDA, 2008). In addition, 'since the 1985 Schengen agreement, and its facilitation of free movement around Europe, the prevention of international drug trafficking and organised crime has become a priority for all member states' (Chatwin, 2007, p. 496) and

> national governments are eager to reap the benefits of unity in the area of controlling organised crime and the illegal trafficking of drugs. However, spillover of this level of European control to areas other than drug trafficking and organised crime prevention has not been as extensive. Trends towards the implementation of harm reduction initiatives and the decriminalisation of the drug user can be observed across Europe, with notable exceptions, but unity of policy in this area does not enjoy the same degree of official encouragement

(Chatwin, 2007, p. 497)

However, Chatwin has concluded that with regard to 'the fight against organised crime and drug trafficking, some progress towards a European drug policy is being made' (Chatwin, 2003, pp. 40–1). Finally, the 'context of a particular country, its size, geographical position and relation to its neighbours, the state of the drug problem and public opinion … political context [and] political ideology' all influence national strategies (Muscat, 2008, p. 9).

Harm reduction in international policy debates

In 1992, the Cooney Report to the European Parliament had advocated the use of needle exchange and methadone treatment programmes (Cooney, 1992). This was evidence of a growing pragmatic approach in Europe based on harm reduction principles, reflecting a significant shift of opinion between 1985 and the early 1990s, very much influenced by awareness of HIV/AIDS and its links to injecting drug use (Stimson, 1995). The European Parliament at the time did not, however, adopt these recommendations.

As illustrated in Table 3.2, there were a number of developments over the 1990s (see also Estievenart, 1995; Kaplan and Leuw, 1996), and in 2004 a former Interpol Chief writing in *Le Monde* felt able to declare the 'war on drugs' lost. Raymond Kendall said that it was time for an alternative approach — 'harm reduction' — and called for Europe to take the lead in an international movement to reform policy when the UN drug conventions came up for renewal in 2008. He said:

> Policies based solely on criminal sanctions have failed to demonstrate effectiveness. Economic corruption increases, organised crime prospers and developing economies are hard hit by military and environmental (crop eradication) interventions that have no apparent positive effect. At the same time, the marginalisation of drug users is compounded. There is therefore an urgent need for a multi-dimensional and integrated approach, which aims at reducing both supply and demand, and which also integrates harm reduction strategies designed to protect the health of the individual drug user as well as the well-being of society as a whole
>
> (Le Monde, 26 October 2004)

Is Europe now leading the policy case for harm reduction? Judged in terms of where things were a few decades ago, Europe does appear to have a recognisably shared approach and countries have coordinated their policies. Importantly, Europe tends increasingly to speak with one voice on the international stage.

EU drugs policy respects the International Drugs Conventions and implements the five principles of international drug policy adopted at the UN General Assembly Special Session (UNGASS) on Drugs of June 1998 (United Nations, 1998). These principles are: *shared responsibility* — de-emphasising the distinction between producing and consuming countries; an emphasis on *multilateralism* — recognising that unilateral action to single out particular countries is ineffective; a *balanced approach* — controlling demand as well as controlling supply; *development mainstreaming* — the drugs problem is complex and attention to sustainable development is critical; and *respect for human rights*.

The EU is also playing an active role in developing UN drug policy, notably promoting the emphasis on demand reduction. For example, the Action Plan on Demand Reduction that followed the 1998 UNGASS resolution rested on a set of guiding principles on demand reduction, based to an extent on ideas of harm reduction, though the term itself was not allowed — 'adverse consequences of drug use' was preferred. In this way, European ideas can be seen to be penetrating to the international level. More recently the EU also supported the UNGASS reviews, for example by preparing resolutions for the Commission on Narcotic Drugs (CND) meetings. A thematic paper drafted by the EMCDDA on the role of syringe provision in the reduction of infectious disease incidence and prevalence was presented to the HDG before the 2005 CND session and formed the basis of a mutually agreed position from EU Member States (EMCDDA, 2004).

The EU's influence is partly levered by financial contributions: for example, between 1971 and 1998 the total contribution to UN drugs-related activities through UNODC from EU countries amounted to $535 million. Currently, EU countries contribute at least half of the UNODC budget. Additionally, in international cooperation activities with countries that want to sign association agreements with the EU, like Iran and Afghanistan, drug-related issues are raised, with human rights being discussed routinely. Particular attention is also given to assisting third countries, especially those applying for future membership of the EU, and countries that are main transit points for drugs reaching the EU. The EU thus reaches out to Latin America and the Caribbean, to central and south-east Asia and to West and South Africa.

According to one drug policy researcher:

> The European Union is now mainly a single voice at international meetings with a strong and explicit harm reduction tone even though there are signs of modest retreat from some of the boundaries of harm reduction

(Reuter, 2009, p. 512)

In its evaluation of the EU drugs action plan 2005–08, the European Commission also concluded that the EU is increasingly speaking with one voice in international fora, notably in the UN CND (European Commission, 2008). It noted that the EU maintained a unified position in the UNGASS review process and that during the CND Working Sessions in 2006–08, the successive EU Presidencies delivered joint EU statements on the follow-up to UNGASS, drug demand reduction, illicit drug trafficking and supply, the International Narcotics Control Board (INCB) and policy directives to strengthen the UNODC Drug Programme, and the role of the CND as its governing body. The Commission, on behalf of the European Community, delivered its traditional statement on precursors at each CND session. However, the Commission warned that a harmonised approach among EU actors during the plenary meetings had to be maintained to ensure the EU speaks with one voice (European Commission, 2008). The EU positioned a paper in 2009 to CND noting the importance of harm reduction, but the inclusion of the words 'harm reduction' in the final UN statement were resisted, as they were a decade earlier in 1998 (International Drug Policy Consortium, 2009). Yet, while Europe may be seen to speak with one voice at the highest elite level, it is important to note that differences remain between and within countries, and groups organise to put pressure on these elites (see box on p. 73).

Voices against harm reduction

Drug abuse is a global problem ... Even though the world is against drug abuse, some organizations and local governments actively advocate the legalisation of drugs and promote policies such as 'harm reduction' that accept drug use and do not help drug users to become free from drug abuse. This undermines the international efforts to limit the supply of and demand for drugs. 'Harm reduction' is too often another word for drug legalisation or other inappropriate relaxation efforts, a policy approach that violates the UN Conventions. There can be no other goal than a drug-free world. Such a goal is neither utopian nor impossible.

(Declaration of World Forum Against Drugs, Stockholm, Sweden, 2008)

Step-by-step development

It appears therefore that in drug policy as in other policy areas, incremental change has been the explicit strategy of those aiming at 'closer European Union' (that is, achieving an increasing proportion of common positions in policy statements), and has been actively pursued by the key actors within the dominant institutions of the EU (Hantrais, 1998; Clarke, 2001, p. 34).

While enlargement might have been expected to lead to greater diversity within Europe on drug issues, oddly, convergence or harmonisation have in many ways followed the expansion of the EU. EU accession instruments had an impact on drug policy convergence and the adoption of harm reduction in new Member States. This is partly because the accession countries were keen to drop all vestiges of the former Soviet system and were open to demonstrating their adherence to European values and policies. The deliberate policy of institution building within the EU encouraged this process, including the coordination of activities aimed at *synchronisation* in the conduct of reviews, publishing of strategies and action plans and attention to the value of information and evaluation. Drugs as an issue can serve these purposes very well since drug misuse is at face value something all agree to be a bad thing: through the process of deliberating on drug policy, networks develop, institutions are formed and the wider aspects of a European approach are learnt, such as transparency, justification by reference to evidence, dialogue, and involvement of civil society.

For instance, the European Union PHARE ([2]) programmes exercised influence over candidate countries aiming to meet the requirements for accession. The European Commission funded a multi-beneficiary drug programme within PHARE, and the EU included national drug policy as an area of focus in its accession talks with candidate countries, which all signed the UN Conventions. Many candidate countries made the prevention of trafficking of illicit drugs an area of special attention and focus.

[2]   Acronym deriving from the original title of the EU assistance programme, Pologne Hongrie Assistance pour la Réstructuration Economique.

There have thus been a number of steps in the path towards convergence: the shared experience of practitioners, especially those involved in tackling the heroin, HIV/AIDS and hepatitis C epidemics and treating injecting drug users (IDUs); an increasingly shared perception of the problem, partly encouraged by dialogue around the development of information resources; the development of a common language to support the discourse; and the adoption of a set of common methods and reporting standards.

Forums and networks have also played a role in developing shared understandings and approaches to the European drug problem. With the Frankfurt Resolution of November 1990, representatives from the cities of Amsterdam, Frankfurt, Hamburg and Zurich resolved that attempts at eliminating drugs and drug consumption were a failure and that a new model was needed to cope with drug use in European cities (http://www.realitaeten-bureau.de/en_news_04.htm). This led to the setting up of European Cities on Drug Policy (ECDP), which helped open up the debate for a Europe-wide harm reduction drug policy approach. The direct involvement of user groups as well as epidemiologists and medical and criminal justice and other practitioners has been another important factor. ENCOD (European Coalition for Just and Effective Drug Policies) is a European network of about 156 organisations and individual citizens affected by and concerned about current drug policies. Another important network is the International Drug Policy Consortium — 'promoting objective and open debate of drug policies'; this brings together NGOs and professionals who specialise in issues related to illegal drugs, while the International Harm Reduction Association (IHRA) has influence through its efforts to promote a harm reduction approach to all psychoactive substances on a global basis.

On the other hand, there have continued below the surface to be strong opposing currents of opinion on drug policy (see box on p. 73). In April 1994, the Stockholm resolution aimed to promote a drug-free Europe and established European Cities Against Drugs (now with 264 signatory municipalities in 30 countries). In this process, Sweden played a leading role (http://www.ecad.net/resolution).

Conclusion

Some have noted 'a clear trend across Europe towards the recognition of harm reduction as an important component of mainstream public health and social policies towards problem drug use', representing something of a 'sea change in European drug policies' (Hedrich et al., 2008, p. 512). This convergence appears to have been strongly influenced by the production of EU drugs strategies from 1999 onwards, and the development of concrete, measurable targets, action plans and evaluation strategies. Hedrich et al. note:

> By including harm reduction as a key objective of drug policy, EU action plans not only reflect what was already happening in some Member States in response to serious public health challenges but [also] that European instruments further consolidated harm reduction as one of the central pillars of drug policy.

(Hedrich et al., 2008, p. 514)

Convergence towards 'policy consensus' was thus 'mediated by EU guidance while not originating from it' (Hedrich et al., 2008, p. 507).

The evidence reviewed in this chapter supports a conclusion of a progressive although limited convergence in European drug policies and that harm reduction is both an element and an indicator of this convergence. Opioid substitution treatment and needle and syringe programmes have become part of the common response in Europe for reducing problems related to drug injecting. This is characterised as a 'new public health' response to injecting drugs and HIV/AIDS (see also Rhodes and Hedrich, 2010).

EU drugs policy mixes traditional law enforcement approaches with an increasing focus on public health. A public health approach could be seen as relatively humane, sympathetic to those affected by drug use — both users, and families and communities — and as following ethical principles (see also Fry, 2010). The public health model still, however, rests on a 'disease' conception of drug use, framing it as an infectious and communicable disease that can be regulated from above, using a package of measures including surveillance and monitoring and aiming at containment. The starting point is recognising that the disease is present, even if measures should try to prevent or eliminate it. The main concern is to reduce the risk of transmission and its development into an epidemic. This conception has grown in power with the arrival of HIV/AIDS, exacerbated more recently by hepatitis C. It is a feature of this model also to assume that some members of populations are more vulnerable than others and that, although the underlying causes may need to be understood and tackled, in the short term the focus should be on targeting these groups. The priority is to focus on containing and managing the disease. This approach, based on scientific evidence and filtered through a range of regulatory and advisory bodies, produces directives, recommendations and guidance documents to which national governments are expected to respond. These increasingly influence national policies, partly because national governments want to 'show willing', be part of and signed up to the European Project, and also in some cases because governments do not actually consider drugs to be as important an issue as others on their busy agendas, so they do not bother to contest the matter.

In reality, implementation, a crucial element in the policy process, is influenced by the degree of acceptance by those involved of the measures suggested. Treatment professionals, service providers and budget holders influence the shape of service responses, and the wider society — of non-governmental pressure groups, drug users themselves and families and communities — may agree or disagree about the basic values on which these recommendations are based.

Overall, however, within Europe, a coordinated and increasingly coherent 'middle ground' policy on drugs appears to be emerging, within which harm reduction has an accepted place. But there is continuing tension between opposing views. A compromise may hold for a while, but with changing circumstances and conditions further policy adaptations are likely to appear on the agenda.

Acknowledgements

The research on which this chapter is based was supported by an Emeritus Fellowship awarded to Susanne MacGregor by The Leverhulme Trust, for which we are very grateful. We would like to thank reviewers of drafts of this chapter for their valuable comments, which we have endeavoured to take into account. Any errors or faults of interpretation remain our responsibility.

References

Bergeron, H. and Griffiths, P. (2006), 'Drifting towards a more common approach to a more common problem: epidemiology and the evolution of a European drug policy', in Hughes, R., Lart, R. and Higate, P. (eds), *Drugs: policy and politics*, Open University Press, Milton Keynes, pp. 113–24.

Chatwin, C. (2003), *On the possibility of policy harmonisation for some illicit drugs in selected member states of the European Union,* Sheffield University, PhD thesis.

Chatwin, C. (2007), 'Multi-level governance: the way forward for European illicit drug policy?', *International Journal of Drug Policy* 18, pp. 494–502.

Clarke, J. (2001), 'Globalisation and welfare states: some unsettling thoughts', in Sykes, R., Palier, B. and Prior, P. M. (eds), *Globalisation and European welfare states*, Palgrave, Houndsmill, pp. 19–37.

Cook, C., Bridge, J. and Stimson, G. V. (2010), 'The diffusion of harm reduction in Europe and beyond', in European Monitoring Centre for Drugs and Drug Addiction (EMCDDA), *Harm reduction: evidence, impacts and challenges*, Rhodes, T. and Hedrich, D. (eds), Scientific Monograph Series No. 10, Publications Office of the European Union, Luxembourg.

Cooney, P. (1992), *Report of the Committee of Inquiry on the spread of organised crime linked to drug trafficking in the Member States of the Community*, 23 April, European Parliament, meeting documents, A3-0358/91.

EMCDDA (European Monitoring Centre for Drugs and Drug Addiction) (2004), *A European perspective on responding to blood borne infections among injecting drug users: a short briefing paper*, European Monitoring Centre for Drugs and Drug Addiction, Lisbon. Available at http://www.emcdda.europa.eu/html.cfm/index5777EN.html.

EMCDDA (2008), *The state of the drugs problem in Europe*, European Monitoring Centre for Drugs and Drug Addiction, Lisbon.

EMCDDA (2009), *The state of the drugs problem in Europe*, European Monitoring Centre for Drugs and Drug Addiction, Lisbon.

Estievenart, G. (ed.) (1995), *Policies and strategies to combat drugs in Europe*, European University Institute, Martinus Nijhoff Publishers, Florence.

Eurobarometer (2006), 'TNS Opinion and Social', *Public opinion in the European Union*, Standard Eurobarometer, 66, Autumn, European Commission. Available from http://ec.europa.eu/public_opinion/archives/eb/eb66/eb66_en.htm.

European Commission (2008), *Commission staff working document. Accompanying the communication from the Commission to the Council and the European Parliament on an EU drugs action plan (2009–2012) — report of the final evaluation of the EU drugs action plan (2005–2008)*, {COM(2008) 567} {SEC(2008) 2455} {SEC(2008) 2454}, European Community, Brussels. Available at http://eur-lex.europa.eu/SECMonth.do?year=2008&month=09.

Fry, C. (2010), 'Harm reduction: an "ethical" perspective', in Chapter 4, 'Perspectives on harm reduction: what experts have to say', in European Monitoring Centre for Drugs and Drug Addiction (EMCDDA), *Harm reduction: evidence, impacts and challenges*, Rhodes, T. and Hedrich, D. (eds), Scientific Monograph Series No. 10, Publications Office of the European Union, Luxembourg.

Hantrais, L. (1998), 'European and supranational dimensions', in Alcock, P., Erskine, A. and May, M. (eds), *The student's companion to social policy*, Blackwell, Oxford, pp. 199–204.

Hartnoll, R. L. (2003), 'Drug epidemiology in the European institutions: historical background and key indicators', *Bulletin on Narcotics* LV (1 and 2), pp. 53–71.

Hedrich, D., Pirona, A. and Wiessing, L. (2008), 'From margin to mainstream: the evolution of harm reduction responses to problem drug use in Europe', *Drugs: education, prevention and policy* 15, pp. 503–17.

Hungarian Civil Liberties Union (2009), *Public poll survey on drug policy attitudes in 6 EU Member States*, HCLU. Available at http://eudrugpolicy.org/files/eudrugpolicy/PollReportEDPI.pdf.

International Drug Policy Consortium (2009), *The 2009 Commission on Narcotic Drugs and its high level segment: report of proceedings*, IDPC Briefing Paper, April 2009.

Kaplan, C. D. and Leuw, E. (1996), 'A tale of two cities: drug policy instruments and city networks in the European Union', *European Journal of Criminal Policy and Research* 4, pp. 74–89.

Kendall, R. (2004), 'Drugs: war lost, new battles' [Drogues: guerre perdue, nouveaux combats], *Le Monde* 26 October — opinion editorial.

Muscat, R. and members of the Pompidou research platform (2008), *From a policy on illegal drugs to a policy on psychoactive substances,* Council of Europe Publishing, Strasbourg.

Official Journal of the European Union (2008) Official Journal of the European Union C 326, 20.12.2008, Part IV: Notices from European Union Institutions and Bodies: Council, *EU Drugs Action Plan for 2009–2012*. Available at: http://eur-lex.europa.eu/JOIndex.do?year=2008&serie=C&textfield2=326&Submit=Search&_submit=Search&ihmlang=en.

Reuter, P. (2009), 'Ten years after the United Nations General Assembly Special Session (UNGASS): assessing drug problems, policies and reform proposals', *Addiction* 104, pp. 510–17.

Rhodes, T. and Hedrich, D. (2010), 'Harm reduction and the mainstream', in European Monitoring Centre for Drugs and Drug Addiction (EMCDDA), *Harm reduction: evidence, impacts and challenges*, Rhodes, T. and Hedrich, D. (eds), Scientific Monograph Series No. 10, Publications Office of the European Union, Luxembourg.

Stimson, G. V. (1995), 'AIDS and injecting drug use in the United Kingdom, 1987–1993: the policy response and the prevention of the epidemic', *Social Science and Medicine* 41, pp. 699–716.

United Nations (1998), 'UN General Assembly Twentieth Special Session World Drug Problem 8–10 June'. United Nations, New York. Available at http://www.un.org/documents.

United Nations (2008), 'Economic, Social and Economic Council, Commission on Narcotic Drugs, fifty-first session', *The world drug problem: fifth report of the Executive Director*, United Nations, Vienna, 10–14 March (E/CN.7/2008). Available at http://www.unodc.org.

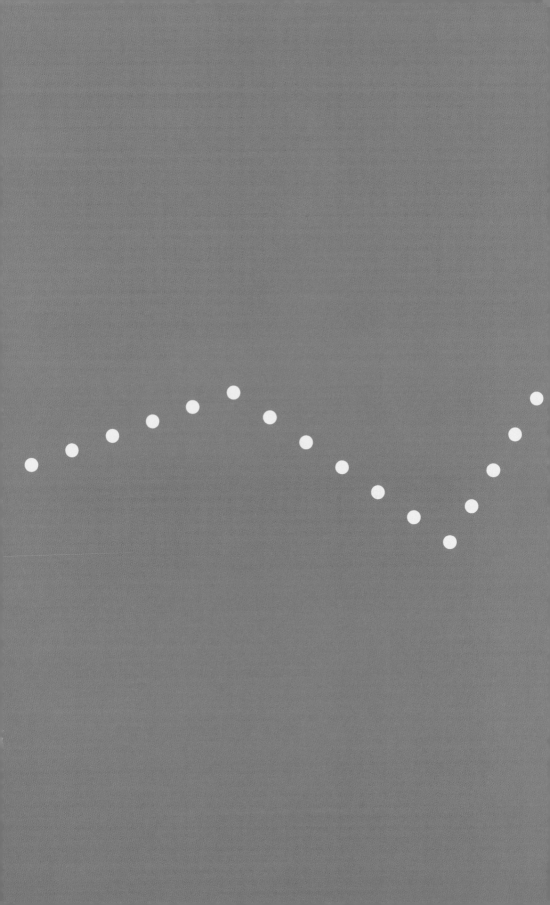

Chapter 4
Perspectives on harm reduction — what experts have to say

Jürgen Rehm, Benedikt Fischer, Matthew Hickman, Andrew Ball, Rifat Atun, Michel Kazatchkine, Mat Southwell, Craig Fry, Robin Room

Harm reduction is usually used as an umbrella term to define interventions, programmes and policies that seek to reduce the health, social and economic harms of substance use to individuals, communities and societies. But definitions of harm reduction are also contested. At the same time, a variety of challenges face the development and implementation of harm reduction policies in Europe and elsewhere. We invited nine international experts to reflect upon harm reduction. Between them, they reflect expertise in international public health policy and development (including representatives of the World Health Organization and Global Fund), the health and social sciences, medical ethics and user involvement. Their topics focus on challenges regarding:

- strengthening the concept and evidence-base (Rehm and Fischer);
- preventing hepatitis C (Hickman);
- broadening the scope of interventions (Ball);
- scaling up coverage (Atun and Kazatchkine);
- generating genuine user involvement (Southwell);
- the ethics of policy decision-making (Fry); and
- how best to think about and define what we mean by harm (Room).

Harm reduction in an open and experimenting society

Jürgen Rehm and Benedikt Fischer

Over the past 25 years 'harm reduction' has played an increasingly prominent and explicit role in substance use policy and interventions, especially in Western Europe and Australia, but also in North America to some extent. Although people have struggled with the concept in terms of its clarity, and there has been ideological opposition to it since its inception, its fundamental significance is that it departs from the traditionally dominant approach by which the severity of substance use problems is principally defined by the extent, quantity or frequency of substance use by an individual or within a population. The implied logic of this conventional approach to substance use suggested that abstinence, and thus reducing the prevalence of use ought to be main goals of substance use, interventions or policy.

Although the principles of harm reduction stretch back several decades, harm reduction practice was symbolically re-invented during the early phase of the HIV/AIDS epidemic among injecting drug users (IDUs) in the 1980s. This was a time when health workers started providing clean syringes to IDUs — rather than seeking to achieve their abstinence from drug use — in order to halt the spread of HIV. Since then, harm reduction initiatives and frameworks have been established for all areas of substance use, albeit not without substantial difficulty or opposition.

Critics of harm reduction have claimed that the concept of 'harm' is not objectively defined, and therefore does not provide a strong empirical basis for the implementation and evaluation of harm reduction measures (Rehm and Fischer, 1997; Leshner, 2008; Hall, 2007). Further, it has been suggested that harm reduction approaches appear to sanction or even enable substance use, and therefore may facilitate the 'legalisation' of illicit substances, and thus may send out 'the wrong message' (DuPont, 1996). Finally, an often-cited argument is that harm reduction measures for illicit drugs contravene international drug control treaties, although such criticisms have been rejected both in theory and in practice (Room, 2003). For each of the main substantive substance use arenas (alcohol, tobacco, illicit drugs), there are distinct harm reduction debates and initiatives. We summarise some of these below, before sketching out an evidence- and experimental-based approach to implementing interventions based on harm reduction principles.

Harm reduction in different fields of substance use: commonalities and differences

The term harm reduction has somewhat distinct connotations in different fields of substance use.

Alcohol

In the alcohol field there has been recognition for some time now that abstinence may not be the ideal or most feasible outcome of policy or therapeutic interventions, as consistent light to moderate alcohol use without heavy drinking occasions has been shown to confer health benefits (Pearl, 1926; Rehm et al., 2004b; Rehm et al., 2003). Even though abstinence for everybody is not the main goal of alcohol policy in Western societies anymore, approaches to reduce consumption in a given country or region are still presented as harm reduction (Room, 2004). However, the current use of the term has evolved, and in the debates at the World Health Assembly towards establishing a global strategy to reduce alcohol-attributable harm, harm reduction has been framed in different ways by many players.

Despite differences of emphasis, there is an emerging consensus among alcohol experts:

- that abstinence may not necessarily be the only goal of a public health approach for the population and not even necessarily the goal of treatment for individuals who enter the treatment system (see 'controlled drinking' approaches as one kind of therapy, or so-called 'wet hostels' as one form of intervention, Podymov et al., 2006);
- that patterns and practices of drinking predominantly influence the alcohol-related harm experienced (Rehm et al., 2003);
- and that this harm from drinking is to a substantial extent also influenced by the environment and the context of drinking (Rehm et al., 2004a).

Following this perspective, the risk behaviour of so-called 'binge drinking' (Gmel et al., 2003) has become the focus of many preventive and therapeutic interventions. Here, the advice might be to replace the consumption of two bottles of wine in one setting on a Friday with drinking one glass of wine daily in conjunction with a meal. This change of drinking patterns results in about the same amount of alcohol being consumed, but typically leads to much less health and social harm.

However, closer examination shows that despite changes of language and examples, the interventions proposed are often still the same as 40 years ago within a supposedly different paradigm. As some of the accepted truths of the field (that is, that higher availability of alcohol leads to more harm under all circumstances) have been empirically challenged (example: Sweden has experienced much higher availability of alcohol in the past years, but not necessarily higher consumption or alcohol-attributable harm), the global strategy will need a much closer examination of what interventions produce which effects under what circumstances, and less debate on how we label the successful interventions.

Tobacco

Many have argued that harm reduction cannot be applied to tobacco smoking, since smoking even small quantities of tobacco is associated with significant health risks (Institute of Medicine, 2001). However, changing realities have led to a new focus on harm reduction and smoking, at least in high-income countries (Shiffman et al., 2002; Hatsukami et al., 2004; Hughes, 1995). In many Western countries, smoking is now increasingly concentrated in a population of 'hard-core' smokers who often have symptoms of depression (Fergusson et al., 2003) and/or are economically disadvantaged (Barbeau et al., 2004). Such people may not be able to quit their tobacco consumption entirely, but may be good candidates for harm reduction measures — for example, practices of controlled smoking supported by alternative nicotine delivery mechanisms — that lower the risks associated with their smoking. In addition, harm reduction may offer alternative interventions for smokers that are less punitive or stigmatising in an increasingly harsh 'anti-smoking' climate (Poland, 2000).

Some attention has been given in this context to alternative or 'safer' nicotine delivery models that eliminate the highly carcinogenic effects of smoked tobacco inhalation by means of 'cleaner' forms of nicotine intake (Ferrence et al., 2000). These range from various culture-specific forms of chewed tobacco products (e.g. 'snus') to nicotine gum or patches. Some have pointed out that 'controlled' or 'reduced' smoking for certain users would at least reduce exposure to harmful tobacco smoke and its consequences (Drinkmann, 2002; Hughes, 2000), if it is not compensated by more harmful ways of inhaling. Studies have yet to demonstrate whether such approaches are really showing an overall benefit for the target groups. Again, an extensive ideological debate will not reduce any of the harms associated with smoking. Rather, well-designed and executed scientific experiments testing the benefits of different types of 'harm reduction' interventions for smokers resistant to quitting may inform the best mix of interventions for different target groups (Rehm and Strack, 1994).

Illicit drugs

Until recently, the harm reduction approach has been equally controversial in the field of illicit drugs (that is, drugs whose consumption is prohibited by law). Although depending on the type of illegal drug, an accumulation of evidence over the past couple of decades points to the substantial risks of death and disease associated with illicit drug use and specifically underlines the crucial role that behavioural, social and environmental factors play in aggravating or mitigating those risks (EMCDDA, 2003). Various harm reduction measures have been used to pragmatically reduce drug-related risks especially in the area of IDU, including needle exchange programmes that are known to reduce transmission risk behaviours for both HIV and hepatitis B and C among IDUs (Vlahov et al., 2001; Kimber et al., 2010). Supervised injection facilities — including many such operations in Europe and Australia, and one facility in North America ('Insite' in Vancouver) — have become a main intervention for IDUs and aim to reduce overdose, infectious disease and public order problems among IDUs by offering a protected and medically supervised drug injecting environment. Overall, the empirical evidence shows some success (Kimber et al., 2003; Hedrich, 2004; Hedrich et al., 2010), but the interpretation is limited by the weak designs applied in many evaluations, often represented by the lack of adequate control groups. This leaves the door open for alternative interpretations of data produced and subsequent ideological debate.

Towards a more evidence-based and experimental approach

Although the term 'harm reduction' has different meanings within and across different fields of substance use, there are some clear conceptual underpinnings. First, the primary emphasis within this paradigm is on the outcomes of substance use rather than on use itself. Second, the major objective of intervention measures is to reduce negative outcomes, regardless of whether or not use is reduced.

As such, harm reduction can be construed as an alternative — welcome or not — to the conventional paradigm underlying substance use interventions or policy, which has been concerned principally with use *per se*. Clearly, all fields of substance use are starkly shaped by an abundance of ideology. Harm reduction is and will remain controversial in this climate, as it challenges or deviates from conventional approaches and norms to substance use, some of which signal that any form of substance use is bad or should not be accepted or 'aided'. Thus, simply renaming the approach may incur some short-lived gains on the rhetorical level, but may not resolve these substantive conceptual dilemmas in the long run. Rather, the use of 'harm reduction' terminology should be avoided at the philosophical or abstract level, and instead should be specified concretely in each instance with regard to what is meant by 'harms', and how 'the reduction of harm' is supposed to occur and to be measured. Thus, harm reduction efforts in practice should be clear in their conception, based on evidence and implemented in a way that allows their effectiveness to be evaluated. This, in consequence, also means that harm reduction measures should be revised or suspended, if they do not deliver the intended or otherwise beneficial outcomes.

In the field of substance use, ideology is a strong current, and a simple label (such as 'harm reduction') can suffice to render certain interventions or measures as unacceptable. We must therefore find ways to move towards a more experimental and evidence-based approach to substance use policy and interventions (Campbell, 1969; Rehm, 2009). Measures such as supervised injection sites should be implemented with clear outcome objectives on a time-limited basis; the progress towards these objectives should be monitored, and if not reached, the available — and typically scarce — resources should be invested in other interventions. Furthermore, experiments on programming options should be construed and implemented *a priori* with control groups, such as the Saturday opening hours for alcohol in Sweden, where the policy was implemented in one part of the country, with another part of the country serving as the control group (Norström and Skog, 2003). Such control groups are very valuable in distinguishing effects of interventions from secular trends or concomitant events. Another example in this direction would be the proposal for alcohol outlets in Canada to open on Sunday mornings in certain areas to avoid the use of surrogate alcohol by marginalised or poor alcohol addicts (e.g. homeless people) who do not have enough funds to stock their required alcohol supply over the weekend.

It is unlikely that the fundamental philosophical controversy regarding 'harm reduction' will ever diminish or disappear. The only basis for a meaningful continued existence of harm reduction concepts will be a firm linkage with concrete definitions and operationalisations, and evidence-based assessments of whether the respective measures deliver on their objectives or not. These principles should also become a consistent standard for all policy frameworks relying on the harm reduction concept.

Acknowledgement

This contribution is based on and conceptually expands the contribution 'Harm reduction' by Benedikt Fischer in *Substance abuse in Canada: current challenges and choices* (2005, Canadian Centre on Substance Abuse, Ottawa, pp. 11–15).

References

Barbeau, E., Krieger, N. and Soobader, M-J., (2004), 'Working class matters: socioeconomic disadvantage, race/ethnicity, gender, and smoking in NHIS 2000', *American Journal of Public Health* 94, pp. 269–78.

Campbell, D. T. (1969), 'Reforms as experiments', *American Psychologist* 24, pp. 409–29.

Drinkmann, A. (2002), 'Kontrolliertes Rauchen: Standortbestimmung und Perspektiven', *Suchttherapie* 3, pp. 81–6.

DuPont, R. (1996), 'Harm reduction and decriminalization in the United States: a personal perspective', *Substance Use and Misuse* 31, pp. 1929–45.

EMCDDA (2003), *Annual report: state of the drugs problem in the European Union and Norway*, European Monitoring Centre for Drugs and Drug Addiction, Lisbon.

Fergusson, D., Goodwin, L. and Horwood, L. (2003), 'Major depression and cigarette smoking: results of a 21-year longitudinal study', *Psychological Medicine* 33, pp. 1357–67.

Ferrence, R. G., Slade, J., Room, R. and Pope, M. A. (2000), *Nicotine and public health*, American Public Health Association, Washington.

Gmel, G., Rehm, J. and Kuntsche, E. (2003), 'Binge drinking in Europe: definitions, epidemiology, and consequences', *Sucht* 49, pp. 105–16.

Hall, W. (2007), 'What's in a name?', *Addiction* 102, p. 692.

Hatsukami, D., Henningfield, J. and Kotlyar, M. (2004), 'Harm reduction approaches to reducing tobacco-related mortality', *Annual Review of Public Health* 25, pp. 377–95.

Hedrich, D. (2004), *European report on drug consumption rooms*, European Monitoring Centre for Drugs and Drug Addiction, Lisbon.

Hedrich, D., Kerr, T. and Dubois-Arber, F. (2010), 'Drug consumption facilities in Europe and beyond', in Rhodes, T. (ed.), *Harm reduction: evidence, impacts and challenges*, European Monitoring Centre for Drugs and Drug Addiction, Scientific Monograph Series No. 10, Publications Office of the European Union, Luxembourg.

Hughes, J. (1995), 'Applying harm reduction to smoking', *Tobacco Control* 4, pp. S33–S38.

Hughes, J. (2000), 'Reduced smoking: an introduction and review of the evidence', *Addiction* 95, pp. 3–7.

Institute of Medicine (2001), *Clearing the smoke: assessing the science base for tobacco harm reduction*, Institute of Medicine, Washington, DC.

Kimber, J., Dolan, K., van Beek, I., Hedrich, D. and Zurhold, H. (2003), 'Drug consumption facilities: an update since 2000', *Drug Alcohol Review* 22, pp. 227–33.

Kimber, J., Palmateer, N., Hutchinson, S., Hickman, M. and Rhodes, T. (2010), 'Harm reduction interventions for injecting drug users: evidence of effectiveness', in Rhodes, T. (ed.), *Harm reduction: evidence, impacts and challenges*, European Monitoring Centre for Drugs and Drug Addiction, Scientific Monograph Series No. 10, Publications Office of the European Union, Luxembourg.

Leshner, A. (2008), 'By now, "harm reduction" harms both science and the public health', *Clinical Pharmacology and Therapeutics* 83, pp. 513–14.

Norström, T. and Skog, O. J. (2003), 'Saturday opening of alcohol retail shops in Sweden: an impact analysis', *Journal of Studies on Alcohol and Drugs* 64, pp. 393–401.

Pearl, R. (1926), *Alcohol and longevity*, Knopf, New York.

Podymov, T., Turnbull, J., Coyle, D., Yetisir, E. and Wells, G. (2006), 'Shelter-based managed alcohol administration to chronically homeless people addicted to alcohol', *Canadian Medical Association Journal* 174 (01), pp. 45–49.

Poland, B. (2000), 'The "considerate" smoker in public space: the micro-politics and political economy of "doing the right thing"', *Health & Place* 6, pp. 1–14.

Rehm, J. (2009), 'Making connections — the questions we have to answer', Presentation at the conference on the occasion of the 15th anniversary of the European Monitoring Centre for Drugs and Drug Addiction, 'Identifying Europe's information needs for effective drug policy', EMCDDA, Lisbon.

Rehm, J. and Fischer, B. (1997), 'Measuring harm reduction: implications for alcohol epidemiology', in Plant, M. and Single, E., *Minimising the harm: what works?* Free Association Books, London, pp. 248–61.

Rehm, J. and Strack, F. (1994), 'Kontrolltechniken', in Herrmann, T. and Tack, W., *Methodologische Grundlagen der Psychologie: Enzyklopädie der Psychologie, Forschungsmethoden, Band 1*, Hogrefe, Göttingen, pp. 508–55.

Rehm, J., Room, R., Graham, K., et al. (2003), 'The relationship of average volume of alcohol consumption and patterns of drinking to burden of disease: an overview', *Addiction* 98, pp. 1209–28.

Rehm, J., Fischer, B., Graham, K., et al. (2004a), 'The importance of environmental modifiers of substance use and harm', *Addiction* 99, pp. 663–6.

Rehm, J., Room, R., Monteiro, M., et al. (2004b), 'Alcohol use', in Ezzati, M., Lopez, A. D., Rodgers, A. and Murray, C. J. L. (eds), *Comparative quantification of health risks: global and regional burden of disease attributable to selected major risk factors. Volume 1,* WHO, Geneva, pp. 959–1109.

Room, R. (2003), 'Impact and implications of the international drug control treaties on IDU and HIV/AIDS prevention and policy', in Fischer, B., Rehm, J. and Haydon, E. (eds), *Reducing the risks, harms and costs of HIV/ AIDS and injection drug use: a synthesis of the evidence base for development of policies and programs.* Background paper #4, 2nd annual background dialogue on HIV/AIDS, Health Canada/ UNAIDS/Canadian International Development Agency, Warsaw, Poland.

Room, R. (2004), 'Alcohol and harm reduction, then and now', *Critical Public Health* 14, pp. 329–44.

Shiffman, S., Gitchell, J., Warner, K., et al. (2002), 'Tobacco harm reduction: conceptual structure and nomenclature for analysis and research', *Nicotine and Tobacco Research* 4, pp. S113–S129.

Vlahov, D., Des Jarlais, D., Goosby, E., et al. (2001), 'Needle exchange programs for the prevention of human immunodeficiency virus infection: epidemiology and policy', *American Journal of Epidemiology* 154, pp. S70–S77.

HCV prevention — a challenge for evidence-based harm reduction

Matthew Hickman

Harm reduction applied to substance use, such as injecting, is a form of secondary prevention. Harm reduction aims to prevent the consequence of drug use, that is, to reduce the burden of disease and improve the health of the population (Lenton and Single, 1998). Clearly when onset of drug use or progression to dependence cannot be prevented then it is logical to intervene in order to reduce the potential consequences of drug use, in the same way that once people have developed diabetes, obesity or high blood pressure primary prevention is replaced by other strategies that aim to reduce potential health problems associated with these conditions. In some chronic health problems the natural history requires life-long treatment (such as diabetes) whereas in others the disease or adverse condition can be reversed. The latter is true of substance use, which is often described as a 'chronic relapsing condition' — that is, it may be of long duration with multiple periods of recovery and relapse before final cessation (O'Brien and McLellan, 1996). Harm reduction, therefore, aims to reduce premature mortality and long-term health and social problems during periods of substance use. Replacing the term 'harm reduction' with 'secondary prevention' may please some or annoy others (Hall, 2007; Weatherburn, 2009). But any name change is less important than recognising that harm reduction is like any other public health intervention (Institute of Medicine, 2007).

Evidence is required that a specific harm reduction activity is effective; that harm is reduced in order to justify ongoing support and investment; and that like any public health intervention the evidence is assessed in standard ways and compiled from study designs that can properly test whether exposure to the harm reduction intervention has reduced harm. In the hierarchy of study designs randomised control trials give the strongest evidence — if the research question and exposure lends itself to a trial. Next in the hierarchy come cohort studies and case control designs, which separate and attempt to clarify clearly the relationship between exposure and outcome. Cross-sectional or ecological study designs may corroborate or raise hypotheses — but cannot by themselves test them. Nonetheless it should be possible to generate good-quality evidence (even without a trial), especially by considering consistency of evidence across different studies, different study designs and settings (Rutter, 2007).

Harm reduction or drug harms are collective nouns and cannot be reviewed as a whole. They encompass many forms of harm reduction (encompassing psychological and pharmacological therapies, provision of sterile drug taking equipment, and changes to the risk environment) and multiple harms (from neurocognitive deficit, psychological and psychiatric impairment, crime, family and social problems, and acute and chronic ill-health) (Horne, 2007).

So let us consider a specific area — harm reduction and injecting drug use — associated with marked levels of harm, a range of interventions, and novel intervention development. There is good evidence from trials and well-conducted observational cohort studies that methadone reduces the risk of overdose, and can have a role in reducing HIV infection among injectors (Institute of Medicine, 2007). There is weaker direct evidence but good evidence from cost-effectiveness models that needle and syringe programmes reduce HIV transmission. More challenging for harm reduction, and what I want to focus on, is its role in preventing hepatitis C virus (HCV).

HCV is a comparatively common blood-borne infection that may lead to liver cirrhosis, cancer and death. In the United Kingdom — and many other countries in Europe — 80 % of infections are due to injecting drug use and nearly 0.5 to 1 % of the adult population maybe infected with HCV (De Angelis et al., 2008). The risk of becoming infected with HCV increases with injecting duration, and in many cities in Europe one in two active IDU will be infected with HCV (Hickman et al., 2007). Two key harm reduction interventions that may reduce HCV transmission are: (i) needle and syringe programmes (NSPs), which aim to reduce the use and sharing of injecting equipment that maybe infected with HCV; and (ii) opioid substitution treatment (OST), which in the context of HCV aims to reduce injecting frequency and thereby reduce the probability of sharing and increase coverage of NSPs.

The first challenge and obvious policy question is — what evidence is there that harm reduction reduces HCV transmission? Unfortunately there is very little direct evidence (ACMD, 2009). For example, Jo Kimber, Norah Palmateer and colleagues report overwhelming evidence from reviews and individual studies that NSP and OST reduce self-reported injecting risk (Kimber et al., 2010; Palmateer et al., 2010). However, there is insufficient review-level evidence that NSP or OST are associated with a reduction in HCV incidence.

Does this matter? It might simply be because the studies are too small or underpowered to detect a difference in HCV incidence; if the outcomes are combined (reported sharing and HCV incidence) then the evidence is positive. However, it does matter. Reported injecting risk behaviour change is not a good enough marker of reduced HCV transmission. There are many cross-sectional surveys and longitudinal surveys of IDU that find reported sharing to be a poor predictor of HCV infection — with high rates of HCV among people who report 'never sharing', and comparatively small increased rates of infection among people who report sharing. Reported injecting risk may be misclassified or may be under- or over-reported due to social desirability or other reasons. More importantly, even if a reduction in sharing occurred, without information on HCV incidence we cannot be certain that the reduction was sufficient to reduce HCV transmission. We cannot rule out the possibility that NSP or OST are having no effect on HCV transmission.

However, we know that OST and NSP are beneficial for other health outcomes. So the challenge and policy question should really be — what level of harm reduction is required to reduce HCV transmission? How much extra may be required? We know that in many other European countries HCV prevalence among IDU remains persistently high. In the United Kingdom, HCV prevalence has doubled among recent injectors in the last 10 years — evidence that current interventions and coverage are insufficient (Sweeting et al., 2009). In contrast, there is some evidence that HCV incidence has fallen in Amsterdam (van den Berg et al., 2007a). Indeed there is emerging evidence from the Amsterdam Addiction Cohort (AAC) of a positive intervention effect of harm reduction against HCV incidence (van den Berg et al. 2007b). IDU who were on 'full' harm reduction' (that is, on OST and high coverage NSP — receiving a sufficient number of syringes for the reported number of injections) had an HCV incidence approximately one-third lower than those receiving either OST or NSP. HCV incidence among IDU-receiving 'partial or incomplete harm reduction' was no different from IDU receiving no harm reduction; and there was no evidence of an intervention effect for NSP or OST alone.

The implication of the evidence from AAC is stark and far-reaching. If true, and we observe a similar picture in the United Kingdom (unpublished), then HCV incidence can be reduced, but providing a small amount of harm reduction is insufficient — partial harm reduction will not have an impact on HCV transmission. Further, only the combination of interventions seemed to have an effect. Perhaps the reason why there is no review-level evidence of an intervention effect in the literature is because studies have been investigating a single intervention (e.g. NSP vs. no NSP), and not assessing sites and subjects in OST with high levels of NSP coverage. It is not difficult to see why partial harm reduction may not be enough. If you live in a site where one in two IDU are infected with HCV, and the probability of HCV transmission after sharing an infected syringe is, say, 3.5 %, then you only need to share about 40 times to have a 50:50 chance of being infected with HCV. If you inject 500 times a year then even if you are safe 95 % or more of the time, it does not take many years for your chance of being HCV positive to become very high.

This evidence leads to two further challenges. We need to strengthen the evidence base on what level and combination of harm reduction interventions reduce HCV transmission (Hickman, 2009). This is not trivial. Randomised control trials, at least for OST and NSP, cannot be used, as it would be unethical to randomise interventions that have proven benefit on other health outcomes. This may not be the case for other interventions, which, therefore, could be randomised alongside OST and NSP. Equally, longitudinal studies are expensive and difficult to conduct well and achieve high rates of follow-up. Instead, innovative methods may be required that make use of different serological markers of HCV infection to identify incident infections — and compare HCV incidence against different harm reduction exposures. A further complication is that these studies need to investigate and measure the impact of different combinations of harm reduction intervention.

Finally, the challenge of HCV prevention to harm reduction providers and advocates is that services need to interact and combine. Providing sterile equipment or offering OST may not be enough; but the two need to work together. Reducing injecting frequency and achieving injecting cessation must become prominent goals of HCV harm reduction in order for the reduction in injecting risk and the scale of behaviour change required to prevent HCV to be sustainable.

References

ACMD (Advisory Council on Misuse of Drugs) (2009), *The primary prevention of hepatitis C among infecting drug users*, Hickman, M. (ed.), Home Office, London.

De Angelis, D., Sweeting, M., Ades, A. E., et al. (2009), 'An evidence synthesis approach to estimating hepatitis C prevalence in England and Wales', *Statistical Methods in Medical Research* 18, pp. 361–79.

Hall, W. (2007), 'What's in a name?', *Addiction* 102 (5), p. 692.

Hickman, M. (ed.) (2009), *The primary prevention of hepatitis C among infecting drug users*, Advisory Council on Misuse of Drugs, Home Office, London.

Hickman, M., Hope, V., Brady, T., et al.(2007), 'Hepatitis C virus (HCV) prevalence, and injecting risk behaviour in multiple sites in England in 2004', *Journal of Viral Hepatitis* 14 (9), pp. 645–52.

Horne, G. (ed.) (2007), 'Brain science', *Addiction and drugs*, Academy Medical Sciences, London.

Institute of Medicine (2007) *Preventing HIV infection among injecting drug users in high-risk countries: an assessment of the evidence*, Committee on the Prevention of HIV Infection Among Injecting Drug Users in High-Risk Countries, Institute of Medicine, Washington, DC.

Kimber, J., Palmateer, N., Hutchinson, S., et al. (2010), 'Harm reduction among injecting drug users: evidence of effectiveness', in European Monitoring Centre for Drugs and Drug Addiction (EMCDDA), *Harm reduction: evidence, impacts and challenges*, Rhodes, T. and Hedrich, D. (eds), Scientific Monograph Series No. 10, Publications Office of the European Union, Luxembourg.

Lenton, S. and Single, E. (1998), 'The definition of harm reduction', *Drug and Alcohol Review* 17 (2), pp. 213–19.

O'Brien, C. P. and McLellan, A. T. (1996), 'Myths about the treatment of addiction', *Lancet* 347 (8996), pp. 237–40.

Palmateer, N., Kimber, J., Hickman, M., et al. (2010), 'Evidence for the effectiveness of sterile injecting equipment provision in preventing hepatitis C and HIV transmission among injecting drug users: a review of reviews', *Addiction* (in press).

Rutter, M. (2007), *Identifying the environmental causes of disease*, Academy Medical Sciences, London.

Sweeting, M. J., Hope, V. D., Hickman, M., et al. (2009), 'Hepatitis C infection among injecting drug users in England and Wales (1992–2006): there and back again?', *American Journal of Epidemiology* 170 (3), pp. 352–60.

van den Berg, C. H., Smit, C., Bakker, M., et al. (2007a), 'Major decline of hepatitis C virus incidence rate over two decades in a cohort of drug users', *European Journal of Epidemiology* 22 (3), pp. 183–93.

van den Berg, C., Smit, C., van Brussel, G., Coutinho, R. and Prins, M. (2007b), 'Full participation in harm reduction programmes is associated with decreased risk for human immunodeficiency virus and hepatitis C virus: evidence from the Amsterdam Cohort Studies among drug users', *Addiction* 102 (9), pp. 1454–62.

Weatherburn, D. (2009), 'Dilemmas in harm minimization', *Addiction* 104 (3), pp. 335–9.

Broadening the scope and impact of harm reduction for HIV prevention, treatment and care among injecting drug users

Andrew Ball

Drug use is associated with multiple and changing health risks and harms, requiring increasingly diversified and complex responses. There is an emerging consensus that harm reduction programmes need to be comprehensive and flexible if they are to achieve significant public health outcomes. The example of HIV prevention, treatment and care among injecting drug users illustrates the importance of adopting a broader rather than a more restrictive definition of harm reduction (Ball, 2007a). Harm reduction programmes on the ground need to move beyond single interventions (such as needle exchange programmes and opioid substitution treatment) delivered in isolation, to a comprehensive set of interventions linked in with broader health and social services.

How broad should the harm reduction net be cast? Within the context of HIV and injecting drug use there are multiple intervention points where HIV risk and harm can be reduced, including by decreasing HIV vulnerability and risk, preventing HIV transmission, treating those who are infected and mitigating the impact of HIV on communities. Considering a hierarchy of harm reduction goals, first, interventions can focus on those individuals and populations who are most vulnerable to adopting HIV risk behaviours (such as moving from non-injecting to injecting drug use) or are exposed to HIV risk settings (such as incarceration), but have yet to engage in risk behaviours. The aim of such interventions is to reduce vulnerability by addressing such factors as stigma and discrimination, marginalisation, gender inequity and criminalisation (UNAIDS, 2008). Second, for those who are already engaged in HIV risk behaviours interventions should target those behaviours to reduce risk, such as the use of opioid substitution treatment and needle and syringe programmes to reduce sharing of injecting equipment (Institute of Medicine, 2007). Some injecting drug users are more vulnerable than others, such as female drug users, prisoners and those in rural areas, because their situations prevent them from adopting safer behaviours or accessing prevention services. Third, where individuals are exposed to HIV, interventions for preventing or reducing HIV transmission may be considered, such as the use of antiretroviral drugs for post-exposure prophylaxis and the potential use of HIV vaccines and pre-exposure prophylaxis when they become available (Smith et al., 2005). Fourth, where transmission has already occurred interventions (including antiretroviral treatment) can aim to protect the health of those drug users living with HIV and to prevent onward transmission of HIV to their sexual and drug-using partners and to infants, including via 'positive prevention' interventions (WHO, 2008). Fifth, for those who become ill, treatment and care can reduce HIV-related morbidity and mortality and prevent and manage co-infections and co-morbidities (Ball, 2007b). And finally, interventions can focus on mitigating the social and economic impact of HIV on drug users, their families and communities, such as through social health insurance schemes and care for HIV orphans (Souteyrand et al., 2008; UNICEF, 2007).

Despite multiple opportunities for reducing HIV-related harm among injecting drug users, most harm reduction programmes still focus on a limited number of interventions, particularly those that target specific HIV risk behaviours. Since the mid-1980s, the 'big three' interventions have been risk reduction communication (particularly through community-based outreach), needle and syringe programmes and drug dependence treatment (notably opioid substitution treatment for opioid users). For these interventions the evidence of effectiveness is strong and the feasibility of implementation has been demonstrated in some of the poorest and most difficult settings (Institute of Medicine, 2007; Needle et al., 2005; Wodak and Cooney, 2005; Farrell et al., 2005). In recent years, HIV treatment has been added to the list, with increasing evidence that people living with HIV who use drugs can achieve good outcomes with antiretroviral therapy (Lert and Kazatchkine, 2007). The World Health Organization (WHO), the United Nations Office on Drugs and Crime (UNODC) and the Joint United Nations Programme on HIV/AIDS (UNAIDS) have defined a broader package of interventions for HIV prevention, treatment and care among injecting drug users, adding five interventions to make nine 'priority interventions' (WHO et al., 2009b):

- needle and syringe programmes;
- drug dependence treatment;
- behaviour change communication;
- HIV testing and counselling (WHO and UNODC, 2009);
- HIV treatment and care;
- condom promotion;
- prevention and treatment of sexually transmitted infections (Aral et al., 2005; Coffin et al., 2009);
- prevention and treatment of viral hepatitis (Bottecchia et al., 2007; Hellard et al., 2009; WHO Regional Office for Europe, 2006);
- and tuberculosis prevention, diagnosis and treatment (WHO et al., 2008).

In addition, a programmatic framework is required to take these interventions to scale, including strategies to establish supportive policy and community environments, better engage civil society and other partners, build robust systems for service delivery, and strengthen strategic information to guide responses.

The situation is dynamic, with new developments having implications for how harm reduction programmes might be structured in the future. Research on new HIV prevention interventions needs to be monitored closely to determine their relevance for harm reduction programmes. For example, there is a widening discourse on the role of antiretroviral drugs in the prevention of HIV transmission. A pre-exposure prophylaxis trial in Thailand, involving 2 400 HIV-negative injecting drug users, is studying the safety and efficacy of oral tenofovir for reducing HIV transmission among injecting drug users (CDC, 2009). Whereas the use of antiretroviral post-exposure prophylaxis has become routine practice in many occupational settings, consideration needs to be given to its wider use in non-occupational settings, including for injecting drug users (WHO and ILO, 2007). Recent studies suggest that suppression of viral load through antiretroviral therapy decreases the risk of HIV transmission between HIV-discordant couples (Reynolds et al., 2009). Several modelling exercises have considered the role of antiretroviral therapy in preventing the sexual transmission of HIV (Montaner et al., 2006; Granich et al., 2009), and in controlling HIV epidemics among injecting drug users (Bastani et al., 2010).

Harm reduction programmes should benefit from new developments in HIV/AIDS treatment, care and support. New evidence is emerging that earlier initiation of antiretroviral therapy is associated with better treatment outcomes (NIAID, 2009). This has significant implications for prioritising HIV testing and counselling in harm reduction programmes, to ensure that the HIV status of drug users is determined early so that treatment initiation and prevention efforts may be optimised. The majority of injecting drug users in low- and middle-income countries are unaware of their HIV status. In a survey of 44 low- and middle-income countries in 2008, some 25 countries reported on the percentage of injecting drug users who had received an HIV test and test result in the past 12 months, with a median of only 23 % of injecting drug users knowing their HIV status (WHO et al., 2009a). The promotion of provider-initiated HIV testing and counselling (PITC) and the use of rapid HIV testing technologies is particularly relevant for harm reduction programmes, given that follow-up of individuals may be difficult (WHO and UNODC, 2009). In 2006, out of 44 European countries surveyed, 32 provided PITC specifically for injecting drug users (EuroHIV, 2007). The emergence of simpler, better tolerated and more robust antiretroviral therapy regimens offer opportunities for better treatment outcomes in drug-using populations where treatment adherence and toxicity continue to pose major challenges (Lert and Kazatchkine, 2007). Female drug users should benefit from new approaches to the prevention of mother-to-child transmission of HIV (WHO, 2009) and interventions for addressing gender-based violence (WHO, 2007). There is also increasing recognition that harm reduction programmes should address the broader health care needs of drug users living with HIV, including the prevention and management of common opportunistic infections (notably tuberculosis) (WHO et al., 2008), co-infections (including viral hepatitis and sexually transmitted infections) and co-morbidities (such as mental health disorders), in addition to addressing their sexual and reproductive health needs and rights (GNP+ et al., 2009).

While much attention is given to specific HIV prevention technologies and treatment approaches let us not forget about the broader range of interventions that make for a truly comprehensive response, such as structural interventions for reducing HIV vulnerability and social protection for affected families and communities (Rhodes and Simić, 2005; UNAIDS, 2008). Furthermore, little consideration has been given to the potential role within harm reduction programmes of new or promising biomedical technologies for the prevention of sexual transmission of HIV, such as male circumcision and topical microbicides (Padian et al.,

2008). Today, with the global economic downturn and competing public health and development priorities, we can anticipate ever-louder calls for prioritisation of investments and definition of essential packages of interventions. While this may be an opportunity to bring greater focus to our harm reduction work, we need to ensure that in doing so our public health goals of universal access, health equity and social health protection are not compromised. Certainly, priority must be given to protecting investments in already proven high-impact interventions, such as needle and syringe programmes and opioid substitution treatment. In austere times, can we justify expanding the harm reduction package to include new interventions when coverage of the 'core' harm reduction interventions remains abysmally low in most countries? Decisions will need to be guided by solid evidence. More efficient and effective models of service delivery are required, including the integration of harm reduction interventions into other relevant health services, such as primary health care, sexual and reproductive health, mental health and tuberculosis services. To garner broad support, we need to demonstrate that harm reduction programmes and services contribute to, and are part of, broader health and community systems that strengthen and contribute to broader health and development outcomes — that harm reduction is a public good worth investing in.

References

Aral, S. O., St Lawrence, J. S., Dyatlovb, R. and Kozlovb, A. (2005), 'Commercial sex work, drug use, and sexually transmitted infections in St. Petersburg, Russia', *Social Science and Medicine* 60 (10), pp. 2181–90.

Ball, A. L. (2007a), 'HIV, injecting drug use and harm reduction: a public health response', *Addiction* 102, pp. 197–214.

Ball, A. L. (2007b), 'Universal access to HIV/AIDS treatment for injecting drug users: keeping the promise', *International Journal of Drug Policy* 18, pp. 241–5.

Bastani, P., Hogg, R. S., Marshall, B. et al. (2010), 'Highly active antiretroviral therapy eliminates HIV epidemics in a network model of an injecting drug user community.' Abstract 997. 17th Conference on Retroviruses and Opportunistic Infections, San Francisco, 16–19 February 2010. Available at http://www.retroconference. org/2010/PDFs/997.pdf

Bottecchia, M., Garcia-Samaniego, J. and Soriano, V. (2007), 'The implications of antiviral drugs with activity against hepatitis B virus and HIV', *Current Opinion in Infectious Diseases* 20, pp. 621–8.

CDC (Centers for Disease Control and Prevention) (2009), 'CDC's clinical studies of pre-exposure prophylaxis for HIV prevention', Atlanta: Centers for Disease Control and Prevention. Available at http://www.cdc.gov/hiv/ resources/qa/prep.htm.

Coffin, L. S., Newberry, A., Hagan, H., et al. (2009), 'Syphilis in drug users in low and middle income countries', *International Journal of Drug Policy*, DOI: 10.1016/i.drugpo.2009.02.008.

EuroHIV (2007), *Report on the EuroHIV 2006 survey on HIV and AIDS surveillance in the WHO European Region*, Institute de Veille Sanitaire, St Maurice.

Farrell, M., Gowing, L., Marsden, J., Ling, W. and Ali, R. (2005), 'Effectiveness of drug dependence treatment in HIV prevention', *International Journal of Drug Policy* 16 (Supplement 1), pp. S67–S75.

GNP+, ICW, Young Positives, et al. (2009), *Advancing the sexual and reproductive health and human rights of people living with HIV: a guidance package*, GNP+, Amsterdam.

Granich, R. M., Gilks, C. F., Dye, C., et al. (2009), 'Universal voluntary HIV testing with immediate antiretroviral therapy as a strategy for the elimination of HIV transmission: a mathematical model', *Lancet* 373, pp. 48–57.

Hellard, M., Sacks-Davis, R. and Gold, J. (2009), 'Hepatitis C treatment for injection drug users: a review of the available evidence', *Clinical Infectious Diseases* 49, pp. 561–73.

Institute of Medicine Committee on the Prevention of HIV Infection Among Injecting Drug Users in High-Risk Countries (2007), *Preventing HIV infection among injecting drug users in high-risk countries: an assessment of the evidence*, The National Academies Press, Washington, DC.

Lert, F. and Kazatchkine, M. (2007), 'Antiretroviral HIV treatment and care for injecting drug users: an evidence-based overview', *International Journal of Drug Policy* 18 (4), pp. 255–61.

Montaner, J. S., Hogg, R., Wood, E., et al. (2006), 'The case for expanding access to highly active antiretroviral therapy to curb the growth of the HIV epidemic', *Lancet* 368, pp. 531–6.

Needle, R. H., Burrows, D., Friedman, S. R., et al. (2005), 'Effectiveness of community-based outreach in preventing HIV/AIDS among injecting drug users', *International Journal of Drug Policy* 16 (Supplement 1), pp. S45–S57.

NIAID (National Institute of Allergy and Infectious Disease) (2009), 'Starting antiretroviral therapy earlier yields better clinical outcomes: interim review leads to early end of clinical trial in Haiti', NIH News Release, 8 June. Available at http://www3.niaid.nih.gov/news/newsreleases/2009/CIPRA_HT_01.htm.

Padian, N. S., Buvé, A., Balkus, J., Serwadda, D. and Cates, W. (2008), 'Biomedical interventions to prevent HIV infection: evidence, challenges, and the way forward', *Lancet* 372 (9638), pp. 585–99.

Reynolds, S., Makumbi, F., Kagaayi, J., et al. (2009), 'ART reduced the rate of sexual transmission of HIV among HIV-discordant couples in rural Rakai, Uganda', *16th Conference on Retroviruses and Opportunistic Infections, Abstract 52a*.

Rhodes, T. and Simić, M. (2005), 'Transition and the HIV risk environment', *BMJ* 331, pp. 220–3.

Smith, D. K, Grohskopf, L. A., Black, R. J., et al. (2005), 'Antiretroviral postexposure prophylaxis after sexual, injection-drug use, or other nonoccupational exposure to HIV in the United States: recommendations from the US Department of Health and Human Services', *Morbidity and Mortality Weekly Report* 54 (RR02), pp. 1–20.

Souteyrand, Y. P., Collard, V., Moatti, J. P., Grubb, I. and Guerma, T. (2008), 'Free care at the point of service delivery: a key component for reaching universal access to HIV/AIDS treatment in developing countries', *AIDS* 22 (Supplement 1), pp. S161–S168.

UNAIDS (Joint United Nations Programme on HIV/AIDS) (2008), 'Addressing societal causes of HIV risk and vulnerability', in *2008 report on the global AIDS epidemic*, UNAIDS, Geneva.

UNICEF (United Nations Children's Fund) (2007), *Enhanced protection for children affected by AIDS*, UNICEF, New York.

WHO (World Health Organization) (2007), *Expert meeting on the primary prevention of intimate partner violence and sexual violence, May 2–3 2007, Geneva, Switzerland: meeting report*, WHO, Geneva. Available at http://www.who.int/violence_injury_prevention/violence/activities/who_ipv_sv_prevention_meeting_report.pdf.

WHO (2008), *Essential prevention and care interventions for adults and adolescents living with HIV in resource-limited settings*, WHO, Geneva.

WHO (2009), 'Rapid advice: use of antiretroviral drugs for treating pregnant women and preventing HIV infection in infants', WHO, Geneva. Available at http://www.who.int/hiv/pub/mtct/rapid_advice_mtct.pdf

WHO Regional Office for Europe (2006), *Prevention of hepatitis A, B and C and other hepatotoxic factors in people living with HIV/AIDS: clinical protocol for the WHO European Region*, WHO, Copenhagen.

WHO and ILO (International Labour Organization) (2007), *Post-exposure prophylaxis to prevent HIV infection: joint WHO/ILO guidelines on post-exposure prophylaxis (PEP) to prevent HIV infection*, WHO, Geneva.

WHO and UNODC (United Nations Office on Drugs and Crime) (2009), *Guidance on testing and counselling for HIV in settings attended by people who inject drugs: improving access to treatment, care and prevention*, WHO, Manila.

WHO, UNAIDS and UNICEF (2009), *Towards universal access: scaling up priority HIV/AIDS interventions in the health sector: 2009 Progress report*, WHO, Geneva.

WHO, UNODC and UNAIDS (2008), *Policy guidelines for collaborative TB and HIV services for injecting and other drug users: an integrated approach*, WHO, Geneva.

WHO, UNODC and UNAIDS (2009), *Technical guide for countries to set targets for universal access to HIV prevention, treatment and care for injecting drug users*, WHO, Geneva.

Wodak, A. and Cooney, A. (2005), 'Effectiveness of sterile needle and syringe programmes', *International Journal of Drug Policy* 16 (Supplement 1), pp. S31–S44.

Translating evidence into action — challenges to scaling up harm reduction programmes in Europe and Central Asia

Rifat Atun and Michel Kazatchkine

The exceptionality of the HIV/AIDS epidemic has long been acknowledged: it is shaped by and yet also impacts on socio-economic, political, cultural and legal environments, as well as individual beliefs and norms (Rhodes, 2002). This complex interplay of factors influencing the epidemic is particularly evident in concentrated epidemics driven by injecting drug use, as drug use is strongly influenced by macro-environmental factors such as political and economic changes, as well as socio-cultural and legal norms in particular settings. In many cases this leads to stigmatisation, marginalisation and isolation of injecting drug users (IDUs). Whilst evidence strongly suggests that HIV transmission driven by injecting drug use can be halted and reversed through effective multi-component harm reduction programmes (Ball et al., 1998; Institute of Medicine, 2007), this evidence has been overlooked or disregarded by policymakers in many countries. Consequently, in many parts of the world, injecting drug use is still fuelling HIV epidemics. Europe, a setting with contrasting policies to control HIV epidemics amongst IDUs and various levels of success with these policies, provides valuable evidence and a learning example to inform policy decisions on harm reduction programmes.

The countries of western Europe ([1]), through wide-scale implementation of needle and syringe programmes (NSPs), opioid substitution treatment (OST), outreach, and education

---

([1])   These include Albania, Andorra, Austria, Belgium, Bosnia and Herzegovina, Bulgaria, Croatia, Czech Republic, Denmark, Estonia, Finland, former Yugoslav Republic of Macedonia, France, Germany, Greece, Hungary, Iceland, Ireland, Italy, Latvia, Liechtenstein, Lithuania Luxembourg, Malta, Monaco, Montenegro, Netherlands, Norway, Poland, Portugal, San Marino, Serbia, Slovenia, Slovakia, Romania, Spain, Sweden, Switzerland and United Kingdom.

programmes implemented in the late 1980s and 1990s, were able to halt (such as the United Kingdom) or control (such as France, Italy, Spain) IDU-driven HIV epidemics (Stimson, 1995; Matic et al., 2008; Atun et al., 2008). Similarly, the central European countries of the Czech Republic, Poland, Slovakia, and Slovenia, which experienced rapid socio-economic, political and cultural transitions, were also able to stabilise their HIV epidemics at low prevalence by responding early through the implementation of effective control measures and comprehensive harm reduction (Donoghoe, 2006). Consequently, in western and central Europe, as of 2008, the reported number of new cases of HIV amongst injecting drug users had declined: accounting for a smaller proportion of the HIV burden than previously (UNAIDS and WHO, 2008). By contrast, former Soviet Union countries in eastern Europe and central Asia ([2]), which, following the dissolution of the Soviet Union in the early 1990s, were subject to rapid socio-economic, political and cultural transitions, experienced IDU-driven HIV epidemics (Rhodes et al., 1999), which today are persisting and worsening. In eastern European countries, the response to the IDU HIV transmission was slow and compromised by health systems unequipped to handle the rapid increase in the burden of HIV (Rhodes and Simic, 2005). Even now, though harm reduction programmes are being implemented in all countries of eastern Europe, coverage is woefully inadequate to have any impact on the epidemics these countries face (Donoghoe, 2006). This is evidenced by the current trend of rising HIV incidence amongst injecting drug users in eastern Europe (Wiessing et al., 2008). Of particular concern are the persistent inequities in access to prevention and treatment services and access to antiretroviral therapy (Atun et al., 2008; Donoghoe et al., 2007).

To stem the HIV epidemics in eastern Europe, and to address the unacceptable inequities in access to antiretroviral therapy, it is essential to establish and scale-up comprehensive harm reduction programmes that incorporate NSPs and OST and ensure they are implemented in prisons in both western and eastern Europe. However, in many countries this expansion is hindered by inadequate provision in the legislation that protects the human rights of IDUs and by laws that criminalise injecting drug use and harm reduction programmes. This contributes to deep stigmatisation, and further isolation of this particularly at-risk group. However, in addition to legislative and regulatory barriers, other factors influence the scale-up of harm reduction programmes. We consider here the published literature to identify 'barriers' and 'enablers' to scaling up harm reduction programmes in Europe in order to better understand the challenges that need to be addressed to translate evidence into action.

Health system organisation

Many countries in eastern Europe have inherited vertically organised health systems, with parallel subsystems for HIV prevention and care, and substance use. These services are delivered by highly specialised providers, with little structural and operational integration of the services provided. This leads to fragmentation of services, prevents continuity of care and creates barriers for IDUs, a marginalised group who have poor access to services (Atun, 2006).

[2]   These include Armenia, Azerbaijan, Belarus, Georgia, Moldova, Russian Federation, Ukraine, while central Asian countries include Kazakhstan, Kyrgyz Republic, Tajikistan, Turkmenistan and Uzbekistan.

This structural anomaly, which served well in the past, is not suited to the rapid implementation and scale-up of integrated responses to the IDU-driven HIV (and hepatitis) epidemics faced by these countries. Consequently, services that offer a suitable package of prevention, treatment and care are very limited in number, and when available they are largely inaccessible (Bobrova et al., 2007). For example, in Ukraine, the policy that permits only narcologists to prescribe OST has hindered scale-up of integrated harm reduction services (Bruce et al., 2006). As a result, only 0.1 % of IDUs are reached by this effective treatment (Matic et al., 2008).

Ukraine is not alone in this practice; limiting the prescribing of OST to narcologists is common in most east European health systems — a feature that deters IDUs from seeking and adhering to effective treatment (Donoghoe, 2006). However, experience suggests that with appropriate service design these structural barriers can be overcome. In the Russian Federation, where similar structural rigidities exist and where consequently only 1–4 % of IDUs are reached by NSPs (Wiessing et al., 2009), decentralisation of these activities by including peer network and pharmacy distribution has boosted service coverage in areas where new service delivery models have been adopted (Sarang et al., 2008; Sharma et al., 2007). In contrast, evidence from transition countries such as Croatia, Lithuania, Poland and Slovenia, which soon after transition in the 1990s adopted integrated models of treatment and care for HIV positive IDUs, suggests increased service accessibility for patients (Sarang et al., 2007). In countries such as Ireland, the Netherlands, Norway, Sweden, and the United Kingdom, where in addition to specialised community- or hospital-based clinics general practitioners also provide HIV care and treatment services, service coverage and usage are high, with users reporting high satisfaction with services provided in the community and by general practitioners (Atun, 2006).

Political support and leadership

In western Europe, early in the HIV epidemic, support for harm reduction programmes by political leaders created an enabling environment for rapid introduction and scale-up of OST, NSPs and treatment and care programmes for IDUs. For example, in 1993 an initiative that introduced harm reduction in France was followed between 1995 and 2003 by the rapid scale-up of OST services. This led to a reduction in unsafe injection practices and a decline in HIV prevalence from 40 % to 20 % in the same period (Emmanuelli and Desenclos, 2005). In the United Kingdom, the health authorities, which enjoy substantial operational autonomy, were able to provide local leadership to establish service delivery units to quickly implement NSPs, outreach services, and integrated models of OST where a range of doctors could prescribe methadone (Stimson, 1995).

In contrast, experience in eastern Europe is one of lack of leadership and political commitment to harm reduction. In Armenia, Russia, Tajikistan and Turkmenistan lack of obvious political support for harm reduction has meant that critical activities such as needle and syringe provision were not mainstreamed within the national HIV response, while the total prohibition of OST meant a comprehensive programme could not be mounted. A lack of political support and negative perceptions on harm reduction as a 'Western concept' at odds with the culture and norms in Russia has meant limited public funds being allocated to programmes to address the needs of IDUs (Tkatchenko-Schmidt et al., 2007). A strongly hostile legislative environment and socio-cultural intolerance in many countries to drug use further hindered attempts to develop NSPs and fuelled the practice of syringe sharing amongst IDUs who feared searches by police for injection equipment and possible incarceration (Rhodes et al., 2004). Likewise, Ukraine, one of the first eastern European countries to implement OST pilot projects, has been slow in scaling up these programmes due to resistance amongst the political leadership and some providers coupled with a shortage of financial resources and trained healthcare professionals. To date, there are only high-threshold services in the country (Matic et al., 2008, Schumacher et al., 2007).

Insufficient domestic financing

An important barrier to scaling up harm reduction programmes in eastern Europe relates to limited domestic funding allocated to HIV programmes, especially to prevention activities and targeted interventions for high-risk groups (Matic et al., 2008; Dehne et al., 2000). Though Belarus in its national AIDS programme had plans to set up NSPs nationwide, these could not be established due to financial shortfalls for programme implementation (Sarang et al., 2007).

The Global Fund to Fight AIDS, Tuberculosis and Malaria has provided much-needed funding for programmes targeting injecting drug users and other at-risk groups, such as sex workers and men who have sex with men. Between 2004 and the end of 2008 the Global Fund, the largest donor globally for harm reduction programmes, had invested US $920 million in funding to support HIV programmes that include harm reduction components. Of this $920 million, around $180 million was specifically for harm reduction activities (Atun and Kazatchkine, 2010). In many countries of eastern Europe, the Global Fund is the sole funder of harm reduction programmes. In Ukraine, a Global Fund grant enabled the scale-up of a pilot buprenorphine substitution programme (Matic et al., 2008).

Whilst the much-needed expansion in international funding for harm reduction is a welcome development, domestic investment targeting the needs of IDUs must also be expanded to increase access and service coverage, and to ensure sustainability. There are encouraging signs of increased investment and good coverage levels in some central and eastern European countries. For example, in the Czech Republic, where harm reduction programmes are primarily government funded, a coverage level of 82 % has been reached (Atun, 2006), while Estonia has agreed to continue funding through domestic activities that were initiated with Global Fund investments (Matic et al., 2008).

Involvement of the civil society

Evidence points to a critically important role played by civil society and grassroots organisations in the establishment of harm reduction activities (Sharma et al., 2008). In western Europe, early in the epidemic, the engagement of civil society positively influenced the national policies on HIV control and enabled the development of a multisectoral response to IDU-driven HIV epidemics. A multisectoral response, which was instrumental in the control of the HIV epidemic, also resulted in the design of community-driven user-friendly services (Atun et al., 2008). In France, non-governmental organisations (NGOs) played a central role in persuading the government to develop policies that enabled the establishment of harm reduction programmes for IDUs (Emmanuelli and Desenclos, 2005). In contrast, when the IDU-driven epidemics began in eastern Europe few NGOs were working there, particularly in the field of drug-use, and those that were had little or no government support (Sarang et al., 2007). In these countries a lack of civil society involvement in the response has severely handicapped efforts aimed at scaling up prevention and harm reduction services to reach high-risk populations (Atun et al., 2008). In spite of a lack of political support, networks advocating for harm reduction, such as the Open Society Institute and the Eurasian Harm Reduction Network, have played an instrumental role in advocacy, raising awareness about the problems faced by injecting drug users and disseminating and developing vital information to key stakeholders (Sarang et al., 2007). And in recent years, the World Health Organization Regional Office for Europe has appointed both a harm reduction adviser and a communicable diseases advocacy and community relations adviser, two positions unique in WHO and which have facilitated UN work on these issues across Europe.

Conclusion

The evidence shows a variable and generally weak response to IDU-driven HIV epidemics in eastern Europe. This contrasts with the successful responses mounted in western European countries. While the evidence for a positive impact of harm reduction programmes in controlling IDU-driven HIV epidemics is strong, in Europe the introduction and scaling up of harm reduction programmes has been driven less by the evidence and more by the socio-cultural and political context prevailing in different countries. Evidence from published studies clearly demonstrates that success in the scaling up of harm reduction activities is shaped by political leadership, the legal environment, health system organisation, the availability of domestic financing and the engagement of civil society.

Countries in western Europe that have implemented integrated, multisectoral and multi-component interventions, supported by legal and social policies, have succeeded in controlling IDU-driven HIV epidemics. By contrast, in much of eastern Europe a lack of enabling socio-cultural and political environment and weak civil society has hindered the development of policies to translate evidence into action, in spite of the obvious need to rapidly scale-up harm reduction programmes to curb the HIV epidemic amongst IDUs.

In eastern Europe, as well as Central Asia, evidence alone is not enough to influence the development of policies that will enable the scaling up of comprehensive harm reduction programmes. Translating evidence into action will depend not on the strength of the evidence on the effectiveness of harm reduction but on addressing many of the complex factors that interact to create a receptive or, in the case of some eastern European countries, a hostile context for its adoption.

In eastern European countries successful scaling up and effective service coverage will depend on strong political leadership, a reform of the legal and regulatory norms to create a more enabling environment and respect the human rights of IDUs, sustained domestic funding, the strengthening of civil society and their robust engagement in advocacy and service provision, the planning and delivery of harm reduction programmes, as well as the organisation of vertically structured health systems to create client-centred services. Most critically, in eastern Europe, harm reduction interventions must be rooted in an understanding of the social and economic factors that lead to the initiation of drug use and that increase drug users' vulnerability. This, in turn, demands the greater engagement of drug users in programme design to provide insights on how best to address and serve their needs. But first, this marginalised group must be given the opportunity to enjoy human rights — like any other citizen. However, in many European settings we are far from achieving this objective.

References

Atun, R. A. (2006), 'How European health systems have reacted to HIV/AIDS epidemic', in Matic, S., Lazarus, J. V. and Donoghoe, M. C. (eds), *HIV/AIDS in Europe: moving from death sentence to chronic disease management*, World Health Organization Regional Office for Europe, Denmark.

Atun, R. A. (2008), 'Scaling up of harm reduction programs: the Global Fund Experience', presented at the International Harm Reduction Association's 20th International Conference, *Harm Reduction and Human Rights*, 20–23 April, Bangkok, Thailand.

Atun, R. and Kazatchkine, M. (2010), 'The Global Fund's leadership on harm reduction: 2002–09', *International Journal of Drug Policy* (in press).

Atun, R. A., McKee, M., Coker, R. and Gurol-Urganci, I. (2008), 'Health systems' responses to 25 years of HIV in Europe: inequities persist and challenges remain', *Health Policy* 86, pp. 181–94.

Ball, A. L. (2007), 'HIV, injecting drug use and harm reduction: a public health response', *Addiction* 102, pp. 684–90.

Ball, A. L., Rana, S. and Dehne, K. L. (1998), 'HIV prevention among injecting drug users: responses in developing and transitional countries', *Public Health Reports* 113 (S1), pp. 170–81.

Bobrova, N., Sarang, A., Stuikyte, R. and Lezhentsev, K. (2007), 'Obstacles in provision of anti-retroviral treatment to drug users in Central and Eastern Europe and Central Asia: a regional overview', *International Journal of Drug Policy* 18, pp. 313–18.

Bruce, D. R., Dvoryak, S., Sylla, L. and Altice, F. L. (2006), 'HIV treatment access and scale-up for delivery of opiate substitution therapy with buprenorphine for IDUs in Ukraine: program description and policy implications', *International Journal of Drug Policy* 18, pp. 326–8.

Dehne, K. L., Pokrovskiy, V., Kobyshcha, Y. and Schwartlander, B. (2000), 'Update on the epidemics of HIV and other sexually transmitted infections in the newly independent states of the former Soviet Union', *AIDS*, 14 (S3), pp. S75–S84.

Donoghoe, M. C. (2006), 'Injecting drug use, harm reduction and HIV/AIDS', in Matic, S., Lazarus, J. V. and Donoghoe, M. C. (eds), *HIV/AIDS in Europe: moving from death sentence to chronic disease management*, World Health Organization Europe, Denmark.

Donoghoe, M. C., Bollerup, A. R., Lazarus, J. V., Nielsen, S. and Matic, S. (2007), 'Access to highly active antiretroviral therapy for injecting drug users in the European region 2002–2004', *International Journal of Drug Policy* 18, pp. 271–80.

Emmanuelli, J. and Desenclos, J. C. (2005), 'Harm reduction interventions, behaviors and associated health outcomes in France, 1996–2003', *Addiction* 100, pp. 1690–700.

Institute of Medicine (2007), *Preventing HIV infection among injecting drug users in high-risk countries: an assessment of the evidence*, National Academy of Sciences, Washington, DC.

Matic, S., Lazarus, J. V., Nielsen, S. and Laukamm-Josten, U. (eds) (2008), *Progress on implementing the Dublin Declaration on partnership to fight HIV/AIDS in Europe and Central Asia*, World Health Organization Europe, Denmark.

Rhodes, T. (2002), 'The "risk environment": a framework for understanding and reducing drug-related harm', *International Journal of Drug Policy* 13, pp. 85–94.

Rhodes, T. and Simic, M. (2005), 'Transition and HIV risk environment', *BMJ* 331, pp. 220–3.

Rhodes, T., Ball, A., Stimson, G. V., et al. (1999), 'HIV infection associated with drug injecting in the Newly Independent States, eastern Europe: the social and economic context of epidemics', *Addiction* 94 (9), pp. 1323–36.

Rhodes, T., Sarang, A., Bobrik, A., Bobkov, E. and Platt, L. (2004), 'HIV transmission and HIV prevention associated with injecting drug use in the Russian Federation', *International Journal of Drug Policy* 15, pp. 1–16.

Sarang, A., Stuikyte, R. and Bykov, R. (2007) 'Implementation of harm reduction in Central and Eastern Europe and Central Asia', *International Journal of Drug Policy* 18, pp. 129–35.

Sarang, A., Rhodes, T. and Platt, L. (2008), 'Access to syringes in three Russian cities: implications for syringe distribution and coverage', *International Journal of Drug Policy* 19S, pp. S25–S36.

Schumacher, J. E., Fischer, G. and Qian, H. Z. (2007), 'Policy drives harm reduction for drug abuse and HIV/AIDS prevention in some developing countries', *Drug and Alcohol Dependence* 91, pp. 300–05.

Sharma, M., Burrows, D. and Bluthenthal, R. N. (2008), 'Improving coverage and scale-up of HIV prevention, treatment and care for injecting drug users: moving the agenda forward', *International Journal of Drug Policy* 19S, pp. S1–S4.

Stimson, G. V. (1995), 'AIDS and injecting drug use in the United Kingdom, 1987–1993: the policy response and the prevention of the epidemic', *Social Sciences & Medicine* 41 (5), pp. 669–716.

Tkatchenko-Schmidt, E., Renton, A., Gevorgyan, R., Davydenko, L. and Atun, R. A. (2007), 'Prevention of HIV/AIDS among injecting drug users in Russia: opportunities and barriers to scaling-up of harm reduction programmes', *Health Policy* 85, pp. 162–71.

UNAIDS (Joint United Nations Programme on HIV/AIDS) and WHO (World Health Organization) (2008), *2008 report on the global AIDS epidemic*, UNAIDS, WHO, Geneva. Available at http://data.unaids.org/pub/GlobalReport/2008/jc1510_2008_global_report_pp29_62_en.pdf.

Wiessing, L., van de Laar, M. J., Donoghoe, M. C., et al. (2008), 'HIV among injecting drug users in Europe: increasing trends in the East', *Eurosurveillance* 13 (50), pp. 1–3.

Wiessing, L., Likatavicius, G., Klempova, D., et al. (2009), 'Associations between availability and coverage of HIV-prevention measures and subsequent incidence of diagnosed HIV infection among injection drug users', *American Journal of Public Health* 99 (6), pp. 1049–52.

People who use drugs and their role in harm reduction

Mat Southwell

Drug taking is in part about an engagement with risk and it is therefore unsurprising to find that people who use drugs tend to be 'risk takers' (Measham et al., 2001). People come to drug taking with an understanding that drug use involves risk, and that this may be attractive in and of itself. Most people who use drugs engage in drug use with an understanding that they are managing the interplay between the positive effects of a drug (pleasure maximisation) and the risks associated with administering or taking a drug (harm reduction).

As such, people who use drugs can be defined as calculated risk takers. This challenges the orthodox addiction archetypes that describe people who use drugs as victims either of substances with some type of pseudo-magical quality or of the 'evil drug dealers' who peddle these drugs (Booth, 1997). Those of us who choose and defend the right to take mind-altering substances are not denying or minimising the actual risks involved in taking drugs. However, risk does not automatically result in harm and the factors informing harm are complex, multifaceted, and influenced by both internal and external factors. Too often drug policies seek simple and universal solutions to the complex world of drug taking. This results in a mismatch between political and policy discourses and the reality of drug taking on the ground, which serves to distance people who use drugs, resulting in a general distrust of official guidance.

It is important to understand that the term 'risk' normally defines the likelihood of specific eventualities, which may have either beneficial or adverse consequences. For the person using drugs, the risk or potential of pleasure maximisation is judged against the risk that harm may arise from drug taking. This assessment of comparative risk is best undertaken in a value-free context, which allows people to make hopefully informed decisions about whether to use drugs or not, and, for some, to make informed decisions about which drugs to use, by which routes and in what amounts.

Such a value-free environment may be desirable but it clearly does not exist. Drugs prevention measures are driven by a moralistic opposition to intoxication, which has its roots in the temperance movement. Drug prevention sets out to persuade young people in particular not to take drugs, by ignoring the pleasure features of these drugs and by playing up risks.

Learning to live with drugs

In fact, anti-drugs campaigns are arguably primarily about a discourse between politicians and adult voters, designed to show that a particular political party is 'tough on crime'. This abuse of drugs prevention is unethical and can have dangerous, if unintended, consequences. Drugs prevention is usually pharmacocentric, focusing on drug-related risks in isolation from an understanding of youth culture or the individual lives of young people. Historically, drug use has been part of an 'outsider' identity and some come to drug use in search of belonging and community (Fleming, 2001). The United Kingdom Government's anti-heroin campaign of the 1980s, 'Heroin screws you up' (http://drugtrain.net/drugs/heroin/heroin_screws_you_up.html), was shown in post-campaign testing to have attracted young people to adopt heroin use, as they identified with the alienated and isolated young people portrayed in the campaign's gritty black and white posters (Hastings et al., 2004). When this information entered the public domain, government responded by condemning the researcher and excluding him from undertaking further official research. This hardly reflects a commitment to science but effectively illustrates the value-laden nature of this field.

The harm reduction movement has been ambivalent about its engagement with drugs prevention, fearing that opposition might lead to further accusations of being 'pro-drugs'. However, the harm reduction movement needs to lobby for value-free drugs education that provides young people with objective information about different drugs, their effects and risk profiles. If governments are serious about reducing young people's engagement in drug taking and, particularly, in harmful drug use, then it is likely that addressing young people's motivation, education, and social circumstances will have a greater impact than pushing simplistic anti-drugs messages.

The need for harm reduction is becoming ever more pressing as young people gain access to a diverse range of drugs. Significantly, these drugs are increasingly taken outside the cultural and social settings that often hold community knowledge and learning. In archaic societies, Shamans acted as the guardians of the oral history of a community, gathering and disseminating learning between groups and generations. The demonisation of drugs, and the people who take them, creates a huge disincentive for peer leaders to stand up and model this function within modern-day communities. As such, young people often operate as if they are the first group ever to take drugs (Jay, 2000). This maximises risk by forcing new generations to engage in drug taking without the benefit of the knowledge and learning of previous generations.

User involvement in harm reduction

Harm reduction is most comfortably and effectively delivered with people who have chosen to have a sustained relationship with drug taking. However, even in this setting there are tensions about the role and contribution of people who use drugs. It is important to recognise that while many harm reduction services are delivered by professionals, much harm reduction innovation emerges from within drug using communities. Let us not forget that a drug user group established the world's first needle exchange back in 1984 (Buning et al., 1990; Stimson, 2007), in response to hepatitis B.

This structural response follows the natural desire to avoid risk where possible while in search of pleasure maximisation. Friedman identified that people who injected drugs in New York responded to seeing their peers falling sick in the 1980s, with what was later identified as HIV/AIDS, by reducing needle sharing and this led to a leveling off of infection rates (Friedman et al., 1999). Needle exchange subsequently provided injectors with the technology to act on this organic learning, leading to actual reductions in infection rates.

This process of organic harm reduction has been seen among a number of drug using populations. For example, people who smoke crack correctly sought to exclude the cause of 'black lung', cigarette ash and other impurities, by constructing or sourcing ash-free glass pipes while continuing to smoke crack. While such strategies have been known about since the mid-1990s, stimulant pipe distribution schemes have not been widely adopted. There needs to be greater investment in the interface between drug using communities and the professional field. Drug user organisations should be key players in this environment. It is noteworthy that innovation around crack harm reduction has largely come from drug user groups or practitioners with experiential, as well as professional, expertise. Partnerships between academics, practitioners and drug user organisations need to be strengthened to ensure that knowledge in all three domains is considered and where appropriate translated into accessible practice or peer support interventions.

Spontaneous trends away from injecting, towards non-injecting routes of administration, have been identified in a number of European settings and in New York. Research would indicate that such switches in route of administration reflect a commitment to health, a desire to reduce levels of dependency, or a wish to increase self-control. However, these changes have also been shown to be significantly influenced by the type, cost and quality of drugs. As such, route transition changes are only likely to occur when reasonably priced, good quality drugs are available in a suitable form. Strang and colleagues have questioned whether some type of market manipulation might be helpful in supporting such trends (Hunt et al., 1999). However, in reality this conflicts with demand reduction thinking that sees the disruption of the drug supply chain as a positive objective.

Finally, people who use drugs and their organisations can uniquely operate as 'consumer advocates' within illicit drug scenes. These models are still underdeveloped and have yet to be subjected to scientific scrutiny. However, strategies for promoting consumer rights and ethical trading standards offer another positive opportunity for influencing the context within which drug taking takes place. Some suppliers of drugs have shown themselves willing to support harm reduction messages, operating as secondary needle exchange providers and acting as conduits for health education messages to be transmitted to key populations of drugs users (Southwell, 2008).

People who use drugs need to become routine partners in harm reduction, supporting the identification, development and promotion of harm reduction strategies. Resources need to be allocated to properly support the translation and dissemination of peer and academic learning into practice and peer support interventions.

References

Booth, J. B. (1997), *The myth of addiction* (2nd edition), Harwood Academic Publishers, Newark.

Buning, E. C., van Brussel G. H. and van Santen, G. (1990), 'The "methadone by bus" project in Amsterdam', *British Journal of Addiction* 85, pp. 1247–50.

Fleming, P. (2001), *The role of treatment services in motivating and deterring treatment entry: exploring the views of opioid-dependent drug users*, Wells Healthcare Communications Ltd, England.

Friedman, S. R., Curtis, R., Neaguis, A., Jose, B. and Des Jarlais, D. D. (1999), *Social networks, drug injectors' lives and HIV/AIDS*, Kluwer Academy, New York.

Hastings, G., Stead, M. and Webb, J. (2004), 'Fear appeals in social marketing: strategic and ethical reasons for concern', *Psychology and Marketing* 21, pp. 961–86.

Hunt, N., Griffiths, P., Southwell, M., Stillwell, G. and Strang, J. (1999), 'Preventing and curtailing injecting drug use: opportunities for developing and delivering "route transition interventions", *Drug and Alcohol Review* 18, pp. 441–51.

Jay, M. (2000), *Emperors of dreams: drugs in the nineteenth century*, Dedalus, Cambridge.

Measham, F., Aldridge, J. and Parker, H. (2001), *Dancing on drugs: risk, health, and hedonism in the British club scene*, Free Association Books, London.

Southwell, M. (2008), 'Consumer action and drug supply networks', unpublished report. Available at http://tinyurl.com/consumeractiondealers.

Stimson, G. V. (2007), 'Harm reduction — coming of age: a local movement with global impact', *International Journal of Drug Policy* 18, pp. 67–9.

Harm reduction — an 'ethical' perspective

Craig Fry

In its short history, the harm reduction specialty field of public health has routinely pushed the boundaries of evidence and policy, and tested our moral imagination in relation to the place of drug use and users in society and possible community responses. Each new harm reduction policy and programme proposal has been met with intense and often ongoing public scrutiny (e.g. condom distribution, needle and syringe programmes, maintenance and substitution pharmacotherapy, heroin prescription, supervised injecting).

The unwavering response to this scrutiny from within the harm reduction movement has been to argue that its 'pragmatic' drug policies and interventions are justified because the available evidence shows they work to reduce drug harms (Hunt et al., 2006; Ritter and Cameron, 2006). The reduction of harms associated with the use and misuse of psychoactive substances would appear to be a straightforward goal, and one on which there ought to be widespread agreement. Harm reduction in the most general sense can be considered an ethical project if we accept that harm reduction measures assist in alleviating drug-related harm. Less drug harm is a good thing.

But there is more. Harm reduction has only recently started to grapple critically with the definitional challenges and uncertainties inherent in its core goal (for example, what is drug harm? How can drug harms be measured? How do we balance drug harms and benefits?). Likewise, this field is only now beginning to awaken to the difficult normative questions that come with a focus on drug use harm (for example, what should we do to address drug harms? Whose drug harms matter most? Are some types of drug harm acceptable?).

Harm reduction, at least mainstream harm reduction, has for the most part argued that the best way to address the definitional, measurement and evaluative challenges it faces is through evidence-based scientific approaches. Here, 'facts' are separated from 'values' in the quest for universally valid (and therefore compelling) and value-neutral or 'objective' scientific facts that are untainted by 'subjective' moral evaluations (Weatherburn, 2009).

As this monograph shows, the evidence base in support of harm reduction policies, programmes and interventions has grown in size, complexity and sophistication. Indeed, so successful has harm reduction been judged by its advocates that we are starting to see claims emerge that the scientific debate about the value or positive impact of harm reduction is now over (Wodak, 2007). Harm reduction works.

However, there is still significant government opposition to harm reduction measures in some of the world's most populous countries that arguably need such measures the most. This opposition has been mostly attributed to the moralising by some powerful interests in society about the permissibility of drug misuse and of policy responses that are not abstinence-based. However, the debate has also increasingly been about the authority of science and scientific knowledge as the primary arbiter of what may be regarded as acceptable social policy. Indeed, in the health and drug policy arena we are finally coming to accept the existence of 'blurred boundaries' between science and politics (Gottweis, 2008), and their implications for both the definition of and proposed responses to 'health problems'.

Diverse perspectives exist on drug policy issues and these are informed, for better or worse, by a variety of value and belief systems. 'Evidence' has a social character in terms of the underlying values and beliefs that influence how it is defined, collected, reported and used. Harm reduction today must accommodate uncertainty and diverse values.

When there are disputes and uncertainty about the 'facts' in harm reduction, 'values' cannot be separated from the equation, precisely because value positions are the reason disputes and uncertainty exist in the first place. In the broader context of science and public policy critique there is a growing recognition that disputes on what constitutes 'good evidence' can compromise communication among scientists, policymakers and the public, and in turn constrain the types of public policy questions that are addressed (Kinzig et al., 2003).

We may well ask, then, whether the continued emphasis on evidence-based over values-based approaches is consistent with the 'pragmatism' that has so often been attributed as a harm reduction hallmark. It has been suggested that harm reduction's silence on moral and value issues (in favour of scientific argument) undermines the movement's ability to engage critics who would claim that abstinence and law enforcement are the only morally acceptable solutions to drug problems (Hathaway and Tousaw, 2008).

The time has come for harm reduction to establish its ethical credentials (Irwin and Fry, 2007). I use 'ethical' and 'ethics' here to refer to a critical orientation towards values and normative considerations, and less so to moral philosophy or any particular ethical theory or framework. For me the question 'Is harm reduction ethical?' is first and foremost a query about whether or not harm reduction is, or perhaps can be, reflexive or 'in touch' with the diverse value perspectives underpinning it.

In the last few years there has been increasing attention to the task of articulating the moral underpinnings of harm reduction. It has been discussed in relation to communitarian ethics (Fry et al., 2005), virtue ethics (Christie et al., 2008), deontology and utilitarianism and more (Kleinig and Einstein, 2006; Kleinig, 2008). Special theme issues in leading journals have appeared on harm reduction ethics (Fry et al., 2008), scholarly monographs (Kleinig and Einstein, 2006) and empirical research on this theme is also emerging (Solai et al., 2006; Phillips and Bourne, 2008).

What is particularly encouraging is that a range of perspectives, both theoretical and applied, are emerging on harm reduction ethics. Contributions are coming from moral philosophy, public health, nursing, anthropology, sociology, human rights and so on. These provide rich and varied sources to draw from, and help to highlight an appropriately pluralistic 'harm reduction ethics'. Values-based approaches such as these are starting to gain recognition as an additional resource that can be employed to guide and evaluate harm reduction initiatives.

Harm reduction as defined in this monograph is a sophisticated evidence-based approach to drug policy, programmes and interventions. For a long time now in harm reduction the goal has been to strive for agreement around what the scientific evidence shows is the impact of harm reduction initiatives. Despite significant achievements in this area, tensions and uncertainties remain about the authority of scientific knowledge here.

Diverse value perspectives exist in the harm reduction domain, and we might rightly ask what else could harm reduction do in addition to devising ever-more sophisticated models and collecting more precise data? Evidence-based harm reduction has rendered harm reduction/drug policymaking no less a political project.

An appropriate new focus for the future may be to ask, 'What should be the relative places of evidence and ethics in harm reduction/drug policy decision-making?' Considering such a question would require us to adopt the perspective of 'interested participants' rather than 'detached observers'. In doing so we would need to also accept that science alone is insufficient for making the case for harm reduction and achieving a wider consensus on the full range of normative criteria for action in this area.

For example, beyond the usual utilitarian 'cost–benefit' analyses, we might also strive to clarify what competing interests exist in harm reduction (e.g. in the case of funding sources and regulation from different industries) and how these may be reconciled. We might also consider, what are the obligations and responsibilities of harm reduction professionals? What are the justifications (if any) for prioritising the desires and preferences of individuals over the interests of wider groups and collectivities?

'Ethics engagement' in harm reduction does not commit us to a punitive moral stance on drug use or users; rather, it can help to evaluate these perspectives directly (Fry et al., 2005).

One practical form this could take is the development of a harm reduction code of ethics as a way to orientate practitioners, researchers, policymakers and the community towards considering core values in harm reduction work. A harm reduction code of ethics could assist practitioners in balancing diverse value sets and ethical perspectives in relation to the ethical challenges encountered. It could also serve to facilitate debate on topical ethical dilemmas, and the development of applied ethics resources to enhance harm reduction practice (for example, guidelines, professional development, etc).

We are entering a new phase in public health where the central place of values and ethical considerations is gaining greater acknowledgment. A commitment to making harm reduction values explicit requires that we consider 'ethics' as a tool to enhance, rather than restrict, harm reduction practice (in the same way we think of scientific, empirical, clinical and other practice tools). The future focus of harm reduction advocates will be to work towards enhancing intervention coverage and intensity. Evidence-based approaches will of course continue to guide these developments. The harm reduction field could also benefit from applying values-based approaches in order to establish once and for all its ethical credentials.

Acknowledgements

Craig Fry is supported by an NHMRC Australian Public Health Training Fellowship #519556, the Murdoch Childrens Research Institute (Children's Bioethics Center), and the University of Melbourne (Centre for Applied Philosophy and Public Ethics).

References

Christie, T. K., Groarke, L. and Sweet, W. (2008), 'Virtue ethics as an alternative to deontological and consequential reasoning in the harm reduction debate', *International Journal of Drug Policy* 19, pp. 52–8.

Fry, C., Treloar, C. and Maher, L. (2005), 'Ethical challenges and responses in harm reduction research: promoting applied communitarian ethics', *Drug and Alcohol Review* 24, pp. 449–59.

Fry, C. L., Khoshnood, K., Power, R. and Sharma, M. (2008), 'Harm reduction ethics: acknowledging the values and beliefs behind our actions', *International Journal of Drug Policy* 19, pp. 1–3.

Gottweis, H. (2008), 'Participation and the new governance of life', *BioSocieties* 3, pp. 265–86.

Hathaway, A. D. and Tousaw, K. I. (2008), 'Harm reduction headway and continuing resistance: insights from safe injection in the city of Vancouver', *International Journal of Drug Policy* 19, pp. 11–16.

Hunt, N., Trace, M. and Bewley-Taylor, D. (2006), *Reducing drug related harms to health: an overview of the global evidence*, Report 4, Beckley Foundation Drug Policy Programme, United Kingdom.

Irwin, K. and Fry, C. L. (2007), 'Strengthening drug policy and practice through ethics engagement: an old challenge for a new harm reduction', *International Journal of Drug Policy* 18, pp. 75–83.

Kinzig, A., Starrett, D., Arrow, K., et al. (2003), 'Coping with uncertainty: a call for a new science–policy forum', *Ambio* 32, pp. 330–5.

Kleinig, J. (2008), 'The ethics of harm reduction', *Substance Use and Misuse* 43, pp. 1–16.

Kleinig, J. and Einstein, S. (eds) (2006), *Ethical challenges for intervening in drug use: policy, research and treatment issues*, Sam Houston State University, Huntsville.

Phillips, R. E. and Bourne, H. (2008), 'The impact of worker values on client outcomes within a drug treatment service', *International Journal of Drug Policy* 19, pp. 33–41.

Ritter, A. and Cameron, J. (2006). 'A review of the efficacy and effectiveness of harm reduction strategies for alcohol, tobacco and illicit drugs', *Drug and Alcohol Review* 25 (6), pp. 611–24.

Solai, S., Dubois-Arber, F., Benninghoff, F. and Benaroyo, L. (2006), 'Ethical reflections emerging during the activity of a low threshold facility with supervised drug consumption room in Geneva, Switzerland', *International Journal of Drug Policy* 17, pp. 17–22.

Weatherburn, D. (2009), 'Dilemmas in harm minimization', *Addiction* 104, pp. 335–9.

Wodak, A. (2007), 'Ethics and drug policy', *Psychiatry* 6, pp. 59–62.

The ambiguity of harm reduction — goal or means, and what constitutes harm?

Robin Room

Harm reduction, or harm minimisation, is at the heart of classic approaches to public health, so it is no surprise that the modern use of the terms with reference to illegal drugs has been anticipated in other fields. For instance, in 1970 the sociologist Kettil Bruun wrote a policy piece in Finnish entitled, 'The minimisation of alcohol damage' (Bruun, 1970), and the same formulation and way of thinking was soon picked up in English language discussions (e.g. Room, 1975).

As applied initially in the alcohol field, the focus of the terms was clearly on the intended outcome of the action. The terms identified an overall goal, without specifying the means of achieving it, which could be diverse, including market controls that reduce levels of consumption and interventions to make the drinking environment safer. In the context of the 1970s, the implicit contrast of a 'harm minimisation' approach was not with abstinence as a universal goal, but with an 'alcoholism' approach, which tended to channel all interventions through the gate of clinical care and cure of alcoholism (Room, 1984).

In the alcohol field, 'harm minimisation' was later reinvented as a term imported from the drugs field (e.g. Plant et al., 1997), and with a correspondingly narrower focus on contextual means of reducing harm from heavy use. There are certainly earlier examples of such classic 'harm reduction' approaches in the alcohol field (e.g. Dumont, 1967; Drew, 1980), but there had been no explicit general framing for them.

In the drug field, the meaning in terms of a focus on goals has also been implicit since 'harm reduction' emerged as a term and indeed as a social and professional movement in the 1980s. But the dominant meaning of the term has focused not on goals but on means: harm reduction, in the context of the AIDS epidemic, was primarily applied to strategies that reduced the risk for heavy injection drug users, by such means as offering a switch to an oral opiate, offering sterile needles, or offering a safe place to inject. The discussion of 'what is harm reduction?' currently on the International Harm Reduction Association's website starts from a definition in terms of approaches that 'aim to reduce the … harms'. But then it implicitly contrasts harm reduction with 'approaches that aim for reductions in … consumption'. However, there is still ambiguity about whether reducing consumption can be a harm reduction goal; the IHRA discussion goes on to backtrack slightly, contrasting an approach requiring abstinence with a harm reduction approach involving 'more pragmatic choices such as limiting … intake' (IHRA, 2009).

For many in the drugs harm reduction movement, the term also includes an ethical component, and should be defined in such a way that punitive abstinence-oriented approaches, even if reducing harm was their goal, would be contrasted to harm reduction rather than included in the term (CCSA, 1996). The IHRA website discussion expresses this in terms of a second 'pillar' of harm reduction, a 'human rights approach' alongside the 'pragmatic public health approach'.

A specific adaptation in the context of Australian politics has been the differentiation of 'harm minimisation' from 'harm reduction'. In the era of a national government that rejected safe injection sites as a strategy, and tended to reject 'harm reduction' as an overall policy, a compromise formulation was reached that drug policies aimed at 'harm minimisation' as a goal, with abstinence-based strategies included as one set of strategies fitting within harm minimisation (Blewett, 2004).

The distinction between 'harm minimisation' and 'harm reduction' served the political needs of a particular time in Australia, but it invites confusion, so that even researchers focused on political rhetoric may miss the distinction (e.g. Bessant, 2008). In general, the meaning of the terms remains somewhat ambiguous, with some wavering over time. Thus in 2004 the 'definitive interpretation' of 'harm reduction' on the website of the International Harm Reduction Association explicitly included an abstinence strategy as a 'special subset of harm reduction' (Room, 2004); now, as we have noted, the discussion of the term on the same website contrasts harm reduction with aiming to reduce consumption. The issue of whether harm reduction refers to goals or to means remains unsettled.

Another issue that is of increasing importance in the context of ideas of harm reduction is what counts as harm. The usual procedure in economic studies of the social costs of drug use is to count up all public expenditures and many private costs that are considered to be attributable to drug use (e.g. Collins and Lapsley, 2008). These costs include many that would not occur if the drug use remained at the same level but the societal response to it changed — for instance, if possession and use are decriminalised. The argument has been put forward for some time that an effort should be made to 'separately take into account the resources expended in social responses to drug use and its control, and the subsidiary harms caused by those responses' (Fischer et al., 1997). As attention increases to measuring specifically the harms from illicit drug use (Melberg, 2009), rather than just the fact of the drug use itself, this issue of separating out the harms arising from the societal response (easy in principle, not so easy in practice) will take on greater salience. Reducing the two kinds of harm can point policy in very different directions. If the harm arises from heavy use per se, reducing or eliminating use or changing the mode of use are the logical first choices for reducing the harm. But if the harm results from the criminalisation per se, decriminalising is a logical way of reducing the harm.

Few would argue against the proposition that harm reduction or harm minimisation as a goal will have a continuing importance in drug policy. In this context, it is time to get serious about defining what constitutes harm, and to what it can be attributed — whether to the drug use itself and consequent events and behaviours, or to the social and societal reactions to the drug use. Harm reduction as a set of strategies in reducing the problems of heavy drug use will have a continuing place in the overall set of strategies for managing drug use and reducing drug problems. But, as the passions of the era of the 'war on drugs' fade, they are likely to be fitted into place as a routine part of the treatment and other social handling of heavy drug use.

References

Bessant, J. (2008), 'From "harm minimization" to "zero tolerance" drugs policy in Australia: how the Howard government changed its mind', *Policy Studies* 29 (2), pp. 197–214.

Blewett, N. (2004), 'Harm minimization and Australia's national drug strategies', presented at the 15th International Conference on the Reduction of Drug Related Harm, Melbourne, Australia, 20–24 April.

Bruun, K. (1970), 'Alkoholihaitat mahdollisimman vähäisiksi' (The minimisation of alcohol damage), *Alkoholipolitiikka* 35, pp. 185–91. Abstracted in *Drinking and Drug Practices Surveyor* 8 (15), p. 47 (1973).

CCSA National Working Group on Policy (1996), *Harm reduction: concepts and practices — a policy discussion paper*, Canadian Centre on Substance Abuse, Ottawa. Also published as a paper by D. Riley et al. in *Substance Use and Misuse* 34, pp. 9–24 (1999).

Collins, D. J. and Lapsley, H. M. (2008), *The costs of tobacco, alcohol and illicit drug abuse to Australian society in 2004/05*, National Drug Strategy Monograph Series No. 64, Canberra. Available at http://www.health.gov.au/internet/drugstrategy/publishing.nsf/Content/mono64.

Drew, L. R. H. (1980), 'Prevention of alcohol-related brain damage', *Medical Journal of Australia* 672, p. 48.

Dumont, M. P. (1967), 'Tavern culture: the sustenance of homeless men', *American Journal of Orthopsychiatry* 37 (5), pp. 935–45.

Fischer, B., Kendall, P., Rehm, J. and Room, R. (1997), 'Charting WHO-goals for licit and illicit drugs for the year 2000: are we "on track"?' *Public Health* 111, pp. 271–5.

IHRA (2009), 'What is harm reduction?' International Harm Reduction Association, North Melbourne, Vic., Australia. Available at http://www.ihra.net/Whatisharmreduction (accessed 23 May 2009).

Melberg, H-O. (2009), 'Is it possible to quantify human suffering? Results from a Nordic survey', presented at the 3rd annual meeting of the International Society for the Study of Drug Policy, Vienna, 2–3 March.

Plant, M., Single, E. and Stockwell, T. (eds) (1997), *Alcohol: minimizing the harm — what works?* Free Association Books, London.

Room, R. (1975), 'Minimizing alcohol problems', in Chafetz, M. (ed.), *Proceedings of the fourth annual alcoholism conference of the National Institute on Alcohol Abuse and Alcoholism: research, treatment and prevention*, DHEW Publication No. (ADM)76-284, US Government Printing Office, Washington, DC, pp. 379–93.

Room, R. (1984), 'Alcohol control and public health', *Annual Review of Public Health* 5, pp. 293–317.

Room, R. (2004), 'Alcohol and harm reduction, then and now', *Critical Public Health* 14, pp. 329–44.

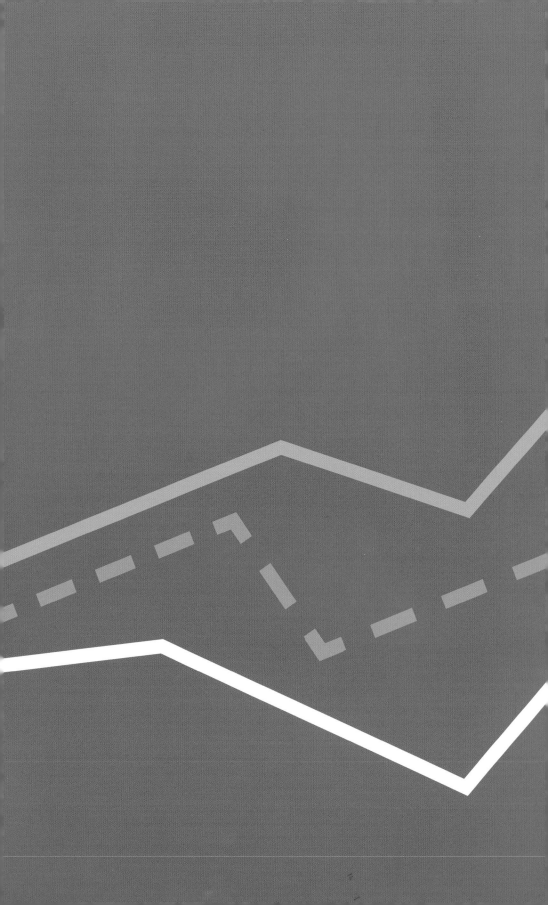

Evidence and impacts

PART II

Chapter 5
Harm reduction among injecting drug users — evidence of effectiveness

Jo Kimber, Norah Palmateer, Sharon Hutchinson, Matthew Hickman, David Goldberg and Tim Rhodes

Abstract

This chapter synthesises and evaluates the available direct evidence relating to the impact of needle and syringe programmes (NSPs), opioid substitution treatment (OST), drug consumption rooms (DCRs), and peer naloxone distribution (PND) on HIV/hepatitis C (HCV) incidence/prevalence, injecting risk behaviour and overdose-related mortality. To achieve this, we conducted a review of reviews; a systematic and explicit method used to identify, select and critically appraise relevant findings from secondary level research (systematic reviews and/or meta-analyses) into an evidence briefing. In the absence of high-quality reviews, appraisal of the evidence was supplemented with a targeted review of the primary literature. We find that there is sufficient review-level evidence that OST reduces HIV transmission, while the evidence in support of NSPs reducing HIV transmission is more tentative, and for DCRs currently insufficient. There is tentative evidence that OST has limited effectiveness in reducing HCV transmission, and insufficient evidence to support or discount NSPs or DCRs' ability to reduce HCV transmission. There is sufficient review-level evidence that NSPs, OST and DCRs reduce self-reported injecting risk behaviour. There is sufficient review evidence that OST reduces risk of overdose mortality, but insufficient evidence to support or discount the effect of DCRs or PND on overdose deaths at the community level. Our review shows evidence in support of a variety of harm reduction interventions but highlights an uneven presence of high-quality review evidence. Future evaluation of harm reduction programmes should prioritise methodologically robust study designs.

Keywords: injecting drug use, review methods, and needle syringe programmes, opioid substitution treatment, drug consumption rooms, peer naloxone distribution.

Introduction

Injecting drug use is a global and regional public health problem, with an estimated 15.9 million injecting drug users (IDUs) worldwide and prevalence rates in European Union (EU) Member States ranging between 0.6 and 15.1 per 1 000 population aged 15–65 years (EMCDDA, 2009; Mathers et al., 2008). IDUs, especially opiate users, experience excess morbidity and mortality, being approximately 10 times more likely to die compared to their non-IDU peers (Bargagli et al., 2006; Degenhardt et al., 2004; Degenhardt et al., 2006).

The primary causes of IDU-related morbidity and mortality are blood-borne viruses (BBVs) and drug overdose (Degenhardt et al., 2006). The prevention of BBV infections and drug overdose deaths among IDUs in community and custodial settings is a key objective of the EU drug strategy (European Commission, 2007). Interventions that directly target these harms include: needle and syringe programmes (NSPs) and opioid substitution treatment (OST); supervised drug consumption rooms (DCRs), and peer naloxone distribution (PND).

NSPs provide sterile needle/syringes and other injecting equipment to IDUs. Delivery is diverse and can include 'primary' fixed site, mobile and/or outreach services and 'secondary' access via community pharmacies, other health services and/or vending machines (WHO, 2007). NSPs operate across all EU Member States (EMCDDA, 2008; see also Cook et al., 2010).

OST is prescribed to dependent users to diminish the use and effects of illicit opiates. Treatment is most efficacious when it is continuous and given at adequate doses (Amato et al., 2005; Faggiano et al., 2003; Ward et al., 1997). Community-based OST is available across all EU Member States and prison-based OST is officially available in the majority of Member States, although overall accessibility is limited (EMCDDA, 2008; see also Stevens et al., 2010). It is estimated that in 2007 more than 650 000 opioid users received OST in Europe, and the most commonly prescribed forms are methadone maintenance treatment (MMT) and buprenorphine maintenance treatment (BMT) (EMCDDA, 2008).

DCRs offer a low-threshold environment to use pre-obtained drugs hygienically and to access targeted safer injecting advice and intervention in case of overdose (Kimber et al., 2003; see also Hedrich et al., 2010). DCRs have been operating in Europe for more than 25 years and are available in 59 cities across Germany, Luxembourg, the Netherlands, Norway, Spain and Switzerland (EMCDDA, 2008).

Peer naloxone distribution (PND) or 'take-home naloxone' programmes provide the antagonist drug, with training to IDUs and/or carers to improve their capacity for effective intervention at opioid-related overdose (Darke and Hall, 1997). Naloxone is currently available on a take-home basis in Italy (where it is widely dispensed by addiction services), Germany, Spain, Lithuania and Norway (Reitox, 2008). PND pilots have also taken place (Dettmer et al., 2001; McAuley et al., 2009; Strang et al., 2008) and are underway (National Treatment Agency, 2009; Parmar, 2008) in the United Kingdom.

The availability and delivery of harm reduction interventions can be controversial outside of the public health arena and vulnerable to shifts in the political environment at the local, national and international level (Bewley-Taylor, 2002; Broadhead et al., 1999; Small, 2007). This re-enforces the need for policymakers to have access to up-to-date evidence briefings on the targeted outcomes and effectiveness of the relevant interventions.

In this chapter we synthesise and evaluate the available evidence relating to the impact of NSPs, OST and DCRs on HIV and HCV incidence/prevalence, injecting risk behaviour, and OST, DCRs and PND on overdose-related mortality. We will focus on evidence synthesised in previous evidence reviews, and where necessary supplement with a review of the recently published primary literature.

Methods

Our evaluation of the evidence is based primarily on the 'review of reviews', or tertiary level research method (Kelly et al., 2002). This is a systematic and explicit method to identify, select, and critically appraise relevant findings from secondary level research (i.e. systematic reviews and/or meta-analyses) into an evidence briefing.

We have drawn substantively on our recent review of reviews of harm reduction interventions (Palmateer et al., 2008; Palmateer et al., 2010). Our inclusion criteria were English language systematic reviews, syntheses, or meta-analyses that examined the effectiveness of NSPs, OST and DCRs in relation to HIV and HCV incidence/prevalence and/or injecting risk behaviour outcomes. For this chapter we have updated our previous review of reviews (Palmateer et al., 2008) by searching for any new reviews published between March 2007 and August 2009 and by conducting additional searches for relevant English language systematic reviews, syntheses, or meta-analyses that examined the effectiveness of OST, DCRs and PND in preventing overdose.

Databases searched were: CINAHL, Cochrane Library, EMBASE, IBSS, MEDLINE, and PsycINFO. To identify grey literature and minimise English language publication bias we also searched publications of key international agencies for harm reduction. These included: the European Monitoring Centre for Drugs and Drug Addiction (EMCDDA), the National Institute on Drug Abuse (NIDA), the United States Institute of Medicine, the United Nations Office on Drugs and Crime (UNODC), and the World Health Organization (WHO). All databases were searched from 1980 to March 2009 except CINAHL, which was searched from 1982 to March 2009. At the screening stage it was apparent that reviews from the 1980s and 1990s had been superseded by more recent reviews and we restricted our appraisal of reviews published from 2000 onwards.

Abstracts were screened and evaluated by two reviewers to determine if the paper met the inclusion criteria. If there was disagreement regarding the relevance of an abstract the full paper was retrieved for further evaluation. In the event of a lack of consensus a decision was reached by discussing points of disagreement.

Selected reviews were critically appraised using a tool that considers the rigour of the methods used to identify the relevant literature, the appraisal of the primary literature, the quality of the analysis in the case of meta-analysis, and the appropriateness of the conclusions (Kelly et al., 2002; Palmateer et al., 2010).

Reviews rated 1 or 2 were included as high-quality ('core') reviews. Reviews rated 3 were retained as 'supplementary', not considered to be of sufficient quality to rely on the author's conclusions but viewed as providing complementary information on the effectiveness of the interventions.

From each review, we extracted information on the reviewers' assessment of the evidence and the number, design and findings of the relevant primary studies. The level of review evidence that supported or discounted the effect of an intervention was classified as: (i) sufficient; (ii) tentative; (iii) insufficient; or (iv) no evidence from reviews. These classifications are based on a framework (Table 5.1) that considers the quality of the reviews, the reviewers' conclusions and the designs/findings of the primary studies (Ellis et al., 2003).

Table 5.1: Types of evidence statements and the level of evidence that was required to support each statement

Evidence statement	Level of evidence
Sufficient evidence from reviews to either support or discount the effectiveness of an intervention	• Clear statement from one or more core reviews based on multiple robust studies. *Or,* • Consistent evidence across multiple robust studies within one or more core reviews, in the absence of a clear and consistent statement in the review(s).
Tentative evidence from reviews to either support or discount the effectiveness of an intervention	• A tentative statement from one or more core reviews based on consistent evidence from a small number of robust studies or multiple weaker studies. *Or,* • Consistent evidence from a small number of robust studies or multiple weaker studies within one or more core reviews, in the absence of a clear and consistent statement in the review(s). *Or,* • Conflicting evidence from one or more core reviews, with the stronger evidence weighted towards one side (either supporting or discounting effectiveness) and a plausible reason for the conflict. *Or,* • Consistent evidence from multiple robust studies within one or more supplementary reviews, in the absence of a core review.
Insufficient evidence from reviews to either support or discount the effectiveness of an intervention	• A statement of insufficient evidence from a core review. *Or,* • Insufficient evidence to either support or discount the effectiveness of an intervention (either because there is too little evidence or the evidence is too weak), in the absence of a clear and consistent statement of evidence from (a) core review(s). *Or,* • Anything less than consistent evidence from multiple robust studies within one or more supplementary reviews.
No evidence	• No core or supplementary reviews of the topic identified, possibly due to a lack of primary studies.

Source: Modified from Ellis et al., 2003.

Consistent with an evidence-based medicine approach (Glaziou and Heneghan, 2009; Sackett et al., 1996), study designs considered to provide more 'robust' evidence of effect were controlled trials, longitudinal cohort and case-control designs, while ecological, serial cross-sectional and cross-sectional designs were considered to provide 'weaker' evidence of effect. We do not discount the importance of different study designs and data sources, including cross-sectional and qualitative studies, to evaluate the process and impact of public health interventions (Petticrew, 2009), but our aim here is to assess quality of the review-level evidence.

With regard to our interpretation of the reviews' reported results of primary studies, a 'positive' finding refers to an observed reduction in the stated outcome associated with the intervention, a 'negative' finding refers to an increase in the outcome associated with the intervention, and 'no association' refers to no statistically significant effect. Where a review reported a finding as positive or negative, it was assumed that the result was statistically significant at the 5 % level even if this was not explicitly stated; where a review reported 'no association' it was assumed that this indicated a non-statistically significant result (Palmateer et al., 2010).

A priori we recognise that no or weak evidence of effectiveness may primarily reflect the quality and/or number of studies available and does not necessarily indicate a lack of intervention effectiveness. We also acknowledge that the history of harm reduction interventions has to a large extent (and necessarily) been driven by community actions and pragmatic public health policies (See also Cook et al., 2010), with some interventions implemented in the absence of high-quality trials or intervention-based research.

Additionally, in the absence of a recent review for an intervention and/or outcome, we supplemented our evaluation of the review-level evidence with a review of subsequently published primary literature using the same search strategy and assessment of evidence quality. Thus we undertook primary literature searches for NSPs and HCV incidence prevalence from 2003, OST and overdose from 2003, DCRs for all outcomes from 2004, and PND and overdose from 2004.

Results

The results of the review of reviews literature search are presented in Figure 5.1. We identified nine (five core and four supplementary) reviews of the effectiveness of NSPs, 11 (three core, six supplementary, two meta-analyses) of OST, four (three supplementary, one meta-analysis) of DCRs, and one supplementary review of PND (Table 5.2).

Figure 5.1: Papers identified in the review of reviews

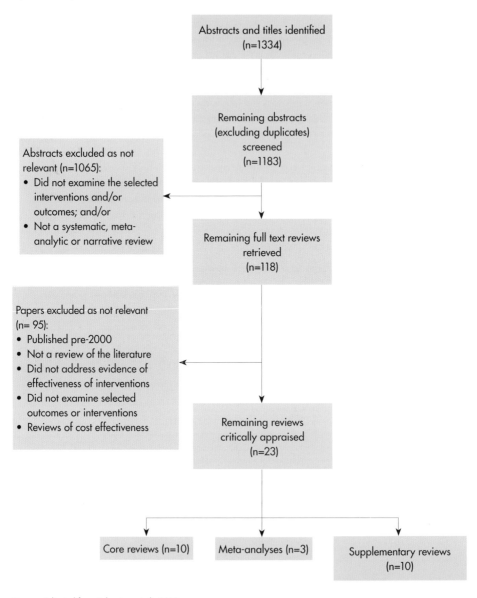

Source: Adapted from Palmateer et al., 2010.

Table 5.2: Summary of reviews by intervention and outcomes

A) Needle syringe provision: needle syringe programmes, pharmacy access and vending machines

Authors and date	Title	Inclusion criteria/ terms of reference	Dates covered	Interventions covered	Critical assessment	No. of studies by outcome
Dolan et al., 2003a	Prison-based syringe exchange programmes: a review of international research and development	Review published and unpublished studies on prison NSPs and interviews with prison NSP experts	Not specified. Publications up to 2002	Prison NSPs	Supplementary review	6 HIV 6 HCV
Gibson et al., 2001	Effectiveness of syringe exchange programs in reducing HIV risk behaviour and HIV seroconversion among IDUs	Review published studies of the effectiveness of syringe exchange programs in reducing HIV risk behaviour and HIV seroconversion among IDUs, regardless of design. Also included studies that examined effects of syringe exchange on HBV and HCV seroconversion	1989 to end 1999	NSPs	Core review	3 HCV 6 HIV 23 self-reported injecting risk behaviour (SR-IRB)
Islam and Conigrave, 2007	Assessing the role of syringe dispensing machines and mobile van outlets in reaching hard-to-reach and high-risk groups of injecting drug users (IDUs): a review	Examine the available evidence for the effectiveness of syringe dispensing machines and mobile van or bus based NSPs in making services accessible to hard-to-reach and high-risk groups of IDUs	Not specified	Vending machines	Supplementary review	1 SR-IRB
Jones et al., 2008	A review of the effectiveness and cost-effectiveness of needle and syringe programmes for injecting drug users	Review of review of NSP effectiveness in BBV prevention. Primary review NSP effectiveness and cost effectiveness with respect to optimal provision of NSPs by type, coverage, additional service provision, and provision alongside OST	1990 to (not specified). Publication dates to 2008	NSPs	Core review — 'review of reviews'	4 HIV 2 HCV 5 SR-IRB

Table 5.2 (continued)

Authors and date	Title	Inclusion criteria/ terms of reference	Dates covered	Interventions covered	Critical assessment	No. of studies by outcome
Käll et al., 2007	The effectiveness of needle exchange programmes for HIV prevention: a critical review	Review studies of NSPs with HIV incidence or prevalence outcomes	Up to Dec 2005	NSPs	Core review	13 HIV
Stöver and Nelles, 2003	Ten years of experience with needle and syringe exchange programmes in European prisons	Summarise results of prison NSPs based on 10 years' experience in Switzerland, Germany, Spain and Moldova	Not specified. Publication dates up to 2003	Prison NSPs	Supplementary review	6 HIV 6 HCV 9 SR-IRB
Tilson et al., 2007	Preventing HIV infection among injecting drug users in high-risk countries: an assessment of the evidence	Review published and unpublished literature on the effectiveness of HIV prevention interventions (drug dependence treatment, sterile needle and syringe access, and outreach and education programmes) for IDUs	1980 to January 2006	NSPs, pharmacy NSPs, vending machines, provision of other injecting equipment	Core review	5 HCV 11 HIV 24 SR-IRB
Wodak and Cooney, 2004	Effectiveness of sterile needle and syringe programming in reducing HIV/AIDS among injecting drug users	Evaluate evidence on the effectiveness of sterile needle and syringe programming (including other injecting paraphernalia) for HIV prevention among IDUs in different contexts using Bradford-Hill criteria	1989 to 2002	NSPs, pharmacy NSPs, vending machines	Core review	1 HCV 10 HIV 28 SR-IRB
Wright and Tompkins, 2006	A review of the evidence for the effectiveness of primary prevention interventions for hepatitis C among injecting drug users	Review intervention or observational studies describing a primary prevention intervention targeting IDUs to reduce HCV incidence/prevalence	Up to end 2002	NSPs	Supplementary review	11 HCV

Source: Adapted from Palmateer et al., 2010.

B) Opiate substitution treatment

Authors and date	Title	Inclusion criteria/ terms of reference	Dates covered	Interventions covered	Critical assessment	No. studies by outcome
Amato et al., 2005	*Overview of the systematic reviews of the effectiveness of opiate maintenance therapies: available research to inform clinical practice and research*	Summarise major findings of five Cochrane reviews on OST for opioid dependence	Up to 2003	Outcomes included retention in treatment, use of heroin and other drugs, and mortality	Meta-analysis	2 OD
Best et al., 2000	*Overdosing on opiates*	Review how opiate overdoses occur and can be prevented	Not specified. Publication dates up to 2000	OST, PND, DCRs	Supplementary review	6 OD
Caplehorn et al., 1996	*Methadone maintenance and addicts' risk of fatal heroin overdose*	Use data on dependent heroin users' risk of death or the effect of MMT on that risk	1966 to (not specified). Publication dates up to 2005	MMT	Meta-analysis	5 OD
Darke and Hall, 2003	*Heroin overdose: research and evidence based intervention*	Examine research on heroin overdose and how this informs evidence-based intervention	Not specified. Publication dates to 2002	Drug treatment, PND, non-injecting routes of administration, DCRs	Supplementary review	5 OD
Gowing et al., 2008	*Substitution treatment of injection opioid users for prevention of HIV infection*	Systematic review to assess the effect of OST for opioid dependent IDUs on rates of HIV infections, and high-risk behaviours	Up to July 2003	OST	Core review	5 HIV 24 SR-IRB

Table 5.2, B) (continued)

Authors and date	Title	Inclusion criteria/ terms of reference	Dates covered	Interventions covered	Critical assessment	No. of studies by outcome
Sorensen and Copeland, 2000	Drug abuse treatment as an HIV prevention strategy: a review	Systematically review evidence on whether drug abuse treatment prevents HIV infection	1988 to 1998	MMT and other drug treatments (e.g. inpatient, outpatient, drug free, residential)	Core review	6 HIV 19 SR-IRB
Sporer, 2003	Strategies for preventing heroin overdose	Not specified	Not specified. Publication dates to 2002	MMT, PND	Supplementary review	6 OD
Stallwitz and Stöver, 2007	The impact of substitution treatment in prisons: a literature review	Review published an unpublished literature on effectiveness of prison-based OST	1990 to (not specified). Publication dates up to 2006	MMT	Supplementary review	4 SR-IRB
Tilson et al., 2007	Preventing HIV infection among injecting drug users in high-risk countries: an assessment of the evidence	Review published and unpublished literature on the effectiveness of HIV prevention interventions for IDUs	Up to January 2006	OST and NSP	Core review	4 HIV 21 SR-IRB
Wright and Tompkins, 2006	A review of the evidence for the effectiveness of primary prevention interventions for hepatitis C among injecting drug users	Review evidence on interventions targeting IDUs to reduce prevalence or incidence of HCV	Up to April 2003	MMT, NSP, behavioural interventions, bleach, DCRs,	Supplementary review	6 HCV
WHO, 2007	Effectiveness of interventions to manage HIV in prisons: opioid substitution therapies and other drug dependence treatment	Review published and unpublished evidence on drug treatment in preventing HIV in prison	Not specified. Publication dates up to 2006	Prison settings: OST, therapeutic communities, counselling, 'boot camp'	Supplementary review	2 HCV 1 HIV 8 SR-IRB

C) Drug consumption rooms

Authors and date	Title	Inclusion criteria/ terms of reference	Dates covered	Interventions covered	Critical assessment	No. studies by outcome
Hedrich, 2004	European report on drug consumption rooms	Describe DCR history, practice and evidence on individual and public health outcomes	Up to end 2003	DCR process indicators and health outcomes	Supplementary review	1 HCV 1 HIV 13 SR-IRB 2 OD
Kerr et al., 2007	The role of safer injection facilities in the response to HIV/ AIDS among injection drug users	Review published articles, novel abstracts, and reviews of grey and non-English literature on health impacts of DCRs	Up to June 2007	DCRs	Supplementary review	10 SR-IRB 5 OD
Milloy and Wood, 2009	Emerging role of supervised injecting facilities in human immunodeficiency virus prevention	Use available peer reviewed estimates of relationship between DCR use and syringe sharing	Up to 2009	DCRs	Meta-analysis	3 SR-IRB
Wood et al., 2006	Summary of findings from the evaluation of a pilot medically supervised safer injecting facility	Summarise key evaluation findings including HIV risk behaviour and use of addiction treatment services	2005 to 2006	Overview of Vancouver DCR evaluation studies	Supplementary review	3 SR-IRB 1 OD process

D) Peer naloxone distribution

Authors and date	Title	Inclusion criteria/ terms of reference	Dates covered	Interventions covered	Critical assessment	No. studies by outcome
Baca and Grant, 2005	Take home naloxone to reduce heroin death	Summarise evidence on take home naloxone, focusing on evidence from addiction and emergency medicine	January 1990 to June 2004	Process indicators of naloxone distribution	Supplementary review	2 OD process

Needle and syringe programmes ([1])

Effects on HIV incidence/prevalence

Evidence of the effects of NSPs on HIV incidence/prevalence was considered in four core reviews (Gibson et al., 2001; Käll et al., 2007; Tilson et al., 2007; Wodak and Cooney, 2004), which included a total of 18 primary studies with HIV incidence or prevalence outcomes.

Tilson et al., 2007, the most recent and rigorous of these reviews, identified 13 relevant studies: four prospective cohort (Bruneau et al., 1997; Mansson et al., 2000; Schechter et al., 1999; Strathdee et al., 1997), two case-control (Patrick et al., 1997; van Ameijden et al., 1992), three ecological (Des Jarlais et al., 2005b; Hurley et al., 1997; MacDonald et al., 2003), and two serial cross-sectional studies (Des Jarlais et al., 2005a; Hammett et al., 2006). Other studies included in their discussion were Des Jarlais et al. (1995) and Coutinho (2005).

Two of the prospective cohort studies (Bruneau et al., 1997; Strathdee et al., 1997) found NSP participation was associated with a higher incidence of HIV seroconversion. Tilson et al., 2007 highlighted that these findings may have been related to several factors, including: restrictive service delivery characteristics; high-risk IDUs being more likely to use the NSP (selection bias); and the availability of clean injecting equipment from other sources (dilution bias).

The authors also refer to four ecological studies demonstrating declining HIV incidence/prevalence in the context of NSP provision or expansion (Des Jarlais et al., 1995; Des Jarlais et al., 2005b; Hurley et al., 1997; MacDonald et al., 2003). Tilson et al. concluded that: 'The evidence of the effectiveness of [NSPs] in reducing HIV prevalence is considered modest, based on the weakness of these study designs' (2007, p. 149). Their conclusions are consistent with the equivocal results from cohort and case-control studies; this review also undertook the most rigorous evaluation of the primary studies and also considered outcomes related to HIV incidence/prevalence separately from injecting risk behaviour.

Käll and colleagues (2007) identified 13 studies examining NSPs and changes in HIV incidence/prevalence outcomes published to the end of 2005, including 11 studies identified in other reviews and two additional studies (Amundsen et al., 2003; Valente et al., 2001). With regard to HIV seroincidence, in seven studies there was no reported association with NSPs (Amundsen et al., 2003; MacDonald et al., 2003; Patrick et al., 1997; Schechter et al., 1999; Schoenbaum et al., 1996; Valente et al., 2001; van Ameijden et al., 1992); one study found a positive effect (Des Jarlais et al., 1996), and one study found a negative effect (Bruneau et al., 1997).

The authors also highlighted three longitudinal studies with a negative baseline association between NSP use and HIV seroprevalence (Bruneau et al., 1997; Millson et al., 2003; Strathdee et al., 1997) and three ecological studies of seroprevalence that found protective

---

([1]) This section on NSPs is largely based on Palmateer et al., 2010.

effects of NSPs (Health Outcomes International et al., 2002; Hurley et al., 1997), but argued that these studies did not control for probable confounding from differences in the stage of the HIV epidemic relative to the introduction of NSPs. Käll and colleagues concluded that 'the effectiveness of NEPs to reduce HIV among IDUs is overrated. Errors in categorising studies in favour of NEPs have been made (Wodak and Cooney, 2004; Wodak and Cooney, 2006) and studies claiming positive results have not been adequately scrutinized' (2007, p. 6).

Wodak and Cooney (2004) did not consider separately the effects of NSPs on HIV transmission versus injecting risk behaviour, and this may have led to the evidence of reduced injecting risk behaviour having a bearing on conclusions drawn with respect to HIV incidence/prevalence: 'There is compelling evidence that increasing the availability and utilization of sterile injecting equipment by IDU reduces HIV infection substantially' (p. 28). Of the 38 studies they reviewed, 10 were relevant to HIV (Bruneau et al., 1997; Des Jarlais et al., 1996; Heimer et al., 1993; Hurley et al., 1997; Ljungberg et al., 1991; MacDonald et al., 2003; Monterroso et al., 2000; Patrick et al., 1997; Schechter et al., 1999; Strathdee et al., 1997); five had positive findings (Des Jarlais et al., 1996; Heimer et al., 1993; Hurley et al., 1997; Ljungberg et al., 1991; MacDonald et al., 2003), two had negative findings (Bruneau et al., 1997; Strathdee et al., 1997), and three did not find an association (Monterroso et al., 2000; Patrick et al., 1997; Schechter et al., 1999). Four of the five positive findings were generated by studies with weaker designs (Heimer et al., 1993; Hurley et al., 1997; Ljungberg et al., 1991; MacDonald et al., 2003).

Gibson et al. (2001) reviewed studies published up until 1999, all of which were covered in the reviews discussed above. They gave consideration to potential bias in studies with negative results, but not for those with protective findings. They concluded that there is 'Substantial evidence that syringe exchange programmes are effective in preventing [HIV risk behaviour and] HIV seroconversion among IDU' (p. 1338). However, as for Wodak and Cooney, their conclusions seemed inconsistent with the HIV studies reviewed: two cohort studies showed an increased risk of HIV infection associated with NSPs (Bruneau et al., 1997; Strathdee et al., 1997), one (meta-analysis using cohort data) showed a protective effect of NSPs (Des Jarlais et al., 1996), and three (one cohort, two case-control) showed no association (Patrick et al., 1997; Schechter et al., 1999; van Ameijden et al., 1992).

The United Kingdom National Institute for Clinical Excellence' review of optimal NSP service delivery (Jones et al., 2008) included a review of reviews component on HIV prevention that evaluated the four reviews considered above. Consistent with our assessment, they concluded:

> There is evidence from two good-quality systematic reviews [Wodak and Cooney, 2004; Gibson et al., 2001] to support the effectiveness of NSPs in reducing HIV infection among IDUs. However, findings from two other systematic reviews [Tilson et al., 2007; Käll et al., 2007], including one good quality review [Tilson et al., 2007], suggest that the evidence may be less convincing.
>
> (Jones et al., 2008, pp. 31–2)

Pharmacy access

Evidence of the effectiveness of pharmacy access to needles/syringes in reducing HIV prevalence was examined in one core review (Wodak and Cooney, 2004), which identified two relevant studies (Hunter et al., 1995; Nelson et al., 1991). A serial cross-sectional study observed that declines in HIV prevalence in the United Kingdom coincided with a period of increased access to needles/syringes through pharmacies and NSPs (Hunter et al., 1995). Second, a cross-sectional survey found a lower HIV prevalence in diabetic IDUs, who had ready access to sterile syringes through pharmacies, compared with non-diabetic IDUs (Nelson et al., 1991). They also referred to two studies as evidence of 'replication of findings': an ecological study that found pharmacy exchange was a common characteristic of cities that had maintained HIV prevalence rates of less than 5 % over the previous five years (Des Jarlais et al., 1995), and a rapid assessment study that attributed a low HIV infection rate in Georgia in part to the availability of syringes in pharmacies (De Jong et al., 1999).

Wodak and Cooney (2004) concluded that 'There is reasonable evidence that pharmacy availability of sterile injecting equipment does provide specific benefits in addition to those derived from NSPs' (p. 29). We note, however, that this is based on a small number of primary studies with weaker designs.

Vending machines

One core review (Wodak and Cooney, 2004) reported the results of a cross-sectional study of IDUs (Obadia et al., 1999), which found that primary users of vending machines were less likely to be HIV positive, although this was not significant after adjustment in a multivariable model. The authors stated that 'Access to sterile needles and syringes from community pharmacies and syringe vending machines was shown in all nine studies to be effective in reducing risk behaviour and HIV seroprevalence' (p. 18). We note, however, that this conclusion is drawn on one study of vending machines with a weak design.

Prison

Two supplementary reviews (Dolan et al., 2003a; Stöver and Nelles, 2003) reported on HIV and HCV incidence from six prison NSP evaluations in Switzerland, Germany and Spain (Jacob and Stöver, 1997; Jacob and Stöver, 2000; Meyeno et al., 2000; Nelles et al., 1997; Villaneuva, 2002). Based on serological testing in five studies and self-report in one study, no new cases of HIV (or HCV) infections were observed in these prisons during one to two years of follow-up. Both reviews provided limited details about the design and quality of these evaluation studies.

A subsequent German cohort study of prison NSPs and BBV incidence observed four HCV seroconversions among 22 prisoners who were seronegative at baseline during a median 12 months of follow-up (incidence rate 18/100 person years). At least one of these exposures was associated with injecting risk behaviour while in prison (Stark et al., 2006).

Evidence statement for NSPs and HIV incidence/prevalence

Primary NSP

Based on a tentative statement from one core review, supported by consistent evidence from less robust primary studies, we conclude that there is tentative evidence to support the effectiveness of NSPs in reducing HIV incidence/prevalence among IDUs.

Pharmacy access

Despite a tentative statement of effectiveness from a core review, the evidence is based on a small number of primary studies with weak designs. We conclude that there is insufficient review-level evidence to either support or discount the effectiveness of pharmacy access to needles/syringes in reducing HIV prevalence among IDUs.

Vending machines

There is insufficient review evidence to either support or discount the effectiveness of needle/syringe vending machines in reducing HIV transmission among IDUs.

Prison

Given a lack of evidence from core reviews, and evidence of uncertain quality from supplementary reviews, we conclude that there is insufficient review-level evidence to either support or discount the effectiveness of prison NSPs in reducing HIV transmission among IDUs.

Effects on HCV incidence/prevalence

Evidence of the effects of NSPs on HCV incidence/prevalence was considered in three core reviews of NSPs and HIV (Gibson et al., 2001; Tilson et al., 2007; Wodak and Cooney, 2004) and one supplementary review (Wright and Tompkins, 2006). The core reviews, however, were focused on HIV outcomes and none examined HCV in any detail, covering seven primary studies between them. Wodak and Cooney included one study (Hagan et al., 1995), Tilson et al. identified six (Des Jarlais et al., 2005b; Hagan et al., 1995; Hagan and Thiede, 2000; Mansson et al., 2000; Sarkar et al., 2003; Taylor et al., 2000), and Gibson et al. included three (Hagan et al., 1995; Hagan et al., 1999; Lamden et al., 1998).

Wright and Tompkins (2006) focused exclusively on HCV outcomes, and identified nine additional papers (Goldberg et al., 2001; Goldberg et al., 1998; Hernandez-Aguado et al., 2001; Hutchinson et al., 2002; MacDonald et al., 2000; Patrick et al., 2001; Smyth et al., 1999; Somaini et al., 2000; van Ameijden et al., 1993), although three of these present duplicate data (Goldberg et al., 2001; Goldberg et al., 1998; Hutchinson et al., 2002), and the search only included studies published up until 2002. There were seven primary studies with positive findings, but these mainly involved weaker study designs. The stronger study designs (cohorts) mainly showed either no association or negative findings between NSPs and HCV seroconversion.

Tilson et al. (2007) concluded there was moderate evidence that 'HIV prevention programmes that include NSPs have less of an impact on HCV transmission than on HIV transmission' (p. 149). Similarly, in their review of reviews Jones et al. (2008) concluded, 'There is insufficient evidence from two systematic reviews [Wright and Tompkins, 2006; Tilson et al., 2007] to determine the impact of NSPs on hepatitis C infection in IDUs' (p. 32).

In our search of the primary literature published since Wright and Tompkins' we identified three additional cohort studies of HCV incidence and NSP use (Hagan et al., 2004; Roy et al., 2007; van den Berg et al., 2007). Time to HCV seroconversion was not associated with being an NSP user at baseline after a median of 2.1 years' follow-up (Hagan et al., 2004) or with NSP use in the preceding six months (Roy et al., 2007). In the Amsterdam Cohort Study among ever IDUs, NSP use alone was not associated with lower risk of HCV seroconversion but full participation in both NSPs and MMT was associated with a lower risk of HCV infection in ever IDU compared to no participation (van den Berg et al., 2007).

No core or supplementary reviews were identified that examined HCV incidence/prevalence outcomes in relation to pharmacy access or vending machines. For details on prison NSPs and HCV incidence/prevalence see the section 'Prisons', p. 128.

Evidence statement for NSPs and HCV incidence/prevalence

Primary NSP

Based on an absence of clear statements from the core reviews, and inconsistent evidence from the primary studies identified in the core reviews and supplementary review, we conclude there is insufficient review-level evidence to either support or discount the effectiveness of NSPs in reducing HCV transmission among IDUs. Evidence from subsequently published longitudinal primary studies suggests no independent association of NSP use on HCV incidence.

Pharmacy access and vending machines

There is no review-level evidence of the effects of pharmacy access to needles/syringes or vending machines on HCV prevalence/incidence among IDUs.

Prison

Given a lack of evidence from core reviews, and evidence of uncertain quality from supplementary reviews, we conclude that there is insufficient review-level evidence to either support or discount the effectiveness of prison NSPs in reducing HCV transmission among IDUs.

Effects on injecting risk behaviour

The largest body of evidence on the effect of NSPs relates to changes in self-reported injecting risk behaviour. Three core reviews reported on a total of 43 studies, 39 of which showed a positive effect of NSPs in reducing injecting risk behaviour, and 20 of these were cohort studies.

Tilson et al. (2007) identified 25 studies (Bluthenthal et al., 2000; Cox et al., 2000; Des Jarlais et al., 2000; Gibson et al., 2002; Hagan et al., 1993; Hagan and Thiede, 2000; Hammett et al., 2006; Hart et al., 1989; Hartgers et al., 1992; Huo et al., 2005; Keene et al., 1993; Klee et al., 1991; Longshore et al., 2001; Monterroso et al., 2000; Ouellet et al., 2004; Schoenbaum et al., 1996; van Ameijden and Coutinho, 1998; van Ameijden et al., 1994; van den Hoek et al., 1989; Vazirian et al., 2005; Vertefeuille et al., 2000; Vlahov et al., 1997; Watters, 1994; Wood et al., 2002; Wood et al., 2003), 14 of which were longitudinal cohort studies (Bluthenthal et al., 2000; Cox et al., 2000; Gibson et al., 2002; Hagan and Thiede, 2000; Hart et al., 1989; Huo et al., 2005; Monterroso et al., 2000; Ouellet et al., 2004; Schoenbaum et al., 1996; van Ameijden and Coutinho, 1998; van den Hoek et al., 1989; Vertefeuille et al., 2000; Vlahov et al., 1997; Wood et al., 2002) and demonstrated reductions in self-reported needle sharing (lending or borrowing needles/syringes). They concluded that there was 'moderate evidence to show that multi-component HIV prevention programmes that include needle and syringe exchange' are associated with a reduction in self-reported sharing of needles and syringes' (Tilson et al., 2007, p. 154).

Wodak and Cooney (2004) identified 28 primary studies of injecting risk behaviour (defined as needle/syringe borrowing, lending, or reuse). Among these studies, there were 24 positive (Bluthenthal et al., 1998; Bluthenthal et al., 2000; Cox et al., 2000; Des Jarlais et al., 1994; Des Jarlais et al., 2000; Donoghoe et al., 1989; Frischer and Elliott, 1993; Gibson et al., 2002; Gleghorn et al., 1998; Guydish et al., 1995; Guydish et al., 1998; Hartgers et al., 1989; Heimer et al., 1998; Keene et al., 1993; Oliver et al., 1994; Paone et al., 1994; Peak et al., 1995; Power and Nozhkina, 2002; Schoenbaum et al., 1996; Singer et al., 1997; van Ameijden and Coutinho, 1998; van Ameijden et al., 1994; Vlahov et al., 1997; Watters, 1994), one negative (Klee et al., 1991), and three indeterminate (Donoghoe et al., 1992; Hartgers et al., 1992; Klee and Morris, 1995) results relating to the association between NSPs and injecting risk behaviour. The reviewers did not formulate any conclusions specifically regarding injecting risk behaviour.

The 23 studies identified by Gibson et al. (2001) (Bluthenthal et al., 1998; Broadhead et al., 1999; Des Jarlais et al., 1994; Donoghoe et al., 1989; Donoghoe et al., 1992; Frischer and Elliott, 1993; Guydish et al., 1995; Guydish et al., 1998; Hagan et al., 1994; Hartgers et al., 1989; Hartgers et al., 1992; Keene et al., 1993; Klee et al., 1991; Klee and Morris, 1995; Oliver et al., 1994; Paone et al., 1994; Peak et al., 1995; Schoenbaum et al., 1996; Singer et al., 1997; van Ameijden and Coutinho, 1998; van Ameijden et al., 1994; Vlahov et al., 1997; Watters, 1994) were covered in the later core reviews, with the exception of Broadhead et al., 1999, and Hagan et al., 1994. Both studies suggested a protective effect of NSP: Broadhead et al. noted an increase in the reported reuse and sharing of syringes after the closure of an NSP, and Hagan et al. observed a decline in the proportion borrowing used syringes among NSP attendees (pre- vs. post-intervention comparison). The authors concluded that there is substantial evidence that NSPs are effective in preventing HIV risk behaviour among IDUs.

Pharmacy access

Two core reviews examined evidence of the effects of pharmacy access to needle/syringes and injecting risk behaviour and identified a total of seven studies. Tilson et al. (2007) identified two serial cross-sectional studies that compared injecting risk behaviour before and after liberalisation of the laws permitting syringe sale from pharmacies in New York (Pouget et al., 2005) and Connecticut (Groseclose et al., 1995); both found that reports of syringe sharing among IDUs declined. The authors concluded, 'A few studies have examined the impact on drug-related HIV risk, and found suggestive evidence of a reduction' (p. 160). Wodak and Cooney (2004) reported on a further five cross-sectional studies (Caslyn, 1992; Gleghorn et al., 1995; Ingold and Ingold, 1989; Nelson et al., 1991; Richard et al., 2002) and all found pharmacy access was associated with lower levels of injecting risk behaviour.

Vending machines

Two core reviews, Tilson et al. (2007) and Wodak and Cooney (2004), both referred to a pilot study of vending machines in a German prison (Heinemann and Gross, 2001), although their reporting of the study results differs. Wodak and Cooney reported that significant decreases in needle-sharing subsequent to the introduction of the programme were found, whereas Tilson et al. stated that this study showed that IDUs will use vending machines as a source of sterile needles/syringes. Tilson et al. concluded that there was insufficient evidence of the effectiveness of vending machines in reducing HIV risk; the conclusions of Wodak and Cooney are as above, for HIV.

A supplementary review of vending machines (Islam and Conigrave, 2007) identified 37 studies of vending machines that reportedly engaged 'hard to reach and high risk' IDUs, but no details were provided on these studies or changes in injecting risk behaviour associated with access to vending machines.

Prison

A supplementary review (Stöver and Nelles, 2003) reported on nine prison NSP evaluations that had examined injecting risk behaviour. Seven studies found large declines in needle/ syringe sharing or reuse, one study found single cases of sharing and one study found no change in needle sharing. However, few details were provided on the primary study designs or formal data analysis.

Evidence statement for NSPs and self-reported injecting risk behaviour

Primary NSP

Based on consistent evidence across multiple robust studies, as well as moderate to strong statements of evidence in support of an effect of NSPs on self-reported injecting risk behaviour from two core reviews, there is sufficient review-level evidence to support the effectiveness of NSPs in reducing self-reported injecting risk behaviour among IDUs.

Pharmacy access

Based on less robust studies identified within two core reviews, there is tentative review-level evidence to support the effectiveness of pharmacy access to needles/syringes — in addition to dedicated NSPs — in reducing self-reported injecting risk behaviour among IDUs.

Vending machines

Given conflicting statements of evidence from core reviews based on one primary study with a weak design, there is insufficient review-level evidence to either support or discount the effectiveness of vending machines in reducing injecting risk behaviour among IDUs.

Prison

Despite consistent findings across multiple studies in a supplementary review suggesting reductions in injecting risk behaviour, due to a lack of information on the quality of the studies we conclude that there is insufficient review-level evidence to either support or discount the effectiveness of prison NSPs in reducing self-reported injecting risk behaviour among IDUs.

Opiate substitution treatment ([2])

Effects on HIV incidence/prevalence

Evidence of the effects of OST on HIV incidence/prevalence was considered in three core reviews (Gowing et al., 2008; Sorensen and Copeland, 2000; Tilson et al., 2007), which identified eight studies between them (Dolan et al., 2003b; Hartel and Schoenbaum, 1998; Metzger et al., 1993; Moss et al., 1994; Novick et al., 1990; Rhoades et al., 1998; Serpelloni et al., 1994; Williams et al., 1992). These comprised two randomised control trials (RCTs) (Dolan et al., 2003b; Rhoades et al., 1998), four cohort studies (Hartel and Schoenbaum, 1998; Metzger et al., 1993; Moss et al., 1994; Williams et al., 1992), one case-control study (Serpelloni et al., 1994), and one cross-sectional study (Novick et al., 1990).

---

[2] Most of the review-level evidence on the effectiveness of OST relates to MMT, but the findings can be largely taken to refer to OST in general.

Three cohort studies showed the odds of HIV seroconversion were greater for untreated individuals or those with interrupted MMT compared to those who remained continuously in MMT (Metzger et al., 1993; Moss et al., 1994; Williams et al., 1992). A cohort study and case control study showed lower daily dose and more time out of MMT was also associated with higher risk of HIV seroconversion (Hartel and Schoenbaum, 1998; Serpelloni et al., 1994). In an RCT of 50mg versus 80mg MMT no seroconversions occurred in six months of follow-up (Rhoades et al., 1998). A retrospective cohort study found no HIV seroconversions among long-term MMT patients (Novick et al., 1990). An RCT of MMT in prison found no difference in HIV incidence between those in MMT and waitlist controls, although this was in the context of a short period of follow-up and low HIV prevalence (Dolan et al., 2003b).

The conclusions from all three reviews allowed that continuous MMT is associated with lower rates of HIV seroconversion while acknowledging that those who resist treatment or leave treatment may inherently engage in more HIV risk behaviours than those who stay in treatment longer.

Specifically, Gowing et al. (2008), in their Cochrane Review (updated from an earlier version in 2004), concluded, 'Few data ... limit the conclusiveness of any analysis, but these studies consistently indicate lower rates of [HIV] seroconversion associated with substitution treatment. This suggests that reductions in risk behaviour do translate into actual reduction in cases of HIV infection' (p. 22); Tilson et al. (2007) concluded that:

> Modest evidence from prospective cohort and case-control studies shows that continuous opioid agonist maintenance treatment is associated with protection against HIV seroconversion. This association persists after controlling for many confounders. These studies also show that the risk of HIV seroconversion is inversely related to length of time in treatment. However the possibility of bias in these findings from self selection cannot be ruled out.
>
> (Tilson et al., 2007, p. 92)

Finally, Sorensen and Copeland (2000) concluded that:

> Four out of the six studies reviewed ... provided firm evidence for the protective effect of MMT against HIV seroconversion. These findings are more convincing because they are based on biologically verified outcomes ... [but] nearly all the studies are inherently limited by a self-selected treatment sample.
>
> (Sorensen and Copeland, 2000, p. 27)

Prison

One core review of OST (Gowing et al., 2008) and two supplementary reviews of prison OST (Stallwitz and Stöver, 2007; WHO et al., 2007) identified the same RCT described above (Dolan et al., 2003b).

Evidence statement for OST and HIV incidence/prevalence

Based on consistent evidence from three core reviews, there is sufficient review-level evidence to conclude that OST in community settings is effective in reducing HIV seroconversion, especially among those in continuous treatment.

There is insufficient review-level evidence to draw conclusions about the effect of OST on HIV seroconversion in prison settings. Data from one RCT in a jurisdiction with low HIV prevalence found no difference in HIV incidence between those receiving MMT and controls.

Effects on HCV incidence/prevalence

One supplementary review (Wright and Tompkins, 2006) examined evidence of the effects of OST on HCV incidence/prevalence and identified six studies. A cohort and a case-control study found a non-significant trend toward lower HCV incidence among those in MMT compared to those not in treatment (Rezza et al., 1996) or those who have left treatment (Thiede et al., 2000). A Dutch cohort study found MMT (in combination with NSPs) was not associated with any decreases in annual HCV incidence over four years (van Ameijden et al., 1993). Three cohort studies did not find any differences in HCV incidence between those in MMT and those not in MMT (Chamot et al., 1992; Crofts et al., 1997; Selvey et al., 1997).

Wright and Tompkins (2006) concluded that, 'As regards methadone maintenance therapy, whilst it has been successful in reducing the incidence of HIV, the evidence for its effectiveness in reducing HCV incidence is less convincing' (p. 5).

In our primary literature search we identified five community-based studies of HCV and OST published since Wright and Tompkins' review. Three cohort studies suggested a positive impact of OST: HCV incidence was lower among those in continuous OST compared with those with interrupted OST (Hallinan et al., 2004); MMT in the past six months was protective against both primary (non-infected IDUs) and secondary (mono-infected IUDs) HIV and HCV infection (Miller et al., 2004); and HCV incidence was similar among those who were not in OST during follow-up or in OST for up to six months, but was lower amongst those in treatment for 7 to 12 months (Craine et al., 2009). One cohort study found no difference in risk of HCV seroconversion among IDUs recruited from MMT clinics and IDUs recruited from NSPs (Maher et al., 2006) and in the Amsterdam Cohort Study, as described earlier, MMT alone was not associated with lower risk of HCV seroconversion but full participation in both MMT and NSPs was associated with a lower risk of HCV infection (van den Berg et al., 2007).

Prison

Two supplementary reviews of prison OST (Stallwitz and Stöver, 2007; WHO et al., 2007) identified two linked studies (Dolan et al., 2003b; Dolan et al., 2005). There was no difference in HCV incidence between RCT prison MMT and waitlist control groups at five-month follow-up (Dolan et al., 2003b). However, at four-year follow-up, retention in MMT was associated with reduced HCV infection, while short MMT episodes (less than five months) were significantly associated with greater risk of HCV (Dolan et al., 2005).

Evidence statement for OST and HCV incidence/prevalence

Based on consistent evidence showing weak or no association from multiple longitudinal studies within a supplementary review, we conclude that there is tentative review-level evidence of OST having limited impact on HCV transmission. However, taken together with recently published primary studies, the available evidence suggests OST contributes to a reduction in the risk of HCV seroconversion among those in continuous treatment.

There is insufficient review-level evidence to either support or discount the effectiveness of OST with respect to HCV transmission in prison settings. One RCT suggests that retention in MMT from prison to community settings is associated with reduced HCV incidence.

Effects on injecting risk behaviour

Three core reviews examined the effect of OST on injecting risk behaviour. The evidence falls into three broad categories: prevalence and frequency of injection; sharing of injecting equipment; and scores of drug-related risk.

Gowing et al. (2008) identified one RCT (Dolan et al., 2003b) and six cohort studies that reported the prevalence of injecting drug use before and after OST (Camacho et al., 1996; Chatham et al., 1999; Gossop et al., 2000; King et al., 2000; Magura et al., 1991; Teeson et al., 2006); three RCTs (Dolan et al., 2003b; Lott et al., 2006; Strang et al., 2000) and six cohort studies that reported frequency of injection at baseline and follow-up (Batki et al., 1989; Brooner et al., 1998; Camacho et al., 1996; Chatham et al., 1999; Kwiatkowski and Booth, 2001; Simpson et al., 1995); and two cohort studies that examined both the proportion and frequency of injection (Camacho et al., 1996; Chatham et al., 1999). Tilson et al. identified the same studies except Teeson et al., 2006 and Lott et al., 2006. The studies varied in terms of follow-up periods (range 3 to 12 months) and the measurement of frequency of injecting, but all studies showed statistically significant decreases in injecting risk behaviour from baseline to follow-up (Gowing et al., 2008; Tilson et al., 2007).

Sorensen and Copeland (2000) refer to a further nine studies with data on injection prevalence and frequency: one RCT and four cohort studies of in-treatment samples showed retention in MMT was associated with decreases in injection frequency (Abbott et al., 1998; Ball et al., 1998; Iguchi, 1998; Saxon et al., 1994; Shore et al., 1996); and one cohort and three cross-sectional studies comparing those in treatment with non-treatment samples found

MMT associated with fewer injections (Baker et al., 1995; Greenfield et al., 1995; Meandzija et al., 1994; Stark et al., 1996).

Gowing et al. (2008) identified three RCT and six cohort studies that examined the proportion who reported sharing equipment before and after a period of MMT. Tilson et al. (2007) identified the same studies except Teeson et al. (2006) and Schroeder et al. (2006). Eight out of nine (Camacho et al., 1996; Chatham et al., 1999; Dolan et al., 2003b; Gossop et al., 2000; Grella et al., 1996; Margolin et al., 2003; Schroeder et al., 2006; Teeson et al., 2006) found a significant reduction in sharing between baseline and follow-up. The ninth study (King et al., 2000), found a non-significant reduction in reported sharing.

Sorensen and Copeland (2000) additionally reported on one RCT and three cohort studies of in-treatment samples that showed that retention in MMT was associated with decreases in sharing of injecting equipment (Camacho et al., 1996; Magura et al., 1998; Rhoades et al., 1998; Saxon et al., 1994) and one cross-sectional study that found no differences in sharing between new treatment entrants and the rest of the sample (Caslyn et al., 1991). One cohort study and four cross-sectional studies comparing those in treatment with non-treatment found MMT was associated with decreased sharing (Caplehorn and Ross, 1995; Greenfield et al., 1995; Klee et al., 1991; Longshore et al., 1993; Stark et al., 1996) and one cross-sectional study found no differences in sharing (Baker et al., 1995).

Gowing et al. (2008) identified four RCTs, one cohort and two cross-sectional studies comparing drug-related HIV risk scores among those in and out of OST (Abbott et al., 1998; Avants et al., 1998; Baker et al., 1995; Chatham et al., 1999; Mark et al., 2006; Marsch et al., 2005; Sees et al., 2000). Tilson et al. (2007) identified the same studies except Mark et al. (2006) and Marsch et al. (2005). Four studies (Abbott et al., 1998; Avants et al., 1998; Chatham et al., 1999; Marsch et al., 2005) found significant decreases in drug-related HIV risk behaviour scores before and after OST. Sees et al. (2000) found no significant difference in mean risk scores between intake and six-month follow-up between MMT and methadone detoxification groups. Finally, Baker et al. (1995) and Mark et al. (2006) compared the drug risk scores for those currently in OST and not in OST and in both studies the mean score was significantly lower for the cohort receiving OST at the time of interview.

The conclusions of all three core reviews allowed that OST was associated with reductions in self-reported prevalence and frequency of injection, sharing of injecting equipment and injecting risk behaviour risk scores. Gowing et al. (2008) concluded:

> Substitution treatment is associated with a significant decrease in the proportion of participants reporting injecting drug use and in the frequency of injection … [and] a significant decrease in the sharing of injecting equipment … studies that reported [injecting risk behaviour] scores also showed a significant reduction is risk associated with substitution treatment.

(Gowing et al., 2008, pp. 19–20)

Tilson et al. (2007) concluded:

> Moderate to strong evidence from one RCT and a number of observational studies show that patients receiving methadone maintenance treatment report reductions in several drug-related HIV risk behaviours, including frequency of injecting and sharing of injecting equipment. These patients also had lower summary scores of drug-related risk behaviour compared with pre-treatment levels.
>
> (Tilson et al., 2007, p. 89)

Sorensen and Copeland (2000) concluded,

> 26 out of 28 studies showed positive results in reducing HIV risk behaviours … In this review both longitudinal studies of in-treatment samples and studies comparing treatment patients with other samples found very strong evidence that drug abuse treatment decreases the risk of HIV infection by decreasing needle-use. The evidence is less strong, but still substantial, that drug abuse treatment changes the needle use patterns of participants (e.g. less needle-sharing, more use of sterile needles).
>
> (Sorensen and Copeland, 2000, pp. 27–8)

Prison

Two supplementary reviews examined prison OST and injecting risk behaviour (Stallwitz and Stöver, 2007; WHO et al., 2007). WHO et al. identified seven studies of prison-based OST and injecting risk behaviour (Bayanzadeh et al., undated; Boguña, 1997; Dolan et al., 1996; Dolan et al., 1998; Dolan et al., 2003b; Heimer et al., 2005; Heimer et al., 2006), although some of these studies reported very similar findings from the same data set (i.e. Heimer et al., 2005 and 2006; Dolan et al., 1996 and 1998). Stallwitz and Stöver (2007) also referred to three studies included in WHO et al. (Boguña, 1997; Dolan et al., 1998; Dolan et al., 2003b). Across all studies, opioid-using IDUs who received MMT in prison reported injecting significantly less frequently than those not receiving MMT in prison. WHO et al. concluded: 'Prison-based OST programmes appear to be effective in reducing the frequency of injecting drug use and associated sharing of injecting equipment, if a sufficient dosage is provided and treatment is provided for longer periods of time' (p. 9).

Evidence statement for OST and injecting risk behaviour

Based on consistent evidence from multiple robust studies in three core reviews there is sufficient review-level evidence to support the effectiveness of OST in reducing the frequency of injection, the sharing of injecting equipment and injecting risk behaviour scores.

Based on consistent evidence from two supplementary reviews there is tentative evidence to support the effectiveness of prison-based OST in reducing injecting risk behaviour among IDUs in prison by reducing frequency of injection of heroin and other opiate use.

Effects on overdose-related mortality

We identified two meta-analyses (Amato et al., 2005; Caplehorn et al., 1996) and three supplementary narrative reviews that considered OST and overdose-related mortality (Best et al., 2000; Darke and Hall, 2003; Sporer, 2003). Between them they referred to 14 primary studies (Caplehorn et al., 1994; Cushman, 1977; Darke and Ross, 1999; Darke et al., 2000; Davoli et al., 1993; Fugelstad et al., 1995; Gearing and Schweitzer, 1974; Gronbladh et al., 1990; Gunne and Gronbladh, 1981; McGregor et al., 2002; Poser et al., 1995; van Ameijden et al., 1999; Yancovitz et al., 1991; Zador et al., 1996).

Amato et al. (2005) synthesised the results of five systematic reviews of OST effectiveness in treating opioid dependence. However, they were only able to pool data for all cause mortality for MMT versus waiting list/no treatment from two controlled studies (Gunne and Gronbladh, 1981; Yancovitz et al., 1991) and found non-significant trend suggestive of a reduced risk of death in MMT (RR 0.15, CI 0.02-1.0). The authors concluded, 'Death within the time frames of a clinical trial is a rare event, even in a high risk population like opiate users … for the statistical power needed to study mortality, big RCTs or long follow-up periods are required' (p. 325).

Caplehorn et al. (1996) conducted a meta-analysis of mortality in and out of MMT based on the results of the aforementioned RCT (Gunne and Gronbladh, 1981) and five cohort studies (Caplehorn et al., 1994; Cushman, 1977; Gearing and Schweitzer, 1974; Gronbladh et al., 1990; Poser et al., 1995) from Sweden, Germany, Australia and the United States. MMT reduced risk of death by 75 % (relative risk 0.25, CI 0.19-0.33), due almost entirely to decreases in deaths due to overdose. Notably the included results were all from high-dose programmes. They concluded:

> Addicts were one-quarter as likely to die while in methadone maintenance treatment because they were less likely to die from heroin overdose or suicide. These are most probably direct, pharmacological effects of methadone and are likely to be dose-dependent. This conclusion gives strong support to the argument that all heroin addicts should have access to high-dose, long term maintenance treatment.
>
> (Caplehorn et al., 1996, p. 190)

Other studies referred to in the three supplementary reviews (Best et al., 2000; Darke and Hall, 2003; Sporer, 2003) highlight that overall risk of overdose death is reduced significantly while in treatment compared to never being in treatment or after leaving treatment. An Italian case-control study of 4 200 IDUs found the risk of overdose death was over three times higher among those who left MMT compared to those still in treatment, and over seven times higher in the first 12 months after leaving treatment (Davoli et al., 1993). In a Swedish cohort study of 472 HIV-infected IDUs, risk of death by overdose or trauma was reduced by 75 % while in MMT compared to never being in treatment (Fugelstad et al., 1995).

A trend toward a dose-dependent reduction in the risk of overdose death was also observed in a Dutch cohort study, where the risk of death among those on 55 mg or more was a third of that in patients on lower doses (van Ameijden et al., 1999). Additionally systematic audits of coronial data on heroin-related deaths in Australia have shown that around 98 % of deaths occurred among individuals not enrolled in MMT at the time of their death (Darke and Ross, 1999; Darke et al., 2000; McGregor et al., 2002; Zador et al., 1996).

Conclusions from all three supplementary reviews consistently supported that being in OST is associated with a substantial reduction in the risk of opioid overdose compared to no treatment or after leaving treatment. Best et al. (2000) also highlighted that the risk of overdose death during treatment is greatest during induction and that risk of death out of treatment is greatest immediately after leaving/being dropped from treatment.

We identified four longitudinal primary studies of OST and overdose-related mortality published since 2003, which all found significant reductions in mortality risk during treatment compared to when out of treatment (Brugal et al., 2005; Clausen et al., 2008; Davoli et al., 2007; Degenhardt et al., 2009).

An Italian prospective cohort study of 10 454 heroin users entering treatment found those retained in MMT had a 90 % reduced risk of death compared to those not in treatment (Davoli et al., 2007). Similarly in a Spanish cohort of 5 049 heroin users entering treatment, risk of overdose death was seven times greater for those not in MMT at the time of death (Brugal et al., 2005). A Norwegian prospective data linkage study of mortality among 3 789 heroin users who applied for OST showed risk of overdose death was reduced by 80 % while in treatment compared to OST waiting list or after leaving treatment (Clausen et al., 2008). In an Australian state-wide OST retrospective data linkage study of 42 676 individuals entering treatment over a 20-year period, OST contributed to a 29 % reduction in mortality (mostly due to overdose and trauma) across the entire cohort (Degenhardt et al., 2009).

Finally, an ecological study of access to OST and overdose deaths in France during a rapid scale-up of OST (particularly BMT) suggests that as the number of drug users in OST increased, there was a concurrent rapid decline in the annual number of opioid related overdose deaths (Emmanuelli and Desenclos, 2005).

Prison

WHO et al. (2007) note recent release from prison as a significant risk factor for drug overdose and the importance of drug treatment through-care. They identified one study of prison MMT and post-release mortality (Dolan et al., 2005). In a four-year follow-up of 382 prison-based MMT RCT participants, no deaths occurred while participants were in MMT, but 17 died out of MMT (untreated mortality rate of 2.0 per 100 person-years, 95 % CI, 1.2-3.2). Eight deaths were from drug overdose, four had never received MMT and four had ceased MMT prior to release from prison.

Evidence statement for OST and overdose

Based on consistent evidence from one meta-analysis and multiple robust studies in supplementary reviews, there is sufficient review-level evidence to support the effectiveness of OST in reducing the risk of opioid overdose death. Recently published high-quality primary studies also support that OST reduces risk of overdose death for those retained in treatment compared to those waiting for treatment or who have left treatment.

There is insufficient review evidence to support or discount the effectiveness of prison-based OST and overdose prevention. Findings from one post-RCT follow-up study suggest that retention in prison based OST after release was associated with reduced mortality.

Supervised drug consumption facilities

Effects on HIV and HCV incidence/prevalence

A supplementary review (Hedrich, 2004) identified two linked studies that examined the effect of DCR on operation BBV incidence/prevalence in Sydney (MSIC Evaluation Committee, 2003). No evidence of an increase or decrease in the incidence of notifications for HIV, HCV or HBV infections in the DCR locality compared to control localities were attributable to the operation of the DCR (MSIC Evaluation Committee, 2003). It was acknowledged a priori that low population prevalence of these infections and the limited coverage of one DCR made it unlikely there would be a detectable community-level impact on BBV incidence (MSIC Evaluation Committee, 2003). Complimentary case-control and serial cross-sectional studies of HCV incidence and HCV prevalence respectively among IDUs in the DCR locality found HCV incidence was stable and that a trend towards increased HCV prevalence was consistent with national trends among IDUs (MSIC Evaluation Committee, 2003).

Hedrich (2004) concluded:

> Few data are available regarding the impact of the rooms on the incidence of infectious diseases among clients. Methodologically, it is difficult to establish a causal effect of the rooms per se that can be distinguished from the effects of the gamut of health promotion and harm reduction activities aimed at preventing drug-related infectious diseases.
>
> (Hedrich, 2004, p. 77)

Evidence statement for DCRs and HIV/HCV incidence/prevalence

There is insufficient review-level or primary evidence to support or discount the effect of DCRs on HIV or HCV prevalence/incidence.

Effects on injecting risk behaviour

Two supplementary reviews (Hedrich, 2004; Kerr et al., 2007), a synthesis of Vancouver evaluation findings (Wood et al., 2006) and a meta-analysis (Milloy and Wood, 2009) examined evidence of the effect of DCR use on self-reported (and in some instances staff-reported) injecting risk behaviour.

Hedrich (2004) identified 13 studies of DCRs and injecting risk behaviour (Benninghoff and Dubois-Arber, 2002; Benninghoff et al., 2003; Jacob et al., 1999; Linssen et al., 2000; Meijer et al., 2001; Minder Nejedly and Bürki, 1996; MSIC Evaluation Committee, 2003; Poschadel et al., 2003; Reyes Fuentes, 2003; Ronco et al., 1996; van der Poel et al., 2003; Zurhold et al., 2001). These comprised mostly serial and single cross-sectional studies with small sample sizes. However, they consistently showed a positive impact of DCR use on injecting-related risk behaviour, including: improved knowledge and/or practice of injecting hygiene and safer use (Benninghoff and Dubois-Arber, 2002; Benninghoff et al., 2003; Jacob et al., 1999; Linssen et al., 2000; Meijer et al., 2001; MSIC Evaluation Committee, 2003; Poschadel et al., 2003; van der Poel et al., 2003; Zurhold et al., 2001); increased use of sterile injecting equipment for all injections (Minder Nejedly and Bürki, 1996; MSIC Evaluation Committee, 2003; Reyes Fuentes, 2003; Ronco et al., 1996); decreases in needle syringe and other equipment sharing (Benninghoff and Dubois-Arber, 2002; Benninghoff et al., 2003; Dubois-Arber et al., 1999; MSIC Evaluation Committee, 2003).

Hedrich concluded:

> Clients of consumption rooms report improved knowledge of safer use and injection techniques as well as reductions in risk behaviour. Positive behavioural changes are confirmed by staff, although this process is sometimes slow. Despite methodological limitations, it is likely that safer use education given at consumption rooms has contributed to this. Effects increase with length and frequency of service use and behaviour changes are sustained outside the facilities.
>
> (Hedrich, 2004, p. 77)

Kerr et al. (2007) referred to seven of the same studies as Hedrich (2004) (Benninghoff and Dubois-Arber, 2002; Benninghoff et al., 2003; Jacob et al., 1999; Meijer et al., 2001; Minder Nejedly and Bürki, 1996; Ronco et al., 1996; van der Poel et al., 2003) and Kerr et al. (2007) and Wood et al. (2006) both referred to three studies of DCR use and injecting risk behaviour from the prospective IDU cohort studies of the Vancouver evaluation (Kerr et al., 2005; Stoltz et al., 2007; Wood et al., 2005). The prevalence of syringe sharing decreased in the cohort after the facility opened and only among DCR users (Kerr et al., 2005). Regular DCR use was associated with reduced syringe lending by HIV-infected IDUs and reduced syringe borrowing by HIV-negative IDUs (Wood et al., 2005). DCR use was independently associated with decreased reuse of syringes, increased use of sterile water and increased use of alcohol swabbing of injection sites (Stoltz et al., 2007).

Milloy and Wood (2009) combined the effects of DCR use on syringe sharing from Canadian (Kerr et al., 2005; Wood et al., 2005) and Spanish (Bravo et al., 2009) cohort studies. Their pooled estimate of 0.31 (95 % confidence interval 0.17-0.55) represented a 69 % reduction in the likelihood of syringe sharing among DCR users.

Evidence statement for DCRs and injecting risk behaviour

Based on consistent evidence from multiple studies identified in two supplementary reviews and a meta-analysis we conclude there is tentative review-level evidence that DCR use is associated with reduced injecting risk behaviour and improvements in injecting practices and hygiene, especially for injections that occur on DCR premises, and among those who are regular DCR users.

Effects on overdose mortality

Two supplementary reviews (Hedrich, 2004; Kerr et al., 2007) identified an ecological study of DCRs and overdose mortality. A time series study of drug-related deaths in four German cities found a significant association between the operation of DCRs (often in multiple sites) and the reduction of drug-related deaths (Poschadel et al., 2003). Hedrich (2004) also described another time series study of DCR operation and overdose deaths and ambulance call-outs to suspected opioid overdoses in Sydney, which was inconclusive due to confounding changes in the drug market after the opening of the DCR that led to a significant reduction in heroin use (MSIC Evaluation Committee, 2003).

Potential deaths prevented by DCR operation have also been estimated. Hedrich (2004) reported on a multiplier estimation study from Sydney that suggested that clinical intervention staff prevented at least four deaths per year (MSIC Evaluation Committee, 2003). Hedrich (2004) also applied a mortality rate of 2 % to data on annual supervised drug consumption episodes in Germany (Poschadel et al., 2003), assuming that one 'person year of active use' equals 1 000 consumptions, and estimated that at least 10 deaths per year were prevented by the operation of DCRS in Germany.

Hedrich (2004) concluded:

> There is some evidence ... that consumption rooms can contribute to a reduction in drug-related deaths at community level. The robustness of these analyses remains to be verified by further research data based on longitudinal analyses in different contexts that reproduce these results across time or geographic location ... There is no evidence at all that consumption rooms contribute to increased morbidity or mortality risks among drug users. Millions of drug consumptions have been supervised and thousands of emergencies been treated — with no deaths from overdose.

(Hedrich, 2004, p. 77)

Evidence statement for DCRs and overdose deaths

There is insufficient review-level evidence to support or discount the effect of DCRs on reduction of overdose deaths at the community level. One time-series study found DCR operation was associated with reduced drug-related deaths at a city level. Process data show no overdose deaths have occurred on DCR premises and clinical and epidemiological data suggest it is likely that a proportion of overdoses treated in DCR settings would have been fatal if they had occurred elsewhere.

Peer naloxone distribution

We identified one supplementary review of PND to reduce heroin deaths (Baca and Grant, 2005), which reported limited process outcomes of two early PND programmes (Bigg, 2002; Dettmer et al., 2001).

The process evaluation literature on PND has grown considerably since that review and we identified nine subsequently published primary studies (Galea et al., 2006; Green et al., 2008; Piper et al., 2008; Seal et al., 2005; Sherman et al., 2009; Strang et al., 2008; Tobin et al., 2009; Wagner et al., 2009).

Taken together, the evidence from four prospective studies (Seal et al., 2005; Strang et al., 2008; Tobin et al., 2009; Wagner et al., 2009) and three cross-sectional studies (Green et al., 2008; Piper et al., 2008; Sherman et al., 2009) suggests that overdose prevention training with PND increases participants' knowledge, confidence and skills to respond effectively in case of overdose. Evidence from five prospective studies (Galea et al., 2006; Seal et al., 2005; Strang et al., 2008; Tobin et al., 2009; Wagner et al., in press) and three cross-sectional studies (Dettmer et al., 2001; Piper et al., 2008) suggests PND trainees subsequently intervene at overdose using naloxone with very high reported rates of survival in cases where the outcome of intervention is known.

Effects on overdose mortality

We identified one ecological study that examined the impact of PND on overdose mortality at the community level. In Chicago, a large-scale PND programme has been operating since 2001 with more than 3 500 vials of naloxone prescribed and 319 naloxone reversals reported by programme participants. Coronial data showed that the upward trend in heroin overdose deaths annually in Chicago prior to the PND programme, which increased four-fold between 1996 and 2000, reversed in 2001, with a 20 % decrease in 2001 and a 10 % decreases in 2002 and 2003 (Maxwell et al., 2006).

Evidence statement for PND and overdose

There is insufficient review-level evidence to draw conclusions about the effect of PND on overdose deaths. Recently published primary studies consistently point to the feasibility and uptake of PND programmes. One ecological study suggests the operation of a large PND programme may have played a role in reducing overdose deaths at the city level.

Discussion

Drawing substantively upon our previous work in this area (Palmateer et al., 2008; Palmateer et al., 2010), we have used a review of reviews methodology to evaluate the evidence relating to the effectiveness of selected harm reduction interventions on key indicators of injecting-related morbidity and mortality: NSPs, OST, DCRs on HIV and HCV incidence/prevalence and injecting risk behaviour; and OST, DCRs, and PND on overdose-related deaths.

We find that there is sufficient review-level evidence that OST reduces HIV transmission, while the review evidence in support of NSPs reducing HIV transmission is more tentative, and for DCRs currently insufficient. We find there is tentative review-level evidence that OST has limited effectiveness in reducing HCV transmission, and insufficient evidence to support or discount that NSPs or DCRs reduce HCV transmission. We find there is sufficient review-level evidence that NSPs, OST and DCRs reduce self-reported injecting risk behaviour and tentative review-level evidence to suggest that pharmacy access, in addition to primary NSP, is effective in reducing injecting risk behaviour. There is sufficient review-level evidence that OST is effective in reducing opioid overdose related mortality but insufficient review-level evidence to support or discount the effectiveness of DCRs and PND in reducing overdose deaths at the community level.

Our findings highlight a lack of high-quality reviews for some harm reduction interventions and/or outcomes we considered. In some cases this reflects a lack of primary studies (e.g. DCRs and PND). It also appears that previous reviews of NSPs may have overstated the evidence of effectiveness in BBV prevention from the available studies. In general, we found that reviews gave more consideration to issues of bias and limitations in studies with negative findings than in studies with positive (protective) findings, and thus may have ascribed less importance to negative studies when synthesising the evidence (Palmateer et al., in press).

As highlighted earlier, an assessment of insufficient or tentative review-level evidence does not equate to evidence for lack of intervention effectiveness. Such assessments are inevitably related to the methodological limitations of primary studies as well as the reviews (Palmateer et al., 2010). For example, one of the criticisms of studies investigating NSPs' effectiveness in preventing BBVs is that they do not accurately measure the coverage or intensity of the intervention delivered (that is, the amount of injecting equipment distributed) (Lurie, 1997).

Further consideration of the limitations of the primary studies helps to explain our finding of a discrepancy between the results of individual-level (i.e. cohort and case-control) and ecological studies of NSP effectiveness (Palmateer et al., 2010). First, individual-level, non-randomised studies are highly susceptible to bias. In cohort studies, for example, two groups, such as NSP attenders and non-attenders, are usually compared to the outcome. This measurement of the exposure to the intervention has generally been limited because: (i) these groups are 'self-selecting' and thus may be inherently different with respect to characteristics, including injecting risk, that can influence the outcome (Lurie, 1997), and (ii) the distinction between exposed and unexposed groups may also be inadequate (for example, unexposed individuals may have access to clean needles/syringes from other sources or exposed individuals may still be engaging in injecting risk despite high uptake of NSP), potentially diluting the effect size (Gibson et al., 2001).

Ecological studies, by contrast, are more likely to report a positive association: because one cannot isolate the effects of a single intervention in an ecological study, such studies may in fact be measuring the impact of several interventions. This is illustrated in the Amsterdam Cohort Study (ACS), which found that MMT or NSP use alone were not associated significantly with HIV or HCV seroconversion, but that full participation in both programmes was associated with a lower incidence of HCV and HIV infection, suggesting that only the combination of these interventions might contribute to the reduction of the transmission of these infections (van den Berg et al., 2007).

All of the evidence for NSP, DCR and PND effectiveness is based on observational study designs, that is, exposure has not been randomised. Observational studies, as discussed above, are generally at risk of confounding and selection bias. However, it is logistically and ethically difficult to conduct a randomised trial for interventions such as NSPs and DCRs, which have face validity and have already been widely introduced (Hall and Kimber, 2005; Lurie, 1997). A feasible alternative study design is a community-randomised trial (e.g. comparing a basic package of harm reduction services with an enhanced package) where participants are randomised on a group basis, rather than an individual basis, thereby avoiding some of the biases associated with observational designs (Tilson et al., 2007).

Another methodological issue is that the primary studies might not have been adequately powered to detect an impact. Few of the reviews addressed this issue in their reporting of the studies and, therefore, it was usually unclear whether equivocal findings were due to a lack of power or truly represented no association (Palmateer et al., 2010).

The reliance on self-reported behaviour is a problem for epidemiological studies examining the effectiveness of harm reduction interventions. Self-reported behaviour by drug users can be reliable (Darke, 1988; Goldstein et al., 1995); however, it is unclear whether this applies to all behaviours. Limitations, for example, in the reliability self-reported injecting risk behaviour may explain our finding of greater strength of evidence for behavioural measures than for biological measures. Differential reporting of risk behaviour between exposed and unexposed groups could bias measures of the effectiveness of an intervention, for example if IDUs exposed to NSPs are more sensitised to the risks of sharing and more reluctant to report this behaviour than unexposed individuals (Palmateer et al., 2010). Second, some modelling studies (Vickerman et al., 2006) have suggested that the association between injecting risk behaviour and HIV/HCV transmission does not follow a dose-response relationship; rather, a reduction in injecting risk has to surpass a threshold level before changes in HIV/HCV transmission are observed. Consequently, a sub-threshold change in injecting risk behaviour may have no impact on HIV/HCV incidence, thereby limiting the usefulness of injecting risk behaviour as a proxy measure for the effectiveness of an intervention (Palmateer et al., 2010).

We acknowledge that we may have missed potentially relevant reviews by limiting our search to English language reviews, although we attempted to expand the search, and reduce publication bias, by examining the grey literature. In particular in the reviews of DCRs, prison NSPs and prison OST there is good coverage of non-English language studies. We also aimed to address potential gaps in the review evidence by undertaking searches of recently published primary literature.

Another limitation of the review of reviews methodology is the reliance on the reviewers' identification of the relevant studies and their accounts of the designs and findings of the primary studies. In considering the primary evidence, we used the study design as a proxy for study quality; however, other factors — for example sample size and recruitment strategy — affect the integrity of a study's results. The likelihood of having missed primary studies is a possibility for outcomes that core reviews did not specifically set out to examine: we attempted to compensate for this by including the studies identified by supplementary reviews (Palmateer et al., 2010).

We have also focused our evaluation of harm reduction programmes on a subset of interventions and outcomes. This is not to suggest that other interventions (e.g. education information and counselling) or outcomes (e.g. health and social functioning) that we have not examined are not important components of these programmes. Additionally, we have focused on the 'direct' evidence of effectiveness of the selected interventions (that is, changes in biological or behavioural outcomes).

Implications for harm reduction practice and evaluation

In most European countries, harm reduction interventions developed in response to community-level identified needs, and were often introduced in the absence of methodologically rigorous evaluation. We have found the quality of evidence on intervention impacts to be lacking in some cases, but this is not uncommon for behavioural interventions in public health more generally and harm reduction interventions in HIV prevention are the subject of much evaluation research. Our assessment of the quality of evidence does not suggest that policymakers should disinvest from harm reduction programmes. Rather, the provision and increase in coverage of interventions needs to be used as an opportunity to conduct better research into the effectiveness of these interventions.

Conclusions and recommendations

European countries face a challenge in reducing/maintaining low prevalence of BBVs among IDUs and reducing drug overdose mortality. Good quality research is fundamental to formulating policy on the development, scale-up and continued investment in public health interventions targeting IDUs. We recommend a step change in evaluations of harm reduction interventions so that future evaluations: (i) include both biological and behavioural outcomes and are powered to detect changes in the outcome of interest; (ii) consider complete packages of harm reduction interventions rather than single interventions; (iii) consider randomised, especially community-level, designs where possible, and report evaluation findings to CONSORT and TREND guidelines (Des Jarlais et al., 2004; Moher et al., 2001); (iv) and compare additional interventions or increased coverage/intensity of interventions with current availability (Palmateer et al., 2010).

References

Abbott, P. J., Weller, S. B., Delaney, H. D. and Moore, B. A. (1998), 'Community reinforcement approach in the treatment of opiate addicts', *American Journal of Drug and Alcohol Abuse* 24 (1), pp. 17–30.

Amato, L., Davoli, M., Perucci, C. A., et al. (2005), 'An overview of systematic reviews of the effectiveness of opiate maintenance therapies: available evidence to inform clinical practice and research', *Journal of Substance Abuse Treatment* 28, pp. 321–9.

Amundsen, E. J., Eskild, A., Stigum, H., Smith, E. and Aalen, O. O. (2003), 'Legal access to needles and syringes/needle exchange programmes versus HIV counselling and testing to prevent transmission of HIV among intravenous drug users: a comparative study of Denmark, Norway and Sweden', *European Journal of Public Health* 13, pp. 252–8.

Avants, S. K., Margolin, A., Kosten, T. R., Rounsaville, B. J. and Schottenfeld, R. S. (1998), 'When is less treatment better? The role of social anxiety in matching methadone patients to psychosocial treatments', *Journal of Consulting and Clinical Psychology* 66 (6), pp. 924–31.

Baca, C. T. and Grant, K. J. (2005), 'Take-home naloxone to reduce heroin death', *Addiction* 100 (12), pp. 1823–31.

Baker, A., Kochan, N., Dixon, J., Wodak, A. and Heather, N. (1995), 'HIV risk-taking behaviour among injecting drug users currently, previously and never enrolled in methadone treatment', *Addiction* 90 (4), pp. 545–54.

Ball, J. C., Lange, W. R., Myers, R. P. and Friedman, S. (1998), 'Reducing the risk of AIDS through methadone maintenance treatment', *Journal of Health and Social Behavior* 29, pp. 214–26.

Bargagli, A. M., Hickman, M., Davoli, M., et al. (2006), 'Drug-related mortality and its impact on adult mortality in eight European countries', *European Journal of Public Health* 16 (2), pp. 198–202.

Batki, S. L., Sorensen, J. L., Gibson, D. R. and Maude-Griffin, P. (1989), 'HIV-infected i.v. drug users in methadone treatment: outcome and psychological correlates: a preliminary report', *NIDA Research Monograph* 95, pp. 405–6.

Bayanzadeh, S. A., et al. (2004), 'A study of the effectiveness of psychopharmacological intervention in reducing harm/high risk behaviours among substance user prisoners'.

Benninghoff, F. and Dubois-Arber, F. (2002), 'Résultats de l'étude de la clientèle du Cactus BIEL/BIENNE 2001', Institut universitaire de médecine sociale et préventive, Lausanne.

Benninghoff, F., Solai, S., Huissoud, T. and Dubois-Arber, F. (2003), 'Evaluation de Quai 9 "Espace d'acceuil et d'injection" à Genéve: période 12/2001–12/2000', Institut universitaire de médecine sociale et préventive, Lausanne.

Best, D., Man, L. H., Zador, D., et al. (2000), 'Overdosing on opiates: part II — prevention', *Drug and Alcohol Findings* (5), pp. 4–18.

Bewley-Taylor, D. (2002), 'Challenging the UN drug control conventions: problems and possibilities', *International Journal of Drug Policy* 14 (2), pp. 171–9.

Bigg, D. (2002), 'Data on take home naloxone are unclear but not condemnatory', *BMJ* 324 (7338), p. 678.

Bluthenthal, R. N., Kral, A. H., Erringer, E. A. and Edlin, B. R. (1998), 'Use of an illegal syringe exchange and injection-related risk behaviors among street-recruited injection drug users in Oakland, California, 1992 to 1995', *Journal of Acquired Immune Deficiency Syndromes and Human Retrovirology* 18 (5), pp. 505–11.

Bluthenthal, R. N., Kral, A. H., Gee, L., Erringer, E. A. and Edlin, B. R. (2000), 'The effect of syringe exchange use on high-risk injection drug users: a cohort study', *AIDS* 14 (5), pp. 605–11.

Boguña, J. (1997), 'Methadone maintenance programmes', in O'Brien, O. (ed.), *Report of the 3rd European Conference on Drug and HIV/AIDS Services in Prison*, Cranstoun Drug Services, London, pp. 68–70.

Bravo, M. J., Royuela, L., Brugal, M. T., Barrio, G. and Domingo-Salvany, A. (2009), 'Use of supervised injection facilities and injection risk behaviours among young drug injectors', *Addiction* 104 (4), pp. 614–19.

Broadhead, R. S., van Hulst, Y. and Heckathorn, D. D. (1999), 'The impact of a needle exchange's closure', *Public Health Reports* 114, pp. 439–47.

Brooner, R., Kidorf, M., King, V., et al. (1998), 'Drug abuse treatment success among needle exchange participants', *Public Health Reports* 113 Supplement 1, pp. 129–39.

Brugal, M. T., Domingo-Salvany, A., Puig, R., et al. (2005), 'Evaluating the impact of methadone maintenance programmes on mortality due to overdose and AIDS in a cohort of heroin users in Spain', *Addiction* 100 (7), pp. 981–9.

Bruneau, J., Lamothe, F., Franco, E., et al. (1997), 'High rates of HIV infection among injection drug users participating in needle exchange programs in Montreal: results of a cohort study', *American Journal of Epidemiology* 146 (12), pp. 994–1002.

Camacho, L. M., Bartholomew, N. G., Joe, G. W., Cloud, M. A. and Simpson, D. D. (1996), 'Gender, cocaine and during-treatment HIV risk reduction among injection opioid users in methadone maintenance', *Drug and Alcohol Dependence* 41 (1), pp. 1–7.

Caplehorn, J. and Ross, M. (1995), 'Methadone maintenance and the likelihood of risky needle-sharing', *International Journal of the Addictions* 30, pp. 685–98.

Caplehorn, J., Dalton, M. and Petrenas, A. (1994), 'Retention in methadone maintenance and heroin addicts' risk of death', *Addiction* 89, pp. 203–07.

Caplehorn, J., Dalton, M. S., Haldar, F., Petrenas, A. M. and Nisbet, J. G. (1996), 'Methadone maintenance and addicts' risk of fatal heroin overdose', *Substance Use and Misuse* 31 (2), pp. 177–96.

Caslyn, D. A. (1992), 'Ineffectiveness of AIDS education and HIV antibody testing in reducing high risk behaviours among injecting drug users', *American Journal of Public Health* 82, pp. 573–5.

Caslyn, D. A., Saxon, A., Freeman, G. and Whittaker, S. (1991), 'Needle practices among intravenous drug users in an area where needle purchase is still legal', *AIDS* 5, pp. 187–93.

Chamot, E., de Saussure, P., Hirschel, B., Deglon, J. J. and Perrin, L. H. (1992), 'Incidence of hepatitis C, hepatitis B and HIV infections among drug users in a methadone-maintenance programme', *AIDS* 6 (4), pp. 430–1.

Chatham, L. R., Hiller, M. L., Rowan-Szal, G. A., Joe, G. W. and Simpson, D. D. (1999), 'Gender differences at admission and follow-up in a sample of methadone maintenance clients', *Substance Use and Misuse* 34 (8), pp. 1137–65.

Clausen, T., Anchersen, K. and Waal, H. (2008), 'Mortality prior to, during and after opioid maintenance treatment (OMT): a national prospective cross-registry study', *Drug and Alcohol Dependence* 94, pp. 151–7.

Cook, C., Bridge, J. and Stimson, G. V. (2010), 'The diffusion of harm reduction in Europe and beyond', in European Monitoring Centre for Drugs and Drug Addiction (EMCDDA), *Harm reduction: evidence, impacts and challenges*, Rhodes, T. and Hedrich, D. (eds), Scientific Monograph Series No. 10, Publications Office of the European Union, Luxembourg.

Coutinho, R. (2005), 'Needle exchange: the Amsterdam experience', in *Institute of Medicine workshop on the prevention of HIV among injecting drug users in high-risk countries*, Institute of Medicine Committee on the Prevention of HIV Infection Among Injecting Drug Users in High-Risk Countries, Geneva.

Cox, G. M., Lawless, M. C., Cassin, S. P. and Geoghegan, T. W. (2000), 'Syringe exchanges: a public health response to problem drug use', *Irish Medical Journal* 93, pp. 143–6.

Craine, N., Hickman, M., Parry, J. V., et al. (2009), 'Incidence of hepatitis C in drug injectors: the role of homelessness, opiate substitution treatment, equipment sharing, and community size', *Epidemiology and Infection* 137 (9), pp. 1255–65.

Crofts, N., Nigro, L., Oman, K., Stevenson, E. and Sherman, J. (1997), 'Methadone maintenance and hepatitis C virus infection among injecting drug users', *Addiction* 92 (8), pp. 999–1005.

Cushman, P. J. (1977), 'Ten years of methadone maintenance treatment: some clinical observations', *American Journal of Drug and Alcohol Abuse* 4, pp. 543–53.

Darke, S. (1988), 'Self-report among injecting drug users: a review', *Drug and Alcohol Dependence* 51 (3), pp. 253–63.

Darke, S. and Hall, W. (1997), 'The distribution of naloxone to heroin users', *Addiction* 92 (9), pp. 1195–9.

Darke, S. and Hall, W. (2003), 'Heroin overdose: research and evidence-based intervention', *Journal of Urban Health* 80 (2), pp. 189–200.

Darke, S. and Ross, J. (1999), 'Heroin-related deaths in south western Sydney: 1992–1996', *Drug and Alcohol Review* 18, pp. 39–45.

Darke, S., Ross, J., Zador, D. and Sunjic, S. (2000), 'Heroin-related deaths in New South Wales, Australia, 1992–1996', *Drug and Alcohol Dependence* 60, pp. 141–50.

Davoli, M., Perucci, C. A., Forastiere, F., et al. (1993), 'Risk factors for overdose mortality: a case control study within a cohort of intravenous drug users', *International Journal of Epidemiology* 22 (2), pp. 272–7.

Davoli, M., Bargagli, A. M., Perucci, C. A., et al. (2007), 'Risk of fatal overdose during and after specialist drug treatment: the VEdeTTE study, a national multi-site prospective cohort study', *Addiction* 102 (12), pp. 1954–9.

De Jong, W., Tsagarelli, T. and Schouten, E. (1999), 'Rapid assessment of injection drug use and HIV in the Republic of Georgia', *Journal of Drug Issues* 29 (4), pp. 843–60.

Degenhardt, L., Hall, W., Lynskey, M. and Warner-Smith, M. (2004), 'Illicit drug use', in Ezzati, M., Lopez, A., Rodgers, A. and Murray, C. (eds), *Comparative quantification of health risks: global and regional burden of disease attributable to selected major risk factors*, World Health Organization, Geneva.

Degenhardt, L., Hall, W. and Warner-Smith, M. (2006), 'Using cohort studies to estimate mortality among injecting drug users that is not attributable to AIDS', *Sexually Transmitted Infections* 82, pp. 56–63.

Degenhardt, L., Randall, D., Hall, W., et al. (2009), 'Mortality among clients of a state-wide opioid pharmacotherapy program over 20 years: risk factors and lives saved', *Drug and Alcohol Dependence* 105 (1–2), pp. 9–15.

Des Jarlais, D. C., Friedman, S. R., Sotheran, J. L., et al. (1994), 'Continuity and change within an HIV epidemic: injecting drug users in New York City, 1984 through 1992', *JAMA* 271 (2), pp. 121–7.

Des Jarlais, D. C., Hagan, H., Friedman, S. R., et al. (1995), 'Maintaining low HIV seroprevalence in populations of injecting drug users', *JAMA* 274 (15), pp. 1226–31.

Des Jarlais, D. C., Marmor, M., Paone, D., et al. (1996), 'HIV incidence among injecting drug users in New York City syringe-exchange programmes', *Lancet* 348 (9033), pp. 987–91.

Des Jarlais, C., Perlis, T., Friedman, S. R., et al. (2000), 'Behavioral risk reduction in a declining HIV epidemic: injection drug users in New York City, 1990–1997', *American Journal of Public Health* 90 (7), pp. 1112–16.

Des Jarlais, D., Lyles, C., Crepaz, N. and TREND Group (2004), 'Improving the reporting quality of nonrandomized evaluations of behavioral and public health interventions: the TREND statement', *American Journal of Public Health* 94 (3), pp. 361–6.

Des Jarlais, D. C., Perlis, T., Arasteh, K., et al. (2005a), 'HIV incidence among injection drug users in New York City, 1990 to 2002: use of serologic test algorithm to assess expansion of HIV prevention services', *American Journal of Public Health* 95 (8), pp. 1439–44.

Des Jarlais, D. C., Perlis, T., Arasteh, K., et al. (2005b), 'Reductions in hepatitis C virus and HIV infections among injecting drug users in New York City, 1990–2001', *AIDS* 19 (Supplement 3), pp. S20–S25.

Dettmer, K., Saunders, B. and Strang, J. (2001), 'Take home naloxone and the prevention of deaths from opiate overdose: two pilot schemes', *British Medical Journal* 322 (7291), pp. 895–6.

Dolan, K., Hall, W. and Wodak, A. (1996), 'Methadone maintenance reduces injecting in prison', *British Medical Journal* 312, p. 1162.

Dolan, K., Wodak, A. and Hall, W. (1998), 'Methadone maintenance treatment reduces heroin injection in NSW prisons', *Drug and Alcohol Review* 17 (2), pp. 153–8.

Dolan, K., Rutter, S. and Wodak, A. D. (2003a), 'Prison-based syringe exchange programmes: a review of international research and development', *Addiction* 98 (2), pp. 153–8.

Dolan, K. A., Shearer, J., MacDonald, M., et al. (2003b), 'A randomised controlled trial of methadone maintenance treatment versus wait list control in an Australian prison system', *Drug and Alcohol Dependence* 72 (1), pp. 59–65.

Dolan, K. A., Shearer, J., White, B., et al. (2005), 'Four-year follow-up of imprisoned male heroin users and methadone treatment: mortality, re-incarceration and hepatitis C infection', *Addiction* 100 (6), pp. 820–8.

Donoghoe, M. C., Stimson, G. V., Dolan, K. and Alldritt, L. (1989), 'Changes in HIV risk behaviour in clients of syringe-exchange schemes in England and Scotland', *AIDS* 3 (5), pp. 267–72.

Donoghoe, M. C., Dolan, K. and Stimson, G. V. (1992), 'Life-style factors and social circumstances of syringe sharing in injecting drug users', British Journal of Addiction 87, pp. 993–1003.

Dubois-Arber, F., Jeannin, A. and Spencer, B. (1999), 'Evaluation of the AIDS prevention strategy in Switzerland (6th synthesis report 1996–1998)', Institut universitaire de medicine sociale e preventitive, Lausanne.

Ellis, S., Barnett-Page, E., Morgan, A., et al. (2003), HIV prevention: a review of reviews assessing the effectiveness of interventions to reduce the risk of sexual transmission, Health Development Agency, London.

EMCDDA (2008), The state of the drugs problem in Europe: annual report 2008, European Monitoring Centre for Drugs and Drug Addiction, Lisbon.

EMCDDA (2009), The state of the drugs problem in Europe: annual report 2009, European Monitoring Centre for Drugs and Drug Addiction, Lisbon.

Emmanuelli, J. and Desenclos, J. C. (2005), 'Harm reduction interventions, behaviours and associated health outcomes in France, 1996–2003', Addiction 100 (11), pp. 1690–700.

European Commission (2007), Report from the Commission to the European Parliament and the Council on the implementation of the Council recommendation of 18 June 2003 on the prevention and reduction of health-related harm associated with drug dependence, COM (2007) 199 final, Commission of the European Communities, Brussels.

Faggiano, F., Vigna-Taglianti, F., Versino, E. and Lemma, P. (2003), 'Methadone maintenance at different dosages for opioid dependence', Cochrane Database of Systematic Reviews 3, p. CD002208.

Frischer, M. and Elliott, L. (1993), 'Discriminating needle exchange attenders from non-attenders', Addiction 88 (5), pp. 681–7.

Fugelstad, A., Rajs, J., Böttiger, M. and Gerhardsson de Verdier, M. (1995), 'Mortality among HIV-infected intravenous drug addicts in Stockholm in relation to methadone treatment', Addiction 90 (5), pp. 711–16.

Galea, S., Worthington, N., Piper, T. M., et al. (2006), 'Provision of naloxone to injection drug users as an overdose prevention strategy: early evidence from a pilot study in New York City', Addictive Behaviors 31 (5), pp. 907–12.

Gearing, F. R. and Schweitzer, M. D. (1974), 'An epidemiologic evaluation of long term methadone maintenance treatment for heroin addiction', American Journal of Epidemiology 100, pp. 101–12.

Gibson, D. R., Flynn, N. M. and Perales, D. (2001), 'Effectiveness of syringe exchange programs in reducing HIV risk behavior and HIV seroconversion among injecting drug users', AIDS 15 (11), pp. 1329–41.

Gibson, D. R., Brand, R., Anderson, K., et al. (2002), 'Two- to sixfold decreased odds of HIV risk behavior associated with use of syringe exchange', Journal of Acquired Immune Deficiency Syndromes 31 (2), pp. 237–42.

Glaziou, P. and Heneghan, C. (2009), 'A spotter's guide to study designs', Evidence Based Medicine 14, pp. 37–8.

Gleghorn, A. A., Jones, T. S., Doherty, M. C., Celentano, D. D. and Vlahov, D. (1995), 'Acquisition and use of needles and syringes by injecting drug users in Baltimore, Maryland', Journal of Acquired Immune Deficiency Syndromes and Human Retrovirology 10 (1), pp. 97–103.

Gleghorn, A. A., Wright-De Aguero, L. and Flynn, C. (1998), 'Feasibility of one-time use of sterile syringes: a study of active injection drug users in seven United States metropolitan areas', Journal of Acquired Immune Deficiency Syndromes and Human Retrovirology 18 (Supplement 1), pp. S30–S36.

Goldberg, D., Cameron, S. and McMenamin, J. (1998), 'Hepatitis C virus antibody prevalence among injecting drug users in Glasgow has fallen but remains high', Communicable Disease and Public Health 1 (2), pp. 95–7.

Goldberg, D., Burns, S., Taylor, A., et al. (2001), 'Trends in HCV prevalence among injecting drug users in Glasgow and Edinburgh during the era of needle/syringe exchange', *Scandinavian Journal of Infectious Diseases* 33 (6), pp. 457–61.

Goldstein, M. F., Friedman, S. R., Neaigus, A., et al. (1995), 'Self-reports of HIV risk behavior by injecting drug users: are they reliable?' *Addiction* 90 (8), pp. 1097–104.

Gossop, M., Marsden, J., Stewart, D. and Rolfe, A. (2000), 'Patterns of improvement after methadone treatment: 1 year follow-up results from the National Treatment Outcome Research Study', *Drug and Alcohol Dependence* 60 (3), pp. 275–86.

Gowing, L., Farrell, M., Bornemann, R., Sullivan, L. and Ali, R. (2008), 'Substitution treatment of injecting opioid users for prevention of HIV infection', *Cochrane Database of Systematic Reviews* (2), DOI: 10.1002/14651858. CD004145.pub3.

Green, T. C., Heimer, R. and Grau, L. E. (2008), 'Distinguishing signs of opioid overdose and indication for naloxone: an evaluation of six overdose training and naloxone distribution programs in the United States', *Addiction* 103 (6), pp. 979–89.

Greenfield, L., Bigelow, G. E. and Brooner, R. (1995), 'Validity of intravenous drug abusers' self-reported changes in HIV high-risk drug use behaviors', *Drug and Alcohol Dependence* 39 (2), pp. 91–98.

Grella, C. E., Anglin, M. D., Rawson, R., Crowley, R. and Hasson, A. (1996), 'What happens when a demonstration project ends: consequences for a clinic and its clients', *Journal of Substance Abuse Treatment* 13 (3), pp. 249–56.

Gronbladh, L., Ohlund, L. S. and Gunne, L. M. (1990), 'Mortality in heroin addiction: impact of methadone treatment', *Acta Psychiatrica Scandinavica* 82, pp. 22–37.

Groseclose, S. L., Weinstein, B., Jones, T. S., et al. (1995), 'Impact of increased legal access to needles and syringes on practices of injecting-drug users and police officers: Connecticut, 1992–1993', *Journal of Acquired Immune Deficiency Syndromes and Human Retrovirology* 10 (1), pp. 82–9.

Gunne, L. M. and Gronbladh, L. (1981), 'The Swedish methadone maintenance program: a controlled study', *Drug and Alcohol Dependence* 7, pp. 249–56.

Guydish, J., Clark, G., Garcia, D. and Bucardo, J. (1995), 'Evaluation of needle exchange using street-based survey methods', *Journal of Drug Issues* 25, pp. 33–41.

Guydish, J., Bucardo, J., Clark, G. and Bernheim, S. (1998), 'Evaluating needle exchange: a description of client characteristics, health status, program utilization, and HIV risk behavior', *Substance Use and Misuse* 33 (5), pp. 1173–96.

Hagan, H. and Thiede, H. (2000), 'Changes in injection risk behavior associated with participation in the Seattle needle-exchange program', *Journal of Urban Health* 77 (3), pp. 369–82.

Hagan, H., Des Jarlais, D. C., Purchase, D., et al. (1993), 'An interview study of participants in the Tacoma, Washington, syringe exchange', *Addiction* 88 (12), pp. 1691–7.

Hagan, H., Des Jarlais, D. C. and Friedman, S. (1994), *Risk for human immunodeficiency virus and hepatitis B virus in users of the Tacoma syringe exchange program*, National Academy Press, Washington, DC.

Hagan, H., Des Jarlais, D. C., Friedman, S. R., Purchase, D. and Alter, M. J. (1995), 'Reduced risk of hepatitis B and hepatitis C among injection drug users in the Tacoma syringe exchange program', *American Journal of Public Health* 85 (11), pp. 1531–7.

Hagan, H., McGough, J. P., Thiede, H., et al. (1999), 'Syringe exchange and risk of infection with hepatitis B and C viruses', *American Journal of Epidemiology* 149 (3), pp. 203–13.

Hagan, H., Thiede, H. and Des Jarlais, D. C. (2004), 'Hepatitis C virus infection among injection drug users: survival analysis of time to seroconversion', *Epidemiology* 15 (5), pp. 543–9.

Hall, W. and Kimber, J. (2005), 'Being realistic about benefits of supervised injecting facilities', *Lancet* 366 (9482), pp. 271–2.

Hallinan, R., Byrne, A., Amin, J. and Dore, G. J. (2004), 'Hepatitis C virus incidence among injecting drug users on opioid replacement therapy', *Australian and New Zealand Journal of Public Health* 28 (6), pp. 576–8.

Hammett, T. M., Kling, R., Johnston, P., et al. (2006), 'Patterns of HIV prevalence and HIV risk behaviors among injection drug users prior to and 24 months following implementation of cross-border HIV prevention interventions in northern Vietnam and southern China', *AIDS Education and Prevention* 18 (2), pp. 97–115.

Hart, G. J., Carvell, A. L., Woodward, N., et al. (1989), 'Evaluation of needle exchange in central London: behaviour change and anti-HIV status over one year', *AIDS* 3 (5), pp. 261–5.

Hartel, D. M. and Schoenbaum, E. (1998), 'Methadone treatment protects against HIV infections: two decades of experience in the Bronx, New York City', *Public Health Reports* 113 (Supplement 1), pp. S107–S115.

Hartgers, C., Buning, E. C., van Santen, G. W., Verster, A. D. and Coutinho, R. A. (1989), 'The impact of the needle and syringe-exchange programme in Amsterdam on injecting risk behaviour', *AIDS* 3 (9), pp. 571–6.

Hartgers, C., van Ameijden, E. J., van den Hoek, J. A. and Coutinho, R. A. (1992), 'Needle sharing and participation in the Amsterdam Syringe Exchange program among HIV-seronegative injecting drug users', *Public Health Reports* 107 (6), pp. 675–81.

Health Outcomes International, National Centre in HIV Epidemiology & Clinical Research and Drummond, M. (2002), *Return on investment in needle & syringe programs*, Commonwealth Department of Health and Aging, Canberra.

Hedrich, D. (2004), *European report on drug consumption rooms*, European Monitoring Centre for Drugs and Drug Addiction, Lisbon.

Hedrich, D., Kerr, T. and Dubois-Arber, F. (2010), 'Drug consumption facilities in Europe and beyond', in European Monitoring Centre for Drugs and Drug Addiction (EMCDDA), *Harm reduction: evidence, impacts and challenges*, Rhodes, T. and Hedrich, D. (eds), Scientific Monograph Series No. 10, Publications Office of the European Union, Luxembourg.

Heimer, R., Cantani, H., Newman, R. G., Zambrano, J., Brunet, A. and Ortiz, A. (2006), 'Methadone maintenance in prison: evaluation of a pilot program in Puerto Rico', *Drug and Alcohol Dependence* 83 (2), pp. 122–9.

Heimer, R., Kaplan, E. H., Khoshnood, K., Jariwala, B. and Cadman, E. C. (1993), 'Needle exchange decreases the prevalence of HIV-1 proviral DNA in returned syringes in New Haven, Connecticut', *American Journal of Medicine* 95 (2), pp. 214–20.

Heimer, R., Khoshnood, K., Bigg, D., Guydish, J. and Junge, B. (1998), 'Syringe use and reuse: effects of syringe exchange programs in four cities', *Journal of Acquired Immune Deficiency Syndromes and Human Retrovirology* 18 (Supplement 1), pp. S37–S44.

Heimer, R., Zambrano, J. A., Brunet, A. et al. (2005), 'Methadone maintenance treatment in a men's prison in Puerto Rico: a pilot program', *Journal of Correctional Healthcare* 11 (3), pp. 295–305.

Heinemann, A. and Gross, U. (2001), 'Prevention of blood-borne virus infections among drug users in an open prison by syringe vending machines', *Sucht* 47 (2), pp. 57–65.

Hernandez-Aguado, I., Ramos-Rincon, J. M., Avinio, M. J., et al. (2001), 'Measures to reduce HIV infection have not been successful to reduce the prevalence of HCV in intravenous drug users', *European Journal of Epidemiology* 17 (6), pp. 539–44.

Hunter, G. M., Donoghoe, M. C., Stimson, G. V., Rhodes, T. and Chalmers, C. P. (1995), 'Changes in the injecting risk behaviour of injecting drug users in London, 1990–1993', *AIDS* 9 (5), pp. 493–501.

Huo, D., Bailey, S. L., Garfein, R. S. and Ouellet, L. J. (2005), 'Changes in the sharing of drug injection equipment among street-recruited injection drug users in Chicago, Illinois, 1994–1996', *Substance Use and Misuse* 40 (1), pp. 63–76.

Hurley, S. F., Jolley, D. J. and Kaldor, J. M. (1997), 'Effectiveness of needle-exchange programmes for prevention of HIV infection', *Lancet* 349 (9068), pp. 1797–800.

Hutchinson, S. J., McIntyre, P. G., Molyneaux, P., et al. (2002), 'Prevalence of hepatitis C among injectors in Scotland 1989–2000: declining trends among young injectors halt in the late 1990s', *Epidemiology and Infection* 128 (3), pp. 473–7.

Iguchi, M. Y. (1998), 'Drug abuse treatment as HIV prevention: changes in social drug use patterns might also reduce risk', *Journal of Addictive Diseases* 17 (4), pp. 9–18.

Ingold, F. R. and Ingold, S. (1989), 'The effects of the liberalization of syringe sales on the behavior of intravenous drug users in France', *Bulletin on Narcotics* 41, pp. 67–81.

Islam, M. M. and Conigrave, K. M. (2007), 'Assessing the role of syringe dispensing machines and mobile van outlets in reaching hard-to-reach and high-risk groups of injecting drug users (IDUs): a review', *Harm Reduction Journal* 4 (14), DOI: 10.1186/1477-7517-4-14.

Jacob, J. and Stöver, H. (1997), 'Clean needles for Saxon prisoners', *Prison Report* Spring, pp. 22–3.

Jacob, J. and Stöver, H. (2000), 'Drug use, drug control, and drug services in German prisons: contradictions, insufficiencies and innovative approaches', in Shewan, D. and Davies, J. (eds), *Drug use and prisons: an international perspective*, Overseas Publishers Association, Amsterdam, pp. 57–87.

Jacob, J., Rottman, J. and Stöver, H. (1999), *Entstehung und Praxis eines Gesundheitsraumangebotes für Drogenkonsumierende. Abschlußbericht der einjährigen Evaluation des 'drop-in Fixpunkt'*, Hannover, Bibliotheks und Informationssystem der Universität Oldenburg, Oldenburg.

Jones, L., Pickering, L., Sumnall, H., McVeigh, J. and Bellis, M. A. (2008), *A review of the effectiveness and cost-effectiveness of needle and syringe programmes for injecting drug users*, Centre for Public Health, John Moores University, Liverpool.

Käll , K., Hermansson, U., Amundsen, E. J. and Ronnback, S. (2007), 'The effectiveness of needle exchange programmes for HIV prevention: a critical review', *Journal of Global Drug Policy and Practice* 1. Available at http://www.globaldrugpolicy.org/1/3/1.php (accessed 20 October 2009).

Keene, J., Stimson, G. V., Jones, S. and Parry-Langdon, N. (1993), 'Evaluation of syringe-exchange for HIV prevention among injecting drug users in rural and urban areas of Wales', *Addiction* 88 (8), pp. 1063–70.

Kelly, M., Swann, C., Killoran, A., et al. (2002), *Methodological problems in constructing the evidence base in public health*, Health Development Agency, London.

Kerr, T., Tyndall, M., Li, K., Montaner, J. and Wood, E. (2005), 'Safer injection facility use and syringe sharing in injection drug users', *Lancet* 366 (9482), pp. 316–18.

Kerr, T., Kimber, J., De Beck, K. and Wood, E. (2007), 'The role of safer injection facilities in the response to HIV/AIDS among injection drug users', Current HIV Reports 4, pp. 158–64.

Kimber, J., Dolan, K., van Beek, I., Hedrich, D. and Zurhold, H. (2003), 'Drug consumption facilities: an update since 2000', Drug and Alcohol Review 22, pp. 227–33.

King, V. L., Kidorf, M. S., Stoller, K. B. and Brooner, R. K. (2000), 'Influence of psychiatric comorbidity on HIV risk behaviors: changes during drug abuse treatment', Journal of Addictive Diseases 19 (4), pp. 65–83.

Klee, H. and Morris, J. (1995), 'The role of needle exchanges in modifying sharing behaviour: cross-study comparisons 1989–1993', Addiction 90 (12), pp. 1635–45.

Klee, H., Faugier, J., Hayes, C. and Morris, J. (1991), 'The sharing of injecting equipment among drug users attending prescribing clinics and those using needle-exchanges', British Journal of Addiction 86, pp. 217–23.

Kwiatkowski, C. F. and Booth, R. E. (2001), 'Methadone maintenance as HIV risk reduction with street-recruited injecting drug users', Journal of Acquired Immune Deficiency Syndromes 26 (5), pp. 483–9.

Lamden, K. H., Kennedy, N., Beeching, N. J., et al. (1998), 'Hepatitis B and hepatitis C virus infections: risk factors among drug users in northwest England', Journal of Infection 37 (3), pp. 260–9.

Linssen, L., de Jong, W. and Wolf, J. (2000), Gebruiksruimten: Een systematisch overzicht van de voorziening en de effecten ervan, Trimbos-Instituut, ontwikkelcentrum Social Verslavingsbeleid, Utrecht.

Ljungberg, B., Christensson, B., Tunving, K., et al. (1991), 'HIV prevention among injecting drug users: three years of experience from a syringe exchange program in Sweden', Journal of Acquired Immune Deficiency Syndromes 4 (9), pp. 890–5.

Longshore, D., Hsieh, S., Danila, B. and Anglin, M. D. (1993), 'Methadone maintenance and syringe sharing', International Journal of the Addictions 29, pp. 983–96.

Longshore, D., Bluthenthal, R. N. and Stein, M. D. (2001), 'Needle exchange program attendance and injection risk in Providence, Rhode Island', AIDS Education and Prevention 13 (1), pp. 78–90.

Lott, D., Strain, E. C., Brooner, R., Bigelow, G. and Johnson, R. (2006), 'HIV risk behaviours during pharmacologic treatment for opioid dependence: a comparison of levomethadyl acetate hydrochloride, buprenorphine, and methadone', Journal of Substance Abuse Treatment 31 (2), pp. 187–94.

Lurie, P. (1997), 'Invited commentary: le mystere de Montreal', American Journal of Epidemiology 146 (12), pp. 1003–6; discussion pp. 1007–10.

McAuley, A., Lindsay, G., Woods, M. and Louttit, D. (2009), 'Responsible management and use of a personal take-home naloxone supply: a pilot project', Drugs: Education Prevention and Policy, DOI: 10.1080/09687630802530712.

MacDonald, M. A., Wodak, A. D., Dolan, K. A., et al. (2000), 'Hepatitis C virus antibody prevalence among injecting drug users at selected needle and syringe programs in Australia, 1995–1997: collaboration of Australian NSPs', Medical Journal of Australia 172 (2), pp. 57–61.

MacDonald, M., Law, M. G., Kaldor, J. M., Hales, J. and Dore, G. J. (2003), 'Effectiveness of needle and syringe programmes for preventing HIV transmission', International Journal of Drug Policy 14 (5–6), pp. 353–7.

McGregor, C., Ali, R., Lokan, R., Christie, P. and Darke, S. (2002), 'Accidental fatalities among heroin users in South Australia, 1994–1997: toxicological findings and circumstances of death', Addiction Research and Theory, pp. 335–46.

Magura, S., Siddiqui, Q., Shapiro, J., et al. (1991), 'Outcomes of an AIDS prevention program for methadone patients', *International Journal of the Addictions* 26 (6), pp. 629–55.

Magura, S., Nwakeze, P. and Demsky, S. (1998), 'Pre-and in-treatment predictors of retention in methadone treatment using survival analysis', *Addiction* 93 (1), pp. 51–60.

Maher, L., Jalaludin, B., Chant, K. G., et al. (2006), 'Incidence and risk factors for hepatitis C seroconversion in injecting drug users in Australia', *Addiction* 101 (10), pp. 1499–508.

Mansson, A. S., Moestrup, T., Nordenfelt, E. and Widell, A. (2000), 'Continued transmission of hepatitis B and C viruses, but no transmission of human immunodeficiency virus among intravenous drug users participating in a syringe/needle exchange program', *Scandinavian Journal of Infectious Diseases* 32 (3), pp. 253–8.

Margolin, A., Avants, S. K., Warburton, L. A., Hawkins, K. A. and Shi, J. (2003), 'A randomized clinical trial of a manual-guided risk reduction intervention for HIV-positive injection drug users', *Health Psychology* 22 (2), pp. 223–8.

Mark, H. D., Nanda, J., Davis-Vogel, A., et al. (2006), 'Profiles of self-reported HIV-risk behaviours among injection drug users in methadone maintenance treatment, detoxification, and needle exchange programs', *Public Health Nursing* 23 (1), pp. 11–19.

Marsch, L. A., Bickel, W. K., Badger, G. J. and Jacobs, E. A. (2005), 'Buprenorphine treatment for opioid dependence: the relative efficacy of daily, twice and thrice weekly dosing', *Drug and Alcohol Dependence* 77 (2), pp. 195–204.

Mathers, B. M., Degenhardt, L., Wiessing, L., et al. (2008), 'Global epidemiology of injecting drug use and HIV among people who inject drugs: a systematic review', *Lancet* 372 (9651), pp. 1733–45.

Maxwell, S., Bigg, D., Stanczykiewicz, K. and Carlberg-Racich, S. (2006), 'Prescribing naloxone to actively injecting heroin users: a program to reduce heroin overdose deaths', *Journal of Addictive Diseases* 25 (3), pp. 89–96.

Meandzija, B., O'Connor, P. G., Fitzgerald, B., Rounsaville, B. J. and Kosten, T. R. (1994), 'HIV infection and cocaine use in methadone maintained and untreated intravenous drug users', *Drug and Alcohol Dependence* 36 (2), pp. 109–13.

Meijer, G., de Jong, A., Koeter, M. and Bieleman, B. (2001), *Gebruik van de straat: Evaluatie gebruiksruimte binnenstad-Zuid Groningen*, INTRAVAL, Groningen-Rotterdam.

Metzger, D. S., Woody, G. E., McLellan, A. T., et al. (1993), 'Human immunodeficiency virus seroconversion among intravenous drug users in- and out-of-treatment: an 18-month prospective follow-up', *Journal of Acquired Immune Deficiency Syndromes* 6 (9), pp. 1049–56.

Meyeno, C., Zulaica, D. and Parras, F. (2000), 'Prisons: needle exchange programmes in prisons in Spain', *Canadian HIV/AIDS Policy & Law Newsletter* 5, pp. 20–21.

Miller, C. L., Wood, E., Spittal, P. M., et al. (2004), 'The future face of coinfection: prevalence and incidence of HIV and hepatitis C virus coinfection among young injection drug users', *Journal of Acquired Immune Deficiency Syndromes* 36 (2), pp. 743–9.

Milloy, M. and Wood, E. (2009), 'Emerging role of supervised injecting facilities in human immunodeficiency virus prevention', *Addiction* 104 (4), pp. 620–1.

Millson, P., Myers, T., Calzavara, L., et al. (2003), 'Regional variation in HIV prevalence and risk behaviours in Ontario injection drug users (IDU)', *Canadian Journal of Public Health* 94, pp. 431–5.

Minder Nejedly, M. and Bürki, C. M. (1996), *Monitoring HIV risk behaviours in a street agency with injection room in Switzerland*, Medizinischen Fakultät, Universität Bern, Bern.

Moher, D., Schulz, K., Altman, D. and CONSORT Group (2001), 'The CONSORT statement: revised recommendations for improving the quality of reports of parallel-group randomised trials', *Lancet* 357 pp. 1191–4.

Monterroso, E. R., Hamburger, M. E., Vlahov, D., et al. (2000), 'Prevention of HIV infection in street-recruited injection drug users: the Collaborative Injection Drug User Study (CIDUS)', *Journal of Acquired Immune Deficiency Syndromes* 25 (1), pp. 63–70.

Moss, A. R., Vranizan, K., Gorter, R., et al. (1994), 'HIV seroconversion in intravenous drug users in San Francisco, 1985–1990', *AIDS* 8 (2), pp. 223–31.

MSIC Evaluation Committee (2003), *Final report of the evaluation of the Sydney Medically Supervised Injecting Centre*, University of New South Wales, Sydney.

National Treatment Agency (2009), 'Life saving kits to be given to families of injecting drug users in groundbreaking scheme'. Available at http://www.nta.nhs.uk/media/media_releases/2009_media_releases/ life_saving_kits_to_be_given_to_families_of_injecting_drug_users.aspx.

Nelles, J., Dobler-Mikola, A. and Kaufmann, B. (1997), 'Provision of syringes and prescription of heroin in prison: the Swiss experience in the prisons of Hindelbank and Oberschongrun,' in Nelles, J. and Fuhrer, A. (eds), *Harm reduction in prison*, Peter Lang, Bern, pp. 239–62.

Nelson, K. E., Vlahov, D., Cohn, S., et al. (1991), 'Human immunodeficiency virus infection in diabetic intravenous drug users', *JAMA* 266 (16), pp. 2259–61.

Novick, D. M., Joseph, H., Croxson, T. S., et al. (1990), 'Absence of antibody to human immunodeficiency virus in long-term, socially rehabilitated methadone maintenance patients', *Archives of Internal Medicine* 150, pp. 97–9.

Obadia, Y., Feronia, I., Perrin, V., Vlahov, D., and Moatti, J. P. (1999), 'Syringe vending machines for injection drug users: an experiment in Marseille, France', *American Journal of Public Health* 89 (12), pp. 1852–4.

Oliver, K. J., Maynard, H., Friedman, S. R. and Des Jarlais, D. C. (1994), 'Behavioral and community impact of the Portland Syringe Exchange Program', paper presented at the Proceedings of a Workshop on Needle Exchange and Bleach Distribution Programs, Washington, DC.

Ouellet, L., Huo, D. and Bailey, S. L. (2004), 'HIV risk practices among needle exchange users and nonusers in Chicago', *Journal of Acquired Immune Deficiency Syndromes* 37 (1), pp. 1187–96.

Palmateer, N., Kimber, J., Hickman, M., et al. (2008), *Evidence for the effectiveness of harm reduction interventions in preventing hepatitis C transmission among injecting drug users*, Prevention Working Groups of the Advisory Council on the Misuse of Drugs and the Hepatitis C Action Plan for Scotland, Glasgow.

Palmateer, N., Kimber, J., Hickman, M., et al. (2010), 'Evidence for the effectiveness of sterile injecting equipment provision in preventing hepatitis C and HIV transmission among injecting drug users: a review of reviews', *Addiction* , DOI:10.1111/j.1360-0443.2009.02888.x.

Paone, D., Des Jarlais, D. C., Caloir, S., et al. (1994), 'New York City syringe exchange: an overview', paper presented at the Proceedings of a Workshop on Needle Exchange and Bleach Distribution Programs, Washington, DC.

Parmar, M. (2008), 'NALoxone InVEstigation (N-ALIVE) pilot randomised controlled trial (RCT)'. Available at http://www.controlled-trials.com/ISRCTN34044390/.

Patrick, D. M., Strathdee, S. A., Archibald, C. P., et al. (1997), 'Determinants of HIV seroconversion in injection drug users during a period of rising prevalence in Vancouver', *International Journal of STD & AIDS* 8 (7), pp. 437–45.

Patrick, D. M., Tyndall, M. W., Cornelisse, P. G., et al. (2001), 'Incidence of hepatitis C virus infection among injection drug users during an outbreak of HIV infection', *Canadian Medical Association Journal* 165 (7), pp. 889–95.

Peak, A., Rana, S., Maharjan, S. H., Jolley, D. and Crofts, N. (1995), 'Declining risk for HIV among injecting drug users in Kathmandu, Nepal: the impact of a harm-reduction programme', *AIDS* 9 (9), pp. 1067–70.

Petticrew, M. (2009), 'Systematic reviews in public health: old chestnuts and new challenges', *Bulletin of the World Health Organization* 87 (3), pp. 163–163A.

Piper, T. M., Stancliff, S., Rudenstine, S., et al. (2008), 'Evaluation of a naloxone distribution and administration program in New York City', *Substance Use and Misuse* 43 (7), pp. 858–70.

Poschadel, S., Höger, R., Schnitzler, J. and Schreckenberger, D. (2003), *Evaluation der Arbeit der Drogenkonsumräume in der Bundesrepublik Deutschland: Endbericht im Auftrag des Bundesministeriums für Gesundheit*, Nomos-Verlags-Gesellschaft, Baden-Baden.

Poser, W., Koc, J. and Ehrenreich, H. (1995), 'Methadone maintenance treatment', *British Medical Journal* 310, pp. 463.

Pouget, E. R., Deren, S., Fuller, C. M., et al. (2005), 'Receptive syringe sharing among injection drug users in Harlem and the Bronx during the New York State Expanded Syringe Access Demonstration Program', *Journal of Acquired Immune Deficiency Syndromes* 39 (4), pp. 471–7.

Power, R. and Nozhkina, N. (2002), 'The value of process evaluation in sustaining HIV harm reduction in the Russian Federation', *AIDS* 16 (2), pp. 303–04.

Reitox (2008), 'National reports to the EMCDDA on new developments, trends and in-depth information on selected issues', EMCDDA. Available at http://www.emcdda.europa.eu/publications/searchresults?action=list&type=PUBLICATIONS&SERIES_PUB=w203.

Reyes Fuentes, V. C. (2003), *15 Jahre Fixerraum Bern. Auswirkungen auf soziale und medizinische Aspekte bei Drogenabhängigen*, University of Bern, Bern.

Rezza, G., Sagliocca, L., Zaccarelli, M., et al. (1996), 'Incidence rate and risk factors for HCV seroconversion among injecting drug users in an area with low HIV seroprevalence', *Scandinavian Journal of Infectious Diseases* 28 (1), pp. 27–9.

Rhoades, H., Creson, D., Elk, R., Schmitz, J. and Grabowski, J. (1998), 'Retention, HIV risk, and illicit drug use during treatment: methadone dose and visit frequency', *American Journal of Public Health* 88, pp. 34–9.

Richard, A. J., Mosier, V. and Atkinson, J. S. (2002), 'New syringe acquisition and multi-person use of syringes among illegal drug users', *Journal of Public Health Policy* 23 (3), pp. 324–43.

Ronco, C., Spuhler, G., Coda, P. and Schopfer, R. (1996), 'Evaluation der Gassenzimmer I, II und III in Basel', *Sozial und Praventivmedizin* 41, pp. S58–S68.

Roy, E., Alary, M., Morissette, C., et al. (2007), 'High hepatitis C virus prevalence and incidence among Canadian intravenous drug users', *International Journal of STD and AIDS* 18 (1), pp. 23–7.

Sackett, D. L., Rosenberg, J., Muir Gray, J. A., Haynes, R. B. and Richardson, W. S. (1996), 'Evidence based medicine: what it is and what it isn't', *British Medical Journal* 312, pp. 71–2.

Sarkar, K., Mitra, S., Bal, B., Chakraborty, S. and Bhattacharya, S. K. (2003), 'Rapid spread of hepatitis C and needle exchange programme in Kolkata, India', *Lancet* 361 (9365), pp. 1301–2.

Saxon, A., Calsyn, D. and Jackson, T. (1994), 'Longitudinal changes in injection behaviors in a cohort of injection drug users', *Addiction* 89, pp. 191–202.

Schechter, M. T., Strathdee, S. A., Cornelisse, P. G., et al. (1999), 'Do needle exchange programmes increase the spread of HIV among injection drug users? An investigation of the Vancouver outbreak', *AIDS* 13 (6), pp. F45–51.

Schoenbaum, E. E., Hartel, D. M. and Gourevitch, M. N. (1996), 'Needle exchange use among a cohort of injecting drug users', *AIDS* 10 (14), pp. 1729–34.

Schroeder, J., Epstein, D., Umbricht, A. and Preston, K. (2006), 'Changes in HIV risk behaviours among patients receiving combined pharmacological and behavioral interventions for heroin and cocaine dependence', *Addictive Behaviors* 31 (5), pp. 868–79.

Seal, K. H., Thawley, R., Gee, L., et al. (2005), 'Naloxone distribution and cardiopulmonary resuscitation training for injection drug users to prevent heroin overdose death: a pilot intervention study', *Journal of Urban Health* 82 (2), pp. 303–11.

Sees, K. L., Delucchi, K. L., Masson, C., et al. (2000), 'Methadone maintenance vs 180-day psychosocially enriched detoxification for treatment of opioid dependence: a randomized controlled trial', *JAMA* 283 (10), pp. 1303–10.

Selvey, L. A., Denton, M. and Plant, A. J. (1997), 'Incidence and prevalence of hepatitis C among clients of a Brisbane methadone clinic: factors influencing hepatitis C serostatus', *Australian and New Zealand Journal of Public Health* 21 (1), pp. 102–04.

Serpelloni, G., Carrieri, M. P., Rezza, G., et al. (1994), 'Methadone treatment as a determinant of HIV risk reduction among injecting drug users: a nested case-control study', *AIDS Care* 6 (2), pp. 215–20.

Sherman, S. G., Gann, D. S., Tobin, K. E., et al. (2009), '"The life they save may be mine": diffusion of overdose prevention information from a city sponsored programme', *International Journal of Drug Policy* 20 (2), pp. 137–42.

Shore, R., Marmor, M., Titus, S. and Des Jarlais, D. (1996), 'Methadone maintenance and other factors associated with intraindividual temporal trends in injection drug use', *Journal of Substance Abuse Treatment* 13, pp. 241–8.

Simpson, D. D., Joe, G. W., Rowan-Szal, G. and Greener, J. (1995), 'Client engagement and change during drug abuse treatment', *Journal of Substance Abuse* 7 (1), pp. 117–34.

Singer, M., Himmelgreen, D., Weeks, M. R., Radda, K. E. and Martinez, R. (1997), 'Changing the environment of AIDS risk: findings on syringe exchange and pharmacy sales of syringes in Hartford, CT', *Medical Anthropology* 18 (1), pp. 107–30.

Small, D. (2007), 'Fools rush in where angels fear to tread: playing God with Vancouver's supervised injection facility in the political borderland', *International Journal of Drug Policy* 18 (1), pp. 18–26.

Smyth, B. P., Keenan, E. and O'Connor, J. J. (1999), 'Evaluation of the impact of Dublin's expanded harm reduction programme on prevalence of hepatitis C among short-term injecting drug users', *Journal of Epidemiology and Community Health* 53 (7), pp. 434–5.

Somaini, B., Wang, J. and Persozo, M. (2000), 'A continuing concern: HIV and hepatitis testing and prevalence among drug users in substitution programmes in Switzerland', *AIDS Care* 12, pp. 449–60.

Sorensen, J. L. and Copeland, A. L. (2000), 'Drug abuse treatment as an HIV prevention strategy: a review', *Drug and Alcohol Dependence* 59 (1), pp. 17–31.

Sporer, K. A. (2003), 'Strategies for preventing heroin overdose', *British Medical Journal* 326 (7386), pp. 442–44.

Stallwitz, A. and Stöver, H. (2007), 'The impact of substitution treatment in prisons: a literature review', *International Journal Drug Policy* 18 (6), pp. 464–74.

Stark, K., Herrmann, U., Ehrhardt, S. and Bienzle, U. (2006), 'A syringe exchange programme in prison as prevention strategy against HIV infection and hepatitis B and C in Berlin, Germany', *Epidemiology and Infection* 134 (4), pp. 814–19.

Stark, K., Muller, R., Bienzle, U. and Guggenmoos-Holzmann, I. (1996), 'Methadone maintenance treatment and HIV risk-taking behaviour among injecting drug users in Berlin', *Journal of Epidemiology and Community Health* 50 (5), pp. 534–7.

Stevens, A., Stöver, H. and Brentari, C. (2010), 'Criminal justice approaches to harm reduction in Europe', in European Monitoring Centre for Drugs and Drug Addiction (EMCDDA), *Harm reduction: evidence, impacts and challenges*, Rhodes, T. and Hedrich, D. (eds), Scientific Monograph Series No. 10, Publications Office of the European Union, Luxembourg.

Stoltz, J. A., Wood, E., Small, W., et al. (2007), 'Changes in injecting practices associated with the use of a medically supervised safer injection facility', *Journal of Public Health (Oxford)* 29 (1), pp. 35–9.

Stöver, H. and Nelles, J. (2003), 'Ten years of experience with needle and syringe exchange programmes in European prisons', *International Journal of Drug Policy* 14 (5–6), pp. 437–44.

Strang, J., Marsden, J., Cummins, M., et al. (2000), 'Randomized trial of supervised injectable versus oral methadone maintenance: report of feasibility and 6-month outcome', *Addiction* 95 (11), pp. 1631–45.

Strang, J., Manning, V., Mayet, S., et al. (2008), 'Overdose training and take-home naloxone for opiate users: prospective cohort study of impact on knowledge and attitudes and subsequent management of overdoses', *Addiction* 103 (10), pp. 1648–57.

Strathdee, S. A., Patrick, D. M., Currie, S. L., et al. (1997), 'Needle exchange is not enough: lessons from the Vancouver injecting drug use study', *AIDS* 11 (8), pp. F59–65.

Taylor, A., Goldberg, D., Hutchinson, S., et al. (2000), 'Prevalence of hepatitis C virus infection among injecting drug users in Glasgow 1990–1996: are current harm reduction strategies working?' *Journal of Infection* 40 (2), pp. 176–83.

Teeson, M., Ross, J., Darke, S., et al. (2006), 'One year outcomes for heroin dependence: findings from the Australian Treatment Outcome Study (ATOS)', *Drug and Alcohol Dependence* 83 (2), pp. 174–80.

Thiede, H., Hagan, H. and Murrill, C. S. (2000), 'Methadone treatment and HIV and hepatitis B and C risk reduction among injectors in the Seattle area', *Journal of Urban Health* 77 (3), pp. 331–45.

Tilson, H., Aramrattana, A., Bozzette, S., et al. (2007), 'Preventing HIV infection among injecting drug users in high risk countries: an assessment of the evidence', *Institute of Medicine*, Washington, DC.

Tobin, K. E., Sherman, S., Beilenson, P., Welsh, C. and Latkin, C. A. (2009), 'Evaluation of the Staying Alive programme: training injection drug users to properly administer naloxone and save lives', *International Journal of Drug Policy* 20 (2), pp. 131–6.

Valente, T., Foreman, R. K., Junge, B. and Vlahov, D. (2001), 'Needle-exchange participation effectiveness and policy: syringe relay, gender, and the paradox of public health', *Journal of Urban Health* 78, pp. 340–9.

van Ameijden, E. J. and Coutinho, R. A. (1998), 'Maximum impact of HIV prevention measures targeted at injecting drug users', *AIDS* 12 (6), pp. 625–33.

van Ameijden, E. J., van den Hoek, J. A., van Haastrecht, H. J. and Coutinho, R. A. (1992), 'The harm reduction approach and risk factors for human immunodeficiency virus (HIV) seroconversion in injecting drug users, Amsterdam', *American Journal of Epidemiology* 136 (2), pp. 236–43.

van Ameijden, E. J., van den Hoek, J. A., Mientjes, G. H. and Coutinho, R. A. (1993), 'A longitudinal study on the incidence and transmission patterns of HIV, HBV and HCV infection among drug users in Amsterdam', *European Journal of Epidemiology* 9 (3), pp. 255–62.

van Ameijden, E. J., van den Hoek, A. R. and Coutinho, R. A. (1994), 'Injecting risk behavior among drug users in Amsterdam, 1986 to 1992, and its relationship to AIDS prevention programs', *American Journal of Public Health* 84 (2), pp. 275–81.

van Ameijden, E. J., Langendam, M. W. and Coutinho, R. A. (1999), 'Dose-effect relationship between overdose mortality and prescribed methadone dosage in low-threshold maintenance programs', *Addictive Behaviours* 24 (4), pp. 559–63.

van den Berg, C., Smit, C., van Brussel, G., Coutinho, R. A. and Prins, M. (2007), 'Full participation in harm reduction programmes is associated with decreased risk for human immunodeficiency virus and hepatitis C virus: evidence from the Amsterdam Cohort Studies among drug users', *Addiction* 102, pp. 1454–62.

van den Hoek, J. A., van Haastrecht, H. J. and Coutinho, R. A. (1989), 'Risk reduction among intravenous drug users in Amsterdam under the influence of AIDS', *American Journal of Public Health* 79 (10), pp. 1355–7.

van der Poel, A., Barendregt, C. and van de Mheen, D. (2003), 'Drug consumption rooms in Rotterdam: an explorative description', *European Addiction Research* 9, pp. 94–100.

Vazirian, M., Nassirimanesh, B., Zamani, S., et al. (2005), 'Needle and syringe sharing practices of injecting drug users participating in an outreach HIV prevention program in Tehran, Iran: a cross-sectional study', *Harm Reduction Journal* 2, p. 19.

Vertefeuille, J., Marx, M. A., Waimar, T., et al. (2000), 'Decline in self-reported high-risk injection-related behaviors among HIV-seropositive participants in the Baltimore needle exchange program', *AIDS and Behavior* 4 (4), pp. 381–8.

Vickerman, P., Hickman, M., Rhodes, T. and Watts, C. (2006), 'Model projections on the required coverage of syringe distribution to prevent HIV epidemics among injecting drug users', *Journal of Acquired Immune Deficiency Syndromes* 42 (3), pp. 355–61.

Villanueva, M. G. (2002), 'Programa de Intercambia de Jeringuillas en el Centre Penitenciario de Pamplona', *Rev Esp Sanid Penit* 4, pp. 18–23.

Vlahov, D., Junge, B., Brookmeyer, R., et al. (1997), 'Reductions in high-risk drug use behaviors among participants in the Baltimore needle exchange program', *Journal of Acquired Immune Deficiency Syndromes and Human Retrovirology* 16 (5), pp. 400–06.

Wagner, K., Valente, T., Casanova, M., et al. (in press), 'Evaluation of an overdose prevention and response training programme for injection drug users in the Skid Row area of Los Angeles, CA', *International Journal of Drug Policy,* DOI: 10.1016/j.drugpo.2009.01.003.

Ward, J., Mattick, R. P. and Hall, W. (1997), *Methadone maintenance treatment and other opioid replacement therapies,* Harwood Academic Press, Amsterdam.

Watters, J. (1994), 'Syringe and needle exchange as HIV/AIDS prevention for injecting drug users', *Journal of the American Medical Association* 271, pp. 115–20.

WHO (World Health Organization) (2007), *Guide to starting and managing needle and syringe programmes,* World Health Organization, Geneva.

WHO, UNAIDS (Joint United Nations Programme on HIV/AIDS) and UNODC (United Nations Office on Drugs and Crime) (2007), *Effectiveness of interventions to manage HIV in prisons: opioid substitution therapies and other drug dependence treatment,* WHO, Geneva.

Williams, A. B., McNelly, E. A., Williams, A. E. and D'Aquila, R. T. (1992), 'Methadone maintenance treatment and HIV type 1 seroconversion among injecting drug users', *AIDS Care* 4 (1), pp. 35–41.

Wodak, A. and Cooney, A. (2004), *Effectiveness of sterile needle and syringe programming in reducing HIV/AIDS among injecting drug users*, WHO, Geneva.

Wodak, A. and Cooney, A. (2006), 'Do needle syringe programs reduce HIV infection among injecting drug users? A comprehensive review of the international evidence', *Substance Use and Misuse* 41 (6–7), pp. 777–813.

Wood, E., Tyndall, M. W., Spittal, P. M., et al. (2002), 'Factors associated with persistent high-risk syringe sharing in the presence of an established needle exchange programme', *AIDS* 16 (6), pp. 941–3.

Wood, E., Kerr, T., Spittal, P. M., et al. (2003), 'An external evaluation of a peer-run "unsanctioned" syringe exchange program', *Journal of Urban Health* 80 (3), pp. 455–64.

Wood, E., Tyndall, M., Stoltz, J., et al. (2005), 'Factors associated with syringe sharing among users of a medically supervised safer injecting facility', *American Journal of Infectious Diseases* 1 (1), pp. 50–4.

Wood, E., Tyndall, M., Montaner, J., and Kerr, T. (2006), 'Summary of findings from the evaluation of a pilot medically supervised safer injecting facility', *Canadian Medical Association Journal* 175 (11), pp. 1399–404.

Wright, N. M. J. and Tompkins, C. N. E. (2006), 'A review of the evidence for the effectiveness of primary prevention interventions for hepatitis C among injecting drug users', *Harm Reduction Journal* 3 (27), DOI: 10.1186/1477-7517-3-27.

Yancovitz, S., Des Jarlais, D., Peskoe-Peyser, N., et al. (1991), 'A randomised trial of an interim methadone maintenance clinic', *American Journal of Public Health* 81, pp. 1185–91.

Zador, D., Sunjic, S. and Darke, S. (1996), 'Heroin related deaths in New South Wales in 1992: toxicological findings and circumstances', *Medical Journal of Australia* 164, pp. 204–07.

Zurhold, H., Kreuzfeld, N., Degwitz, P. and Verthein, U. (2001), *Drogenkonsumräume: Gesundheitsförderung und Minderung öffentlicher Belastungen in europäischen Grossstädten*, Lambertus, Freiburg.

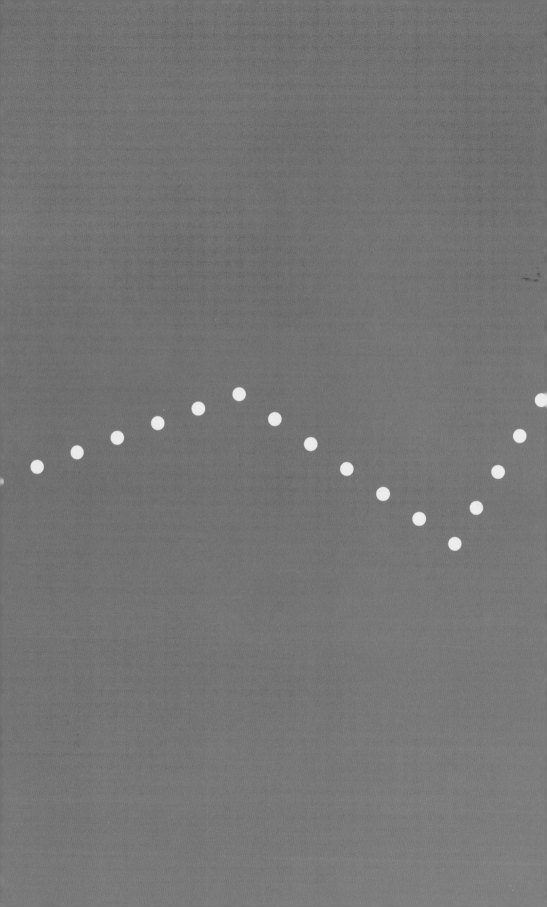

Chapter 6
The effect of epidemiological setting on the impact of harm reduction targeting injecting drug users

Peter Vickerman and Matthew Hickman

Abstract

Hepatitis C (HCV) and HIV cause substantial morbidity and mortality, and are both easily transmitted through contaminated syringes. Although reducing the transmission of HCV and HIV through injecting drug use is critical to preventing both infections, there is little evidence that interventions targeting injecting drug users (IDUs) reduce the transmission of either HIV or HCV.

A recent systematic review suggested a strong positive relationship between the prevalence of HIV and HCV in different IDU populations, but with considerable variability in different settings. This analysis uses a dynamic HIV and HCV transmission model to investigate the possible reasons for these observed trends, and to explore whether HIV and/or HCV prevalence could be used as proxy markers for the relative impact of an IDU intervention in different settings. By varying the HIV and HCV transmission probabilities and other non-setting specific HIV/HCV natural history parameters, a dynamic compartmental model of HIV and HCV transmission was fitted, to observe trends in HIV and HCV prevalence from different settings. Using multivariate linear regression, the output from the 'best-fitting' simulated epidemics was used to identify factors that determine the type of HIV and HCV epidemic that occurs. These simulated epidemics were then used to project the impact of a generic intervention that reduced syringe sharing amongst all IDUs or just low- or high-risk IDUs, and to explore whether the impact projections correlated with HIV and/or HCV prevalence.

Results showed that the relative HCV to HIV transmission probability was the main factor determining how well the model agreed with the observed HIV and HCV prevalence trends. The 'best-fitting' model projections suggest that the relative HIV to HCV prevalence in different epidemic scenarios is positively correlated to the relative proportion of and level of risk behaviour among the high-risk IDUs. Indeed, the projected impact of the generic intervention was also strongly correlated with the baseline HIV and HCV prevalence of the simulated epidemic, with more impact (HIV/HCV infections averted and relative decrease in HIV/HCV incidence) occurring in higher HCV prevalence settings but less impact occurring, except for HIV infections averted, in higher baseline HIV prevalence settings. Lastly, a generic intervention among IDUs had less impact on the HCV epidemic compared to the HIV epidemic in most scenarios. However, when the intervention reached only lower-risk IDUs, it had only little impact on the HIV epidemic and greater impact on the HCV epidemic.

We conclude that the trends and variability in HIV and HCV prevalence observed in different epidemiological settings may be mainly due to differences in the heterogeneity of IDU risk behaviour. The HIV and HCV prevalence in a setting could be proxy markers for the relative impact of an intervention.

Keywords: injecting drug use, HIV, hepatitis C, mathematical modelling.

Introduction

Hepatitis C (HCV) and HIV cause substantial morbidity and mortality. Worldwide, 40 million people are estimated to be infected with HIV (UNAIDS, 2004a) and 170 million with HCV (WHO, 2000a). HCV and HIV can easily be transmitted through contaminated syringes (Baggaley et al., 2006; De Carli et al., 2003), and, while HIV infection rates vary widely (UNAIDS, 2004b), HCV infection rates are often very high amongst injecting drug users (IDUs) (Health Protection Agency, 2004; Wiessing and Nardone, 2006). Similarly to HIV, HCV infection is an important public health concern in Europe and elsewhere, because the majority of HCV infections do not resolve (Micallef et al., 2006) but become chronic and over time lead to cirrhosis of the liver, and possibly liver cancer and death (Limburg, 2004).

A worldwide systematic ecological analysis by the authors has shown that there is a strong positive relationship between the prevalence of HIV and that of HCV in different IDU populations, with the mean HIV prevalence generally being negligible if HCV prevalence is less than 30 % and thereafter increasing linearly with HCV prevalence (Vickerman et al., 2009a). Although this suggests that HCV prevalence could be used as a proxy indicator for injection-related HIV risk, there was substantial variability around the relationship when HCV prevalence is greater than 30 %, suggesting that other factors, such as the stage of the HIV epidemic and heterogeneity in IDU risk behaviour, may also play a role. This variability in HIV and HCV prevalence exists in all world regions, with the HIV prevalence in different European settings varying between 0 % and 70 % (Muga et al., 2007) and the HCV prevalence varying between 2.8 % (Danis et al., 2007) and 98 % (Westh et al., 1993). Overall, HIV prevalence in Europe is low; with high rates of prevalence being found in local studies. Nonetheless, despite this variability, the systematic review suggests that HCV prevalence could be used as a proxy indicator for injection-related HIV risk — and as a target or threshold level to minimise the possibility of an HIV outbreak.

Modelling health harm and its reduction

Reducing the transmission of HCV and HIV through injecting drug use is critical to the overall prevention of these infections in most countries. Epidemiological studies have shown that needle exchange and opioid substitution therapy (OST) interventions can reduce HIV transmission (Gibson et al., 1999; Gibson et al., 2001). However, the evidence for interventions impacting on HCV transmission is modest (Des Jarlais et al., 2005; Goldberg et al., 2001; van den Berg et al., 2007), with only one European study showing that full harm reduction (syringe distribution and OST) can reduce not only HIV incidence by 57 %, but also HCV incidence by 64 % (van den Berg et al., 2007). This lack of evidence is partly due to a relative dearth of epidemiological studies that estimate the impact of IDU interventions on HCV incidence, probably due to their high cost and difficulties in following up 'chaotic' IDUs (Craine et al., 2009). Although it is not the gold standard for evaluating interventions, modelling can play an important role in these difficult situations by translating intermediate intervention outcomes (HIV/HCV prevalence trends and/or even decreases in IDU risk behaviour) into projected decreases in HIV/HCV incidence or number of infections averted. Indeed, modelling can also answer 'what if' questions that would otherwise be very difficult to answer with epidemiological studies.

Numerous model analyses have provided important insights into the potential impact and cost-effectiveness of different intervention strategies for IDUs in Europe, the United States, Eastern Europe, Asia and Australia (Blower et al., 1991; Kaplan and Heimer, 1994; Kretzschmar and Wiessing, 1998; Kretzschmar and Wiessing, 2008; Murray et al., 2003; Vickerman et al., 2006b; Vickerman et al., 2007). However, most studies have focused on HIV, with the small number of HCV modelling analyses being hampered by simplified epidemiology of HCV or IDU risk behaviour, or uncertainty surrounding key behavioural or biological parameters (Kretzschmar and Wiessing, 2004; Murray et al., 2003; Pollack, 2001; Vickerman et al., 2007).

Despite this, a number of analyses have fit HCV models to epidemiological data from one setting (Hutchinson et al., 2006; Murray et al., 2003; Vickerman et al., 2007; Vickerman et al., 2009b), mainly to estimate the impact of changes in syringe distribution/sharing. However, this model fitting strategy may not adequately calibrate an HCV transmission model, because one epidemic profile will contain insufficient information to fully understand the nature of HCV epidemics in other settings. This was emphasised in two studies by the first author of this chapter, which found that very different model parameterisations could accurately fit the HCV prevalence data from London, United Kingdom (Vickerman et al., 2007) or Rawalpindi, Pakistan (Vickerman et al., 2009b).

Few epidemiological or modelling analyses have considered the impact on the transmission of both HIV and HCV of an intervention targeting IDUs (Kwon et al., 2009; Murray et al., 2003; Vickerman et al., 2009b), and none have explored how impact could vary by the extent of baseline HIV and HCV epidemic occurring in a setting. In an attempt to fill this knowledge gap and to reduce the parametric uncertainty around modelling HCV, this analysis uses a joint HIV and HCV transmission mathematical model, fitted to the observed trends between HIV and HCV prevalence, to explore how the impact of a generic intervention (any one that reduces the extent of syringe sharing among IDUs) varies across different epidemiological scenarios. The model's biological parameters are calibrated by determining which set of 'biological parameters' (HIV and HCV transmission and natural history parameters) most accurately produces the observed relationship between HIV and HCV prevalence when IDU behavioural parameters are widely varied to produce different epidemics. The simulated epidemics for this 'biological' parameter set are then used to explore how the impact of a generic intervention varies by HIV and HCV prevalence. More complex 'realistic' interventions (i.e., combinations of interventions, including treatment) were not modelled because it was not the main focus of the study, but impact estimates were made amongst high- and low-frequency syringe sharers in order to understand how targeted IDU interventions may differentially impact on HIV and HCV.

Methods

There were a number of stages to this analysis, many of which built on the work of previous analyses. First, the HIV and HCV transmission mathematical model and different 'biological' parameter sets (includes HIV and HCV transmission probabilities and non-setting specific natural history parameters — see Table 6.1 for all 'biological' parameters) that produced model fits in a recent modelling analysis from a specific IDU population (Vickerman et al., 2009b) were used as the basis for this analysis. For each of the biological parameter sets, an extensive uncertainty analysis was undertaken by randomly sampling specific IDU risk behaviour parameters (see parameters in Table 6.1) to produce 100 different behavioural parameter sets and so 100 different simulated HCV and HIV epidemics. These 100 behavioural parameter sets were chosen so that a wide variety of simulated HIV and HCV epidemics would be produced, and the same behavioural parameter sets were used for each biological parameter set. For each parameter set, the simulated epidemic was run until the overall HCV prevalence among IDUs was stable and the HIV epidemic had run for 30 years. The projected HIV/HCV prevalences were then compared to HIV and HCV prevalence trends for different IDU populations from a systematic review to see which biological parameter set produced the highest proportion of HIV and HCV epidemic projections lying within a defined area containing the vast majority of the paired HIV and HCV prevalence estimates from the systematic review. The 100 runs for this 'best fit' biological parameter set were used to explore how the impact of reducing the frequency of syringe sharing by 50 %, either amongst all IDUs or just among low-frequency (sharing syringes less often than once a week) or high-frequency (sharing syringes at least once a week) syringe sharers, varies for epidemics with different endemic HIV and HCV prevalence. Intervention impact was estimated over three years in terms of HIV and HCV infections averted (per 1 000 IDUs) and the relative decrease in HIV and HCV incidence (defined as the decrease of HIV and, respectively, HCV incidence compared to the baseline incidence).

Table 6.1: **Uncertainty ranges used for 'biological' (HIV and HCV) and behavioural model parameters**

Model parameter	Value used	Data source
HIV 'biological' model parameter		
HIV transmission probability per syringe sharing event	0.14–1.41 %	(Baggaley et al., 2006)
Cofactor increase in HIV transmission probability during initial period of high viraemia	7.5–15	(Pilcher et al., 2004a; Quinn et al., 2000; Wawer et al., 2005)
Pre-AIDS period of high viraemia	3–6	(Wawer et al., 2005)
Duration of initial period of high viraemia	1.5–2.5 months	(Pilcher et al., 2004b; Wawer et al., 2005)
Duration of pre-AIDS period of high viraemia	12–24 months	(Wawer et al., 2005)

Table 6.1 (continued)

Model parameter	Value used	Data source
Median duration until severe morbidity or death	75–92 months	(Grover and Shivraj, 2004; Kumarasamy et al., 2003)
HCV 'biological' model parameter		
HCV transmission probability if HIV negative	1.5–14 %	(Baggaley et al., 2006; De Carli et al., 2003; Vickerman et al., 2009b)
HCV transmission probability if HIV positive relative to if HIV negative	RR of 1.0–3.7	(De Carli et al., 2003; Pappalardo, 2003; Vickerman et al., 2009b; Yazdanpanah et al., 2005)
Duration of HCV acute phase of infection	3–24 months	(Cox et al., 2005; Larghi et al., 2002; Vickerman et al., 2007)
Proportion of HCV infecteds that resolve infection		
Amongst HIV negatives	26 % (20–50 %)	(Micallef et al., 2006)
Amongst HIV positives relative to HIV negatives	RR of 0.21–0.58	(Bonacini et al., 2001; Daar et al., 2001; Grebely et al., 2008; Thomas et al., 2000a)
Proportion of resolved infecteds that become immune		
Amongst HIV negatives	0–100 %	(Currie et al., 2008; Dalgard, 2005; Grebely et al., 2006; Mehta et al., 2002; Micallef et al., 2007)
Amongst HIV positives relative to HIV negatives	RR of 0.3–0.5	Little data (Grebely et al., 2006; Mehta et al., 2002)
Effectiveness of cleaning syringes for disinfecting against HCV (mainly water used)	Assumed same effectiveness as HIV	Little data (Kapadia et al., 2002).
Behavioural model parameters		
Duration inject drugs for	5–15 years	NA
Proportion do not share syringes	0–40 %	NA
Frequency of syringe sharing per month amongst high-frequency syringe sharers	4–60	NA
Frequency of syringe sharing per month amongst low-frequency syringe sharers	<4 (less than once per week)	NA
Proportion of IDUs that share with high frequency	5–60 %	NA
Proportion of IDUs that share with low frequency	remainder	NA

Model derivation

A deterministic compartmental model of HCV and HIV transmission developed for a previously published analysis was used (Vickerman et al., 2009b). In brief, the model simulates the transmission of both HCV and HIV amongst IDUs with different levels of needle/ syringe sharing. The model includes three behavioural subgroups of IDUs depending on whether they do not share needles/syringes (do not inject with a previously used needle/ syringe), or share with a low or high frequency. The model simulates the transmission of HCV/HIV over time and includes two sub-groups for those that are new injectors and those that have been injecting for longer. IDUs leave the population if they cease injecting, die or experience severe HIV-related morbidity.

The HCV transmission model assumes that IDUs enter an acute phase of infection once infected, and either resolve their infection after a number of months or progress to lifelong chronic infection. A proportion of those that resolve HCV are assumed to become immune, and the remainder become susceptible again (Aitken et al., 2008; Currie et al., 2008; Dalgard, 2005; Grebely et al., 2006; Micallef et al., 2007). All infecteds develop an antibody response during their acute phase.

The HIV transmission model assumes that once susceptible individuals are infected they progress to a high viraemia phase of infection, following which they progress to a longer stage of low viraemia, a short period of high viraemia pre-AIDS, and then AIDS. Because the focus of the study was to look at the impact of interventions aiming to reduce injecting risks, the model did not simulate the sexual transmission of HIV.

The HCV and HIV models are run in parallel once the HCV transmission model has reached a stable state without HIV. From that point, the model follows the HIV/HCV co-infection state of each IDU and assumes that being HIV infected exacerbates the effects of being HCV infected, both in terms of the secondary transmission and the natural history of HCV. Because of evidence that HIV infection increases both the HCV viral load in co-infected IDUs (Bonacini et al., 2001; Daar et al., 2001; Fishbein et al., 2006; Thomas et al., 2000b; Thomas et al., 2001) and the probability of mother-to-child HCV transmission (Pappalardo, 2003), the HCV secondary transmission probability was assumed to be heightened in HIV/HCV co-infected IDUs. In addition, it was assumed that the probability that an HCV infection resolves was reduced in HIV/HCV co-infected individuals (Bonacini et al., 2001; Daar et al., 2001; Grebely et al., 2007; Mehta et al., 2002; Thomas et al., 2000a), and so was the probability that they develop immunity against HCV (Grebely et al., 2006; Mehta et al., 2002).

This HIV/HCV prevalence model also has an additional component that incorporates the possible effect of a generic intervention. After a certain time the intervention reduces the frequency of syringe sharing amongst IDUs, regardless of whether they share syringes with a low or high frequency, and affects the epidemiology of HIV and HCV in the modelled population.

Model parameter values used for model fitting

The model was parameterised using different biological parameter sets that produced model fits (n=42) to HIV and HCV prevalence data from a specific IDU population (Vickerman et al., 2009b). These parameter sets were obtained during a rigorous fitting process that also sampled across the uncertainty ranges for the behavioural parameters from that setting. The behavioural parameters were mainly obtained from an in-depth survey undertaken in the setting. The 42 biological model parameter sets were from a total of 400 non-setting specific parameter sets that were randomly sampled from parameter uncertainty ranges during the model fitting process. The parameter uncertainty ranges for the biological parameters were obtained from the literature, and included such aspects as the HIV and HCV transmission probabilities, the duration of the HCV acute phase, and proportion of HCV infecteds that resolve infection. See Table 6.1 for the biological parameters and their uncertainty ranges. All parameters had similar ranges amongst the model fits from the previous analysis, except for the HIV and HCV transmission probabilities, which had the ranges of 0.34–1.4 % and 1.5–5.0 %, respectively.

One hundred behavioural parameter sets were randomly sampled from the behavioural parameter uncertainty ranges in Table 6.1, and these parameter sets were used to

Figure 6.1: Weighted HIV and HCV prevalence data from 310 different IDU populations including the defined region for determining whether a model simulation is a model fit or not

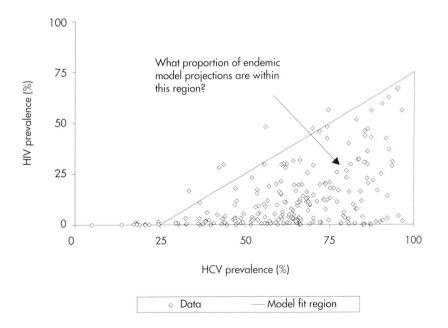

simulate 100 different HIV and HCV epidemics for each biological parameter set. Each epidemic was run until the HCV prevalence changed by <0.05 % in one year and then the HIV epidemic was run for 30 years. The ranges for each behavioural parameter were set to allow the model to produce a wide range of different HIV and HCV epidemics.

For each biological parameter set, the 100 model simulations were compared against collated HIV and HCV prevalence data from different IDU cross-sectional surveys found by our systematic review (Vickerman et. al, 2009a) (see Figure 6.1). This systematic review obtained weighted HIV and HCV prevalence estimates for 310 different IDU populations from peer reviewed journal articles, international AIDS conference abstracts between 2000–08, the European IDU HIV/HCV database (managed by the European Monitoring Centre for Drugs and Drug Addiction) (EMCDDA, 2008), United Kingdom unlinked prevalence monitoring programme (managed by the Health Protection Agency) (Health Protection Agency, 2008), and WHO Multi-City Drug Injection Study Phase II (WHO, 2000b). A model simulation was defined as a fit to the collated HIV/HCV prevalence data if the last time point of the model simulation projected an HIV and HCV prevalence within the region surrounded by a bolded triangle shown in Figure 6.1. The percentage of model runs that were model fits for a particular biological parameter set was used to evaluate its goodness of fit. The model projections for the best-fitting biological parameter set were also validated against available HIV and HCV incidence data from different IDU populations (obtained through a non-systematic literature review) to confirm that the model produced a similar relationship between HIV/HCV incidence and HIV/HCV prevalence.

Intervention impact projections

The biological parameter set with the best goodness of fit was used to explore how the impact of a 50 % reduction in the frequency of syringe sharing will vary by endemic HIV and HCV prevalence in different epidemic settings. A 50 % reduction in syringe sharing was chosen for illustrative purposes, but this figure also reflects an upper bound estimate for what can be achieved with intensive needle and syringe distribution (Foss et al., 2007; Hutchinson et al., 2006). The impact of the intervention was estimated in terms of HIV/HCV infections averted (per 1 000 IDUs) and the relative decrease in HIV/HCV incidence over three years. Scatter plots, partial correlation coefficients and linear regression models (with 'impact' as the independent variable and HIV and HCV prevalence as the dependent variables) were used to assess the relationship between the variables, and the R-squared statistic was used to determine the strength of the association.

Insights from model fitting process

The percentage of model simulations for each biological parameter set that gave endemic HIV and HCV prevalence projections within the bounded area in Figure 6.1 varied widely from 0 % to 78 %. Interestingly, the goodness of fit was largely dependent on the factor difference between the HIV and HCV transmission rate (defined as Ω), with a greater percentage of simulations lying within the bounded area as Ω increases (Figure 6.2). This suggests that the HCV transmission probability must be over three, or potentially even four to five times greater than the HIV transmission probability. Figure 6.2 also shows that one biological parameter set had a much better goodness of fit than the others, with 78 % of the model projections within the bounded area compared to 54 % for the next best-fitting biological parameter set. This biological parameter set was defined as the 'best fit' and was used in the impact analysis.

Figure 6.2: Relationship between the factor difference in the HCV and HIV transmission probabilities and the percentage of model simulations that lie within the bounded area in Figure 6.1

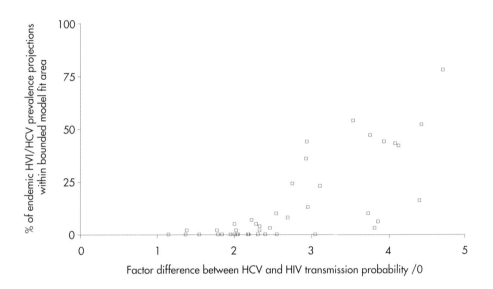

A comparison of available HIV/HCV prevalence and incidence data with the model projections from the best-fitting biological parameter set is shown in Figures 6.3a and b. They show that the model mimics the data reasonably well, except for settings with high HCV prevalence but low HIV prevalence, that is, a low ratio of HIV prevalence to HCV prevalence. This could be due to the model not incorporating enough heterogeneity in risk behaviour, or HIV being more compartmentalised in specific IDU networks, or just the fact that we only included the final time point of the model's projection of HIV and HCV prevalence for each epidemic in the comparison. Including all the model projections over time for each epidemic results in many more lower HIV prevalence projections (result not shown), and the existing model projections also suggest that decreasing the proportion and/or syringe sharing frequency of the high-frequency syringe sharers results in a lower HIV prevalence relative to HCV prevalence (Figure 6.4).

Figure 6.3: Comparison with data of the HIV/HCV prevalence and incidence projections for the 'best fit' biological parameter set

Figure 6.3a: Comparison with HIV/HCV prevalence data

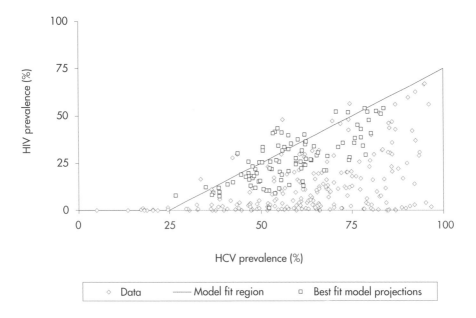

Figure 6.3b: Comparison with HIV/HCV incidence data

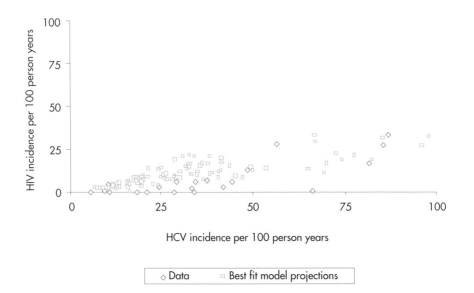

Figure 6.4a: Relationship between relative HIV to HCV prevalence and the proportion of high-risk syringe-sharing IDUs

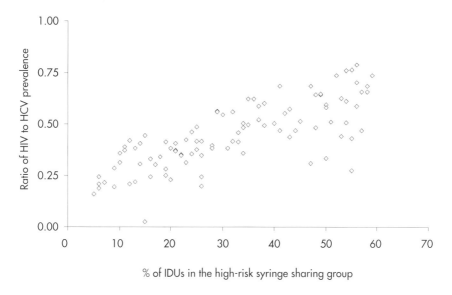

% of IDUs in the high-risk syringe sharing group

Figure 6.4b: Relationship between relative HIV to HCV prevalence and syringe-sharing frequency of high-risk syringe-sharing IDUs

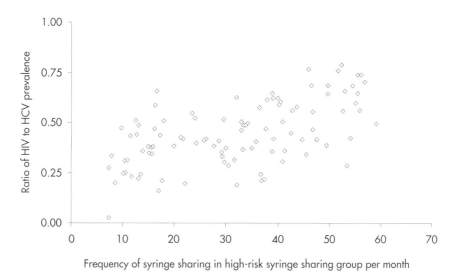

Frequency of syringe sharing in high-risk syringe sharing group per month

Intervention impact projections: overall projections

Figure 6.5 shows that the projected HIV and HCV infections averted due to a 50 % reduction in syringe sharing frequency amongst all IDUs is highly variable, although a similar range of impact projections are obtained for each infection. The number of HIV infections averted is positively correlated with baseline HIV and HCV prevalence and the number of HCV infections averted is negatively correlated with baseline HIV prevalence, but positively correlated with baseline HCV prevalence. These correlations are maintained when the partial correlation coefficients are estimated (see Table 6.2), while controlling for the prevalence of the other infection, with the corresponding linear regression models explaining 50–60 % ($R2=0.5-0.6$) of the variance in the model projections.

Figure 6.5a: Scatter plot to show the relationship between HIV infections averted (per 1 000 IDUs) and HIV prevalence

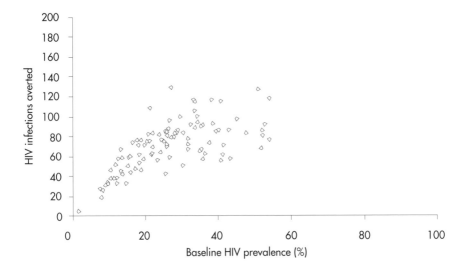

Figure 6.5b: Scatter plot to show the relationship between HIV infections averted (per 1 000 IDUs) and HCV prevalence

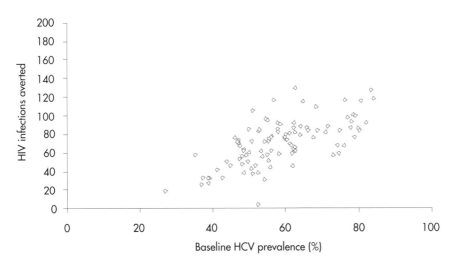

Figure 6.5c: Relationship between HCV infections averted (per 1 000 IDUs) and HIV prevalence

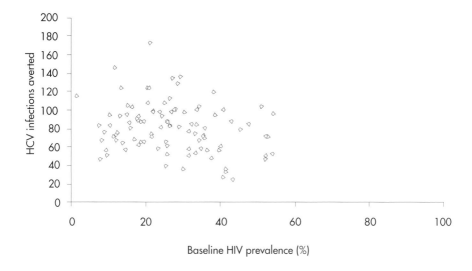

Figure 6.5d: Relationship between HCV infections averted (per 1 000 IDUs) and HCV prevalence

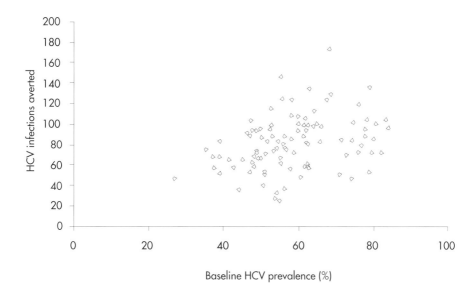

Table 6.2: **Partial correlation coefficients and regression parameters for the relationship between two different measures of intervention impact (HIV and HCV infections averted or relative decrease in HIV and HCV incidence) and baseline HIV and HCV prevalence**

		Partial correlation † with		Linear regression coefficient † with		
		HCV prevalence	HIV prevalence	HCV prevalence	HIV prevalence	R2
Infections averted	HIV	0.33 ↑	0.35 ↑	73.0 ↑	77.3 ↑	0.50
	HCV	0.76 ↑	−0.74 ↓	235.7 ↑	−222.5 ↓	0.60
Relative decrease in incidence	HIV	0.60 ↑	−0.73 ↓	0.81 ↑	−1.15 ↓	0.53
	HCV	0.91 ↑	−0.93 ↓	0.98 ↑	−1.17 ↓	0.87

Notes:

† all partial correlation coefficients and regression coefficients are significant to $p<0.001$.

↑ signifies a positive correlation with that variable and ↓ signifies a negative correlation with that variable.

Similar associations are seen for the relative decrease in HIV or HCV incidence due to the intervention, with both being positively correlated with baseline HCV prevalence and negatively correlated with baseline HIV prevalence. However, although the regression model for the relative decrease in HIV incidence has a similar R2, the regression model for the relative decrease in HCV incidence is a much better fit, explaining 87 % of the variance. The box below explains the implications of these results.

Implications of regression coefficients relating intervention impact projections to baseline HIV and HCV prevalence

For every 10 % increase in baseline HIV prevalence:

- the post-intervention reduction in HIV and HCV incidence decreases by ~12 %;
- the number of HIV infections averted over three years increases by ~8 per 1 000 IDUs reached (which translates to a 10–14 % increase in the number of HIV infections averted if the baseline HIV prevalence was 20 %);
- the number of HCV infections averted over three years decreases by ~22 per 1 000 IDUs (which translates to a 33–50 % decrease if the baseline HCV prevalence was 50 %).

For every 10 % increase in baseline HCV prevalence:

- the post-intervention reduction in HIV incidence increases by 8 % and that of HCV incidence by 10 %;
- the number of HIV infections averted over three years increases by ~7 per 1 000 IDUs reached (which translates to a 10–14 % increase in the number of HIV infections averted if HIV prevalence was 20 %);
- The number of HCV infections averted increases by about ~24 per 1 000 IDUs (which translates to a 33–50 % increase if the baseline HCV prevalence was 50 %).

The existence of these associations is due to the relative HIV prevalence (compared to HCV) being a measure of the proportion and syringe sharing frequency of the high-risk IDUs (Figure 6.4). To attain high HIV prevalence, a larger proportion of IDUs who frequently share syringes is necessary, and so it becomes harder to avert HCV infections and reduce the HIV and HCV incidence because IDUs become re-infected frequently. This effect is not observed in the HIV infections averted because the force of infection (the rate at which susceptible individuals become infected) for HIV is much lower than that for HCV, with the reduced impact on HIV incidence being offset by the higher baseline HIV incidence.

Figure 6.6 suggests that the relative HIV prevalence could be a good predictor of the relative number of HIV vs. HCV infections averted by an intervention. For example, if HIV prevalence is 25 % of HCV prevalence then the model suggests that 40–60 % fewer HIV than HCV infections will be averted, whereas if HIV prevalence is 75 % of HCV prevalence then >50 % more HIV than HCV infections will be averted.

These results occur because the relative HIV to HCV prevalence in a stable epidemic is a measure of relative proportion and level of risk behaviour of the high-risk IDUs. For a low relative HIV prevalence to HCV prevalence, the IDU population must have a smaller and/or 'less risky' high-risk group with lower HIV incidence, and so fewer HIV cases but more HCV cases are averted because fewer of the HCV incident infections are amongst very high-risk IDUs with a high re-infection rate. For a high relative HIV prevalence, the IDU population must have a larger and/or 'more risky' high-risk group with higher HIV incidence, and so more HIV cases but fewer HCV cases are averted because more HCV incident infections are amongst the high-risk IDUs that frequently get re-infected.

Figure 6.6: The model's projected relationship between the relative HIV prevalence compared to HCV prevalence and the relative number of HIV infections averted compared to HCV infections averted

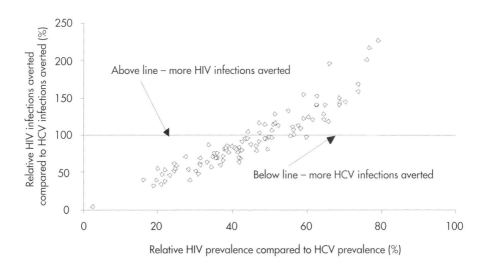

Intervention impact projections: effect of targeting IDUs

Figure 6.7 shows that the targeting of an intervention among IDUs to only those IDUs that have a low- or high-frequency of syringe sharing could have substantial implications for the impact of an intervention. If the intervention just reaches the higher-risk IDUs then a greater impact on HIV transmission can be expected, whereas if the intervention just reaches the lower-risk IDUs then a much greater impact on HCV transmission should be expected. Indeed, little to no decrease in HIV incidence should be expected in this latter case because most HIV transmission occurs amongst the higher-risk IDUs.

Figure 6.7: The model's projected impact on HIV compared to HCV for an intervention that either reaches all IDUs, or just lower- or higher-risk IDUs

Figure 6.7a: Impact on HIV and HCV incidence

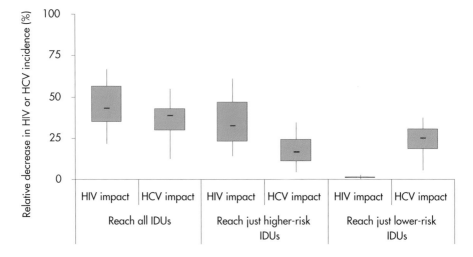

Figure 6.7b: Impact on HIV or HCV infections averted

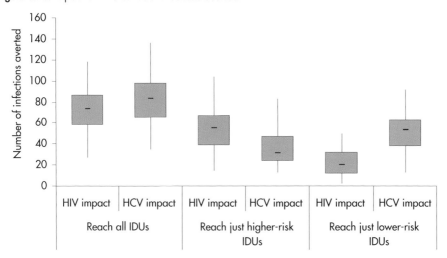

Figure 6.7c: Relative impact on HIV compared to HCV

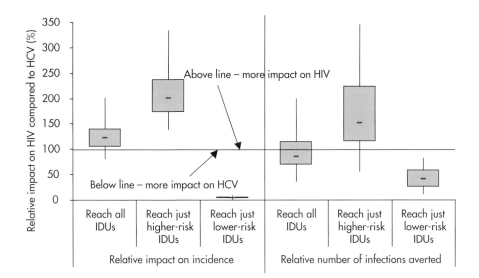

Discussion

This study extensively fit a mathematical model to observed trends between HIV and HCV prevalence in different IDU populations in Europe and beyond. Through fitting the model to a wide range of different joint HIV and HCV epidemics, we were able to explore why different HIV and HCV prevalence trends occur in different settings, project how the impact of an intervention targeting IDUs may vary for different epidemiological settings, and how the impact of the intervention on HCV transmission may compare to the impact on HIV transmission. In addition, as a by-product of the fitting process, estimates for the relative transmissibility of HCV relative to HIV were also produced.

This model analysis should be seen as a significant improvement upon previous modelling analyses because of the effort made to ensure that the model mimics a wide range of observed HIV/HCV epidemics. Indeed, through undertaking this novel method of model fitting, an analysis of the different best-fitting model simulations suggest that heterogeneity in IDU syringe sharing risk behaviour could be a major determinant for the wide range of HIV and HCV epidemics that occur in IDU populations in different settings, including Europe. If this is the case, then the ratio of HIV to HCV prevalence in a stable epidemic setting could be used as a proxy indicator of the heterogeneity in injecting risk behaviour in that IDU population.

Key messages of this research

1. Heterogeneity in IDU risk behaviour could be a major determinant for the wide range of HIV and HCV epidemics that occur in IDU populations in different settings.

2. Model projections suggest that greater intervention impact (more infections averted and greater decrease in incidence) should be expected in higher HCV prevalence settings and less impact in higher HIV prevalence settings, except for the number of HIV infections averted, which increases with HIV prevalence.

3. An intervention will generally result in greater impact on an HIV epidemic than on an HCV epidemic, in terms of either infections averted or relative decreases in incidence. However, when the intervention reaches only lower-risk IDUs, it has only little impact on the HIV epidemic and greater impact on the HCV epidemic.

4. The ratio of HIV to HCV prevalence in a stable epidemic setting could be used as a proxy indicator of the heterogeneity in injecting risk behaviour in an IDU population, and the relative number of HIV and HCV infections that would be averted by an intervention.

Relative impact of intervention in different epidemiological settings

As would be expected, our results show that the number of infections averted by a specific intervention will be highly dependent on the characteristics of the epidemic occurring in a setting. However, our results also highlight that the relative reduction in HIV or HCV incidence attained by an intervention can vary by six fold depending on the type of epidemic occurring. Importantly, the projections imply that the number of infections averted and the associated relative decrease in incidence are both strongly related to the HIV and HCV prevalence in a setting. Generally, greater impact (more infections averted and greater decrease in incidence) is achieved in higher HCV prevalence settings and less impact is achieved in higher HIV prevalence settings, except for the number of HIV infections averted, which increases with HIV prevalence.

These results suggest that the highest impact in terms of reducing HIV/HCV incidence and averting HCV infections should be expected at very high HCV prevalence (>70 %) but low HIV prevalence (<10 %), such as has been recorded in some settings in Belgium, Greece, Ireland or Italy. In contrast, the greatest impact in terms of HIV infections averted occurs at high HIV prevalence (>50 %) as occurs in some settings in Ukraine or Belarus (Vickerman et al., 2006b; Vickerman and Watts, 2002). These results highlight that policymakers should not expect interventions to result in the same impact on incidence, or in the same number of infections averted when initiated in different settings. Indeed, an intervention's cost-effectiveness ratio will vary widely within and between countries, and different coverage levels and reductions in syringe sharing will be required to achieve specific reductions in disease incidence in different settings. This analysis can help in producing these targets and in estimating the relative cost-effectiveness of specific interventions in different settings.

Interestingly, if HIV and HCV infections are considered in a similar light in public health terms, as could be the case in many European settings, then the projections have important implications for how the impact and cost-effectiveness of an intervention is estimated. For example, although less is achieved in reducing HIV/HCV incidence and fewer HCV infections are averted in high HIV prevalence settings, interventions can still have a favourable cost-effectiveness ratio due to many HIV infections being averted. Alternatively, an intervention undertaken in a high HCV but low HIV prevalence setting, as occurs in many European regions, may not be seen as cost-effective if only the cost per HIV infection averted is considered. However, in these settings many more HCV infections will be averted and the intervention is likely to have a large effect on the transmission of both infections. To explore this further, quality-adjusted life year (QALY) weights and HIV and HCV health care costs could be incorporated to give relative weights to the benefits of a HIV or HCV infection averted, so that the cost-effectiveness of different interventions can be compared in different epidemiological settings depending on the level of care provided in that country.

HIV and HCV impact of targeting low- or high-risk IDUs

When the HIV and HCV impact projections are compared further, they suggest that an intervention will generally result in greater decreases in HIV incidence than HCV incidence. This is especially true if the intervention mainly reaches higher-risk IDUs, and highlights that greater coverage and reductions in risk behaviour will frequently be required by interventions to achieve a comparable impact on HCV incidence as well as HIV incidence. This trend also occurs, and is more pronounced, when we look at the relative decrease in HIV or HCV prevalence (results not shown). This has important implications for harm reduction interventions because it suggests that much more needs to be done if the objective of the intervention is a decrease in HCV transmission.

Limitations of analysis

The analysis was limited in a number of ways. First, it used a limited number of biological parameter sets from a previous analysis as the basis for the fitting process. This may have limited the number of model fits that we found and so there may be more uncertainty around our impact projections. The model was only fit against HIV and HCV prevalence trends. A different parameter set may have produced a better fit to other ecological data, such as trends in HIV/HCV co-infection. Behavioural data was not used in the fitting process, and so it was difficult to determine whether the behavioural parameters used would produce similar epidemics in real life. In addition, the transmission of HIV through sexual contact was not incorporated in the model. Although HIV transmission through injecting risk behaviours is likely to dominate in most situations, sexual transmission could play a substantial role in settings where the HIV prevalence is already high but injecting risk behaviours have decreased in recent years. This could affect the relationship not only between HIV and HCV prevalence, but also, and most likely, between HIV incidence and HIV prevalence or HIV incidence and HCV incidence.

Only one intervention was considered in the impact analysis and so it is impossible to determine how the results would vary for other interventions. The impact analysis also assumed the HIV and HCV epidemics were in a stable state. Importantly, epidemics in the exponential or early epidemic stage would have resulted in different impact projections. Lastly, the model was deterministic and did not incorporate the effects on transmission of different syringe sharing behaviours within different risk networks. These more complex syringe sharing structures may affect the prevalence of HIV and HCV in different ways, possibly restricting HIV in small IDU sub-networks, and so could explain the reason why the current model structure was not able to predict very low HIV prevalences with high HCV prevalences. The effect of these complexities on our projections will be explored in future analyses involving more complex models.

Concluding remarks

This analysis used a novel technique to fit a joint HIV/HCV model to HIV and HCV prevalence data from diverse epidemic types, many of which were from European settings. This enabled the model to explore the impact of interventions in different epidemic settings, with the results suggesting that HIV and HCV prevalence could be used as predictors of intervention impact in different settings, including Europe. However, the study should be seen as preliminary because a limited number of 'biological' parameter sets (HIV and HCV transmission probabilities and natural history parameters) were used in the fitting and the model was only fit to HIV/HCV prevalence trends. In addition, the analysis did not explore the impact of interventions such as opioid substitution treatment (OST), HCV and/or HIV antiviral treatments, and/or combined interventions, which may be essential for resulting in large reductions in HIV/HCV incidence in some settings. This has recently been highlighted by a study looking at the long-term impact of intervention activities in Amsterdam (van den Berg et al., 2007), and will be the focus of future work where sufficient attention can be given to subtleties such as how increasing the coverage of OST may increase the coverage of syringe distribution to IDUs on and off OST, and how the behaviour of IDUs may revert after leaving OST. In addition, previous analyses have suggested that reducing the number of people that an IDU shares needles/syringes with and the time that IDUs are initially reached by harm reduction interventions are both important for determining the impact of a harm reduction intervention. These will also be explored further in future analyses.

Acknowledgements

Peter Vickerman designed the study, developed the model, undertook all analyses and wrote the first draft of the chapter. Matthew Hickman contributed to the study concept, helped with interpreting the results, and contributed to writing the manuscript. Tim Rhodes and V. Anna Gyarmathy helped edit the chapter. The views expressed are those of the authors and cannot be taken to reflect the official opinions of the London School of Hygiene and Tropical Medicine. Financial support was provided from a Medical Research Council New Investigators award (held by P.V.) and the European Monitoring Centre for Drugs and Drug Addiction. Lastly, grateful thanks goes to Lucas Wiessing and all contributors to the EMCDDA HIV and HCV prevalence database, which was highly useful for providing data for the meta-analysis used in this model analysis.

References

Aitken, C. K., Tracy, S. L., Revill, P., et al. (2008), 'Consecutive infections and clearances of different hepatitis C virus genotypes in an injecting drug user', *Journal of Clinical Virology* 41, pp. 293–6.

Baggaley, R. F., Boily, M. C., White, R. G., and Alary, M. (2006), 'Risk of HIV-1 transmission for parenteral exposure and blood transfusion: a systematic review and meta-analysis', *AIDS* 20, pp. 805–12.

Blower, S. M., Hartel, D., Dowlatabadi, H., Anderson, R. M. and May, R. M. (1991), 'Drugs, sex and HIV: a mathematical model for New York City', *Philosophical Transactions of the Royal Society B: Biological Sciences* 331, pp. 171–87.

Bonacini, M., Lin, H. J. and Hollinger, F. B. (2001), 'Effect of coexisting HIV-1 infection on the diagnosis and evaluation of hepatitis C virus', *Journal of Acquired Immune Deficiency Syndromes* 26, pp. 340–4.

Cox, A. L., Netski, D. M., Mosbruger, T., et al. (2005), 'Prospective evaluation of community-acquired acute-phase hepatitis C virus infection', *Clinical Infectious Diseases* 40, pp. 951–8.

Craine, N., Hickman, M., Parry, J. V., et al. (2009), 'Incidence of hepatitis C in drug injectors: the role of homelessness, opiate substitution treatment, equipment sharing, and community size', *Epidemiology and Infection* 137 (9), pp. 1255–65.

Currie, S. L., Ryan, J. C., Tracy, D., et al. (2008), 'A prospective study to examine persistent HCV reinfection in injection drug users who have previously cleared the virus', *Drug and Alcohol Dependence* 93, pp. 148–54.

Daar, E. S., Lynn, H., Donfield, S., et al. (2001), 'Relation between HIV-1 and hepatitis C viral load in patients with hemophilia', *Journal of Acquired Immune Deficiency Syndromes* 26, pp. 466–72.

Dalgard, O. (2005), 'Follow-up studies of treatment for hepatitis C virus infection among injection drug users', *Clinical Infectious Diseases* 40 (Supplement 5), pp. S336–S338.

Danis, K., Doherty, L., McCartney, M., McCarrol, J. and Kennedy, H. (2007), 'Hepatitis and HIV in Northern Ireland prisons: a cross-sectional study', *Eurosurveillance* 12, pp. 9–12.

De Carli, G., Puro, V. and Ippolito, G. (2003), 'Risk of hepatitis C virus transmission following percutaneous exposure in healthcare workers', *Infection* 31 (Supplement 2), pp. 22–7.

Des Jarlais, D. C., Perlis, T., Arasteh, K., et al. (2005), 'Reductions in hepatitis C virus and HIV infections among injecting drug users in New York City, 1990–2001', *AIDS* 19 (Supplement 3), pp. S20–S25.

EMCDDA (2008), *Annual report 2008: the state of the drugs problem in the European Union*, European Monitoring Centre for Drugs and Drug Addiction, Lisbon. Available at http://www.emcdda.europa.eu/publications/annual-report/2008.

Fishbein, D. A., Lo, Y., Netski, D., Thomas, D. L. and Klein, R. S. (2006), 'Predictors of hepatitis C virus RNA levels in a prospective cohort study of drug users', *Journal of Acquired Immune Deficiency Syndromes* 41, pp. 471–6.

Foss, A. M., Watts, C. H., Vickerman, P., et al. (2007), 'Could the CARE-SHAKTI intervention for injecting drug users be maintaining the low HIV prevalence in Dhaka, Bangladesh?' *Addiction* 102, pp. 114–25.

Gibson, D. R., Flynn, N. M. and McCarthy, J. J. (1999), 'Effectiveness of methadone treatment in reducing HIV risk behavior and HIV seroconversion among injecting drug users', *Aids* 13, pp. 1807–18.

Gibson, D. R., Flynn, N. and Perales, D. (2001), 'Effectiveness of syringe exchange programs in reducing HIV risk behavior and HIV seroconversion among injecting drug users', *AIDS* 15, pp. 1329–41.

Goldberg, D., Burns, S., Taylor, A., et al. (2001), 'Trends in HCV prevalence among injecting drug users in Glasgow and Edinburgh during the era of needle/syringe exchange', *Scandinavian Journal of Infectious Diseases* 33, pp. 457–61.

Grebely, J., Conway, B., Raffa, J. D., et al. (2006), 'Hepatitis C virus reinfection in injection drug users', *Hepatology* 44, pp. 1139–45.

Grebely, J., Genoway, K., Khara, M., et al. (2007), 'Treatment uptake and outcomes among current and former injection drug users receiving directly observed therapy within a multidisciplinary group model for the treatment of hepatitis C virus infection', *International Journal of Drug Policy* 18, pp. 437–43.

Grebely, J., Genoway, K. A., Raffa, J. D., et al. (2008), 'Barriers associated with the treatment of hepatitis C virus infection among illicit drug users', *Drug and Alcohol Dependence* 93, pp. 141–7.

Grover, G. and Shivraj, S. O. (2004), 'Survival pattern of reported HIV infected individuals in the city of Delhi (India)', *Journal of Communicable Diseases* 36, pp. 83–92.

Health Protection Agency (2004), *Shooting up: infections among injecting drug users in the United Kingdom 2003*, Health Protection Agency, London.

Health Protection Agency (2008), *Shooting up: infections among injecting drug users in the United Kingdom 2007*, Health Protection Agency, London.

Hutchinson, S., Bird, S., Taylor, A. and Goldberg, D. (2006), 'Modelling the spread of hepatitis C virus infection among injecting drug users in Glasgow: implications for prevention', *International Journal of Drug Policy* 17, pp. 211–21.

Kapadia, F., Vlahov, D., Des Jarlais, D. C., et al. (2002), 'Does bleach disinfection of syringes protect against hepatitis C infection among young adult injection drug users?' *Epidemiology* 13, pp. 738–41.

Kaplan, E. H. and Heimer, R. (1994), 'A circulation theory of needle exchange [editorial]', *AIDS* 8, pp. 567–74.

Kretzschmar, M. and Wiessing, L. G. (1998), 'Modelling the spread of HIV in social networks of injecting drug users', *AIDS* 12, pp. 801–11.

Kretzschmar, M. and Wiessing, L. (2004), 'Modelling the transmission of hepatitis C in injecting drug users', in Jager, J. C., Limburg, W., Kretzschmar, M., Postma, M. J. and Wiessing, L. (eds), *Hepatitis C and injecting drug use: impact, costs and policy options*, European Monitoring Centre for Drugs and Drug Addiction, Lisbon.

Kretzschmar, M. and Wiessing, L. (2008), 'New challenges for mathematical and statistical modeling of HIV and hepatitis C virus in injecting drug users', *Aids* 22, pp. 1527–37.

Kumarasamy, N., Solomon, S., Flanigan, T. P., et al. (2003), 'Natural history of human immunodeficiency virus disease in southern India', *Clinical Infectious Diseases* 36, pp. 79–85.

Kwon, J. A., Iversen, J., Maher, L., Law, M. G. and Wilson, D. P. (2009), 'The impact of needle and syringe programs on HIV and HCV transmissions in injecting drug users in Australia: a model-based analysis', *Journal of Acquired Immune Deficiency Syndromes* 51, pp. 462–9.

Larghi, A., Zuin, M., Crosignani, A., et al. (2002), 'Outcome of an outbreak of acute hepatitis C among healthy volunteers participating in pharmacokinetics studies', *Hepatology* 36, pp. 993–1000.

Limburg, W. (2004), *Natural history, treatment and prevention of hepatitis C in injecting drug users: an overview*, in Jager, J. C., Limburg, W., Kretzschmar, M., Postma, M. J. and Wiessing, L. (eds), *Hepatitis C and injecting drug use: impact, costs and policy options*, European Monitoring Centre for Drugs and Drug Addiction, Lisbon.

Mehta, S. H., Cox, A., Hoover, D. R., et al. (2002), 'Protection against persistence of hepatitis C', *Lancet* 359, pp. 1478–83.

Micallef, J. M., Kaldor, J. and Dore, G. J. (2006), 'Spontaneous viral clearance following acute hepatitis C infection: a systematic review of longitudinal studies', *Journal of Viral Hepatitis* 13, pp. 34–41.

Micallef, J. M., Macdonald, V., Jauncey, M., et al. (2007), 'High incidence of hepatitis C virus reinfection within a cohort of injecting drug users', *Journal of Viral Hepatitis* 14, pp. 413–18.

Muga, R., Langohr, K., Tor, J., et al. (2007), 'Survival of HIV-infected injection drug users (IDUs) in the highly active antiretroviral therapy era, relative to sex- and age-specific survival of HIV-uninfected IDUs', *Clinical Infectious Diseases* 45, pp. 370–6.

Murray, J. M., Law, M. G., Gao, Z. and Kaldor, J. M. (2003), 'The impact of behavioural changes on the prevalence of HIV and hepatitus C among injecting drug users', *International Journal of Epidemiology* 32, pp. 708–14.

Pappalardo, B. L. (2003), 'Influence of maternal human immunodeficiency virus (HIV) co-infection on vertical transmission of hepatitis C virus (HCV): a meta-analysis', *International Journal of Epidemiology* 32, pp. 727–34.

Pilcher, C. D., Price, M. A., Hoffman, I. F., et al. (2004a), 'Frequent detection of acute primary HIV infection in men in Malawi', *AIDS* 18, pp. 517–24.

Pilcher, C. D., Tien, H. C., Eron, J. J., Jr., et al. (2004b), 'Brief but efficient: acute HIV infection and the sexual transmission of HIV', *Journal of Infectious Diseases* 189, pp. 1785–92.

Pollack, H. A. (2001), 'Cost-effectiveness of harm reduction in preventing hepatitis C among injection drug users', *Medical Decision Making* 21, pp. 357–67.

Quinn, T. C., Wawer, M. J., Sewankambo, N., et al. (2000), 'Viral load and heterosexual transmission of human immunodeficiency virus type 1. Rakai Project Study Group', *New England Journal of Medicine* 342, pp. 921–9.

Thomas, D. L., Astemborski, J., Rai, R. M., et al. (2000a), 'The natural history of hepatitis C virus infection: host, viral, and environmental factors', *Jama* 284, pp. 450–6.

Thomas, D. L., Astemborski, J., Vlahov, D., et al. (2000b), 'Determinants of the quantity of hepatitis C virus RNA', *Journal of Infectious Diseases* 181, pp. 844–51.

Thomas, D. L., Rich, J. D., Schuman, P., et al. (2001), 'Multicenter evaluation of hepatitis C RNA levels among female injection drug users', *Journal of Infectious Diseases* 183, pp. 973–6.

UNAIDS (2004a), *AIDS epidemic update*, UNAIDS, Geneva, pp. 1–21.

UNAIDS (2004b), *Report on the global HIV/AIDS epidemic*, UNAIDS, Geneva, pp. 1–225.

van den Berg, C., Smit, C., Van Brussel, G., Coutinho, R. A. and Prins, M. (2007), 'Full participation in harm reduction programmes is associated with decreased risk for human immunodeficiency virus and hepatitis C virus: evidence from the Amsterdam cohort studies among drug users', *Addiction* 102, pp. 1454–62.

Vickerman, P. and Watts, C. H. (2002), 'The impact of an HIV prevention intervention for injecting drug users in Svetlogorsk, Belarus: model predictions', *International Journal of Drug Policy* 13, pp. 149–64.

Vickerman, P., Hickman, M., Rhodes, T. and Watts, C. H. (2006a), 'Model projections on the required coverage of syringe distribution to prevent HIV epidemics among injecting drug users', *Journal of Acquired Immune Deficiency Syndromes* 42, pp. 355–61.

Vickerman, P., Kumaranayake, L., Balakireva, O., et al. (2006b), 'The cost-effectiveness of expanding harm reduction activities for injecting drug users in Odessa, Ukraine', *Sexually Transmitted Diseases* 33 (Supplement), pp. S89–S102.

Vickerman, P., Hickman, M. and Judd, A. (2007), 'Modelling the impact of hepatitis C transmission of reducing syringe sharing: London case study', *International Journal of Epidemiology* 36, pp. 396–405.

Vickerman, P., Hickman, M., May, M., Kretzschmar, M. and Wiessing, L. (2009a), 'Can HCV prevalence be used as a measure of injection-related HIV-risk in populations of injecting drug users? An ecological analysis', *Addiction* 105, pp. 311–18.

Vickerman, P., Platt, L. and Hawkes, S. (2009b), 'Modelling the transmission of HIV and HCV amongst injecting drug users in Rawalpindi, a low HCV prevalence setting in Pakistan', *Sexually Transmitted Infections* 85 (Supplement 2), pp. ii23–30.

Wawer, M. J., Gray, R. H., Sewankambo, N. K., et al. (2005), 'Rates of HIV-1 transmission per coital act, by stage of HIV-1 infection, in Rakai, Uganda', *Journal of Infectious Diseases* 191, pp. 1403–09.

Westh, H., Worm, A. M., Jensen, B. L., et al. (1993), 'Hepatitis C virus antibodies in homosexual men and intravenous drug users in Denmark', *Infection* 21, pp. 115–17.

WHO (World Health Organization) (2000a), *Hepatitis C fact sheet*, WHO, Geneva. Available at http://www.who.int/mediacentre/factsheets/fs164/en/.

WHO (2000b), *WHO drug injecting study — phase II operations manual version 4*, des Jarlais D., Friedman, S. and Perlis, T. (eds), WHO, Geneva, 2000. Available at http://www.who.int/substance_abuse/activities/en/WHODrugInjectionStudyOperationsManual.pdf (accessed 1 October 2008).

Wiessing, L. and Nardone, A. (2006), 'Ongoing HIV and viral hepatitis infections in IDUs across the EU, 2001–2005', *Eurosurveillance* 11, pp. E061123 2.

Yazdanpanah, Y., De Carli, G., Migueres, B., et al. (2005), 'Risk factors for hepatitis C virus transmission to health care workers after occupational exposure: a European case-control study', *Clinical Infectious Diseases* 41, pp. 1423–30.

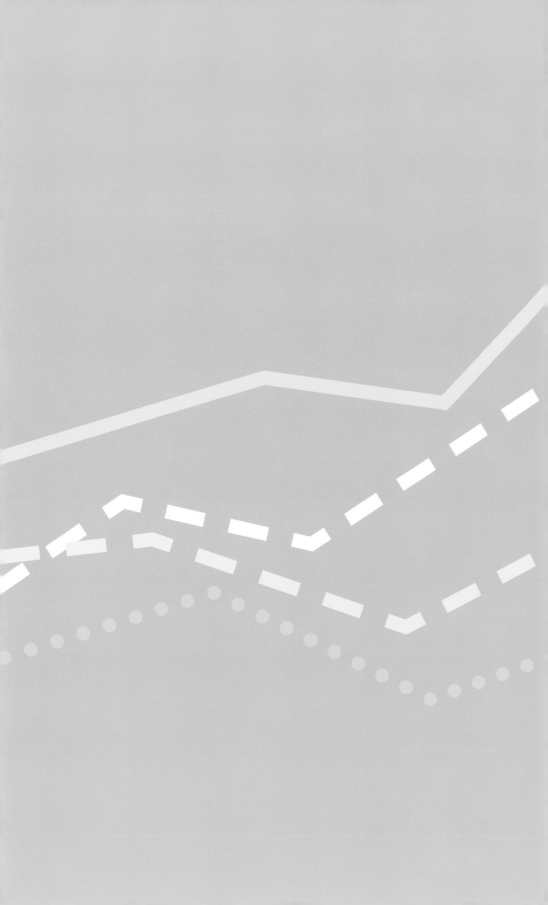

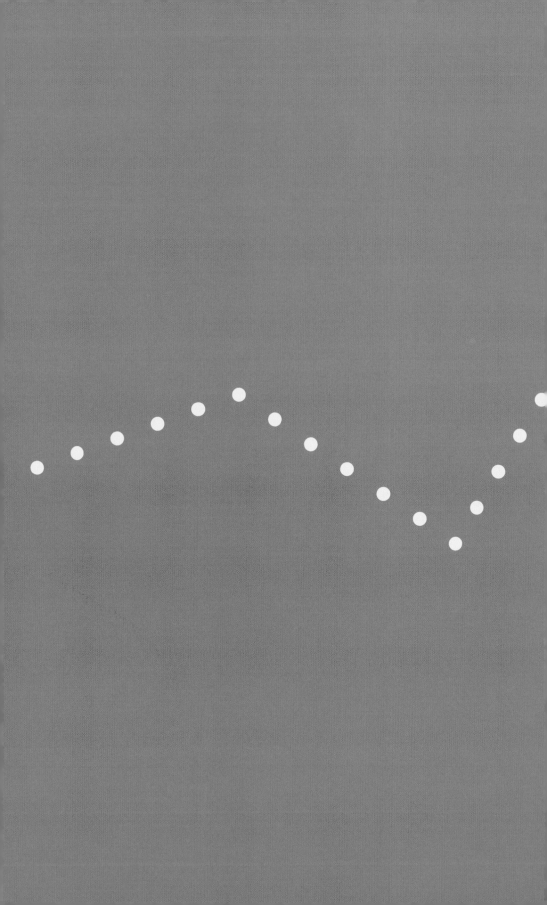

Chapter 7
The fast and furious — cocaine, amphetamines and harm reduction

Jean-Paul Grund, Philip Coffin, Marie Jauffret-Roustide, Minke Dijkstra, Dick de Bruin and Peter Blanken

'The role of the state is not to make people happy but to relieve avoidable suffering.'

(Sir Karl Popper, 1945)

Introduction

Cocaine and amphetamines ('stimulants') are distinct central nervous system stimulants with similar effects (Pleuvry, 2009; Holman, 1994). Cocaine is a crystalline tropane alkaloid extracted from coca leaves. Amphetamines are a subclass of phenylethylamines with primarily stimulant effects, including amphetamine, methamphetamine, methcathinone and cathinone and referred to as 'amphetamines' in this review (Holman, 1994). MDMA (3,4-methylenedioxy-N-methamphetamine or ecstasy) is a substituted amphetamine known for its entactogenic, psychedelic, and stimulant effects (Morgan, 2000). Stimulants can produce increased wakefulness, focus and confidence, elevated mood, feelings of power, and decreased fatigue and appetite; stimulants also produce nervousness or anxiety and, in some cases, psychosis and suicidal thoughts (Holman, 1994; EMCDDA, 2007f; Hildrey et al., 2009; Pates and Riley, 2009). Although there is little evidence that stimulants cause physical dependence, tolerance may develop upon repetitive use and withdrawal may cause discomfort and depression (EMCDDA, 2007f; Pates and Riley, 2009). Users may engage in 'coke or speed binges' alternated with periods of withdrawal and abstinence (Beek et al., 2001).

Epidemiology of stimulant use in the European Union

The European Monitoring Centre for Drugs and Drug Addiction (EMCDDA, 2009) estimates that at least 3.9 % of the total adult population (15–64 years) in European Union (EU) Member States has used cocaine at least once in their lifetime (lifetime prevalence, LTP), but variations in prevalence and patterns are found between countries, demographic and social groups, and specific settings. Higher levels of cocaine use are found in western and southern countries, notably Denmark, Spain, Italy, Ireland and the United Kingdom, with relatively low LTP in most other European countries, ranging from 0.1 % to 8.3 % (EMCDDA, 2009). Cocaine use is concentrated among young adults (15–34 years), with an average LTP of 5.3 %, and more so among young men, with an LTP over 10 % and last year prevalence (LYP) over 5 % in Denmark, Spain, and the United Kingdom (EMCDDA, 2007b). LYP for all EU adults is 1.3 %, ranging from 0 % to 3.1 % by country. LYP among young adults is 2.2 %, ranging from 0.1 % to 5.5 %. Last month prevalence (LMP) for all adults range from 0 % to 1.1 %, two-thirds of whom are young adults (EMCDDA, 2007f).

Cocaine use appears to have increased among young adults since the 1990s and, while prevalence is leveling off or decreasing in many countries (EMCDDA, 2007a), Denmark and Italy report considerable increases as recently as 2005 and Spain, France, Denmark, and the United Kingdom report rapid growth among adults aged 15–24 (EMCDDA, 2007d). Those countries with data on problem cocaine use include Spain, with 4.5 to 6 problem cocaine users per 1 000 adults in 2002, Italy with 2.9 to 4.1 per 1 000 adults in 2005, and England with 5.7 to 6.4 problem crack users per 1 000 adults in 2004/05 (EMCDDA, 2007c).

Cocaine use is elevated in specific social settings and subpopulations, such as nightlife participants with rates from 10 to 60 % (Cohen and Sas, 1993; Cohen and Sas, 1994; Decorte, 2001; EMCDDA, 2007d; Nabben et al., 2007; Grund et al., 2007b; Haasen et al., 2004), sex workers, homeless people, treatment participants and marginalised young adults (EMCDDA, 2007d; Haasen et al., 2004). Largely employed, socially integrated users mostly sniff cocaine and do so occasionally within rather well-defined leisure settings and periods (Prinzleve et al., 2004; Bellis et al., 2003; Cohen and Sas, 1994; Decorte, 2001), with some experiencing periods of often short-lived uncontrolled use (Cohen and Sas, 1994; Decorte, 2001), a finding consistent with laboratory studies in which experienced cocaine users regulate their use (Sughondhabirom et al., 2005). Marginalised users, on the other hand, very often smoke cocaine-base (crack) or inject cocaine, use more frequently and chaotically, and more often use heroin, benzodiazepines or alcohol, while also experiencing a wide array of social-economic and medical problems (Prinzleve et al., 2004; Beek, 2001; Hando et al., 1997).

LTP of amphetamines among EU adults is 3.3 %, ranging from 0.1 % to 11.9 %, with 0.6 % LYP. As with cocaine, more young adults use amphetamines, with 5 % LTP and 1.3 % LYP (EMCDDA, 2008). Amphetamines are more common in nightlife, in particular in specific dance scenes, such as Hardcore, Tekno or Goa (Nabben et al., 2007; Grund et al., 2007b). In contrast to cocaine, amphetamine use is higher in northern, central and eastern parts of the EU, particularly Sweden and Finland, with rising rates among young adults in Austria, Germany, Denmark and southern Italy (Degenhardt et al., 2009). Amphetamine injecting is a long-established problem in the Czech Republic and increasing in Slovakia and Hungary (where methamphetamine use and injection is common) (EMCDDA, 2008; Degenhardt et al., 2009; Griffiths et al., 2008) as well as Estonia and countries across the eastern borders, such as Ukraine, Belarus, Russia and Georgia (Degenhardt et al., 2009; Griffiths et al., 2008; Grund et al., 2009; Grund and Merkinaite, 2009) Users in former Soviet states often produce amphetamine-type stimulants at home (Borodkina et al., 2005; Grund, 2001; Heimer et al., 2007), creating an environment where injecting is common among recreational users, in contrast to western EU countries where a division between integrated (party) and marginalised users of amphetamine seems to exist, similar to that between cocaine snorters and smokers or injectors (Grund, 2001; Grund et al., 2009; Degenhard et al., 2009).

LTP of ecstasy among EU adults is about 3 %, ranging from 0.3 to 7.3 %, with 0.8 % LYP. Among young adults, LTP is 5.6 % and LYP is 1.8 % (EMCDDA, 2008). The geographic diffusion of ecstasy is less clear than that of cocaine and amphetamines, but is associated with diffusion of the electronic dance music culture (House or Techno parties, raves, etc.). Ecstasy is almost exclusively taken orally, most users are well-integrated and few seek treatment barring other drug or alcohol problems (EMCDDA, 2008). Thus, although the potential for harm of ecstasy use is not fictional, the reported burden of harm is very low in the EU compared to those of cocaine and amphetamines. For this reason this review will largely focus on (problem) use of cocaine and amphetamines. Fletcher and colleagues (2010) provide an overview of newly emerging harm reduction interventions aimed at users of ecstasy, amphetamines and other drugs in recreational settings.

In this review we use the term 'stimulant(s)' when discussing cocaine and (meth)amphetamines in general terms. We will use 'cocaine' when discussing this substance in either its salt or base form. 'Smokable cocaine' or colloquial terms like 'crack' will only be used when indicated (as in 'crack pipes'). Note that the term 'crack' is associated with stigma among drug users and some prefer saying they smoke 'free-base', instead of crack. Likewise, we use 'amphetamines' as a much as possible, when discussing amphetamines in general terms and use either 'amphetamine', 'methamphetamine' or '(meth)cathinone' when referring to those specific substances.

Methodology

This review was primarily based on searches in the Medline database for relevant articles. Several search terms were used and generally limited papers to those addressing human subjects and those published after 1990. The overwhelming majority of articles addressed a small number of harms and standardised search terms were unable to identify numerous articles known by the authors to be relevant to risk management among stimulant users. For example, we searched PubMed on 12 October 2008 for clinical trials, metaanalyses, randomised controlled trials, reviews, and practice guidelines involving human subjects with the search terms (cocaine or psychostimulants or amphetamine or methamphetamine) and (health consequences or overdose or cardiac toxicity or HIV or HCV or pregnancy) published after 1990, resulting in 779 papers. After eliminating papers that were not relevant (such as animal studies or medical use of stimulants), there were 287 articles, of which 49 % referred to pregnancy, 21 % to infectious diseases, 10 % to cardiovascular disease, 5 % to neurologic disease, 5 % to other medical problems, 4 % to overdose. Several searches were replicated in World of Science and through university search engines but with few additional relevant papers identified, nor did including more specific search terms related to these topics. A number of articles were identified from authors' previous knowledge and included in the review. With regard to infectious disease, stimulant use and harm reduction, 196 articles were identified in English and French; after examining these articles and selecting a number of other articles, 91 references were included. Only a few peer reviewed publications addressed crack use and harm reduction, and most of these were grey. Mental health issues were investigated in a similar fashion, including a broad search, manual review of the publications, and inclusion of outside sources including published papers, reports, organisational materials, and other grey publications.

Adverse (health) consequences associated with use of stimulants

Key findings

Scientific literature is overwhelmingly weighted toward the harms of stimulants, with minimal literature on harm reduction interventions. Among the myriad of ill health effects associated with stimulants, some are mediated by mode of administration (such as infections, overdose, and pulmonary damage) while others are independent thereof (such as neurologic, cardiovascular and mental health problems). But the distinction between the two categories of stimulant-related harm is subtle and contingent on the broader risk environment. For example:

- Problem stimulant use is associated with poverty, unemployment, homelessness or unstable housing, lower socio-economic status, a variety of other social problems, as well as legal problems and incarceration.
- Adulterants and use of caustic chemicals in drug preparation are stipulated by market conditions beyond the control of individual users.
- Traditional harm reduction programmes may fail to reach problem stimulant users due to opiate-centred services and social barriers to young or female users.
- Innovative service development paired with critical evaluation is necessary in translating the successes of harm reduction for opiates to stimulants.
- There is an important and unmet need for services that enhance the ability of stimulant users to control their intake levels, chaotic behaviour and mental health problems, as well as limit pulmonary, cardiovascular and neurologic harms.
- Stimulant-related harms are aggravated by external factors, such as selected aspects of international drug legislation, policing and public policies in a process of 'contingent causality'.

The risks associated with stimulants include medical harms, such as infectious, cardiovascular, and neurologic and psychiatric morbidity, as well as risks to pregnancy, pulmonary and renal toxicity, overdose and other less common sequelae. Problem stimulant use is also associated with poverty, unemployment, homelessness or unstable housing, lower socio-economic status, a variety of other social problems, as well as legal problems and incarceration. Here we focus primarily on medical health consequences while briefly addressing mental health and other problems associated with stimulant use.

Blood-borne viruses

Transmission of blood-borne viruses is consistently associated with stimulant use (Mitchell et al., 2006), due primarily to high-frequency use and to increased risky sexual behaviors. HIV and hepatitis C (HCV) transmission among stimulant injectors has been associated with higher injecting frequency (Kral et al., 2001; Gibson et al., 2002) and needle sharing (Rotheram-Borus et al., 1999). Frequent cocaine injection is a factor in the failure of selected syringe exchange programmes to prevent HIV transmission (Wood et al., 2002). HCV rates are very high, even among recent initiates to cocaine injection (Maher et al., 2007). In central and eastern Europe, home-produced stimulants such as methcathinone and cathinone are injected up to 10 times daily (Kozlov et al., 2006; Booth et al., 2008; Grund et al., 2009; Chintalova-Dallas et al., 2009) and are associated with increased sexual activity (Kozlov et al., 2006) as well as sharing of equipment in home drug preparation (Grund, 2001; Des Jarlais et al., 2002; Grund and Merkinaite, 2009; Balakireva et al., 2006). In comparison to heroin users, stimulant users are more likely to have unstable social situations, larger drug-using social networks, riskier injection practices (e.g. increased frequency, chaotic drug preparation, injecting in unstable settings) and increased sexual activity (De et al., 2007; Elkashef et al., 2008; Grund et al., 1991b; Kozlov et al., 2006; Chintalova-Dallas et al., 2009; Booth et al., 2008). HCV is also prevalent among non-injection stimulant users, with rates of 2.3–35.3 % among those who sniff or smoke stimulants (Scheinmann et al., 2007) and 2.3–81 % among crack smokers (Fischer et al., 2008; Jauffret-Roustide et al., 2008a; Tortu et al., 2001); many are unaware that they are infected (Roy et al., 2001; Kwiatkowski et al., 2002). Hepatitis B (HBV) infection has also been associated with injection and non-injection drug use (NIDU), although the availability of a vaccine has greatly reduced infection rates (Kottiri et al., 2005). Stimulant use is associated with infrequent condom use (Edlin et al., 1992), amphetamine use preceding sex (Koblin et al., 2006), risk behaviours among young gay men (Celentano et al., 2006), and trading sex for drugs or money (Serraino et al., 1991; Stevens et al., 1998; Tortu et al., 2000; Tortu et al., 2003).

Cocaine smoking is a distinct risk factor for blood-borne virus transmission (Pechansky et al., 2006; Haydon and Fischer, 2005; McCoy et al., 2004; Adimora et al., 2003; Edlin et al., 1994; Chiasson et al., 1991; Haverkos and Steel, 1991), even when adjusted for injection behaviour (Wolff et al., 2007; Osher et al., 2003; Nyamathi et al., 2002; Rosenblum et al., 2001; Roy et al., 2001; Jauffret-Roustide et al., 2006), primarily due to an association with risky sexual behaviour (Hagan et al., 2005; McCoy et al., 2004; Edlin et al., 1994; Lejuez et al., 2005; Campsmith et al., 2000; Gross et al., 2000; Perlman et al., 1999; Word and Bowser, 1997; Centers for Disease Control and Prevention, 1996; Seidman et al., 1994; Edlin et al., 1992), with HIV prevalence estimates from 7.5–23.0 % (Jauffret-Roustide et al., 2006; McCoy et al., 2004; Edlin et al., 1994; Kral et al., 1998; Gyarmathy et al., 2002). Sex work is more frequent among cocaine smokers compared to other drug users (Faruque et al., 1996; Edlin et al., 1994; Campsmith et al., 2000; Fischer et al., 2006; Mehrabadi et al., 2008) and women cocaine smokers are particularly vulnerable as they are exposed to multiple risks associated with both sexual and drug use behaviours, contingent on broader gender relations (Jauffret-Roustide et al., 2008b; Shannon et al., 2008; Maranda et al., 2004; Cotten-Oldenburg et al., 1999; Heffernan et al., 1996; McCoy and Miles, 1992; Balakireva et al., 2006). While sexual transmission of HIV among cocaine smokers is mainly through unprotected intercourse (Haverkos and Steel, 1991), other routes include oral sores and cracked lips from hot pipes in the setting of unprotected fellatio (Faruque et al., 1996; Theall et al., 2003). Recent studies of cocaine smoking and HCV transmission have noted the collective use of glass smoking utensils ('crack pipes' or 'stems') as a potential risk factor. HCV is present in gingival fluid (Suzuki et al., 2005), nasal secretions (McMahon et al., 2004), saliva (Hermida et al., 2002), and crack pipes (Fischer et al., 2008), the last of which are frequently made of glass, metal or other materials that can get extremely hot, have jagged edges, and may break between clenching jaws. Oral sores and burns on lips can result from using these pipes (Ward et al., 2000; Faruque et al., 1996; Porter and Bonilla, 1993) and small blood droplets deposit on the stem of the pipe, possibly transmitting HCV to others with similar sores (Hagan et al., 2005). One study reported that up to 81 % of all cocaine smokers had shared their crack pipes in the previous month (Jauffret-Roustide et al., 2006).

Stimulant use may hasten progression of HIV disease, although data are conflicting. Cocaine use has been associated with poor anti-retroviral initiation and adherence (Brewer et al., 2007), complicated by the interaction of depression, particularly among women (Cook et al., 2007) whose crack use is strongly associated with poor outcomes of HIV disease (Cook et al., 2008). While current or past cocaine use is associated with less favorable laboratory parameters (T cell and viral load) among patients on HIV treatment, past amphetamine use is associated with more favorable parameters (Cofrancesco et al., 2008). Studies of HIV-positive and HIV-negative men who have sex with men demonstrate no change in T cell counts among subjects related to their use of cocaine or amphetamines (Chao et al., 2008), and studies among women showed no difference in CD4 count, viral load, or mortality (Thorpe et al., 2004). References are available to predict possible interactions of HIV medications with illicit drugs (Wynn et al., 2005), but the clinical implication of these interactions remains uncertain (Pal and Mitra, 2006). The hypothesis of a direct immunomodulatory effect of stimulants that could increase vulnerability to HIV and other infections remains unproven (Cabral, 2006).

Other infectious complications

Stimulants have been associated with increased incidence of many sexually transmitted diseases including syphilis, gonorrhea, and chancroid (Bauwens et al., 2002; Friedman et al., 2003; Ross et al., 1999; Ross et al., 2002; Sorvillo et al., 1998; Stoner et al., 2000; Thomas et al., 1996; Centers for Disease Control and Prevention, 1991 and 1993; Chirgwin et al., 1991; Finelli et al., 1993; Martin and DiCarlo, 1994; Oxman et al., 1996; Shuter et al., 1998; Williams and Ekundayo, 2001; Cleghorn et al., 1995), as well as various bacterial infections (Kerr et al., 2005) and tuberculosis (Malakmadze et al., 2005; McElroy et al., 2003). Cocaine use has been independently associated with human papillomavirus infection and progression to cervical lesions (Minkoff et al., 2008). Skin and soft tissue infections (SSTIs) affect 10–30 % of injecting drug users (IDUs) (Binswanger et al., 2000; Murphy et al., 2001; Ciccarone et al., 2001) and are associated with loss of venous access and reliance on intramuscular or subcutaneous injection (Ciccarone and Bourgeois, 2003; Lloyd-Smith et al., 2008; Binswanger et al., 2000). Injecting crack, vint or boltushka (home-made meth-cathinone) is particularly damaging to veins due to the uninformed and unskilled use of chemicals for preparation (Rhodes et al., 2006; Chintalova-Dallas et al., 2009). Jeff or boltushka is injected with large-bore needles that rapidly damage veins. The United Kingdom has recently seen a rise in groin injection, with an estimated 45 % of IDUs in English cities recently injecting into the femoral vein (Maliphant and Scott, 2005; Rhodes et al., 2006). Groin injection has been associated with public use of crack and speedballs and is now common among new initiates and housed IDUs, not just older and homeless users with no other venous access, suggesting a shift from 'risk boundary' to 'acceptable risk' (Rhodes et al., 2006; Rhodes et al., 2007). Cocaine injectors, including women, those with unstable housing, and those who require help injecting, are independently more likely to have SSTIs (Lloyd-Smith et al., 2008).

Shooting Jeff (homemade methcatinone), Pskov, Russia, 1999

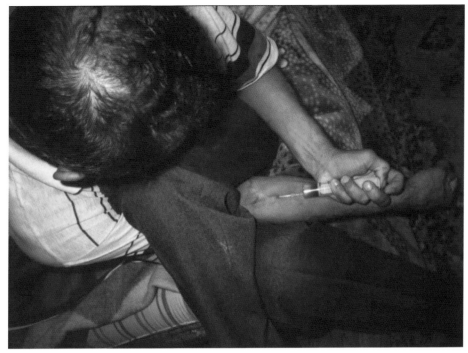

Source: J-P. Grund.

Stimulants are also associated with skin lesions resulting from excessive scratching or picking. Most lesions are not due to delusions, apart from 'Coke Bugs' or 'Meth Mites', which result from the sensation that insects are crawling on or under the skin or that the drug is coming out of the skin. These are hallucinations from prolonged stimulant use and resulting sleep deprivation (Frieden, 2006; Beek et al., 2001; Lee, 2008). Known as delusional parasitosis, this behaviour is associated with MRSA, streptococcal, and polymicrobial SSTIs (Hinkle and Nancy, 2000; Frieden, 2006; Beek et al., 2001; Cohen et al., 2007). Other self-mutilation behaviours observed by outreach workers in Frankfurt include 'working on wounds with giant knives' (primarily males), cutting (primarily females), cigarette burns and excessive fingernail-biting (both sexes) (personal email communication, M. Nickolai, 30 September 2009).

Neurologic effects

Cocaine induces plasticity in the dopaminergic system largely responsible for drug craving, yet the principal neurologic effects of cocaine are related to its cardiovascular effects: strokes, hemorrhages and blood clots. Persistent vasoconstriction may lead to reduced brain perfusion and associated cognitive deficits that may or may not resolve with abstinence (Nnadi et al., 2005). Heavy methamphetamine use also induces dopaminergic plasticity, as well as reduced dopaminergic activity and neuropsychiatric deficits in memory, attention, and executive function (Ferris et al., 2008). Alterations in brain structure and chemistry have been convincingly documented in heavy users of methamphetamine although the clinical implications of these data remain uncertain (Chang et al., 2007). Numerous studies of long-term prescribed amphetamines have failed to demonstrate lasting psychiatric or neurologic deficits, although few are of high quality (Vitiello, 2001). In Central and Eastern Europe, chemical residues of home stimulant production (including potassium permanganate, gasoline, toluene or tetrachlorethylene, sodium hydroxide, or hydrochloric acid) (Grund and Merkinaite, 2009) may have toxic effects and local clinicans have reported 'amphetamine-induced movement disorder' (see e.g. Downes and Whyte, 2005) and declines in cognitive function and memory similar to dementia (Volik, 2008; Chintalova-Dallas et al., 2009). Pseudoephedrine restrictions in the region may have resulted in use of more hazardous precursors such as phenylpropanolamine, associated with hemmorhagic stroke (Horwitz et al., 2000), in production of cathinone (Chintalova-Dallas et al., 2009). In the setting of HIV, stimulants have been associated with more rapid progression of cognitive decline and recent data suggest that stimulants may contribute to HIV-related neuron cell death, particularly within the dopaminergic (Ferris et al., 2008) and hippocampal (Venkatesan et al., 2007) systems (Goodkin et al., 1998; Basso and Bornstein, 2000; Nath et al., 2002; Cadet and Krasnova, 2007; Ferris et al., 2008).

Cardiovascular effects

Cardiovascular toxicities of cocaine are well-established (Vandhuick et al., 2004). Cocaine results in adrenergic activation through effects on norepinephrine and clot formation through activation of platelets, resulting in increased cardiac oxygen demand, coronary artery spasm, and coronary artery thrombosis. 'Cocaine chest pain' is usually not a sign of cardiac ischemia, yet cocaine also increases the risk of true myocardial infarction, aortic dissection, coronary artery dissection, cardiomyopathy, and sudden cardiac death (Steinhauer and Caulfield, 2001; McCord et al., 2008). Injection of any drug is associated with endocarditis (Guerot et al., 2002). Cocaine-induced tachycardia and hypertension play a role in many of these sequelae (Tuncel et al., 2002), accounted for in part by direct reduction in vagal tone (Newlin et al., 2000). Injected cocaine causes a dose-dependent prolongation of the QT segment of the cardiac cycle, raising the risk of potentially fatal arrhythmias (Haigney et al., 2006), particularly among those with genetic predispositions for QT prolongation (Karch, 2005). Overdose of cocaine can result in fatal monomorphic ventricular tachycardia by blocking sodium channels (Bauman and DiDomenico, 2002). Dilated cardiomyopathy may be related to direct toxicity of cocaine through increased programmed death of heart muscle cells (Zhang et al., 1999). Furthermore, prolonged cocaine use accelerates atherosclerosis (Kloner et al., 1992) and accumulation of metabolites in cardiac tissue may have further detrimental effects (Schindler et al., 1995). Clinicians are reluctant to use beta blockers, a key agent in heart disease, to manage cocaine-related disease due to fear of producing unopposed activation of other adrenergic receptors with cocaine (Afonso et al., 2007). Use of alcohol and cocaine together leads to production of cocaethylene, which is believed to increase the cardiotoxic effects of both drugs (Kertesz et al., 2007), increases the tachycardia produced by cocaine, and may increase the tendency toward violent thoughts and threats (Farre et al.,

1997; Pennings et al., 2002). Amphetamines produce substantial increases in blood pressure and heart rate, more marked when the drugs are injected and somewhat buffered among those who also use marijuana (Fleury et al., 2008). Use of ecstasy, amphetamine, and cocaine in a club setting did not result in any excess body temperature compared to use of alcohol and/or cannabis alone; those drugs did, however, result in a relative increase in blood pressure (increase of 40mm Hg systolic) and heart rate (increase of 30 beats/minute) (Mas et al., 1999), perpetuating concerns about possible cardiovascular toxicities (Cole et al., 2005).

Pulmonary and other health effects

Novel interventions: reinventing the 'micro' risk environment

Interventions aimed at reducing harms of cocaine use focus on BBVs and thus on the micro risk environment of drug consumption, providing utensils and practical information for safer use.

Crack kit programmes offer kits that generally include a Pyrex tube, plastic tips, filters, condoms, lip balm, sterile compresses and chewing gum for salivation (Aidslaw, 2007). An evaluation of crack kit distribution in Ottawa (Leonard et al., 2006; Leonard et al., 2007) suggested that sharing of crack pipes decreased dramatically, while crack users reduced injecting and more often smoked cocaine. The Dutch Mainline Foundation offers cocaine information in flyers, on the Internet and on the streets, including a van-based 'health circuit' for cocaine smokers (Boekhout van Solinge, 2001) to check their lung capacity, blood pressure and heart rate. The van is supervised by a trained nurse, providing participatory interaction in which pulmonary and mental health harm reduction and self-regulation strategies are discussed through motivational interviewing techniques (Wittenberg, 2005). Mainline's website and flyers emphasise practical information for managing health risks and controlling cocaine use, including tips for managing coke bugs, the coke shuffle and the urge to scratch (e.g. http://www.cocaineinfo.nl/).

Crack kits are controversial and rarely funded. In Canada and some US cities, crack kits are distributed with regional funding (Small and Drucker, 2008), but some have closed after local opposition (Symington, 2007). At the same time, France is improving access to crack kits (Jauffret-Roustide et al., 2008a) with plans for community-based evaluations. Recent technological developments such as personal vaporisers, similar to E-cigarettes for tobacco smokers, might offer additional opportunities to reduce pulmonary and other bodily harm, as vaporisation and filtering could reduce the amount of combustion products inhaled while offering an acceptable alternative to crack pipes and perhaps even syringes.

Nonetheless, reactive harm reduction measures focused at the micro risk environment of cocaine use do little to mediate the influences in the drug's macro risk environment, upon which risk behaviour and drug related harms are contingent (Rhodes, 2009). This review identifies an important need to apply harm reduction thinking in proactive policymaking towards changing the 'contingent causation' of problem stimulant use with unhealthy drug and social policies and those that influence the public domain.

The most notable pulmonary complication of smoked cocaine, referred to as 'crack lung', is difficult to differentiate from several other associated and life-threatening restrictive, granulomatous, infectious, and hematologic pulmonary diseases and frequently requires open-lung biopsy to diagnose (Terra Filho et al., 2004; Wolff and O'Donnell, 2004). The vasoconstrictor effect of smoked cocaine can also lead to pulmonary hypertension with chronic use (Glauser and Queen, 2007). Asthma exacerbations and eosinophilic pneumonias are also described in relation to inhaled stimulants (Mayaud et al., 2001). Intranasal cocaine use is clearly associated with septal necrosis and perforation (Glauser and Queen, 2007). Use of tobacco is thought to worsen pulmonary outcomes among stimulant smokers or injectors (Wolff and O'Donnell, 2004).

Amphetamine use has been associated with dental disease, although there is dispute as to the degree of destruction that is related to direct toxicity versus diet and personal hygiene (Chi and Milgrom, 2008; Heng et al., 2008). Renal diseases related to stimulants include glomerulonephritites, largely believed to be associated with IDU and contaminants, and tubulointerstitial processes resulting from vasoconstrictive properties in the setting of pre-existing mild renal disease (Crowe et al., 2000; Jaffe and Kimmel, 2006). Uncommon complications include renal infarction and rhabdomyolisis. Concerns with ecstasy use include hyperthermia and rhabdomyolisis with associated renal failure (Hedetoft and Christensen, 1999). Fear of dehydration has led to consumption of large quantities of water that, in individuals without appropriate regulation of antidiuretic hormone, may lead to dilutional hyponatremia and, rarely, death (Crowe et al., 2000). Urinary retention due to bladder neck closure has also been associated with ecstasy use (Crowe et al., 2000). Gastroschesis, or slowed gastric processing of food, has been associated with use of stimulants (Draper et al., 2008), and cocaine use has been associated with intestinal ischemia, likely due to both vasoconstrictor and pro-thrombogenic effects (Glauser and Queen, 2007).

Overdose

Opioids remain the source of most overdose deaths globally, yet in regions such as New York City (Coffin et al., 2003) and Sao Paolo, Brazil (Mesquita et al., 2001), the high prevalence of cocaine use contributes, often in conjunction with opioids, to the majority of overdose deaths. Among cocaine body-packers, overdose can result from the rupture of a container and requires immediate laparotomy for chance of survival (Schaper et al., 2007). Extreme overdose on stimulants can result in profound hyperthermia, with subsequent risks for rhabdomyolisis, seizures, and death (Callaway and Clark, 1994). Overdose on ecstasy without concomitant use of other drugs is notably rare and difficult to define, but may be related to seritonin syndrome (see 'Neurologic effects') (Schifano, 2004). In a survey of all amphetamine-related deaths in Belgium, cardiopulmonary arrest and trauma were the most common direct causes of death, and drug metabolite levels were notably variable (De Letter et al., 2006). Cocaine use is intimately associated with opioid overdose, with combined use of the two drugs substantially increasing the risk of both nonfatal and fatal overdose (Ochoa et al., 2005; Coffin et al., 2003; Coffin et al., 2007). Furthermore, while overdose on opioids is far more likely among IDUs, the rates are closer among injection and non-injection cocaine users (Kaye and Darke, 2004).

Pregnancy and parenting

Stimulant use during pregnancy and parenting has been a major concern, particularly in the United States where fears about a future generation of 'crack babies' inspired legislation and prosecutions against women for stimulant use, marijuana use, or any acts that might be considered risky during pregnancy (Harris and Paltrow, 2003). Risk factors for bad outcomes among drug-using pregnant women include lack of prenatal care, prior premature delivery, and active cigarette smoking (Kuczkowski, 2007; Ness et al., 1999). Cocaine use during pregnancy is more likely than opiates, tobacco, and marijuana to be associated with fetal growth decrements (Schempf, 2007), and is associated with abruptio placenta and premature rupture of membranes; other concerns such as spontaneous abortion, preterm labour, behavioural or developmental disabilities, feeding disturbances, or withdrawal syndromes were confounded by other variables and often better attributed to maternal poverty (Addis et al., 2001). Developmental effects, based on studies utilising vast arrays of tools in an effort to elucidate decrements, remain in doubt by some investigators (Frank et al., 2001), are at most subtle with unclear clinical significance (Lester et al., 2003) and are mediated with educational programmes (Schiller and Allen, 2005). Childhood psychiatric correlates are mediated by psychosocial factors and diminish as children age (Williams and Ross, 2007). There is no risk of direct toxicity to a pregnancy at the time of conception from male cocaine use (Klemmt and Scialli, 2005). A thorough 2005 review of amphetamines and pregnancy found insufficient evidence to evaluate the developmental toxicity of therapeutic amphetamines, with two underpowered cohort studies showing no effect (Golub et al., 2005). Amphetamines have been associated with a 3.5 fold increased risk of fetal growth restriction, while tobacco use had a twofold increased risk (Smith et al., 2006). Early research has demonstrated an association between amphetamine-using mothers and poor perceived quality of life, increased substance use among family and friends, as well as ongoing legal problems (Derauf et al., 2007).

Mental health and social problems

High levels of psychiatric and social comorbidities, in addition to dependence and addiction, are found among chronic stimulant users (Hall et al., 1996; Baker et al., 2004; Darke et al., 2008; Sutcliffe et al., 2009). Chronic amphetamine use is associated with psychosis, usually transient during use or withdrawal but occasionally occuring for several years after discontinuation (Scott et al., 2007). Pre-existing psychotic symptoms can be greatly exacerbated by amphetamine initiation (Hall et al., 1996; Suttcliffe et al., 2009). Stimulant use is also associated with suicide, suicidal ideation, depression, post-traumatic stress disorder, and several personality disorders (Kertesz et al., 2006; Scott et al., 2007). Methamphetamine use has been associated with anti-social personality disorder as well as mania and bipolar mood disorder (Chen et al., 2003). Although methamphetamine has been associated with impulsive or violent behavior, no causal relationship has ever been established (Scott et al., 2007). Compared to cocaine, crack use is associated with higher levels of anxiety, depression paranoia, and psychosis, likely due to intensity of use, physical health, and concurrent social situation rather than route of administration per se (Haasen, 2005). There is a strong association between amphetamine use and attention-deficit hyperactivity disorder (ADHD), which is treated with amphetamine-type medications, leading some investigators to suspect that indviduals with ADHD are drawn to amphetamine use (Jaffe et al., 2005; Scott et al., 2007).

Problem use of stimulants is also associated with social and family problems, including poor interpersonal relationships, child abuse or neglect, job loss, motor vehicle accidents, trading sex for money or drugs, criminal or violent behaviour and homicide (Daley et al., 2002), although convincing causal relationships have not been established. Problem stimulant users are more likely to be unemployed and experience poor coping skills, limited social support, and disorganised lifestyles (Scott et al., 2007), which may play a central role in behavioural problems. Furthermore, the criminal and stigmatised nature of stimulant use, while possibly deterring wider use, serves as a barrier for problem users to participate in productive society (Grabowski et al., 2004).

Harm reduction for stimulant users

Are stimulants too fast and too furious for harm reduction? A relatively new focus for harm reduction programmers, stimulants require rethinking many traditional strategies. Here we discuss the evidence for, and emerging interventions in, harm reduction for stimulant users. We start with a brief review of behavioural and pharmacologic treatment interventions for stimulant dependence and then focus on the stimulant-specific harms discussed in the previous section.

Behavioural and pharmacologic interventions for stimulant users

Challenges for harm reduction for stimulant users

Harm reduction for problem stimulant users is both crucial and feasible, but requires consideration of the unique characteristics of stimulant use. There are many obstacles, including:

- Frequent cocaine injection is a factor in the failure of selected syringe exchange programmes to prevent HIV transmission and in low treatment success and retention.
- Local studies among IDUs in English cities show show that up to 45 % report recent injecting into the femoral vein.
- Cocaine smoking is a growing risk factor for blood-borne virus transmission, due to associations with risky sex and collective use of smoking utensils.
- Female users are exposed to multiple risks associated with both sexual and drug use behaviours, which are contingent on broader gender relations.
- Despite shifts toward smoking drugs in many EU countries, public health efforts remain almost exclusively focused on IDUs.

Independent of mode of administration, stimulant and other drug users must enjoy the fundamental human right to health protection, as stipulated by Article 25 of the Universal Declaration of Human Rights.

Generally, the primary goal of treatment is viewed as inducing abstinence and preventing relapse ('cure'). If abstinence is not (yet) feasible, treatment should aim at reducing or at least stabilising substance use and its consequences ('care'). The ultimate stage of treatment should be lenitive and aim at alleviating suffering ('palliation'). At all stages, crisis intervention, treatment of intoxication and withdrawal, and improving health, psychological and social functioning are self-evident (Health Council of the Netherlands, 2002).

The first line of treatment for problem stimulant use is outpatient psychosocial intervention (American Psychiatric Association, 2007), most notably cognitive behaviour therapy (CBT), contingency management (CM) (Dutra et al., 2008), and motivational interviewing (MI) (Shearer, 2007; EMCDDA, 2007e). In CM a well-described target behaviour (e.g., medication compliance, clinic attendance, stimulant use abstinence, or any other verifiable behaviour) is rewarded whenever the behaviour is demonstrated (Dutra et al., 2008). CM is most effective when cash (as opposed to vouchers) and higher-value incentives are used, and although the effects diminish after the intervention is discontinued, effects of incentives have been demonstrated for up to 12 months thereafter (Lussier et al., 2006; Prendergast et al., 2006).

There is no proven effective pharmacological treatment for cocaine and stimulant use, in spite of the large number of studies on a broad array of pharmaceuticals (for reviews, see: De Lima et al., 2002; EMCDDA, 2007e; Pirona and Hedrich, 2009). More recently, the Cocaine Rapid Efficacy Screening Trial (CREST) tested 19 medications, of which three potentially effective compounds (cabergoline, reserpine and tiagabine) were moved forward to be tested in larger, confirmatory trials (Leiderman, 2005; Kampman et al., 2005). However, in recent larger trials neither tiagabine (Winhusen et al., 2007a) nor reserpine (Winhusen et al., 2007b) were effective in reducing cocaine use compared to placebo. Another approach is to develop a vaccine to prevent cocaine from crossing the blood–brain barrier; the current vaccine needs improvement (Martell et al., 2009) and there are many ethical issues to be addressed even once a vaccine has shown to be effective (see e.g. Hall and Carter, 2004).

More recently, there is growing interest in shifting the focus from abstinence to 'substitution treatment', based on the effectiveness of replacement therapy for nicotine and opiate dependence (Moeller et al., 2008; Shearer, 2008). The rationale for substitution treatment is to replace harmful stimulant drug use 'with safer, licit pharmaceutical drugs, avoiding contaminants and risks associated with hazardous routes of administration, such as injecting (blood-borne viral infections, overdose)' (Shearer, 2008, pp. 302–03). Ultimately, substitution treatment should result in a stabilisation of illicit drug use, thereby enabling the stimulant drug user to benefit from additional psychosocial interventions. Although the evidence to date for substitution treatment of stimulant use is scant (De Lima et al., 2002; Castells et al., 2007), dexamphetamine (SR) and modafinil seem promising candidates for further study. Llosa (1994) and Hurtado-Gumucio (2000) have also documented in non-controlled studies that coca tea, coca leaves and cocaine tablets could be effective in terms of craving, cocaine use and social functioning.

Interventions aimed at reducing adverse (health) consequences associated with stimulant use

Blood-borne viruses

Harm reduction for stimulant injectors relies heavily on the evidence for HIV prevention among heroin injectors (see e.g. Kimber et al., 2010), but demands consideration of the unique setting of stimulant injection. In particular, stimulant injection involves more frequent injection, increased sexual risk behaviours, chaotic injecting behaviour, home production, younger ages and more frequent treatment utilisation. Stimulant injectors should have easy access to large volumes of sterile injection equipment and means of sexual protection, requiring liberal exchange and distribution policies, extended opening hours and, where needed, outreach activities in injecting and sexual risk environments (Beek et al., 2001; Des Jarlais et al., 2009). Proper injection kits should include a range of materials based on local assessment of drug use patterns and the social situation of injectors. One-for-one syringe exchange policies, still in place in various needle and syringe programmes (NSPs) in the EU and Eastern Europe, should be avoided due to the high frequency of stimulant injection.

Harm reduction materials

No table manners without silverware!

- *Silverware*
- *Guidance on table manners*

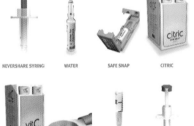

Collage: Jean-Paul Grund. Source images: Exchange Supplies.

Harm reduction kits for injecting drug users may include needles and syringes, disinfectants, alcohol pads, ascorbic or citric acid, filters, single-use cookers, plasters and antibiotic ointments, as well as educational materials. Sometimes other specific (e.g. for home preparation in CEE) or generic (such as vitamins or food) items are included as well.

Longer opening hours for NSPs and liberal exchange policies, political activism and public funding are associated with higher coverage of IDU populations and lower rates of risk behaviour (Templaski et al., 2008; Bluthenthal et al., 2007a; Bluthenthal et al., 2007b). Increased coverage was followed by substantial reductions in HIV prevalence and incidence among IDUs in the United States (Santibanez et al., 2006). Exchange Supplies in the United Kingdom offers syringes with coloured plungers and 'syringe-IDs' (a little colour- and pattern-marked clip for the back of the plunger), developed to allow stimulant injectors in particular to distinguish their personal syringe when injecting collectively (see illustration above).

In response to home-made stimulants, some NSPs in Eastern Europe offer syringes both for injecting and for preparing drugs (Grund and Merkinaite, 2009). Harm reduction networks in Georgia, Russia and Ukraine are developing interventions and information materials for home-made stimulant users. Distributing litmus paper to home-made stimulant users to allow production of less acidic drugs has been proposed but not yet implemented (Agafonova, 2008).

Traditional harm reduction programmes may fail to reach problem stimulant users due to opiate-centered services and social barriers to young or female users (see e.g. Grund and Merkinaite, 2009). Outreach, secondary exchange, or peer-driven strategies are needed to reach those not attending established service programmes (Needle et al., 2005; Coyle et al., 1998; Des Jarlais et al., 2009; Wood et al., 2003; Grund et al., 1992a; Broadhead et al., 1998). An unsanctioned peer-based and all-night NSP, located on the street in Vancouver's open drug scene, was able to reach and deliver harm reduction services to the city's most at risk cocaine injectors (Wood et al., 2003). Syringe dispensing machines (SDMs) and mobile NSPs provide confidential access to sterile equipment at times and places where coverage is poor (Islam and Conigrave, 2007), to younger users (Moatti et al., 2001; Obadia et al., 1999) with shorter injection histories than NSP or pharmacy users, less drug dependence, less access to established services (Stark et al., 1994; Leicht, 1993), less licit income, and lower socioeconomic status (Moatti et al., 2001). Patrons of mobile outlets are likely to be younger, indigenous and female, inject more frequently and do so more often on the street, be engaged in sex work and not be in drug treatment (Miller et al., 2002; Riley et al., 2000; Islam and Conigrave, 2007). SDMs are not advised as stand-alone interventions as there is little chance for health education, but they can serve as strategic adjuncts to conventional NSPs and pharmacy distribution (Islam and Conigrave, 2007; Agnoletto et al., 1993; Cox et al., 2000).

Despite shifts towards smoking drugs in many EU countries, public health efforts remain almost exclusively focused on IDU (Jauffret-Roustide, 2004; Jauffret-Roustide et al., 2008a; Haydon and Fischer, 2005; Cheung, 2000). Canada and several US programmes have implemented specific programmes for cocaine smokers (Boyd et al., 2008; Leonard et al., 2006; Leonard et al., 2007), such as the distribution of so-called 'crack kits', containing supplies to prevent oral or respiratory lesions from smoking (Porter and Bonilla, 1993; Malchy et al., 2008; Collins et al., 2005). Studies of the out-of-treatment cocaine and heroin users suggest that the principles and evidence base of needle exchange (Wodak and Cooney, 2005; Hunt et al., 2003; Hunt et al., 2005; WHO, 2005; WHO et al. and UNODC, 2004) may apply to crack kits or other drug use utensils as well (Grund, 1991a; Grund, 1993; Pizzey and Hunt, 2008).

Although many supervised drug consumption facilities prohibit injected or smoked cocaine due to the chaotic and frenetic nature of use, several supervised injection facilities (SIFs) in the EU now include rooms for smoking cocaine and other drugs (Hunt, 2006), a trend that may extend to Vancouver's SIF (Shannon et al., 2006). Managing a smoking room has proven similar to an injection room; SIFs that do allow cocaine use have not reported major problems (Poschadel et al., 2002; Verthein et al., 2001; Zurhold et al., 2001; Zurhold et al., 2003; Vogt and Zeissler, 2005; Broadhead et al., 2002; Poel, et al., 2003; Hedrich, 2004; IWGDCR, 2006). Programmes targeting smokers should emphasise women through gender-sensitive programmes that have been developed, although few of these have been evaluated (Boyd et al., 2008; Wechsberg et al., 2004; Butters and Erickson, 2003). Programming for women may work better when biological, behavioural, psychological and social characteristics of women are considered and individual and community support measures combined (Latka, 2003), supporting increased autonomy of women over their drug use and sexuality to minimise exposure to BBVs (Jauffret-Roustide et al., 2008b; Gollub, 2008).

Sexually transmitted diseases, bacterial infections and other complications

Ample supply of injection and sexual protection supplies may also contribute to reducing sexually transmitted diseases (STDs) and bacterial infections (Beek et al., 2001; Kerr et al., 2005). Proper injection techniques, antibacterial creams and ointments and rotation of injection sites may help reduce vein loss and effectively treat minor SSTIs (Stern, 1992). Basic hygiene (hand washing, short nails) and vein care as well as simple wound care and training in safer injection may prevent infections in cocaine injectors (Beek et al., 2001; Kerr et al., 2005; Rhodes et al., 2007). Wound and abscess services within NSPs may increase patient–clinician interactions, providing opportunities for referrals to services such as HIV counseling and testing, medical care, and drug treatment at an estimated cost of $5 per patient (Grau et al., 2002). There is no consensus on whether groin injection should be actively discouraged or safer techniques provided (as in the United Kingdom; Maliphant and Scott, 2005; Zador, 2007; Strang et al., 2008), although investigators agree that transitions to groin injection or crack injection should be discouraged (Rhodes et al., 2007).

Neurologic effects

Efforts to reduce the neurologic sequelae of stimulants are primarily related to the use of 'club drugs'. Reducing frequency of use is the most common strategy for reducing the delayed 'comedown' of stimulants, depression, and concerns about neurologic damage (Allott and Redman, 2006). 'Pre-loading' or 'post-loading' with a variety of substances is another approach, involving vitamins, foods, antidepressant medications, sleeping tablets, or amino acids. While there are no data evaluating the effect of these common methods (Kelly, 2009), a combination of amphetamines and most anti-depressant medications poses the risk of a life-threatening reaction known as serotonin syndrome (Copeland et al., 2006). A Dutch website (http://www.cocaineinfo.nl/) provides neurological explanations for the 'Coke Shuffle', advising temporary cessation of use, massage, a warm environment or a visit to the sauna, as this might help to reduce cramps. Sometimes benzodiazepines are prescribed to problem cocaine users, mostly for sleep, but these may also alleviate joint and muscle pains.

Cardiovascular effects

Routine cardiovascular care, involving diet and exercise, management of high blood pressure and cholesterol, as well as reducing other risk factors such as tobacco use, are likely to be the most powerful harm reduction strategies, as they are for the general population. Reducing dosage and frequency of all stimulant use may reduce cardiovascular toxicities, as may reducing concomitant alcohol consumption. Although no controlled studies or specific interventions have been conducted, patients maintained on amphetamines (Vitiello, 2008) and Andean users of low-potency coca products (Knuepfer, 2003) are believed to be at only mild to moderately increased risk of cardiovascular toxicities. As cocaine is directly toxic to heart muscle cells while amphetamines exert toxicity primarily through blood pressure elevation, reducing or discontinuing use with onset of the cardiovascular disease that comes with age is paramount to reducing the harm of these drugs.

Pulmonary and other health effects

While marijuana can be filtered for some reduction in exposure to particulate matter (McPartland and Pruitt, 1997), filtering stimulant drugs is less likely to reduce the impact of these drugs on pulmonary tissue. Nonetheless, providing filters may reduce oropharyngeal exposure to hot embers, thus reducing burns to the mouth and throat. Harm reduction providers in Canada, and the United States offer 'crack kits' that include Pyrex pipes or rubber mouthpieces (Leonard et al., 2006; Leonard et al., 2007; Aidslaw, 2007), which may reduce lacerations to the lips. Mainline in Amsterdam offered street cocaine smokers lung, blood and heart measurements, safer smoking advice and self-regulation training (Boekhout van Solinge, 2001), but roll-out of the methodology in mainstream drug services proved challenging (Bruin et al., 2008). Other strategies to reduce pulmonary damage could include vaporisation and other means to filter out talc and other particles. Sufficient hydration contributes to lip, skin and other organ health. The frequency of pneumonia might be mitigated by pneumococcal vaccination and tuberculosis prevention, diagnosis and treatment.

The American Dental Association has developed a patient folder on 'meth mouth,' that includes drug treatment locators, a guide for parents and 'a calculator to figure out how much it costs to support a drug habit' (American Dental Association, 2005), but provides no advice on oral hygiene. Drug users in Amsterdam can get dental care at a special clinic and referrals to regular dentists. In Frankfurt in the 1990s, the Integrative Drogenhilfe was reportedly successful in finding IDUs dentists in the community using case management and advocacy strategies, as part of a 'Vermittlung in die Normalität' philosophy towards all their clients' health, social and legal problems (personal communication Marion Nickolai, 15 August 2009).

Overdose

Cocaine overdose is frequently cardiovascular (i.e. heart attack, fatal arrhythmia, or stroke) and demands rapid and sophisticated medical management. Concomitant use of opioids, alcohol or other depressant drugs is closely associated with cocaine overdose (Kaye and Darke, 2004), suggesting that limiting other drug use while using cocaine may reduce the risk of overdose. Cardiopulmonary resuscitation delivered by bystanders has been demonstrated to improve outcomes in opioid overdose (Dietze et al., 2002) and may translate to stimulant overdoses. Naloxone will not reverse a stimulant overdose, therefore ensuring rapid access to nonjudgmental medical care without police intervention is essential to reducing fatalities.

Mental health problems

Many mental health problems associated with stimulant use are dose, frequency and mode of administration related, and might be mitigated by specific harm reduction measures. Care providers should use a sensitive, respectful approach toward stimulant users, even when chaotic, and treat people with signs of drug toxicity, such as cocaine-induced psychosis (Beek et al., 2001). Brief interventions among recreational amphetamine users should include information about potential mental health problems arising from regular use (Baker et al., 2004) and more than weekly use or injection should be discouraged (Hall et al., 1996). A randomised-controlled trial of Assertive Community Treatment for chronic crack users in Rotterdam found good programme compliance and improvements in physical and mental health (Henskens, 2004).

Cessation of cocaine injecting or smoking may be necessary for recovery from cocaine-related mental health morbidity (Beek et al., 2001), but self-regulation to control use may also prove helpful (Prinzleve et al., 2002; Haasen et al., 2005; Cramer and Schippers, 1994/1996). Stimulant users often self-medicate with heroin or other downers to control side-effects of anxiety and irritability (Grund, 1993; Decorte, 2001). Acupuncture, while of little use as monotherapy, may reduce cocaine craving when provided as an adjunct treatment (Gates et al., 2006; Kim et al., 2005) and the service may retain users in care (NTA, 2002). In New York, the Lower East Side Harm Reduction Center offers acupuncture, Reiki and other alternative treatments to cocaine users (personal communication Raquel Algarin, 23 November 2009).

Other practical suggestions for dealing with the behavioural peculiarities include immediate and flexible walk-in services (Haasen et al., 2003, Beek et al., 2001) and offering a calming, tranquil environment (Stöver, 2002), similar to 'chill-out' rooms at dance parties. 'Tagesruheräume', or daytime rest rooms, for cocaine injectors and crack smokers have been established in Frankfurt am Main and integrated within a low-threshold drug help centre, which offers counselling, medical and psychiatric care, a consumption room and a shelter in Hamburg (Vogt et al., 2000; Stöver, 2001; Verthein et al., 2001). Organisations such as HIT in Liverpool, Lifeline in Manchester and Mainline in Amsterdam have developed several explicit flyers for cocaine users with tips for managing mental health risks and controlling use of cocaine. While a focus of many programmes, approaches developed for stimulant users are rarely published in the scientific literature.

Pregnancy and parenting

An ethnographic evaluation of drug-using pregnant women demonstrated numerous self-employed harm reduction strategies, such as use of less dangerous substances (e.g. marijuana), reduced dose and frequency, and improved diet and self-care, as well as less helpful strategies like avoiding medical care for fear of stigma or prosecution (Kearney et al.,

1995; Murphy and Rosenbaum, 1999). Long-term outcome data on early intervention programmes for cocaine-exposed children suggest that the impact of poverty far overshadows that of cocaine, and that early intervention can improve developmental outcomes (Kilbride et al., 2000). Furthermore, among cocaine-exposed children who do not receive early interventions, remaining with their birth mothers may result in improved social interactions (Kilbride et al., 2006). Substantial harm reduction efforts around stimulants and pregnancy in North America have been legal defense and policy reform to reduce the criminalisation of women's behaviour during pregnancy (Lester et al., 2004).

Discussion

Appraisal of the quality of evidence reviewed and limitations of the study

Research has established the rationale for many harm reduction interventions for stimulant users (Wodak and Cooney, 2005; Farrell et al., 2005; Hunt et al., 2003; Hunt et al., 2005; WHO et al., 2004). Nonetheless, scientific literature is overwhelmingly weighted toward the harms of stimulants, with minimal literature on harm reduction interventions. Investigations frequently consider stimulants users a subset, rather than the target population of a study. Several interventions for stimulant users, such as providing materials for safer crack smoking or safer groin injection training, remain controversial or illegal and thus systematic evaluations are lacking. Funding mechanisms for evaluating new interventions are also limited, partly due to the reliance of most investigators on HIV funding streams.

Potential harms addressed by harm reduction interventions

The effectiveness of pharmacological and psychosocial interventions for stimulant users is limited (De Lima et al., 2002; EMCDDA, 2007e; Pirona and Hedrich, 2009), thus interventions to stabilise and minimise the negative consequences of ongoing stimulant use are of paramount importance. The evidence suggests that there are no fundamental challenges in adjusting regular harm reduction interventions, such as NSPs and SIFs, towards BBV prevention among problem stimulant users. However, a wide range of health and social problems associated with stimulant use are largely unaddressed by current services (e.g. specific harm reduction approaches to SSTIs have been developed but are not widely implemented (Grau et al., 2002; Kerr et al., 2005)).

Prevention of SSTIs, overdose or pulmonary, neurologic, or cardiovascular damage is a relatively new focus in harm reduction and there is much ground to be gained in prevention and early treatment of these conditions. 'Crack kits' may prove useful in preventing certain infections. Widely available SSTI, and cardiac primary care services, may lessen the burden of disease. The rapidly expanding literature on overdose prevention programming (Sporer and Kral, 2007; Maxwell et al., 2006; Coffin et al., 2007; Coffin, 2008) suggests a need to extend the harm reduction philosophy even further. Innovative service development paired with critical evaluation is necessary in translating the successes of harm reduction towards heroin to stimulant use.

Community-based research, programme evaluations and best practice examples underscore the need for services that enhance the ability of stimulant users to manage their intake levels, chaotic behaviour and mental health problems. Several harm reduction programmes informally aid stimulant users in money management, at times even holding clients' benefit cheques until after a binge. At hundreds, if not thousands, of blogs and Internet discussion lists, users discuss stimulant and other drug use openly and in detail, including many of the harms discussed in this review, dietary advice and 'street pharmacology' approaches to self-regulation (e.g. 'Harm Reduction for Stimulants', http://www.drugs-forum.com/forum/archive/index.php/t-24802.html).

Rhodes and colleagues reported what could be termed an epidemic of groin injecting. When groin injection becomes an 'acceptable risk' (Rhodes et al., 2006), one wonders what other risks have pushed the normalisation of this hazardous behaviour down the injector's 'hierarchy of risk' (Connors, 1992). Rhodes and colleagues not only point towards increasing crack/speedball injection in their explanation, they also emphasise the changing 'risk environment' of drug injecting (Rhodes, 2002). Groin injection is reportedly viewed as 'reliable, speedy, and discreet'. As one of their respondents explained, 'you can do it under a camera' (Rhodes et al., 2006). The omnipresence of camera and human surveillance, zero tolerance towards deviance in the public space and the resulting lack of spaces where homeless IDUs could withdraw to inject in British (and other) cities can thus be seen to engender a risk environment in which 'macro risk factors' synergise the risks of crack injection towards aggravating injecting-related harm (Rhodes, 2002; Rhodes et al., 2006; Rhodes, 2009). Such environmental factors are mostly beyond the scope of harm reduction interventions, which focus primarily on the substance and its users. Nonetheless, in the early 1980s, when cocaine landed in the urban heroin scenes of the Netherlands and injecting was still the dominant mode of drug administration, IDUs did not turn 'en masse' towards groin injecting (Grund et al., 1991b). Instead, smoking cocaine at 'house addresses' became the norm (Grund et al., 1991a; Grund and Blanken, 1993; Blanken et al., 1997).

The harms associated with problem stimulant use interact at multiple levels in the risk environment (Rhodes, 2002; Zinberg, 1984). Not only can specific harms influence one another, but they are also aggravated by external factors, such as international drug legislation, policing and other public policies in a process of 'contingent causality' (Rhodes, 2009). Developing proper and timely responses to such policy-related harms is a crucial challenge to harm reduction. Not because the proper harm reduction tools are absent or cannot be imagined, but because the larger risk environment might make such efforts null and void (Grund et al., 1992b; Rhodes et al., 2006; Gostin, 1998). Policymakers should therefore find ways to reduce the harms from counter-effective drug policies, harsh social policies and policies affecting our public space and private behaviours, and strengthen the ability of drug consumers and society to learn from past experience.

History is full of examples of the acculturation of 'new' psychoactive drugs across various cultures. As part of the mainstream social fabric, most drinking is restrained by explicit and implicit social rules passed from generation to generation. Unfortunately, the collective knowledge on cocaine and amphetamines is accumulated through peer-based learning and not necessarily passed on automatically to new generations of users. The potential to respond in a rational and healthy fashion to 'new' illicit drugs is — among users and policymakers alike — hampered by what Lloyd Johnston termed 'generational forgetting' (Johnston et al., 2004). Yet, this learning is crucial to peacefully controlling problem drug use, a role recently adopted by harm reduction providers in many countries.

Implications for future intervention development, research and policy

There is a strong base of needle exchange programming in many, but not all, EU Member States, but their coverage of the IDU population may vary and stimulant users are poorly reached. Developing sufficient coverage for NSP and other interventions is a clear but complex issue (Des Jarlais et al., 2009) (see Kimber et al., 2010). Therefore, internal and external regulatory barriers, such as one-for-one exchange policies and laws that impede harm reduction programmes from distributing other safer use supplies (e.g. crack pipes and smoking foil) should be reconsidered. While returning used injecting equipment should be encouraged, the strict combination of distribution and collection is an unsavoury choice as it hinders access to ample quantities of injecting equipment at places and times when these are most needed. Therefore, independent distribution and collection schemes should be developed (Des Jarlais et al., 2009; Wood et al., 2003; Grund et al., 1992a).

The volume of injection equipment or condoms provided to clients should be determined based on a thorough assessment of clients' needs and network characteristics (Braine et al., 2008; Friedman et al., 2007; Rothenberg, 2007). All this requires a paradigm shift in service provision — from institutional provider–client relationships to facilitation of peer prevention in user networks (Broadhead et al., 1998) through peer-based outreach and secondary exchange. Syringe vending machines and mobile programmes can be useful adjuncts to 'reaching the unreached' but should be firmly based in flexible, attractive and human-delivered services.

Safer injecting and smoking education and interventions supporting transition to less harmful routes of drug administration, as well as overdose prevention and medical care of vein, skin and other infections should become standard features of SIFs and NSPs, and moved into the mainstream of harm reduction. NSPs and SIFs should not only create a healthy atmosphere, but also a setting that allows for the pleasurable effects of stimulants while minimising negative experiences, possibly by emphasising more controlled and less frenetic use. Relaxation techniques and alternative therapies may help stimulant users to ameliorate some of the mental health effects of heavy or frequent stimulant use, as well as physical complaints such as musculoskeletal pain. Offering sleep and day rest facilities may help to reduce sleep deprivation, which may alleviate the mental health strain of stimulant use. Involving participants in service provision and other activities may further help reduce the frequency and amounts of stimulant use, potentially leading to improvements in mental health and social functioning. Collaborations between various medical specialties, drug users, service providers and researchers in designing harm reduction strategies towards the pulmonary, cardiovascular and neurologic effects of stimulant use are equally important.

The reviewed studies suggest that problem stimulant use requires innovative, integrated and multidisciplinary medical and social services, but also drug and social policies that do not exacerbate the already considerable potential for harm of stimulants. The recent attention being paid to the unintended consequences of drug policy at UNODC is encouraging, but needs to be translated into effective action. At present, international drug and other public policies emphasise maximising harm to reduce casual drug use. Stimulant and other drug users must enjoy the fundamental human right to health protection, as stipulated by Article 25 of the Universal Declaration of Human Rights (General Assembly of the United Nations, 1948). In 1945, at the brink of war and peace, Sir Karl Popper published his influential *The open society and its enemies*, in which he wrote 'The role of the state is not to make people happy but to relieve avoidable suffering.' For the state and its agents to live up to these calls is amongst the principal challenges of harm reduction.

Acknowledgements

The authors would like to gratefully acknowledge Gaelle Guibert and Marc Rondy for conducting parts of the crack literature review for this paper. We thank David Otiashvili and Simona Merkinaite for support with Russian-language literature and Floor van Bakkum, Mika Mikkonen, Shona Shoning and Allan Clear for their help with finding information on various specific topics. We thank Mariette Baas and Lila Oudaya for their assistance in preparing this manuscript.

Further reading

Beek, I. van, Dwyer, R. and Malcom, A. (2001), 'Cocaine injecting: the sharp end of drug related harm', *Drug and Alcohol Review* 20, 333–42.

Bertol, E., Trignano, C., Di Milia, M. G., Di Padua, M. and Mari, F. (2008), 'Cocaine-related deaths: an enigma still under investigation', *Forensic Science International* 7 Apr, 176 (2–3), pp. 121–3.

Darke, S., Kaye, S., McKetin, R. and Duflou, J. (2008), 'Major physical and psychological harms of methamphetamine use', *Drug and Alcohol Review* 27, pp. 253–62.

EMCDDA (European Monitoring Centre for Drugs and Drug Addiction) (2007), *Treatment of problem cocaine use: a review of the literature*, EMCDDA, Lisbon.

EMCDDA (2008), *Treatment of problem cocaine use: a short update*, EMCDDA, Lisbon.

Karch, S. B. (2005), 'Cocaine cardiovascular toxicity', *Southern Medical Journal* August, 98 (8), pp. 794–9.

Leonard, L., DeRubeis, E., Pelude, L., et al. (2007), '"I inject less as I have easier access to pipes": injecting, and sharing of crack-smoking materials, decline as safer crack-smoking resources are distributed', *International Journal of Drug Policy* 19 (3), pp. 1–10.

Pates, R. and Riley, D. (2009), *Interventions for amphetamine misuse*, Wiley-Blackwell, Oxford.

Scheinmann, R., Hagan, H., Lelutiu-Weinberger, C., et al. (2007), 'Non-injection drug use and hepatitis C virus: a systematic review', *Drug and Alcohol Dependence* 89, pp. 1–12.

References

Addis, A., Moretti, M. E., Ahmed Syed, F., Einarson, T. R. and Koren, G. (2001), 'Fetal effects of cocaine: an updated meta-analysis', *Reproductive Toxicology* 15 (4), pp. 341–69.

Adimora, A. A., Schoenbach, V. J., Martinson, F. E., et al. (2003), 'Concurrent partnerships among rural African Americans with recently reported heterosexually transmitted HIV infection', *Journal of Acquired Immune Deficiency Syndromes* 34, pp. 423–9.

Afonso, L., Mohammad, T. and Thatai, D. (2007), 'Crack whips the heart: a review of the cardiovascular toxicity of cocaine', *American Journal of Cardiology* 100 (6), pp. 1040–3.

Agafonova, A. (2008), 'Report from the consultation meeting "Psychostimulants: harm reduction approaches"', Russian Harm Reduction Network, Moscow.

Agnoletto, V., Tradati, C., Ceserani, N., et al. (1998), *Street work and needle exchange machines as complementary strategies of HIV harm reduction among active drug users: an Italian model* (Abstract no. WS-D09-4), *Int Conf AIDS*, Berlin, Germany.

Aidslaw (2007), *Abolition du programme de trousses pour l'usage plus sûr du crack: un geste irresponsable et de courte visée, du Conseil municipal d'Ottawa* (news release). Available at http://www.aidslaw.ca/publications/ interfaces/downloadDocumentFile.php?ref=731 (accessed on 23 January 2010).

Alcabes, P. (2009), *Dread: how fear and fantasy have fueled epidemics from the Black Death to avian flu*, Public Affairs Books, New York.

Allott, K. and Redman, J. (2006), 'Patterns of use and harm reduction practices of ecstasy users in Australia', *Drug and Alcohol Dependence* 82 (2), pp. 168–76.

American Dental Association (2005), 'For the dental patient: methamphetamine use and oral health'. Available at http://www.ada.org/prof/resources/pubs/jada/patient/patient_55.pdf (accessed on 30 September 2009).

American Dental Association (2009), 'Methamphetamine use (meth mouth)'. Available at http://www.ada.org/ prof/resources/topics/methmouth.asp (accessed on 30 September 2009).

American Psychiatric Association (2007), 'Practice guideline for the treatment of patients with substance use disorders' (2nd edition), *American Journal of Psychiatry* 164 (4) (Supplement), pp. 1–124.

Baker, A., Lee, N. K., Claire, M., et al. (2004), 'Drug use patterns and mental health of regular amphetamine users during a reported "heroin drought"', *Addiction* 99, pp. 875–84.

Balakireva, O. M., Grund, J. P. C., Barendregt, C., et al. (2006), *Risk and protective factors in the initiation of injecting drug use: analytical report on a respondent driven sampling study and strategy paper preventing the initiation of injecting drug use among vulnerable adolescents and young people: final report*, UNICEF/UISR, Kiev.

Basso, M. R. and Bornstein, R. A. (2000), 'Neurobehavioural consequences of substance abuse and HIV infection', *Journal of Psychopharmacology* 14 (3), pp. 228–37.

Bauman, J. L. and DiDomenico, R. J. (2002), 'Cocaine-induced channelopathies: emerging evidence on the multiple mechanisms of sudden death', *Journal of Cardiovascular Pharmacology and Therapeutics* 7 (3), pp. 195–202.

Bauwens, J. E., Orlander, H., Gomez, M. P., et al. (2002), 'Epidemic Lymphogranuloma venereum during epidemics of crack cocaine use and HIV infection in the Bahamas', *Sexually Transmitted Diseases* 29, pp. 253–9.

Beek, I. van, Dwyer, R., and Malcom, A. (2001), 'Cocaine injecting: the sharp end of drug related harm', *Drug and Alcohol Review* 20, 333–42.

Bellis, M., Hughes, K., Bennett, A. and Thomson, R. (2003), 'The role of an international nightlife resort in the proliferation of recreational drugs', *Addiction* 98, pp. 1713–21.

Binswanger, I. A., Kral, A. H., Bluthenthal, R. N., Rybold, D. J. and Edlin, B. R. (2000), 'High prevalence of abscesses and cellulitis among community-recruited injection drug users in San Francisco', *Clinical Infectious Diseases* 30, pp. 579–81.

Blanken, P., Barendregt, C., and Hendriks, V. (1997), *Op is op. Niets is voor altijd. Een onderzoek naar het roken van cocaïne-base en zelf-controle mechanismen (IVO-reeks nr. 14)*, IVO, Rotterdam.

Bluthenthal, R., Anderson, R., Flynn, N. and Kral, A. (2007a), 'Higher syringe coverage is associated with lower odds of HIV risk and does not increase unsafe syringe disposal among syringe exchange program clients', *Drug and Alcohol Dependence* 89, pp. 214–22.

Bluthenthal, R., Ridgeway, G., Schell, T., et al. (2007b), 'Examination of the association between syringe exchange program (SEP) dispensation policy and SEP client-level syringe coverage among injection drug users', *Addiction* 102, pp. 638–46.

Boekhout van Solinge, T. (2001), *Op de pof*, Rozenberg, Amsterdam.

Booth, R., Lehman, W., Kwiatkowski, C., et al. (2008), 'Stimulant injectors in Ukraine: the next wave of the epidemic?' *AIDS and Behaviour*, 12 (4), pp. 652–61.

Borodkina, O. I., Baranova, M. V., Girchenko, P. V., et al. (2005), 'The correlation between the type of drug use and HIV prevalence of IDU in different Russian cities', *Russian Journal of HIV/AIDS and Related Problems* 9 (3), pp. 74–5.

Boyd, S., Johnson, J. L. and Moffat, B. (2008), 'Opportunities to learn and barriers to change: crack cocaine use in the Downtown Eastside of Vancouver', *Harm Reduction Journal* 5, p. 34.

Braine, N., Acker, C., Goldblatt, C., Yi, H., Friedman, S. R., and Des Jarlais, D. C. (2008), 'Neighborhood history as a factor shaping syringe distribution networks among drug users at a U.S. syringe exchange', *Soc Netw* 30 (3), pp. 235–46.

Brewer, T. H., Zhao, W., Pereyra, M., et al. (2007), 'Initiating HIV care: attitudes and perceptions of HIV positive crack cocaine users', *AIDS and Behavior* 11 (6), pp. 897–904.

Broadhead, R. S., Heckathorn, D. D., Weakliem,D. L., et al. (1998), 'Harnessing peer networks as an instrument for AIDS prevention: results from a peer-driven intervention', in Needle, R. H., Coyle, S. and Cesari, H. (eds), 'HIV prevention with drug-using populations: current status and future prospects', *Public Health Reports* 113 (Supplement 1), pp. 42–57.

Broadhead, R. S., Altice, F. L., Kerr, T. H. and Grund, J-P. C. (2002), 'Safer injection facilities in North America: their place in public policy and health initiatives', *Journal of Drug Issues* 32 (7), pp. 327–54.

Bruin, D. de, Ossebaard, H., Bakker, I., Aalderen, H. van and Wildschut, J. (2008), 'Hoezo onbereikbaar? Passende hulp voor basecokegebruikers: knelpunten en kansen', *Verslaving, Tijdschrift over Verslavingsproblematiek* 4, no. 1.§.

Butters, J. and Erickson, P. G. (2003), 'Meeting the health care needs of female crack users: a Canadian example', *Women and Health* 37, pp. 1–17.

Cabral, G. A. (2006), 'Drugs of abuse, immune modulation, and AIDS', *Journal of Neuroimmune Pharmacology* 1 (3), pp. 280–95.

Cadet, J. L. and Krasnova, I. N. (2007), 'Interactions of HIV and methamphetamine: cellular and molecular mechanisms of toxicity potentiation', *Neurotoxicity Research* 12 (3), pp. 181–204.

Callaway, C. W. and Clark, R. F. (1994), 'Hyperthermia in psychostimulant overdose', *Annals of Emergency Medicine* 24 (1), pp. 68–76.

Camilleri, A. M. and Caldicott, D. (2005), 'Underground pill testing, down under', *Forensic Science International* 151 (1), pp. 53–8.

Campsmith, M. L., Nakashima, A. K. and Jones, J. L. (2000), 'Association between crack cocaine use and high-risk sexual behaviours after HIV diagnosis', *Journal of Acquired Immune Deficiency Syndromes* 25, pp. 192–8.

Castells, X., Casas, M., Vidal, X. et al. (2007), 'Efficacy of central nervous stimulant treatment for cocaine dependence: a systematic review and meta-analysis of randomized controlled clinical trials', *Addiction* 102 (12), pp. 1871–87.

Celentano, D. D., Valleroy, L. A., Sifakis, F., et al. (2006), 'Associations between substance use and sexual risk among very young men who have sex with men', *Sexually Transmitted Diseases* 33 (4), pp. 265–71.

Centers for Disease Control and Prevention (1991), 'Alternative case-finding methods in a crack-related syphilis epidemic: Philadelphia', *Morbidity and Mortality Weekly Report* 40, pp. 77–80.

Centers for Disease Control and Prevention (1993), 'Selective screening to augment syphilis case-finding — Dallas, 1991', *Morbidity and Mortality Weekly Report* 42, pp. 424–7.

Centers for Disease Control and Prevention (1996), 'Continued sexual risk behaviour among HIV-seropositive, drug-using men — Atlanta, Washington, D.C., and San Juan, Puerto Rico, 1993', *Morbidity and Mortality Weekly Report* 45, pp. 151–2.

Chang, L., Alicata, D., Ernst, T. and Volkow, N. (2007), 'Structural and metabolic brain changes in the striatum associated with methamphetamine abuse', *Addiction* 102 (Supplement 1), pp. 16–32.

Chao, C., Jacobson, L. P., Tashkin, D., et al. (2008), 'Recreational drug use and T lymphocyte subpopulations in HIV-uninfected and HIV-infected men', *Drug and Alcohol Dependence* 94 (1–3), pp. 165–71.

Chen, C. K., Lin, S. K., Sham, P. C., et al. (2003), 'Pre-morbid characteristics and co-morbidity of methamphetamine users with and without psychosis', *Psychological Medicine* 33 (8), pp. 1407–14.

Cheung, Y. W. (2000), 'Substance abuse and developments in harm reduction', *Canadian Medical Association Journal* 162, pp. 1697–700.

Chi, D. and Milgrom, P. (2008), 'The oral health of homeless adolescents and young adults and determinants of oral health: preliminary findings', *Special Care Dentistry* 28 (6), pp. 237–42.

Chiasson, M. A., Stoneburner, R. L., Hildebrandt, D. S., et al. (1991), 'Heterosexual transmission of HIV-1 associated with the use of smokable freebase cocaine (crack)', *AIDS* 5, pp. 1121–6.

Chintalova-Dallas, R., Case, P., Kitsenko, N. and Lazzarini, Z. (2009), 'Boltushka: a homemade amphetamine-type stimulant and HIV risk in Odessa, Ukraine', *International Journal of Drug Policy* 20, pp. 347–51.

Chirgwin, K., DeHovitz, J. A., Dillon, S. and McCormack, W. M. (1991), 'HIV infection, genital ulcer disease, and crack cocaine use among patients attending a clinic for sexually transmitted diseases', *American Journal of Public Health* 81, pp. 1576–9.

Ciccarone, D. and Bourgois, P. (2003), 'Explaining the geographical variation of HIV among injection drug users in the United States', *Substance Use and Misuse* 38, pp. 2049–63.

Ciccarone, D., Bamberger, J., Kral, A., et al. (2001), 'Soft tissue infections among injection drug users: San Francisco, California, 1996–2000', *Morbidity and Mortality Weekly Report* 50 (19), pp. 381–84.

Cleghorn, F.R., Jack, N., Murphy, J.R. et al. (1995), 'HIV-1 prevalence and risk factors among sexually transmitted disease clinic attenders in Trinidad', *AIDS* 9, pp. 389–94.

Coffin, P. (2008), *Overdose: a major cause of preventable death in central and eastern Europe and central Asia*, Eurasian Harm Reduction Network, Vilnius.

Coffin, P. O., Galea, S., Ahern, J., et al. (2003), 'Opiates, cocaine and alcohol combinations in accidental drug overdose deaths in New York City, 1990–98', *Addiction* 98 (6), pp. 739–47.

Coffin, P. O., Tracy, M., Bucciarelli, A., et al. (2007), 'Identifying injection drug users at risk of nonfatal overdose', *Academic Emergency Medicine* 14 (7), pp. 616–23.

Cofrancesco, J. Jr., Scherzer, R., Tien, P. C., et al. (2008), 'Illicit drug use and HIV treatment outcomes in a US cohort', *Aids* 22 (3), pp. 357–65.

Cohen, A. L., Shuler, C., McAllister, S., et al. (2007), 'Methamphetamine use and methicillin-resistant staphylococcus aureus skin infections', *Emerging Infectious Diseases* 13 (11), pp. 1707–13.

Cohen, P. and Sas, A. (1993), *Ten years of cocaine: a follow-up study of 64 cocaine users in Amsterdam*, Department of Human Geography, Universiteit van Amsterdam, Amsterdam, pp. 1–126.

Cohen, P. and Sas, A. (1994), 'Cocaine use in Amsterdam in non deviant subcultures', *Addiction Research* 2 (1), pp. 71–94.

Cole, J. C., Sumnall, H. R., Smith, G. W. and Rostami-Hodjegan, A. (2005), 'Preliminary evidence of the cardiovascular effects of polysubstance misuse in nightclubs', *Journal of Psychopharmacology* 19 (1), pp. 67–70.

Collins, C. L., Kerr, T., Tyndall, M. W. S., et al. (2005), 'Rationale to evaluate medically supervised safer smoking facilities for non-injection illicit drug users', *Canadian Journal of Public Health* 96, pp. 344–7.

Connors, M. M. (1992), 'Risk perception, risk taking and risk management among intravenous drug users: implications for AIDS prevention', *Social Science and Medicine* 34 (6), pp. 591–601.

Cook, J. A., Burke-Miller, J. K., Cohen, M. H., et al. (2008), 'Crack cocaine, disease progression, and mortality in a multicenter cohort of HIV-1 positive women', *Aids* 22 (11), pp. 1355–63.

Cook, J. A., Grey, D. D., Burke-Miller, J. K., et al. (2007), 'Illicit drug use, depression and their association with highly active antiretroviral therapy in HIV-positive women', *Drug and Alcohol Dependence* 89 (1), pp. 74–81.

Copeland, J., Dillon, P. and Gascoigne, M. (2006), 'Ecstasy and the concomitant use of pharmaceuticals', *Addictive Behaviours* 31 (2), pp. 367–70.

Cotten-Oldenburg, N. U., Jordan, B. K., Martin, S. L. and Kupper, L. (1999), 'Women inmates' risky sex and drug behaviours: are they related?' *American Journal of Drug and Alcohol Abuse* 25, pp. 129–49.

Cox, G., Lawless, M., Cassin, S. P. and Geoghegan, T. W. (2000), 'Syringe exchanges: a public health response to problem drug use', *Irish Medical Journal* 93 (5), pp. 143–6.

Coyle, S. L., Needle, R. H. and Normand, J. (1998), 'Outreach based HIV prevention for injecting drug users: a review of published outcome data', in Needle, R. H., Coyle, S. and Cesari, H. (eds), *HIV prevention with drug-using populations: current status and future prospects*, Public Health Reports, 113 (Supplement 1), pp. 19–30.

Cramer, E. A. S. M. and Schippers, G. M. (1994/1996), *Zelfcontrole en ontwenning van harddrugs, Eindrapport van een onderzoek naar de ontwikkeling en evaluatie van een zelfcontrole programma voor druggebruikers*, Nijmegen: UNRAB.

Crowe, A. V., Howse, M., Bell, G. M. and Henry, J. A. (2000), 'Substance abuse and the kidney', *QJM* 93 (3), pp. 147–52.

Daley, D. C., Mercer, D. and Carpenter, G. (2002), *Drug counseling for cocaine addiction: the collaborative cocaine treatment study model*, National Institute on Drug Abuse, Bethesda, Maryland.

Darke, S., Kaye, S., McKetin, R. and Duflou, J. (2008), 'Major physical and psychological harms of methamphetamine use', *Drug and Alcohol Review*, pp. 253–62.

De, P., Cox, J., Boivin, J. F., Platt, R. W. and Jolly, A. M. (2007), 'Rethinking approaches to risk reduction for injection drug users: differences in drug type affect risk for HIV and hepatitis C virus infection through drug-injecting networks', *Journal of Acquired Immune Deficiency Syndromes* 46 (3), pp. 355–61.

De Lima, M. S., De Oliviera Soares, B. G., Reisser, A., et al. (2002), 'Pharmacological treatment of cocaine dependence: a systematic review', *Addiction* 97 (8), pp. 931–49.

De Letter, E. A., Piette, M. H., Lambert, W. E. and Cordonnier, J. A. (2006), 'Amphetamines as potential inducers of fatalities: a review in the district of Ghent from 1976–2004', *Medicine, Science and the Law* 46 (1), pp. 37–65.

Decorte, T. (2001), *The taming of cocaine: cocaine use in European and American cities*, VUB University Press, Brussel.

Degenhardt, L., Mathers, B., Guarinieri, M. , Panda, S., Phillips, B., Strathdee, S. A., Tyndall, M., Wiessing, L., Wodak, A., Howard, J., on behalf of the Reference Group to the United Nations on HIV and injecting drug use (2010), 'Meth/amphetamine use and associated HIV: Implications for global policy and public health', (corrected proof, 01 February 2010), *International Journal of Drug Policy*, 21, DOI: 10.1016/j.drugpo.2009.11.007.

Derauf, C., Lagasse, L. L., Smith, L. M., et al. (2007), 'Demographic and psychosocial characteristics of mothers using methamphetamine during pregnancy: preliminary results of the infant development, environment, and lifestyle study (IDEAL)', *American Journal of Drug and Alcohol Abuse* 33 (2), pp. 281–9.

Des Jarlais, D. C., Grund J-P. C., Zadoretzky, C., et al. (2002), 'HIV risk behaviour among participants of syringe exchange programmes in central/eastern Europe and Russia', *International Journal of Drug Policy* 13, pp. 165–74.

Des Jarlais, D. C., McKnight, C., Goldblatt, C. and Purchase, D. (2009), 'Doing harm reduction better: syringe exchange in the United States', *Addiction*, 104 (9), pp. 1441–6.

Dietze, P., Cantwell, K. and Burgess, S. (2002), 'Bystander resuscitation attempts at heroin overdose: does it improve outcomes?', *Drug and Alcohol Dependence* 67 (2), pp. 213–18.

Downes, M. A. and Whyte, I. M. (2005), 'Amphetamine-induced movement disorder', *Emergency Medicine Australia* 17, pp. 277–80.

Draper, E. S., Rankin, J. and Tonks, A. M., et al. (2008), 'Recreational drug use: a major risk factor for gastroschisis?', *American Journal of Epidemiology* 167 (4), pp. 485–91.

Dutra, L., Stathopoulou, G., Basden, S. L., et al. (2008), 'A meta-analytic review of psychosocial interventions for substance use disorders', *American Journal of Psychiatry* 165 (2), pp. 179–87.

Edlin, B. R., Irwin, K. L., Ludwig, D. D., et al. (1992), 'High-risk sex behaviour among young street-recruited crack cocaine smokers in three American cities: an interim report', The Multicenter Crack Cocaine and HIV Infection Study Team, *Journal of Psychoactive Drugs* 24, pp. 363–71.

Edlin, B. R., Irwin, K. L., Faruque, S., et al.(1994), 'Intersecting epidemics: crack cocaine use and HIV infection among inner-city young adults', Multicenter Crack Cocaine and HIV Infection Study Team, *New England Journal of Medicine* 331, pp. 1422–7.

Elkashef, A., Vocci, F., Hanson, G., et al. (2008), 'Pharmacotherapy of methamphetamine addiction: an update', *Substance Abuse* 29 (3), pp. 31–49.

EMCDDA (European Monitoring Centre for Drugs and Drug Addiction) (2007a), *Annual report 2007: highlights*, Figure 7. Available at http://www.emcdda.europa.eu/html.cfm/index42367EN.html (accessed on 19 July 2009).

EMCDDA (2007b), Statistical bulletin, Figure GPS-13. Available at http://www.emcdda.europa.eu/stats09/gpsfig13 (accessed on 19 July 2009).

EMCDDA (2007c), Statistical bulletin, Table PDU-2. Available at http://www.emcdda.europa.eu/stats07/pdutab02b (accessed on 19 July 2009).

EMCDDA (2007d), Statistical bulletin 2007. Available at http://www.emcdda.europa.eu/stats07/GPS (accessed on 19 July 2009).

EMCDDA (2007e), *Treatment of problem cocaine use: a review of the literature*, EMCDDA, Lisbon. Available at http://www.emcdda.europa.eu/html.cfm/index40152EN.html (accessed on 17 December 2009).

EMCDDA (2007f), *Cocaine and crack cocaine: a growing public health issue*, EMCDDA, Lisbon. Available at http://www.emcdda.europa.eu/html.cfm/index44746EN.html (accessed on 23 January 2010).

EMCDDA (2008), *Annual report*. Available at http://www.emcdda.europa.eu/publications/annual-report/2008 (accessed on 19 July 2009).

EMCDDA (2009), Statistical bulletin 2009. Available at http://www.emcdda.europa.eu/stats09/gps (accessed on 19 July 2009).

Farre, M., De La Torre, R., Gonzalez, M. L., et al. (1997), 'Cocaine and alcohol interactions in humans: neuroendocrine effects and cocaethylene metabolism', *Journal of Pharmacology and Experimental Therapeutics* 283 (1), pp. 164–76.

Farrell, M., Marsden, J., Ling, L., Ali, R. and Gowing, L. (2005), *Effectiveness of drug dependence treatment in preventing HIV among injecting drug users: evidence for action technical paper*, World Health Organization, Geneva.

Faruque, S., Edlin, B. R., McCoy, C. B., et al. (1996), 'Crack cocaine smoking and oral sores in three inner-city neighborhoods', *Journal of Acquired Immune Deficiency Syndromes and Human Retrovirology* 13, pp. 87–92.

Ferris, M. J., Mactutus, C. F. and Booze, R. M. (2008), 'Neurotoxic profiles of HIV, psychostimulant drugs of abuse, and their concerted effect on the brain: current status of dopamine system vulnerability in NeuroAIDS', *Neuroscience and Behavioural Reviews* 32 (5), pp. 883–909.

Finelli, L., Budd, J. and Spitalny, K.C. (1993), 'Early syphilis: relationship to sex, drugs, and changes in high-risk behaviour from 1987–1990', *Sexually Transmitted Diseases* 20, pp. 89–95.

Fischer, B., Rehm, J., Patra, J., et al. (2006), 'Crack across Canada: comparing crack users and crack non-users in a Canadian multi-city cohort of illicit opioid users', *Addiction* 101, pp. 1760–70.

Fischer, B., Powis, J., Firestone, C. M., Rudzinski, K. and Rehm, J. (2008), 'Hepatitis C virus transmission among oral crack users: viral detection on crack paraphernalia', *European Journal of Gastroenterology & Hepatology* 20, pp. 29–32.

Fletcher, A., Calafat, A., Pirona, A. and Olszewski, D. (2010), 'Young people, recreational drug use and harm reduction', in European Monitoring Centre for Drugs and Drug Addiction (EMCDDA), *Harm reduction: evidence, impacts and challenges*, Rhodes, T. and Hedrich, D. (eds), Scientific Monograph Series No. 10, Publications Office of the European Union, Luxembourg.

Fleury, G., De La Garza, R., Mahoney, J. J., Evans, S. E. and Newton, T. F. (2008), 'Predictors of cardiovascular response to methamphetamine administration in methamphetamine-dependent individuals', *American Journal on Addictions* 17 (2), pp. 103–10.

Frank, D. A., Augustyn, M., Knight, W. G., Pell, T. and Zuckerman, B. (2001), 'Growth, development, and behavior in early childhood following prenatal cocaine exposure: a systematic review', *JAMA* 285 (12), pp. 1613–25.

Frieden, J. (2006), 'Skin manifestations may signal crystal meth use: think "meth mites" when patients are picking at their skin and think they have insects crawling on them', Skin disorders, *Family Practice News*. Available at http://www.accessmylibrary.com/coms2/summary_0286-12689367_ITM (accessed on 19 July 2009).

Friedman, S. R., Flom, P. L., Kottiri, R., et al. (2003), 'Drug use patterns and infection with sexually transmissible agents among young adults in a high-risk neighbourhood in New York City', *Addiction* 98, pp. 159–69.

Friedman, S. R., Bolyard, M. and Mateu-Gelabert, P. (2007), 'Some data-driven reflections on priorities in AIDS network research', *AIDS and Behaviour* 11 (5), pp. 641–51.

Gates, S., Smith, L. A. and Foxcroft, D. R. (2006), 'Auricular acupuncture for cocaine dependence', *Cochrane Database of Systematic Reviews* 1, CD005192.

General Assembly of the United Nations (1948), *The Universal Declaration of Human Rights*. Available at http://www.un.org/en/documents/udhr/.

Gibson, D. R., Leamon, M. H. and Flynn, N. (2002), 'Epidemiology and public health consequences of methamphetamine use in California's Central Valley', *Journal of Psychoactive Drugs* 34, pp. 313–19.

Glauser, J. and Queen, J. R. (2007), 'An overview of non-cardiac cocaine toxicity', *Journal of Emergency Medicine* 32 (2), pp. 181–6.

Gollub, E. L. (2008), 'A neglected population: drug-using women and women's methods of HIV/STI prevention', *AIDS Education and Prevention* 20, pp. 107–20.

Golub, M., Costa, L., Crofton, K., et al. (2005), 'NTP-CERHR Expert Panel Report on the reproductive and developmental toxicity of amphetamine and methamphetamine', *Birth Defects Research Part B: Developmental and Reproductive Toxicology* 74 (6), pp. 471–584.

Goodkin, K., Shapshak, P., Metsch, L. R., et al. (1998), 'Cocaine abuse and HIV-1 infection: epidemiology and neuropathogenesis', *Journal of Neuroimmune Pharmacology* 83 (1–2), pp. 88–101.

Gostin, L. O. (1998), 'The legal environment impeding access to sterile syringes and needles: the conflict between law enforcement and public health', *Journal of Acquired Immune Deficiency Syndromes and Human Retrovirology* 18 (Supplement 1), pp. S60–S70.

Grabowski, J., Rhoades, H., Stotts, A., et al. (2004), 'Agonist-like or antagonist-like treatment for cocaine dependence with methadone for heroin dependence: two double-blind randomized clinical trials', *Neuropsychopharmacology* 29 (5), pp. 969–81.

Grau, L.E., Arevalo, S., Catchpool, C., Heimer, R. for the Diffusion of Benefit through Syringe Exchange Study Team (2002), 'Expanding harm reduction services through a wound and abscess clinic', *American Journal of Public Health* 92, pp. 1915–17.

Griffiths, P., Mravcik, V., Lopez, D. and Klempova, D. (2008), 'Quite a lot of smoke but very limited fire: the use of methamphetamine in Europe', *Drug and Alcohol Review* 27 (3), pp. 236–42.

Gross, M., Holte, S. E., Marmor, M., et al. (2000), 'Anal sex among HIV-seronegative women at high risk of HIV exposure', The HIVNET Vaccine Preparedness Study 2 Protocol Team, Journal of Acquired Immune Deficiency Syndromes 24, pp. 393–8.

Grund, J-P. C. (1993), Drug use as a social ritual: functionality, symbolism and determinants of self-regulation, Addiction Research Institute (IVO), Rotterdam. Available at http://www.drugtext.org/library/books/grund01/grundcon.html.

Grund, J-P. C. (2001), 'A candle lit from both sides: the epidemic of HIV infection in central and eastern Europe', in McElrath, K. (ed.), HIV and AIDS: a global view, Greenwood Press, Westport, CT.

Grund, J-P. C. and Blanken, P. (1993), From 'Chasing the dragon' to 'Chinezen': the diffusion of heroin smoking in the Netherlands, Addiction Research Institute (IVO), Rotterdam. Available at http://www.drugtext.org/library/books/grund/CHASDRAG.html.

Grund, J-P. C. and Merkinaite, S. (2009), Young people and injecting drug use in selected countries of Central and Eastern Europe, Young IDUs Working Group, EHRN, Vilnius.

Grund, J-P.C., Adriaans, N.F.P. and Kaplan, C.D. (1991a), 'Changing cocaine smoking rituals in the Dutch heroin addict population', British Journal of Addiction 86, pp. 439–48.

Grund, J-P. C., Kaplan, C. D. and Adriaans, N. F. P. (1991b), 'Needle sharing in the Netherlands: an ethnographic analysis', American Journal of Public Health 81, pp. 1602–07.

Grund, J-P. C., Blanken, P., Adriaans, N. F. P., et al. (1992a), 'Reaching the unreached: targeting hidden IDU populations with clean needles via known users', Journal of Psychoactive Drugs 24 (1), pp. 41–7.

Grund, J-P. C., Stern, L. S., Kaplan, C. D., Adriaans, N. F. P. and Drucker, E. (1992b), 'Drug use contexts and HIV-consequences: the effect of drug policy on patterns of everyday drug use in Rotterdam and the Bronx', British Journal of Addiction 87, pp. 381–92.

Grund, J-P. C., Öfner, P. J. and Verbraeck, H. T. (2007a), Marel o Del, kas kamel, le Romes duvar (God hits whom he chooses, the Rom gets hit twice): an exploration of drug use and HIV risks among the Roma of central and eastern Europe, L'Harmattan, Budapest.

Grund, J-P. C., Reinerie, P., Smits, M. and Albert, G. (2007b), 'Uitgaan en genotmiddelengebruik in Den Haag: gegevens over 2006–2007 uit de panelstudie', Epidemiologisch Bulletin 42 (4), pp. 2–10. Available at http://www.denhaag.nl/Docs/ocw/GGD/Epibul/Epi%20nr%204%202007.pdf.

Grund, J-P.C., Zabransky, T., Irwin, K. and Heimer R. (2009), 'Stimulant use in central and eastern Europe: how recent social history shaped current drug consumption patterns', in Pates, R. and Riley, D. (eds), Interventions for amphetamine misuse, Wiley Blackwell, Oxford.

Guerot, E., Sanchez, O., Diehl, J. L. and Fagon, J. Y. (2002), 'Acute complications in cocaine users', Ann Med Interne (Paris) 153 (3 Supplement), pp. 1S27–31.

Gyarmathy, V. A., Neaigus, A., Miller. M., Friedman, S. R. and Des, J. (2002), 'Risk correlates of prevalent HIV, hepatitis B virus, and hepatitis C virus infections among noninjecting heroin users', Journal of Acquired Immune Deficiency Syndromes 30, pp. 448–56.

Haasen, C., Prinzleve, M., Zurhold, H., et al. (2003), Support needs for cocaine and crack users in Europe, Zentrum für Interdisziplinäre Suchtforschung, Hamburg.

Haasen, C., Prinzleve, M., Zurhold, H., et al. (2004), 'Cocaine use in Europe: a multi-centre study', European Addiction Research, 10 (4), pp. 139–46.

Haasen, C., Prinzleve, M., Gossop, M., et al. (2005), 'Relationship between cocaine use and mental health problems in a sample of European cocaine powder or crack users', *World Psychiatry* 4, pp. 173–6.

Hagan, H., Thiede, H. and Des Jarlais, D. C. (2005), 'HIV/hepatitis C virus co-infection in drug users: risk behaviour and prevention', *AIDS* 19 (Supplement 3), pp. S199–S207.

Haigney, M. C., Alam, S., Tebo, S., et al. (2006), 'Intravenous cocaine and QT variability', *Journal of Cardiovascular Electrophysiology* 17 (6), pp. 610–16.

Hall, W. and Carter, L. (2004), 'Ethical issues in using a cocaine vaccine to treat and prevent cocaine abuse and dependence', *Journal of Medical Ethics* 30 (4), pp. 337–40.

Hall, W., Hando, J., Darke, S. and Ross, J. (1996), 'Psychological morbidity and route of administration among amphetamine users in Sydney, Australia', *Addiction* 91, pp. 81–7.

Hando, J., Flaherty, B. and Rutter, S. (1991), 'An Australian profile on the use of cocaine', *Addiction* 92, pp. 173–82.

Harris, L. H. and Paltrow, L. (2003), 'Msjama: the status of pregnant women and fetuses in US criminal law', *JAMA* 289 (13), pp. 1697–9.

Haverkos, H. W. and Steel, E. (1991), 'Crack cocaine, fellatio, and the transmission of HIV', *American Journal of Public Health* 81, pp. 1078–9.

Haydon, E., and Fischer, B. (2005), 'Crack use as a public health problem in Canada: call for an evaluation of "safer crack use kits"', *Canadian Journal of Public Health* 96, pp. 185–8.

Health Council of the Netherlands (2002), *Pharmacotherapeutic interventions in drug addiction*, Health Council of the Netherlands, The Hague, publication no. 2002/10.

Hedetoft, C. and Christensen, H. R. (1999), 'Amphetamine, ecstasy and cocaine: clinical aspects of acute poisoning', *Ugeskr Laeger* 161 (50), pp. 6907–11.

Hedrich, D. (2004), *European report on drug consumption rooms*, European Monitoring Centre for Drugs and Drug Addiction (EMCDDA), Portugal.

Heffernan, R., Chiasson, M. A. and Sackoff, J. E. (1996), 'HIV risk behaviours among adolescents at a sexually transmitted disease clinic in New York City', *Journal of Adolescent Health* 18, pp. 429–34.

Heimer, R., Booth, R. E., Irwin, K. S. and Merson, M. H. (2007), 'HIV and drug use in Eurasia', in Twigg, J. L. (ed.), *HIV/AIDS in Russia and Eurasia*, Palgrave Macmillan, Basingstoke.

Heng, C. K., Badner, V. M. and Schiop, L. A. (2008), 'Meth mouth', *New York State Dental Journal* 74 (5), pp. 50–1.

Henskens, R. (2004), 'Grab and hold: randomized controlled trial of the effectiveness of an outreach treatment program for chronic high-risk crack abusers' (dissertatie), GGD Rotterdam, Universiteit van Tilburg.

Hermida, M., Ferreiro, M. C., Barral, S., Laredo, R., Castro, A. and Diz, D. P. (2002), 'Detection of HCV RNA in saliva of patients with hepatitis C virus infection by using a highly sensitive test', *Journal of Virological Methods* 101, pp. 29–35.

Hildrey, Z., Thomas, S. E. and Smith A. (2009), 'The physical effects of amphetamine use', in Pates, R. and Riley, D. (eds), *Interventions for amphetamine misuse*, Wiley-Blackwell, Oxford, pp. 173–204.

Hinkle, Nancy C. (2000), 'Delusory parasitosis', *American Entomologist* 46 (1), pp. 17–25.

Holman, R. B. (1994), 'Biological effects of central nervous system stimulants', *Addiction* 89 (11), pp. 1435–41.

Horwitz, R. I., Hines, H. H., Brass, L. M., Kernan, W. N. and Viscoli, C. M. (2000), *Phenylpropanolamine and risk of hemorrhagic stroke: final report of the hemorrhagic stroke project*, Yale University School of Medicine. Available at http://www.fda.gov/ohrms/dockets/ac/00/backgrd/3647b1_tab19.doc.

Hunt, N. (2006), *Paper C. An overview of models of delivery of drug consumption rooms, supporting evidence to The Report of the Independent Working Group on Drug Consumption Rooms*, Joseph Rowntree Foundation, York.

Hunt, N., Ashton, M., Lenton, S., et al. (2003), *A review of the evidence-base for harm reduction approaches to drug use*, Forward Thinking on Drugs, London.

Hunt, N., Trace, M. and Bewley-Taylor, D. (2005), *Reducing drug-related harms to health: a global overview of the evidence*, Beckley Foundation, London.

Hurtado-Gumucio, J. (2000), 'Coca leaf chewing as therapy for cocaine maintenance', *Annales de Médicine Interne* 151 (Supplement B), pp. 44–8.

Islam, M. M. and Conigrave, K. M. (2007), 'Assessing the role of syringe dispensing machines and mobile van outlets in reaching hard-to-reach and high-risk groups of injecting drug users (IDUs): a review', *Harm Reduction Journal*, 4: 14 (DOI: 10.1186/1477-7517-4-14).

IWGDCR (Independent Working Group on Drug Consumption Room) (2006), *The report of the Independent Working Group on Drug Consumption Rooms*, Joseph Rowntree Foundation, York.

Jaffe, C., Bush, K. R., Straits-Troster, K., et al. (2005), 'A comparison of methamphetamine-dependent inpatients childhood attention deficit hyperactivity disorder symptomatology', *Journal of Addictive Diseases* 24 (3), pp. 133–52.

Jaffe, J. A. and Kimmel, P. L. (2006), 'Chronic nephropathies of cocaine and heroin abuse: a critical review', *Clinical Journal of the American Society of Nephrology* 1 (4), pp. 655–67.

Jauffret-Roustide, M. (2004), *Les drogues: approche sociologique, économique et politique*, La Documentation Française ed., Paris.

Jauffret-Roustide, M., Couturier, E., Le Strat, Y., et al. (2006), 'Estimation de la séroprévalence du VIH et du VHC et profils des usagers de drogues en France, étude InVS-ANRS Coquelicot, 2004', *Bull Epidemiol Hebd* 33, pp. 244–7.

Jauffret-Roustide, M., Rondy, M., Oudaya, L., Pequart, C., Semaille, C. and Desenclos, J. C. (2008a), 'Evaluation d'un outil de réduction des risques visant à limiter la transmission du VIH et des hépatites chez les consommateurs de crack', *Rev Epidemiol Sante Publique*, 56, p. 376.

Jauffret-Roustide, M., Oudaya, L., Rondy, M., et al. (2008b), 'Life trajectory and risk-taking among women drug users', *Med Sci (Paris)* 24 (Spec No. 2), pp. 111–21.

Jauffret-Roustide, M., Le Strat, Y. , Couturier, E., et al. (2009), 'A national cross-sectional study among drug-users: estimates of HCV prevalence and highlight on practical and statistical aspects in the design', *BMC Infectious Diseases* 9, pp. 113–25.

Johnston, L. D., O'Malley, P. M., Bachman, J. G. and Schulenberg, J. E. (2004), *Monitoring the future national results on adolescent drug use: overview of key findings, 2003*, National Institute on Drug Abuse, Bethesda, MD.

Kampman, K. M., Leiderman, D., Holmes, T., et al. (2005), 'Cocaine Rapid Efficacy Screening Trials (CREST): lessons learned', *Addiction* 100 (S1), pp. 102–10.

Karch, S. B. (2005), 'Cocaine cardiovascular toxicity', *Southern Medical Journal* 98 (8), pp. 794–9.

Kaye, S. and Darke, S. (2004), 'Non-fatal cocaine overdose among injecting and non-injecting cocaine users in Sydney, Australia', *Addiction* 99 (10), pp. 1315–22.

Kearney, M. H., Murphy, S. and Rosenbaum, M. (1994), 'Mothering on crack cocaine: a grounded theory analysis', *Social Science & Medicine* 38 (2), pp. 351–61.

Kearney, M. H., Murphy, S., Irwin, K. and Rosenbaum, M. (1995), 'Salvaging self: a grounded theory of pregnancy on crack cocaine', *Nursing Research* 44 (4), pp. 208–13.

Kelly, B. C. (2009), 'Mediating MDMA-related harm: preloading and post-loading among ecstasy-using youth', *Journal of Psychoactive Drugs* 41 (1), pp. 19–26.

Kerr, T., Wood, E. Grafstein, E., et al. (2005), 'High rates of primary care and emergency department use among injection drug users', *Vancouver Journal of Public Health* 27 (1), pp. 62–66 (Doi:10.1093/Pubmed/Fdh189).

Kertesz, S. G., Madan, A., Wallace, D., Schumacher, J. E. and Milby, J. B. (2006), 'Substance abuse treatment and psychiatric comorbidity: do benefits spill over? Analysis of data from a prospective trial among cocaine-dependent homeless persons', *Substance Abuse Treatment, Prevention, and Policy* 1, p. 27.

Kertesz, S. G., Pletcher, M. J., Safford, M., et al. (2007), 'Illicit drug use in young adults and subsequent decline in general health: the coronary artery risk development in young adults (cardia) study', *Drug and Alcohol Dependence* 88 (2–3), pp. 224–33.

Kilbride, H., Castor, C., Hoffman, E. and Fuger, K. L. (2000), 'Thirty-six-month outcome of prenatal cocaine exposure for term or near-term infants: impact of early case management', *Journal of Developmental & Behavioral Pediatrics* 21 (1), pp. 19–26.

Kilbride, H. W., Castor, C. A. and Fuger, K. L. (2006), 'School-age outcome of children with prenatal cocaine exposure following early case management', *Journal of Developmental & Behavioral Pediatrics* 27 (3), pp. 181–7.

Kim, Y. H., Schiff, E., Waalen, J. and Hovell, M. (2005), 'Efficacy of acupuncture for treating cocaine addiction: a review paper,' *Journal of Addictive Diseases* 24, pp. 115–32.

Kimber, J., Palmateer, N., Hutchinson, S., et al. (2010), 'Harm reduction among injecting drug users: evidence of effectiveness', in European Monitoring Centre for Drugs and Drug Addiction (EMCDDA), *Harm reduction: evidence, impacts and challenges*, Rhodes, T. and Hedrich, D. (eds), Scientific Monograph Series No. 10, Publications Office of the European Union, Luxembourg.

Klemmt, L. and Scialli, A. R. (2005), 'The transport of chemicals in semen', *Birth Defects Research Part B: Developmental and Reproductive Toxicology* 74 (2), pp. 119–31.

Kloner, R. A., Hale, S., Alker, K. and Rezkalla, S. (1992), 'The effects of acute and chronic cocaine use on the heart', *Circulation* 85 (2), pp. 407–19.

Knox, E. G. (1989), 'Detection of clusters', in Elliott, P. (ed.), *Methodology of enquiries into disease clustering*, Small Area Health Statistics Unit, London, pp. 17–20.

Knuepfer, M. M. (2003), 'Cardiovascular disorders associated with cocaine use: myths and truths', *Pharmacology and Therapeutics* 97 (3), pp. 181–222.

Koblin, B. A., Husnik, M. J., Colfax, G., et al. (2006), 'Risk factors for HIV infection among men who have sex with men', *Aids* 20 (5), pp. 731–9.

Kottiri, B. J., Friedman, S. R., Euler, G. L., et al. (2005), 'A community-based study of hepatitis B infection and immunization among young adults in a high-drug-use neighborhood in New York City', *Journal of Urban Health* 82, pp. 479–87.

Kozlov, A. P., Shaboltas, A. V., Toussova, O. V., et al. (2006), 'HIV incidence and factors associated with HIV acquisition among injection drug users in St Petersburg, Russia', *AIDS* 20 (6), pp. 901–06.

Kral, A. H., Bluthenthal, R. N., Booth, R. E. and Watters, J. K. (1998), 'HIV seroprevalence among street-recruited injection drug and crack cocaine users in 16 US municipalities', *American Journal of Public Health* 88, pp. 108–13.

Kral, A. H., Bluthenthal, R. N., Lorvick, J., et al. (2001), 'Sexual transmission of HIV-1 among injection drug users in San Francisco, USA: risk factor analysis', *Lancet* 357, pp. 1397–401.

Kuczkowski, K. M. (2007), 'The effects of drug abuse on pregnancy', *Current Opinion in Obstetrics and Gynecology* 19 (6), pp. 578–85.

Kwiatkowski, C. F., Fortuin, C. K. and Booth, R. E. (2002), 'The association between knowledge of hepatitis C virus status and risk behaviours in injection drug users', *Addiction* 97, pp. 1289–94.

Latka, M. (2003), 'Drug-using women need comprehensive sexual risk reduction interventions', *Clinical Infectious Diseases* 37 (Supplement 5), pp. S445–S450.

Lee, C. S. (2008), 'Delusions of parasitosis', *Dermatologic Therapy* 21 (1), pp. 2–7 (US: http://dx.doi.org/10.1111/j.1529-8019.2008.00163.x).

Leicht, A., (1993), *Characteristics and HIV-infection of users of syringe vending-machines and exchanging programs in Berlin/Germany*, Berlin.

Leiderman, D. B. (2005), 'Cocaine Rapid Efficacy Screening Trial (CREST): a paradigm for the controlled evaluation of candidate medications for cocaine dependence', *Addiction* 100 (Supplement 1), pp. 1–11.

Lejuez, C. W., Bornovalova, M. A., Daughters, S. B. and Curtin, J. J. (2005), 'Differences in impulsivity and sexual risk behaviour among inner-city crack/cocaine users and heroin users', *Drug and Alcohol Dependence* 77, pp. 169–75.

Leonard, L., Meadows, E., Pelude, L., et al. (2006), *Results of the evaluation of the City of Ottawa's Public Health Department's Safer Crack Use initiative: a harm reduction success*, Ontario HIV Treatment Network Research Conference, Toronto, 27–28 November.

Leonard, L., De Rubeis, E., Pelude, L., et al. (2007), 'I inject less as I have easier access to pipes: injecting, and sharing of crack-smoking materials, decline as safer crack-smoking resources are distributed', *International Journal of Drug Policy*, pp. 1–10.

Lester, B. M., Lagasse, L., Seifer, R., et al. (2003), 'The Maternal Lifestyle Study (MLS): effects of prenatal cocaine and/or opiate exposure on auditory brain response at one month', *Journal of Pediatrics* 142 (3), pp. 279–85.

Lester, B. M., Andreozzi, L. and Appiah, L. (2004), 'Substance use during pregnancy: time for policy to catch up with research', *Harm Reduction Journal* 1 (1), p. 5.

Llosa, T. (1994), 'The standard low dose of oral cocaine: used for treatment of cocaine dependence', *Substance Abuse* 15 (4), pp. 215–20.

Lloyd-Smith, E., Wood, E., Zhang, R., et al. (2008), 'Risk factors for developing a cutaneous injection-related infection among injection drug users: a cohort study', *BMC Public Health* 8, p. 405.

Lussier, J. P., Heil, S. H., Mongeon, J. A. et al. (2006), 'A meta-analysis of voucher-based reinforcement therapy for substance use disorders', *Addiction* 101 (2), pp. 192–203.

Maher, L., Li, J., Jalaludin, B., Chant, K. G. and Kaldor, J. M. (2007), 'High hepatitis C incidence in new injecting drug users: a policy failure?' *Australian and New Zealand Journal of Public Health* 31 (1), pp. 30–5.

Malakmadze, N., Gonzalez, I. M., Oemig, T., et al. (2005), 'Unsuspected recent transmission of tuberculosis among high-risk groups: implications of universal tuberculosis genotyping in its detection', *Clinical Infectious Diseases* 40, pp. 366–73.

Malchy, L., Bungay, V. and Johnson, J. (2008), 'Documenting practices and perceptions of "safer" crack use: a Canadian pilot study', *International Journal of Drug Policy* 19, pp. 339–41.

Maliphant, J. and Scott, J. (2005), 'Use of the femoral vein ("groin injecting") by a sample of needle exchange clients in Bristol, UK', *Harm Reduction Journal*, 2, p. 6 (DOI:10.1186/1477-7517-2-6).

Maranda, M. J., Han, C. and Rainone, G. A. (2004), 'Crack cocaine and sex', *Journal of Psychoactive Drugs* 36, pp. 315–22.

Martell, B. A., Orson, F. M., Poling, J., et al. (2009), 'Cocaine vaccine for the treatment of cocaine dependence in methadone-maintained patients', *Archives of General Psychiatry* 66 (10), pp. 1116–23.

Martin, D. H. and DiCarlo, R. P. (1994), 'Recent changes in the epidemiology of genital ulcer disease in the United States: the crack cocaine connection', *Sexually Transmitted Diseases* 21, pp. S76–S80.

Mas, M., Farre, M., De La Torre, R., et al. (1999), 'Cardiovascular and neuroendocrine effects and pharmacokinetics of 3, 4-Methylenedioxymethamphetamine in humans', *Journal of Pharmacology and Experimental Therapeutics* 290 (1), pp. 136–45.

Maxwell, S., Bigg, D., Stanczykiewicz, K. and Carlberg-Racich, S. (2006), 'Prescribing naloxone to actively injecting heroin users: a program to reduce heroin overdose deaths', *Journal of Addictive Diseases* 25 (3), pp. 89–96.

Mayaud, C., Boussaud, V., Saidi, F. and Parrot, A. (2001), 'Bronchopulmonary disease in drug abusers', *Revue de pneumologie Clinique* 57 (4), pp. 259–69.

McCord, J., Jneid, H., Hollander, J. E., et al. (2008), 'Management of cocaine-associated chest pain and myocardial infarction: a scientific statement from the American Heart Association Acute Cardiac Care Committee of the Council on Clinical Cardiology', *Circulation* 117 (14), pp. 1897–907.

McCoy, C. B., Lai, S., Metsch, L. R., Messiah, S. E. and Zhao, W. (2004), 'Injection drug use and crack cocaine smoking: independent and dual risk behaviours for HIV infection', *Annals of Epidemiology* 14, pp. 535–42.

McCoy, H. V. and Miles C. A. (1992), 'Gender comparison of health status among users of crack cocaine', *Journal of Psychoactive Drugs* 24, pp. 389–97.

McElroy, P. D., Rothenberg, R. B., Varghese, R. et al. (2003), 'A network-informed approach to investigating a tuberculosis outbreak: implications for enhancing contact investigations', *International Journal of Tuberculosis and Lung Disease* 7, pp. S486–S493.

McMahon, J. M., Simm, M., Milano, D. and Clatts, M. (2004), 'Detection of hepatitis C virus in the nasal secretions of an intranasal drug-user', *Annals of Clinical Microbiology and Antimicrobials*, 3 (6). Available at http://www.ann-clinmicrob.com/content/pdf/1476-0711-3-6.pdf (accessed on 23 January 2010).

McPartland, J. M. and Pruitt, P. L. (1997), 'Medical marijuana and its use by the immunocompromised', *Alternative Therapies in Health and Medicine* 3 (3), pp. 39–45.

Mehrabadi, A., Craib, K. J., Patterson, K., et al. (2008), 'The Cedar Project: a comparison of HIV-related vulnerabilities amongst young Aboriginal women surviving drug use and sex work in two Canadian cities', *International Journal of Drug Policy* 19, pp. 159–68.

Mesquita, F., Kral, A., Reingold, A., et al. (2001), 'Overdoses among cocaine users in Brazil', *Addiction* 96 (12), pp. 1809–13.

Miller, C. L., Tyndall, M., Spittal, P., et al. (2002), 'Risk-taking behaviors among injecting drug users who obtain syringes from pharmacies, fixed sites and mobile van needle exchanges', *Journal of Urban Health* 79 (2), pp. 257–65.

Milloy, M. J., Kerr, T., Tyndall, M., Montaner, J. and Wood, E. (2008), 'Estimated drug overdose deaths averted by North America's first medically-supervised safer injection facility', *PloS ONE* 3 (10), p. E3351.

Minkoff, H., Zhong, Y., Strickler, H. D., et al. (2008), 'The relationship between cocaine use and human papillomavirus infections in HIV-seropositive and HIV-seronegative women', *Infectious Diseases in Obstetrics and Gynecology*, Article ID 587082, 7 pages (DOI: 10.1155/2008/587082).

Mitchell, S. J., Morris, S. R., Kent, C. K., Stansell, J. and Klausner, J. D. (2006), 'Methamphetamine use and sexual activity among HIV-infected patients in care — San Francisco', *AIDS Patient Care and STDs* 20 (7), pp. 502–10.

Moatti, J. P., Vlahov, D., Feroni, I., Perrin, V. and Obadia, Y. (2001), 'Multiple access to sterile syringes for injection drug users: vending machines, needle exchange programs and legal pharmacy sales in Marseille, France', *European Addiction Research* 7, pp. 40–5.

Moeller, F. G., Barrat, E. S., Dougherty, D. M., et al. (2008), 'Use of stimulants to treat cocaine and methamphetamine abuse', *Current Psychiatry Reports* 10 (5), pp. 385–91.

Morgan, M. J. (2000), 'Ecstasy (MDMA): a review of its possible persistent psychological effects', *Psychopharmacology* 152, pp. 230–48.

Murphy, E. L., DeVita, D., Liu, H., et al. (2001), 'Risk factors for skin and soft-tissue abscesses among injection drug users: a case-control study', *Clinical Infectious Diseases* 33, pp. 35–40.

Murphy, S. and Rosenbaum, M. (1999), *Pregnant women on drugs: combating stereotypes and stigma*, Rutgers University Press, New Jersey.

Nabben, T., Benschop, A. and Korf, D. J. (2007), *Antenna 2006. Trends in alcohol, tabak en drugs bij jonge Amsterdammers*, Rozenberg Publishers, Amsterdam.

Nath, A., Hauser, K. F., Wojna, V., et al. (2002), 'Molecular basis for interactions of HIV and drugs of abuse', *Journal of Acquired Immune Deficiency Syndromes* 31 (Supplement 2), pp. S62–S69.

Neaigus, A., Gyarmathy, V. A., Zhao, M., et al. (2007), 'Sexual and other noninjection risks for HBV and HCV seroconversions among noninjecting heroin users', *Journal of Infectious Diseases* 195, pp. 1052–61.

Needle, R. H., Burrows, D., Friedman, S. R., et al. (2005), 'Effectiveness of community-based outreach in preventing HIV/AIDS among injecting drug users', *International Journal of Drug Policy* 16 (Supplement 1), pp. 45–57. (Also at: *Evidence for Action on HIV prevention among Injecting Drug Users*, World Health Organization, Department of HIV/AIDS, Geneva, 2004.) Available at http://www.who.int/hiv/pub/prev_care/en/evidenceforactionalcommunityfinal.pdf (accessed on 23 January 2010).

Ness, R. B., Grisso, J. A., Hirschinger, N., et al. (1999), 'Cocaine and tobacco use and the risk of spontaneous abortion', *New England Journal of Medicine* 340 (5), pp. 333–9.

Newlin, D. B., Wong, C. J., Stapleton, J. M. and London, E. D. (2000), 'Intravenous cocaine decreases cardiac vagal tone, vagal index (derived in lorenz space), and heart period complexity (approximate entropy) in cocaine abusers', *Neuropsychopharmacology* 23 (5), pp. 560–8.

Nnadi, C. U., Mimiko, O. A., Mccurtis, H. L. and Cadet, J. L. (2005), 'Neuropsychiatric effects of cocaine use disorders', *Journal of the National Medical Association* 97 (11), pp. 1504–15.

NTA (2002), 'Treating cocaine/crack dependence', *Research Into Practice: 1a Drug Services Briefing, Drug and Alcohol Findings*, National Treatment Agency for Substance Misuse, London.

Nyamathi, A. M., Dixon, E. L., Robbins, W., et al. (2002), 'Risk factors for hepatitis C virus infection among homeless adults', *The Journal of General Internal Medicine* 17, pp. 134–43.

Obadia, Y., Feroni, I., Perrin, V., Vlahov, D. and Moatti, J. P. (1999), 'Syringe vending machines for injecting drug users: an experiment in Marseille, France', *American Journal of Public Health* 89 (12), pp. 1582–84.

Ochoa, K. C., Davidson, P. J., Evans, J. L., et al. (2005), 'Heroin overdose among young injection drug users in San Francisco', *Drug and Alcohol Dependence* 80 (3), pp. 297–302.

Osher, F. C., Goldberg, R. W., McNary, S. W., et al. (2003), 'Substance abuse and the transmission of hepatitis C among persons with severe mental illness', *Psychiatric Services* 54, pp. 842–7.

Oxman, G. L., Smolkowski, K. and Noell, J. (1996), 'Mathematical modeling of epidemic syphilis transmission: implications for syphilis control programs', *Sexually Transmitted Diseases* 23, pp. 30–9.

Pal, D., Mitra, A. K. (2006), 'MDR- and CYP3A4-mediated drug-drug interactions', *Journal of Neuroimmune Pharmacology* 1 (3), pp. 323–39.

Pates, R. and Riley, D. (2009), 'The psychological and psychiatric effects of amphetamine use', in Pates, R. and Riley, D. (eds), *Interventions for amphetamine misuse*, Wiley-Blackwell, Oxford, pp. 173–204.

Pechansky, F., Woody, G., Inciardi, J., et al. (2006), 'HIV seroprevalence among drug users: an analysis of selected variables based on 10 years of data collection in Porto Alegre, Brazil', *Drug and Alcohol Dependence* 82 (Supplement 1), pp. S109–S113.

Pennings, E. J., Leccese, A. P. and Wolff, F. A. (2002), 'Effects of concurrent use of alcohol and cocaine', *Addiction* 97 (7), pp. 773–83.

Perlman, D. C., Henman, A. R., Kochems, L., et al. (1999), 'Doing a shotgun: a drug use practice and its relationship to sexual behaviours and infection risk', *Social Science & Medicine* 48, pp. 1441–8.

Pirona, A. and Hedrich, D. (2009), *Treatment of problem cocaine use: a short update* (Version 1), EMCDDA, Lisbon. Available at http://www.emcdda.europa.eu/attachements.cfm/att_76877_EN_EMCDDA-cocaine%20 treatment-update.pdf (accessed on 29 November 2009).

Pizzey, R. and Hunt, N. (2008), 'Distributing foil from needle and syringe programmes (NSPs) to promote transitions from heroin injecting to chasing: an evaluation', *Harm Reduction Journal* 5, p. 24.

Pleuvry, N. J. (2009), 'Central nervous system stimulants: basic pharmacology and relevance to anaesthesia', *Anaesthesia and Intensive Care Medicine* 10 (7), pp. 344–7.

Poel, A. van der, Barendregt, C. and Mheen, D. van de (2003), 'Drug consumption rooms in Rotterdam: an explorative description', *European Addiction Research* 9 (2), pp. 94–100.

Popper, K. (1945), *The open society and its enemies* (Vols 1 and 2), George Routledge and Sons, London.

Porter, J. and Bonilla, L. (1993), 'Crack users' cracked lips: an additional HIV risk factor', *American Journal of Public Health* 83, pp. 1490–1.

Poschadel, S., Höger, R., Schnitzler, J. and Schreckenberg, D. (2002), 'Evaluation der Arbeit der Drogenkonsumräume in der Bundesrepublik Deutschland. Endbericht im Auftrag des Bundesministeriums für Gesundheit', ZEUS, Bochum.

Prendergast, M., Podus, D., Finney, J., et al. (2006), 'Contingency management for treatment of substance use disorders: a meta-analysis', *Addiction* 101 (11), pp. 1546–60.

Prinzleve, M., Verthein, U. and Degkwitz, P. (2002), 'Ambulante Suchtakupunktur als Begleittherapie in der Substitutionsbehandlung', Suchttherapie 3, pp. 197–204.

Prinzleve, M., Haasen, C., Zurhold, H., et al. (2004), 'Cocaine use in Europe — a multi-centre study: patterns of use in different groups', European Addiction Research 10 (4), pp. 147–55.

Rhodes, T. (2002), 'The "risk environment": a framework for understanding and reducing drug-related harm', International Journal of Drug Policy 13 (2), pp. 85–94.

Rhodes, T. (2009), 'Risk environments and drug harms: a social science for harm reduction approach', International Journal of Drug Policy 20 (3), pp. 193–201.

Rhodes, T., Stoneman, A., Hope, V., Hunt, N. and Judd, A. (2006), 'Groin injecting in the context of crack cocaine and homelessness: from "risk boundary" to "acceptable risk"?', International Journal of Drug Policy 17, pp. 164–70.

Rhodes, T., Briggs, D., Kimber, J., Jones, S. and Holloway, G. (2007), 'Crack-heroin speedball injection and its implications for vein care: qualitative study', Addiction 102, pp. 1782–90.

Riley, E. D., Safaeian, M., Strathdee, S. et al. (2000), 'Comparing new participants of a mobile versus a pharmacy-based needle exchange program', Journal of Acquired Immune Deficiency Syndromes 24 (1), pp. 57–61.

Rosenblum, A., Nuttbrock, L., McQuistion, H. L., Magura, S. and Joseph, H. (2001), 'Hepatitis C and substance use in a sample of homeless people in New York City', Journal of Addictive Diseases 20, pp. 15–25.

Ross, M. W., Hwang, L. Y., Leonard, L., Teng, M. and Duncan, L. (1999), 'Sexual behaviour, STDs and drug use in a crack house population', International Journal of STD & AIDS 10, pp. 224–30.

Ross, M. W., Hwang, L. Y., Zack, C., Bull, L. and Williams, M. L. (2002), 'Sexual risk behaviours and STIs in drug abuse treatment populations whose drug of choice is crack cocaine', International Journal of STD & AIDS 13, pp. 769–74.

Rothenberg, R. (2007), 'Maintenance of endemicity in urban environments: a hypothesis linking risk, network structure and geography', Sexually Transmitted Infections 83, pp. 10–15 (DOI:10.1136/sti. 2006.017269).

Rotheram-Borus, M. J., Mann, T. and Chabon, B. (1999), 'Amphetamine use and its correlates among youths living with HIV', AIDS Education and Prevention 11 (3), pp. 232–42.

Roy, E., Haley, N., Leclerc, P., Boivin, J. F., Cedras, L. and Vincelette, J. (2001), 'Risk factors for hepatitis C virus infection among street youths', Canadian Medical Association Journal 165, pp. 557–60.

Santibanez, S., Garfein, R., Swartzendruber, A., et al. (2006), 'Update and overview of practical epidemiologic aspects of HIV/AIDS among injection drug users in the United States', Journal of Urban Health 83, pp. 86–100.

Schaper, A., Hofmann, R., Bargain, P., Desel, H., Ebbecke, M. and Langer, C. (2007), 'Surgical treatment in cocaine body packers and body pushers', International Journal of Colorectal Disease 22 (12), pp. 1531–5.

Scheinmann, R., Hagan, H., Lelutiu-Weinberger, C., et al. (2007), 'Non-injection drug use and hepatitis C virus: a systematic review', Drug and Alcohol Dependence 89, pp. 1–12.

Schempf, A. H. (2007), 'Illicit drug use and neonatal outcomes: a critical review', Obstetrical & Gynecological Survey 62 (11), pp. 749–57.

Schifano, F. (2004), 'A bitter pill: overview of ecstasy (MDMA, MDA) related fatalities', Psychopharmacology (Berl) 173 (3–4), pp. 242–8.

Schiller, C. and Allen, P. J. (2005), 'Follow-up of infants prenatally exposed to cocaine', Pediatric Nursing 31 (5), pp. 427–36.

Schindler, C. W., Tella, S. R., Erzouki, H. K. and Goldberg, S. R. (1995), 'Pharmacological mechanisms in cocaine's cardiovascular effects', *Drug and Alcohol Dependence* 37 (3), pp. 183–91.

Scott, J. C., Woods, S. P. and Matt, G. E., et al. (2007), 'Neurocognitive effects of methamphetamine: a critical review and meta-analysis', *Neuropsychology Review* 17 (3), pp. 275–97.

Seidman, S. N., Sterk-Elifson, C. and Aral, S. O. (1994), 'High-risk sexual behaviour among drug-using men', *Sexually Transmitted Diseases* 21, pp. 173–80.

Serraino, D., Franceschi, S., Vaccher, E., et al. (1991), 'Risk factors for human immunodeficiency virus infection in 581 intravenous drug users, northeast Italy, 1984–1988', *International Journal of Epidemiology* 20 (1), pp. 264–70.

Shannon, K., Ishida, T., Morgan, R., et al. (2006), 'Potential community and public health impacts of medically supervised safer smoking facilities for crack cocaine users', *Harm Reduction Journal* 3 (1) (DOI: 10.1186/1477-7517-3-1).

Shannon, K., Rusch, M., Morgan, R., et al. (2008), 'HIV and HCV prevalence and gender-specific risk profiles of crack cocaine smokers and dual users of injection drugs', *Substance Use and Misuse* 43, pp. 521–34.

Shearer, J. (2007), 'Psychosocial approaches to psychostimulant dependence: a systematic review', *Journal of Substance Abuse Treatment* 32 (1), pp. 41–52.

Shearer, J. (2008), 'The principles of agonist pharmacotherapy for psychostimulant dependence', *Drug and Alcohol Review* 27 (3), pp. 301–08.

Shuter, J., Bell, D., Graham, D., Holbrook, K. A. and Bellin, E. Y. (1998), 'Rates of and risk factors for trichomoniasis among pregnant inmates in New York City', *Sexually Transmitted Diseases* 25, pp. 303–07.

Small, D. and Drucker, E. (2008), 'Return to galileo? The inquisition of the international narcotic control board', *Harm Reduction Journal* 5 (16) (DOI: 10.1186/1477-7517-5-16).

Smith, L. M., Lagasse, L. L., Derauf, C., et al. (2006), 'The infant development, environment, and lifestyle study: effects of prenatal methamphetamine exposure, polydrug exposure, and poverty on intrauterine growth', *Pediatrics* 118 (3), pp. 1149–56.

Sorvillo, F., Kovacs, A., Kerndt, P., et al. (1998), 'Risk factors for trichomoniasis among women with human immunodeficiency virus (HIV) infection at a public clinic in Los Angeles County, California: implications for HIV prevention', *American Journal of Tropical Medicine and Hygiene* 58, pp. 495–500.

Sporer, K. A. and Kral, A. H. (2007), 'Prescription naloxone: a novel approach to heroin overdose prevention', *Annals of Emergency Medicine* 49 (2), pp. 172–7.

Stark, K., Leicht, A. and Müller, R. (1994), 'Characteristics of users of syringe vending machines in Berlin', *Sozial und Praventivmedizin* 39 (4), pp. 209–16.

Steinhauer, J. R. And Caulfield, J. B. (2001), 'Spontaneous coronary artery dissection associated with cocaine use: a case report and brief review', *Cardiovascular Pathology* 10 (3), pp. 141–5.

Stern, L. S. (1992), 'Self-injection education for street level sex workers', in O'Hare, P., Newcombe, R., Matthews, A., Buning, E. and Drucker, E. (eds), *The reduction of drug related harm,* Routledge, London.

Stevens, S. J., Estrada, A. L. and Estrada, B. D. (1998), 'HIV sex and drug risk behavior and behavior change in a national sample of injection drug and crack cocaine using women', *Women Health* 27 (1–2), pp. 25–48.

Stoner, B. P., Whittington, W. L., Hughes, J. P., Aral, S. O. and Holmes, K. K. (2000), 'Comparative epidemiology of heterosexual gonococcal and chlamydial networks: implications for transmission patterns', *Sexually Transmitted Diseases* 27, pp. 215–23.

Stöver, H. (2001), *Bestandsaufnahme „Crack-Konsum" in Deutschland: Verbreitung, Konsummuster, Risiken und Hilfeangebote*, BISDRO, Bremen.

Stöver, H. (2002), 'Crack cocaine in Germany: current state of affairs', *Journal of Drug Issues* 32, pp. 413–22.

Strang, J., Zador, D., Lintzeris, N., et al. (2008), 'The fine line between harm reduction and harm production: development of a clinical policy on femoral (groin) injecting', *European Addiction Research* 14 (4), pp. 213–18.

Sughondhabirom, A., Jain, D., Gueorguieva, R. et al. (2005), 'A paradigm to investigate the self-regulation of cocaine administration in humans', *Psychopharmacology* 180 (3), pp. 436–46.

Sutcliffe, C. G., German, D., Sirirojn, B., et al. (2009), 'Patterns of methamphetamine use and symptoms of depression among young adults in northern Thailand', *Drug and Alcohol Dependence* 101, pp. 146–51.

Suzuki, T., Omata, K., Satoh, T., et al. (2005), 'Quantitative detection of hepatitis C virus (HCV) RNA in saliva and gingival crevicular fluid of HCV-infected patients', *Journal of Clinical Microbiology* 43, pp. 4413–7.

Symington, A. (2007), 'Ottawa: crack pipe program cancelled by city council', *HIV/AIDS Policy & Law Review* 12, pp. 29–30.

Templaski, B., Cooper, H., Friedman, S. R., et al. (2008), 'Correlates of syringe coverage for heroin injection in 35 large metropolitan areas in the US in which heroin is the dominant injected drug', *International Journal of Drug Policy* 19, pp. S47–S58.

Terra Filho, M., Yen, C. C., Santos Ude, P. and Munoz, D. R. (2004), 'Pulmonary alterations in cocaine users', Sao Paulo Medical Journal 122 (1), pp. 26–31.

Theall, K. P., Sterk, C. E., Elifson, K. W. and Kidder, D. (2003), 'Factors associated with positive HIV serostatus among women who use drugs: continued evidence for expanding factors of influence', *Public Health Reports* 118, pp. 415–24.

Thomas, J. C., Schoenbach, V. J., Weiner, D. H., Parker, E. A. and Earp, J. A. (1996), 'Rural gonorrhea in the southeastern United States: a neglected epidemic?', *American Journal of Epidemiology* 143, pp. 269–77.

Thorpe, L. E., Ouellet, L. J., Levy, J. R., Williams, I. T. and Monterroso, E. R. (2000), 'Hepatitis C virus infection: prevalence, risk factors, and prevention opportunities among young injection drug users in Chicago, 1997–1999', *Journal of Infectious Diseases* 182, pp. 1588–94.

Thorpe, L. E., Frederick, M., Pitt, J., et al. (2004), 'Effect of hard-drug use on CD4 cell percentage, HIV RNA level, and progression to AIDS-defining class C events among HIV-infected women', *Journal of Acquired Immune Deficiency Syndromes* 37 (3), pp. 1423–30.

Tortu, S., Beardsley, M., Deren, S., et al. (2000), 'HIV infection and patterns of risk among women drug injectors and crack users in low and high sero-prevalence sites', *AIDS Care* 12 (1), pp. 65–76.

Tortu, S., Neaigus, A., McMahon, J. and Hagen, D. (2001), 'Hepatitis C among noninjecting drug users: a report', *Substance Use and Misuse* 36, pp. 523–34.

Tortu, S., Mcmahon, J. M., Hamid, R. and Neaigus, A. (2003), 'Women's drug injection practices in East Harlem: an event analysis in a high-risk community', *AIDS and Behavior* 7 (3), pp. 317–28.

Tortu, S., McMahon, J. M., Pouget, E. R. and Hamid, R. (2004), 'Sharing of noninjection drug-use implements as a risk factor for hepatitis C', *Substance Use and Misuse* 39, pp. 211–24.

Tuncel, M., Wang, Z., Arbique, D., et al. (2002), 'Mechanism of the blood pressure-raising effect of cocaine in humans', *Circulation* 105 (9), pp. 1054–9.

Vandhuick, O., Pistorius, M. A., Jousse, S., et al. (2004), 'Drug addiction and cardiovascular pathologies', *J Mal Vasc* 29 (5), pp. 243–8.

Venkatesan, A., Nath, A., Ming, G. L. and Song, H. (2007), 'Adult hippocampal neurogenesis: regulation by HIV and drugs of abuse', *Cellular and Molecular Life Sciences* 64 (16), pp. 2120–32.

Verthein, U., Haasen, C., Prinzleve, M. et al. (2001), 'Cocaine use and the utilisation of drug help services by consumers of the open drug scene in Hamburg,' *European Addiction Research* 7, pp. 176–83.

Vitiello, B. (2001), 'Long-term effects of stimulant medications on the brain: possible relevance to the treatment of attention deficit hyperactivity disorder', *Journal of Child and Adolescent Psychopharmacology* 11 (1), pp. 25–34.

Vitiello, B. (2008), 'Understanding the risk of using medications for attention deficit hyperactivity disorder with respect to physical growth and cardiovascular function', *Child and Adolescent Psychiatric Clinics of North America* 17 (2), pp. 459–74.

Vogt, I. and Zeissler, E. (2005), *Abschlussbericht der Evaluation des Projektes Rauchraum im Drogennotdienst Frankfurt des Vereins Jugendberatung und Jugendhilfe e.V.*, ISFF, Frankfurt.

Vogt, I., Schmid, M. and Roth, M. (2000), 'Crack-Konsum in der Drogenszene in Frankfurt am Main: Ergebnisse empirischer Studien,' *Wiener Zeitschrift für Suchtforschung* 23, pp. 5–13.

Volik, A. (2008), 'Admixtures in home-made injecting drugs: components of harm and prevention of harmful consequences', *Public Health*, Poltava, Ukraine. [Волик А., Примести в кустарных инъекционных наркотиках: составляющие вреда и профилактика вредных последствий, БФ «Общественное здоровье», Полтава, Украина, 2008 г.].

Ward, H., Pallecaros, A., Green, A. and Day, S. (2000), 'Health issues associated with increasing use of "crack" cocaine among female sex workers in London', *Sexually Transmitted Infections* 76, pp. 292–3.

Wechsberg, W. M., Lam, W. K., Zule, W. A. and Bobashev, G. (2004), 'Efficacy of a woman-focused intervention to reduce HIV risk and increase self-sufficiency among African American crack abusers', *American Journal of Public Health* 94, pp. 1165–73.

Williams, J. H. and Ross, L. (2007), 'Consequences of prenatal toxin exposure for mental health in children and adolescents: a systematic review', *European Child & Adolescent Psychiatry* 16 (4), pp. 243–53.

Williams, P. B. and Ekundayo, O. (2001), 'Study of distribution and factors affecting syphilis epidemic among inner-city minorities of Baltimore', *Public Health* 115, pp. 387–93.

Winhusen, T., Somoza, E. Ciraulo, D. A., et al. (2007a), 'A double-blind, placebo-controlled trial of tiagabine for the treatment of cocaine dependence', *Drug and Alcohol Dependence* 91 (2–3), pp. 141–8.

Winhusen, T., Somoza, E. Ciraulo, D. A., et al. (2007b), 'A double-blind, placebo-controlled trial of reserpine for the treatment of cocaine dependence', *Drug and Alcohol Dependence* 91 (2–3), pp. 205–12.

Wittenberg, S. (2005), *Niet uit het veld te slaan - bereiken van basecokegebruikers op straat*, Amsterdam, Stichting Mainline.

Wodak, A. and Cooney A. (2005), 'Effectiveness of sterile needle and syringe programmes', *International Journal of Drug Policy*, 16S, pp. S31–S44.

Wolff, A. J. and O'Donnell, A. E. (2004), 'Pulmonary effects of illicit drug use', *Clinics in Chest Medicine* 25 (1), pp. 203–16.

Wolff, F. H., Fuchs, S. C., Barcellos, N. T., et al. (2007), 'Risk factors for hepatitis C virus infection in individuals infected with the HIV', *Digestive and Liver Disease* 40 (6), pp. 460–7.

Wood, E., Tyndall, M. W., Spittal, P. M., et al. (2002), 'Factors associated with persistent high-risk syringe sharing in the presence of an established needle exchange programme', *AIDS* 16 (6), pp. 941–3.

Wood, E., Kerr, T., Spittal, P. M., et al. (2003), 'An external evaluation of a peer-run "unsanctioned" syringe exchange program', *Journal of Urban Health*, Bulletin of the New York Academy of Medicine, 80, pp. 455–64.

Word, C. O. and Bowser, B. (1997), 'Background to crack cocaine addiction and HIV high-risk behaviour: the next epidemic', *American Journal of Drug and Alcohol Abuse* 23, pp. 67–77.

WHO (World Health Organization) (2005), *Policy and programming guide for HIV/AIDS prevention and care among injecting drug users*, Department of HIV/AIDS, Geneva.

WHO, UNAIDS (Joint United Nations Programme on HIV/AIDS) and UNODC (United Nations Office on Drugs and Crime) (2004), *Policy brief: provision of sterile injecting equipment to reduce HIV transmission*, General Assembly of the United Nations, Universal Declaration of Human Rights, New York, 10 December, 1948.

WHO, UNODC and UNAIDS (2004), *Substitution maintenance therapy in the management of opioid dependence and HIV/AIDS prevention, Position paper*, WHO, Geneva.

Wynn, G. H., Cozza, K. L., Zapor, M. J., Wortmann, G. W. and Armstrong, S. C. (2005), 'Med-psych drug-drug interactions update — antiretrovirals, part III: antiretrovirals and drugs of abuse', *Psychosomatics* 46 (1), pp. 79–87.

Zador, D. A. (2007), 'Facilitating groin injecting behaviour: harm reduction or harm production? (commentary)', *Addiction* 102, pp. 1791–2.

Zhang, L., Xiao, Y. and He, J. (1999), 'Cocaine and apoptosis in myocardial cells', *Anatomical Record*, 257 (6), pp. 208–16.

Zinberg, N. E. (1984), *Drug, set, and setting: the basis for controlled intoxicant use*, Yale University Press, New Haven.

Zurhold, H., Kreutzfeld, N., Degkwitz, P. and Verthein, U. (2001), *Drogenkonsumräume. Gesundheitsförderung und Minderung öffentlicher Belastungen in europäischen Großstädten*, Lambertus, Freiburg i. Br.

Zurhold, H., Degkwitz, P., Verthein, U. and Haasen, C. (2003), 'Drug consumption rooms in Hamburg, Germany: evaluation of the effects on harm reduction and the reduction of public nuisance', *Journal of Drug Issues* 33 (3), pp. 663–88.

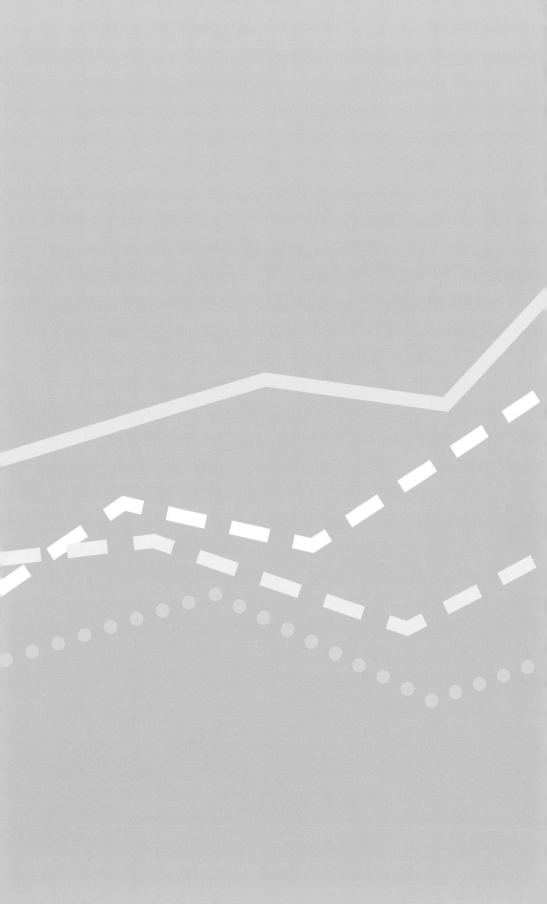

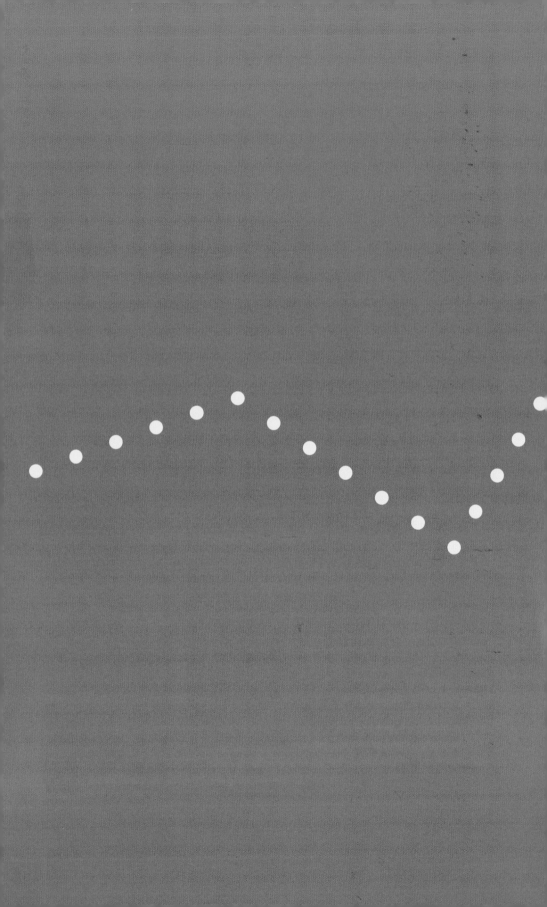

Chapter 8
Harm reduction policies for cannabis

Wayne Hall and Benedikt Fischer

Abstract

This chapter reviews the limited evidence on strategies for reducing the harms arising from cannabis use and from criminal penalties to control its use. It summarises evidence on the harms arising from cannabis use, namely, increased risks of: car crashes among users who drive while intoxicated; the development of cannabis dependence among regular users; psychosis and poorer adolescent psychosocial outcomes; and increased risks of respiratory disease from smoking. Strategies for reducing these risks to users are described, such as, roadside drug testing to deter cannabis-intoxicated driving, and education of users about patterns of use that increase risks of dependence, poor mental health and respiratory problems. The chapter also briefly discusses depenalisation and decriminalisation of cannabis use as strategies to reduce harms arising from cannabis prohibition. It concludes with suggestions for research priorities in how to reduce harms arising from cannabis use and the policies adopted to reduce such use.

Keywords: cannabis-impaired driving, cannabis dependence, respiratory risks, cannabis decriminalisation.

Introduction

Cannabis is the most widely used illicit drug globally, and its use has increased over the past decade. In 2005, around 160 million adults (4 % of the global adult population) were estimated to have used cannabis in the previous year, 10 % more than in the mid 1990s (UNODC, 2007). In the recent World Mental Health Surveys, the lifetime use of cannabis was higher in the United States and New Zealand than in Europe, which, in turn, reported higher rates of use than the Middle East and Africa or Asia (Degenhardt et al., 2008). Because of their larger populations, Asia, Africa and the Americas account for an estimated 31 %, 24 % and 24 % of global cannabis use compared to 19 % in Europe and 2 % in Oceania (UNODC, 2007).

In the United States in 2005, 40 % of the adult population reported using cannabis at some time in their lives and 13 % of adolescents reported use in the past year (SAMHSA, 2006). Cannabis use in most countries begins in the mid to late teens and is most common among people in their early 20s (Degenhardt et al., 2008). Most use is intermittent and time-limited (Bachman et al., 1997), with about 10 % of those who ever use cannabis becoming daily users, and another 20 % to 30 % using weekly (Hall and Pacula, 2003). Cannabis use declines from the early and mid 20s to the early 30s, reflecting major role transitions in early adulthood (e.g. entering tertiary education or full-time employment, marrying, and having children) (Anthony, 2006; Bachman et al., 1997).

Cannabis use in Europe

Cannabis is the most widely used illicit drug among European adolescents and its use is so common that it has been described as an 'illegal everyday drug' (Essau, 2006). In the late 1990s and early 2000s, the median rate of lifetime cannabis use among European adults aged between 18 and 64 years was 15 %, with a range between 31 % in the Czech Republic and 2 % in Romania (EMCDDA, 2006). Rates of lifetime use were higher among younger adults (aged between 15 and 34 years), with a median rate of 21 %, and a range between 3 % in Romania and 45 % in Denmark (EMCDDA, 2006).

Smart and Ogborne (2000) have summarised data on illicit drug use among high school students in 36 European countries during the mid-1990s (circa 1995). The highest prevalence of lifetime cannabis use was found in Scotland (53 %), which was higher than the overall prevalence in the United Kingdom (41 %), followed by the Netherlands (22 %). These rates increased during the 1990s in those countries that have undertaken a series of surveys over that time, namely, the Netherlands, Switzerland, and Norway (Harkin et al., 1997). These trends mirror those in Australia, Canada and the United States (Room et al., 2008).

More recent survey data collected by EMCDDA suggests that cannabis use rates have increased throughout Europe since then, and have recently begun to stabilise. Out of a total population of almost 500 million, 74 million Europeans aged 16 to 64 years have had lifetime experience with cannabis, 23 million in the past year, and 12 million in the past month (see the General Population Survey Tables in EMCDDA, 2009). Highest rates of use were in young adults aged 15–34 years (31 % lifetime, 13 % past year). These rates vary between countries (ranges 3 %–50 % and 1 %–21 % respectively). Average European rates were lower than in the United States (49 % and 21 %), Canada (58 % and 28 %) and Australia (48 % and 20 %) in the mid 2000s.

The probable harms of cannabis use

As argued in more detail elsewhere (Hall and Pacula, 2003; Room et al., 2008), there is reasonable evidence that cannabis use can harm some users. In this chapter we summarise the evidence on those adverse effects most commonly attributed to cannabis use and best supported by epidemiological evidence. We then describe strategies that could be used to reduce these harms arising from cannabis use. We also briefly discuss alternative policy approaches that aim to reduce harms arising from current criminal control policies towards cannabis use.

Cannabis and motor vehicle crashes

Cannabis intoxication produces dose-related impairments in cognitive and behavioural skills that may affect driving (Mann et al., 2008; Ramaekers et al., 2004; Solowij, 1998). Older studies that measured inactive metabolites of tetrahydrocannabinol (THC) could not assess whether drivers were impaired at the time of accidents (Ramaekers et al., 2004). Recent studies measuring THC in blood suggest that cannabis-affected drivers are at a higher risk of being involved in crashes (e.g. Drummer et al., 2004; Gerberich et al., 2003; Mura et al., 2003). Cannabis use appears to increase the risk of motor vehicle crashes by two to three times (Ramaekers et al., 2004) compared with 6 to 15 times for alcohol. It has been estimated that cannabis-affected driving accounted for 2.5 % of fatal accidents in France, compared to 29 % for alcohol (Laumon et al., 2005).

Cannabis dependence

A cannabis dependence syndrome develops in some daily or near-daily users of cannabis (Budney, 2006; Roffman and Stephens, 2006). Cannabis dependence is characterised by marked distress resulting from impaired control over cannabis use and difficulty in ceasing use despite harms caused by it. After tobacco and alcohol, cannabis was the most common form of drug dependence in the US in the 1990s and early 2000s (Anthony, 2006) and in Australia in the late 1990s (Hall et al., 1999). The risk of developing cannabis dependence in the United States is similar to that for alcohol but lower than that for nicotine and the opioids (Anthony et al., 1994). Around 10 % of those who ever use cannabis meet criteria for dependence (Anthony, 2006). This rises to 16 % in persons who initiate in early adolescence (Anthony, 2006).

Over the past two decades, increasing numbers of people have sought professional help for their cannabis use in the United States, Europe and Australia (Hall and Pacula, 2003). In Europe in 2006 there were 390,000 requests for treatment for cannabis dependence (EMCDDA, 2008). This was 21 % of all cases requesting assistance for illicit drugs and second only to opioids (EMCDDA, 2008). Some of this increase may be explained by increased diversion of cannabis users apprehended by the police into treatment programmes, but not all, because increases have also occurred in the Netherlands where cannabis possession has been decriminalised de facto (Dutch National Alcohol and Drug Information System, 2004).

Cannabis and schizophrenia

A 15-year prospective study of 50 465 Swedish conscripts (Andréasson et al., 1987) found that the risk of schizophrenia increased with the number of times cannabis had been used by age 18. A 27-year follow-up of the same cohort (Zammit et al., 2002) also found a dose-response relationship between frequency of cannabis use at baseline and risk of schizophrenia during the follow-up. These relationships persisted after controlling for other drug use and other confounding factors. These findings have been supported by longitudinal studies in the Netherlands (van Os et al., 2002) and Germany (Henquet et al., 2004) and by two small New Zealand cohort studies (Arseneault et al., 2002; Fergusson et al., 2003). The most plausible explanation appears to be that regular cannabis use acts with a variety of other unknown risk factors to precipitate psychoses in vulnerable individuals (Degenhardt and Hall, 2006; Moore et al., 2007).

The respiratory risks of cannabis smoking

Regular smokers of cannabis who do not smoke tobacco have more symptoms of chronic bronchitis and poorer lung function than people who do not smoke either cannabis or tobacco (see Tashkin, 1999). People who smoke cannabis with or without tobacco also seem to be more susceptible to respiratory infections (Tashkin, 1999).

Cannabis smoke is carcinogenic (Marselos and Karamanakos, 1999), making cannabis smoking a potential cause of cancers of the lung and mouth, tongue, and oesophagus (Hall and MacPhee, 2002). Epidemiological studies of head and neck cancer have produced conflicting results: one case control study found an association (Zhang et al., 1999) but a longitudinal study (Sidney et al., 1997) and two other case control studies failed to do so (Llewellyn et al., 2004; Rosenblatt et al., 2004). Case control studies of cannabis smoking and lung cancer have found associations but they have not been able to separate the effects of cannabis from tobacco smoking because most cannabis users in these studies were also daily cigarette smokers (Mehra et al., 2006).

Potential harm reduction strategies for cannabis

The following sections outline some potential harm reduction strategies for cannabis. Some are based on adaptations of similar policies that have been used to reduce harm from other drugs, such as alcohol. In other cases we outline the type of advice that could be given to users to avoid patterns or practices of use that increase the risk of experiencing adverse health outcomes (Swift et al., 2000). With few exceptions, there is little evidence on their effectiveness. Research into the effectiveness of these proposals should be a priority for harm reduction policies for cannabis.

Motor vehicle accidents

It is obvious that cannabis users can avoid cannabis-related vehicle crashes by not driving while intoxicated, but it is uncertain whether cannabis users have responded to education campaigns that urge them not to drive after using. Australia, Norway and Sweden have adopted random roadside drug testing in an effort to discourage cannabis-impaired driving. In Australia, the Victorian state government introduced random roadside saliva testing for cannabis and other drugs in December 2004; other Australian states and territories have since followed (Butler, 2007). Australian legislators have assumed that this policy will substantially reduce cannabis-related road crashes in the same way that random breath testing reduced alcohol related crashes in Australia (Henstridge et al., 1997). Other European countries have adopted the more focused policy of testing for cannabis in saliva or urine on suspicion of use or evidence of impaired driving (Mann et al., 2008).

The illegality of cannabis use has prompted the adoption of a 'zero tolerance' approach in Australia, Norway and Sweden, with the presence of any detectable amount of THC defined as an offence (Butler, 2007). Any road safety benefits of this policy are a by-product of the deterrent effect of enforcing prohibitive drug laws. Proponents of drug testing argue that it will save lives (Jones et al., 2008) but so far there is no evidence that it has done so. This policy needs to be properly evaluated to see if it reduces cannabis-impaired driving at an acceptable social and economic cost (Hall and Homel, 2007). Other approaches that focus on harm reduction would include: developing measures of cannabis-impaired driving, as advocated by Grotenhermen et al. (2007), and encouraging cannabis users to adopt 'designated driver' programmes like those advocated for alcohol users.

Cannabis dependence

An essential first step in reducing the risk of cannabis dependence is informing users of the risk. This can be done by explaining that the risk increases with regular use and is greatest when cannabis is used daily for weeks or months, as is true for alcohol and tobacco dependence. Priorities for research include assessing whether users will accept this advice or what the most persuasive way of delivering it would be.

Screening and brief advice for excessive alcohol consumption in general practice, hospital or even non-medical settings reduces consumption and the problems caused by alcohol (e.g. Shand et al., 2003). The same approach could be adopted for cannabis use disorders in primary care settings, for example among young adults with respiratory problems or symptoms of anxiety and depression, all of which are common among cannabis-dependent individuals who seek help from family physicians (Degenhardt et al., 2001).

Similarly, brief interventions for frequent cannabis users could be targeted at populations and/or settings where cannabis use is known to be high, for example youth mental health services, juvenile justice centres, and among college students (Hall et al., 2008a). Such interventions could advise users to reduce the frequency of cannabis use and not to use it before driving. A 'check-up' approach modelled on the Brief Drinker Check-up (Miller and Sovereign, 1989) provides a promising model for raising the issue of health risks of cannabis use in a non-confrontational way (see Berghuis et al., 2006). This approach has been trialled and evaluated with promising results in a number of studies (Martin and Copeland, 2008; Stephens et al., 2007).

The question of how best to inform young people about the risks of cannabis dependence requires research on young people's views about the type of information that they find most persuasive. In the interim the following are suggestions about what advice could be given:

- Cannabis users can become dependent on cannabis. The risk (around 10 %) is lower than that for alcohol, nicotine and opiates, but the earlier that a young person begins the higher the risk.
- Using cannabis more than weekly increases the risks of developing dependence and other health problems.
- Regular use probably also increases the risk of psychosis in young people who have a family member with a psychosis or other mental disorder, or who have unusual psychological experiences after using cannabis.
- Driving within a few hours of cannabis use increases the risk of both fatal and non-fatal motor vehicle accident involvement and should be avoided, especially after drinking alcohol.

Cognitive behavioural therapy can be used to treat cannabis dependence on an outpatient basis. Rates of abstinence have been modest — for example, around 15 % reported continuous abstinence at six-month follow-ups, according to Copeland et al. (2001) — but cannabis use and cannabis-related problems are substantially reduced (Denis et al., 2006; Roffman and Stephens, 2006). A recent review by Nordstrom and Levin (2007) concluded that while a number of psychotherapies have been found to be effective in treating this disorder, none has been found to be more effective than any other, although offering vouchers as a reward to reinforce negative urine toxicology screens improved abstinence during treatment.

Informing young people about the mental health risks of cannabis use

A major public health challenge will be finding effective ways of explaining the mental health risks of cannabis use to young people. In addition to a possible increased risk of psychosis, young people also need to be informed about the risks of developing dependence, impairing their educational attainment, and possibly increasing their risk of depression (Hall, 2006; Patton et al., 2002). These risks add weight to the prudential argument for discouraging cannabis use by young people.

Policymakers need to be realistic about the impacts of educational messages (Caulkins et al., 2004; White and Pitts, 1998). Small, statistically significant reductions in cannabis use may be observed in well-conducted programmes (Caulkins et al., 2004; Gorman, 1995; Tobler, Lessard, Marshall et al., 1999; White and Pitts, 1998) but the primary impact is on knowledge rather than behaviour (White and Pitts, 1998). Any behaviour change is more likely to occur among less frequent rather than heavier users (Gorman, 1995). Given this, the nature and delivery of the advice may need to differ for different groups facing different levels of risk (Toumbourou et al., 2004). The best way to deliver the advice will depend upon good social marketing research on the views of young people (Grier and Bryant, 2005).

Education about the risks of cannabis use should explain the mental health risks of regular intoxication with alcohol and cannabis; and define the high-risk groups, namely those with a family history of psychosis and those who have had bad experiences with cannabis. Such education needs to be directed not only at cannabis users but also at their peers to increase recognition of these problems among young people so that they can encourage affected peers to cease using or seek help earlier than might otherwise be the case.

A major challenge is framing the magnitude of the risk of psychosis. The risk for any individual increases from around 7 in 1 000 (Saha et al., 2005) to 14 in 1 000, but the consequences of psychosis for those individuals who are vulnerable are serious. The temptation for parents and health educators is to play up the risk, arguing that everyone is at risk because it is difficult to predict which young people are most vulnerable. This strategy is of doubtful effectiveness and may undermine the credibility of the message by being seen to exaggerate the risk.

It is prudent to encourage young people who use cannabis and experience psychotic symptoms to stop, or at the very least to reduce the frequency of their cannabis use. The challenge in implementing this goal is finding effective ways of persuading persons with schizophrenia to stop doing something that they enjoy and to help those who want to stop but find it difficult to do so. Many persons with schizophrenia have characteristics that predict a poor outcome from psychological interventions for cannabis dependence, namely, they lack social support, may be cognitively impaired, are often unemployed, and do not comply with treatment (Kavanagh, 1995; Mueser et al., 1992). There are very few controlled outcome studies of substance abuse treatment in schizophrenia (Lehman et al., 1993). A recent Cochrane review identified only six relevant studies, four of which were small (Jeffery et al., 2004) and found no clear evidence that supported substance abuse treatment in schizophrenia over standard care.

Reducing respiratory risks

The respiratory risks of cannabis smoking could be eliminated if cannabis users adopted eating or ingesting rather than smoking cannabis. This is unlikely to happen, because most long-term users find smoking a more efficient and easier way to titrate their dose of THC than the oral route (Grotenhermen, 2004; Iversen, 2007).

Putatively 'safer' forms of cannabis smoking, such as water pipes, are popular among younger cannabis users in Australia (Hall and Swift, 2000) but United States and Australian (Gowing et al., 2000) research suggests that water pipes deliver more tar per dose of THC than do joints. It is also unclear how much the respiratory risks of cannabis smoking might be reduced if users were to smoke lesser amounts of the more potent cannabis products (Melamede, 2005). There has been too little research to determine whether users can reliably titrate their dose and, if they can, whether in fact they do so (Hall and Pacula, 2003).

It is reasonable to advise cannabis smokers to avoid breath-holding or 'deep inhalation' techniques to maximise the absorption of THC in the lungs. This practice increases the quantities of tar and particulate matter that are retained in the lungs without necessarily increasing the THC delivered. It is also advisable for cannabis users to eliminate the use of tobacco in smoked cannabis preparations because of tobacco's addictiveness and carcinogenicity.

Vaporisers appear to be a more promising way of reducing the carcinogens and toxicants inhaled when cannabis is smoked (Gieringer et al., 2004; Grotenhermen, 2004; Melamede, 2005). These devices are designed to deliver inhaled THC without carcinogens and toxicants. They do so by heating cannabis to a temperature (180°C), which releases THC without burning the plant material. A study by Gieringer et al. (2004) found that vaporisers achieved a similar efficacy in delivery of THC to smoking a cannabis cigarette while very substantially reducing levels of carcinogens. Hazekamp et al. (2006) evaluated the performance of the same device in delivering pure THC and found that it had acceptable safety properties. However, Bloor et al. (2008) found that while vaporisers reduced levels of released ammonia, compared to smoked cannabis these levels (170 ppm) were still well above recommended safe levels (35 ppm) for short-term occupational exposures. These levels of ammonia increase respiratory irritation, but the respiratory effects of long-term intermittent exposure in daily users are unknown.

Abrams et al. (2007) compared the effects of varying doses of cannabis vaporised and smoked in a joint in 18 subjects under double blind conditions. They found that the vaporiser delivered similar amounts of THC and produced similar psychological effects. Sixteen of the 18 subjects preferred the vaporiser. They did not test for delivery of tars and carcinogens but did find lower CO levels in blood when using a vaporiser. Earleywine and Barnwell (2007) found suggestive evidence that vaporisers had reduced respiratory symptoms in a convenience sample of 6 883 cannabis users interviewed via the Internet. The rate of respiratory symptoms (bronchitis, wheeze, breathlessness) among the 150 who reported only using vaporisers was 40 % of that reported by cannabis smokers (after controlling for cigarette smoking, duration of use and amount typically used). The reduction in symptoms among vaporiser users appeared to be larger in heavier cannabis users. More work is needed to evaluate the long-term safety and efficacy of vaporisers in reducing the respiratory risks of cannabis use.

Reducing the harms arising from cannabis control policies

Under current criminal cannabis control policies in many European and other developed countries, cannabis users can nominally be sentenced to prison if caught in possession of cannabis. Even if prison sentences are rarely imposed, the acquisition of a criminal conviction or record for the personal use of cannabis can adversely affect the lives of otherwise law-abiding users (Lenton, 2000) in ways that some have argued are more serious than any harms that result from using cannabis (Wodak et al., 2002), for example, by impeding professional or travel opportunities and adversely affecting personal relationships (Room et al., 2008). The limited research (Erickson, 1980; Lenton et al., 1999a; Lenton et al., 1999b) suggests: that many persons convicted of cannabis offences have no other criminal records; that a criminal conviction adversely affects their employment prospects and their reputations; and that it has a negligible effect on their cannabis use.

The enforcement of cannabis control laws is also often applied in a highly selective, if not discriminatory, way. In Australia in the early 1990s cannabis offenders appearing before the criminal courts were more likely to be unemployed and socially disadvantaged males than were cannabis users in community surveys (Advisory Committee on Illicit Drugs, 1993). Recent US studies show higher rates of arrests for cannabis offences among Hispanic and Black minorities (Gettman, 2000; Human Rights Watch, 2000). It is uncertain to what extent the same is true in European countries with substantial ethnic minorities or immigrant populations.

The non-enforcement or removal of criminal penalties for personal use is one way of reducing the adverse effects of the law on users. The Netherlands was one of the first European countries to do so in 1976 (see box 'De facto cannabis decriminalisation in the Netherlands', p. 243), and Portugal has more recently done so among other European countries (see box 'Cannabis decriminalisation in Portugal', p. 243). In several Australian states, personal cannabis use is subject to a non-criminal 'infringement' or 'expiation' notice, an offence similar to a speeding ticket and punished by a limited fine (Room et al. 2008). Studies of the impact of these changes have typically found that reductions in the severity of penalties for cannabis use have little, if any, impact on rates of population cannabis use in

Australia (e.g. Donnelly et al., 1999), the United States (Pacula et al., 2004) and Europe (Greenwald, 2009; Room et al., 2008). The lack of any evidence of a large impact on rates of use also suggests that this policy may have little or no effect on cannabis-related harms, while at the same time reducing enforcement costs and effects on users (Room et al., 2008).

De facto cannabis decriminalisation in the Netherlands

The Netherlands decriminalised cannabis possession for personal use on a 'de facto' basis from 1976. This means that while personal possession is still formally prohibited by criminal law, the law is not enforced. The Dutch system tolerates cannabis users possessing and buying small amounts of cannabis for personal use, most notably in several hundred 'coffee shops' across the country. Also in the Netherlands, no major changes in cannabis use rates have been observed that could be unambiguously attributed to this policy, and use rates are lower than the EU average. This approach aims to separate the cannabis market from that of other illicit drugs. While this de facto decriminalisation has been well-supported politically and socially in the Netherlands, it has recently come under some pressure from neighbouring countries concerned about 'drug tourism' (Chatwin, 2003; MacCoun and Reuter, 1997; Pakes, 2004; Room et al., 2008). The Dutch government has responded to these concerns by reducing the number of coffee shops and the amount of cannabis that can be sold.

Cannabis decriminalisation in Portugal

Portugal formally decriminalised use of all illicit drugs by changing its drug control laws in 2001. Cannabis use and possession remains illegal but it is treated as an 'administrative violation'. Drug use offenders are brought to the attention of 'Dissuasion Commissions' who typically suspend any punitive proceedings. In serious cases, such as those of repeat offenders, administrative penalties — like fines, suspension of driver's licence or community service orders — can be imposed and problematic users can be referred to treatment. Since these reforms, no significant changes have been observed in cannabis use, which remains low compared to other EU countries and North America. The number of drug use infractions has been stable since the reforms, which have been well-accepted politically and by the general public (Greenwald, 2009; Hughes and Stevens, 2007; Room et al., 2008).

An unintended consequence of depenalisation via civil penalties can be an increase in numbers of persons fined or diverted into non-criminal interventions (e.g., education or treatment measures) by the police, an effect referred to as 'net widening'. This occurs because the police find it easier and less time-consuming to enact non-criminal measures (e.g. impose a fine) than to formally arrest and process a criminal charge. If a substantial proportion of offenders do not pay their fines, more cannabis users may end up in prisons for fine-default than would be the case if cannabis use remained as a criminal offence (Room et al., 2008). The removal or the non-enforcement of any penalties for personal use (as in the Netherlands) avoids this problem (Hall and Pacula, 2003; Room et al., 2008), as does allowing non-custodial ways to enforce the payment of fines (Room et al., 2008).

Research priorities for cannabis harm reduction

Research is needed on the effectiveness of these policies that aim to reduce the harms of cannabis use. Among the priorities for future inquiry are the following questions:

- What do cannabis users believe are the harms of using cannabis?
- Does the type of evidence presented about these adverse effects persuade them?
- Are they prepared to act on advice about how to reduce these harms?
- Does roadside drug testing deter cannabis users from driving while intoxicated? If so, does this reduce motor vehicle accident fatalities? Does it do so at an acceptable social and economic cost? Are there better ways than deterrence policies to reduce risks related to cannabis and driving?
- Do adolescent users accept that cannabis use can be harmful? Are they prepared to act on harm reduction advice? Are brief interventions in medical or non-medical settings effective in changing risk patterns of use or practices?
- Does the use of vaporisers substantially reduce the respiratory risks of cannabis smoking?
- Do cannabis users titrate their doses of cannabis products?

Among priorities for research on the effects of harm reduction measures such as depenalisation and decriminalisation are the following:

- Do depenalisation or decriminalisation policies result in changes in patterns or rates of cannabis use, or attitudes towards cannabis use, especially among vulnerable/high-risk populations (e.g., youth/students)?
- Will more tolerant policies for cannabis use reduce access or exposure to other illicit drugs?
- Do decriminalisation approaches result in tangible savings of public resources (e.g., enforcement time) without increasing the prevalence of harmful cannabis use (e.g., numbers seeking treatment for cannabis dependence)?

Conclusions

Cannabis is the most widely used illicit drug in Europe, as it is globally. While cannabis use clearly does not result in harms that are comparable to those of alcohol or tobacco, its use is associated with significant potential risks and harms. Based on existing evidence, a number of these risks and harms are modifiable by harm reduction approaches directed at users. This more pragmatic, 'public health' approach that builds on experiences from the alcohol field requires substantial additional research and policy engagement. Its utility is still hindered by the century-old illegal status of cannabis in most European jurisdictions.

Driving under the influence of cannabis has been given considerable attention in recent years. Governments in Australia, Norway and Sweden have implemented random roadside saliva testing to detect the presence of cannabis in drivers to reduce cannabis-impaired driving and prevent accidents as a primary harm. However, the scope of this policy might be overly punitive in penalising drivers who are not actually impaired by cannabis while driving. Thus, the effectiveness, cost-effectiveness and social effects of this policy remains to be evaluated.

Given the existing knowledge around the acute and long-term harms associated with cannabis use, and key predictors of these effects, there appears to be considerable room for interventions with or advice to cannabis users towards reducing the odds or severity of problems resulting from use. For example, harm reduction advice that could be given to current cannabis users includes the following:

- Avoid more than weekly use to minimise the risks of developing mental health problems or dependence.

- Avoid smoking as a route of administration or use a vaporiser instead, rather than smoke a bong or joint.

- If you smoke cannabis, avoid deep inhalation or breath-holding practices in order to reduce the risks of respiratory problems.

- Do not drive or use machinery when intoxicated.

There is a need for research on how to effectively convey such messages, and to measure their potential impacts on individual and/or population levels of harm from cannabis use.

There is reasonable evidence that removing criminal penalties for personal possession and use of cannabis reduces some of the harms of current control policy incurred by users who come to the attention of criminal control. This policy can reduce the extensive social and economic harms of use prohibition (rather than the effects of cannabis use) without producing large increases in the prevalence of cannabis use, as recent policy reform experiments in a number of countries have suggested. Such efforts would also help to bring cannabis use more into a policy framework of public health rather than repressive control. They may facilitate steps towards a more integrated and rational regulation of all commonly used psychoactive substances guided by their potential to cause harm and evidence on the benefits and costs of different interventions (Nutt et al. 2007).

References

Abrams, D., Vizoso, H., Shade, S., Jay, C., Kelly, M. and Benowitz, N. (2007), 'Vaporization as a smokeless cannabis delivery system: a pilot study', Clinical Psychopharmacology & Therapeutics 82, pp. 572–8.

Advisory Committee on Illicit Drugs (1993), Cannabis and the law in Queensland: a discussion paper, Queensland Criminal Justice Commission, Brisbane.

Andréasson, S., Engstrom, A., Allebeck, P. and Rydberg, U. (1987), 'Cannabis and schizophrenia: a longitudinal study of Swedish conscripts', Lancet 2, pp. 1483–6.

Anthony, J. C. (2006), 'The epidemiology of cannabis dependence', in Roffman, R. A. and Stephens, R. S. (eds), Cannabis dependence: its nature, consequences and treatment, Cambridge University Press, Cambridge, UK, pp. 58–105.

Anthony, J. C., Warner, L. and Kessler, R. (1994), 'Comparative epidemiology of dependence on tobacco, alcohol, controlled substances and inhalants: basic findings from the National Comorbidity Survey', *Experimental and Clinical Psychopharmacology* 2, pp. 244–68.

Arseneault, L., Cannon, M., Poulton, R., et al. (2002), 'Cannabis use in adolescence and risk for adult psychosis: longitudinal prospective study', *BMJ* 325, pp. 1212–13.

Bachman, J. G., Wadsworth, K. N., O'Malley, P. M., et al. (1997), *Smoking, drinking, and drug use in young adulthood: the impacts of new freedoms and new responsibilities*, Lawrence Erlbaum, Mahwah, NJ.

Begg, S., Vos, T., Barker, B., Stanley, L. and Lopez, A. D. (2007), *The burden of disease and injury in Australia 2003*, AIHW, Canberra. Available from http://www.aihw.gov.au/publications/index.cfm/title/10317.

Berghuis, J. P., Swift, W., Roffman, R., Stephens, R. and Copeland, J. (2006), 'The teen cannabis check-up: exploring strategies for reaching young cannabis users', in Roffman, R. A. and Stephens, R. S. (eds), *Cannabis dependence: its nature, consequences and treatment*, Cambridge University Press, Cambridge, UK, pp. 275–92.

Bloor, R. N., Wang, T. S., Spanel, P. and Smith, D. (2008), 'Ammonia release from heated "street" cannabis leaf and its potential toxic effects on cannabis users', *Addiction* 103, pp. 1671–7.

Budney, A. J. (2006), 'Are specific dependence criteria necessary for different substances: how can research on cannabis inform this issue?', *Addiction* 101 (Supplement 1), pp. 125–33.

Butler, M. (2007), 'Australia's approach to drugs and driving', *Of Substance: The National Magazine on Alcohol, Tobacco, and Other Drugs* 5, pp. 24–6.

Cameron, L. and Williams, J. (2001), 'Cannabis, alcohol and cigarettes: substitutes or complements?', *Economic Record* 77, pp. 19–34.

Caulkins, J. P., Pacula, R. L., Paddock, S. and Chiesa, J. (2004), 'What we can — and cannot — expect from school-based drug prevention', *Drug and Alcohol Review* 23, pp. 79–87.

Chatwin, C. (2003), 'Drug policy developments within the European Union: the destabilizing effects of Dutch and Swedish drug policies', *British Journal of Criminology* 43, pp. 567–82.

Copeland, J., Swift, W., Roffman, R. and Stephens, R. (2001), 'A randomized controlled trial of brief cognitive-behavioral interventions for cannabis use disorder', *Journal of Substance Abuse Treatment* 21, pp. 55–64.

Degenhardt, L. and Hall, W. D. (2006), 'Is cannabis a contributory cause of psychosis?', *Canadian Journal of Psychiatry* 51, pp. 556–65.

Degenhardt, L., Hall, W. D. and Lynskey, M. T. (2001), 'The relationship between cannabis use, depression and anxiety among Australian adults: findings from the National Survey of Mental Health and Well-being', *Social Psychiatry and Psychiatric Epidemiology* 36, pp. 219–27.

Degenhardt, L., Hall, W. D., Warner-Smith, M. and Lynskey, M. T. (2004), 'Illicit drug use', in Ezzati, M., Lopez, A., Rodgers, A. and Murray, C. (eds), *Comparative quantification of health risks: global and regional burden of disease attributable to selected major risk factors*, World Health Organization, Geneva, Vol. 1, pp. 1109–76.

Degenhardt, L., Chiu, W., Sampson, N., et al. (2008), 'Toward a global view of alcohol, tobacco, cannabis and cocaine use: findings from the WHO World Mental Health Surveys', *PLoS Medicine* 5, p. e141.

Denis, C., Lavie, E., Fatseas, M. and Auriacombe, M. (2006), 'Psychotherapeutic interventions for cannabis abuse and/or dependence in outpatient settings', *Cochrane Database of Systematic Reviews 3*, CD005336.

Donnelly, N., Hall, W. D. and Christie, P. (1995), 'The effects of partial decriminalisation on cannabis use in South Australia, 1985 to 1993', *Australian Journal of Public Health* 19, pp. 281–7.

Donnelly, N., Hall, W. D. and Christie, P. (1999), *Effects of the Cannabis Expiation Notice Scheme on levels and patterns of cannabis use in South Australia: evidence from the National Drug Strategy Household Surveys 1985–1995*, Australian Government Publishing Service, Canberra.

Drummer, O. H., Gerostamoulos, J., Batziris, H., et al. (2004), 'The involvement of drugs in drivers of motor vehicles killed in Australian road traffic crashes', *Accident Analysis and Prevention* 36, pp. 239–48.

Dutch National Alcohol and Drug Information System (2004), 'Treatment demand of cannabis clients in outpatient addiction care in the Netherlands (1994–2001)', *LADIS Bulletin*.

Earleywine, M. (2002), *Understanding marijuana: a new look at the scientific evidence*, Oxford University Press, Oxford.

Earleywine, M. and Barnwell, S. S. (2007), 'Decreased respiratory symptoms in cannabis users who vaporize', *Harm Reduction Journal* 4, p. 11.

EMCDDA (2006), *Annual report 2006: the state of the drugs problem in Europe*, European Monitoring Centre for Drugs and Drug Addiction, Lisbon. Available at http://www.emcdda.europa.eu/publications/annual-report/2006.

EMCDDA (2008), *Annual report 2008: the state of the drugs problem in Europe*, European Monitoring Centre for Drugs and Drug Addiction, Lisbon. Available at http://www.emcdda.europa.eu/attachements.cfm/att_64227_EN_EMCDDA_AR08_en.pdf.

EMCDDA (2009), *General population surveys (GPS)*, Statistical bulletin, 2009, tables. European Monitoring Centre for Drugs and Drug Addiction, Lisbon. Available at http://www.emcdda.europa.eu/stats09/gps.

Erickson, P. G. (1980), *Cannabis criminals: the social effects of punishment on drug users*, Addiction Research Foundation, Toronto.

Essau, C. (2006), 'Epidemiological trends and clinical implications of adolescent substance abuse in Europe', in Liddle, H. A. and Rowe, C. L. (eds), *Adolescent substance abuse: research and clinical advances*, Cambridge University Press, Cambridge, UK, pp. 129–47.

Fergusson, D. M. and Horwood, L. J. (2000), 'Does cannabis use encourage other forms of illicit drug use?', *Addiction* 95, pp. 505–20.

Fergusson, D. M., Horword, L. J. and Swain-Campbell, N. (2002), 'Cannabis use and psychosocial adjustment in adolescence and young adulthood', *Addiction* 97, pp. 1123–35.

Fergusson, D. M., Horwood, L. J. and Swain-Campbell, N. R. (2003), 'Cannabis dependence and psychotic symptoms in young people', *Psychological Medicine* 33, pp. 15–21.

Gerberich, S. G., Sidney, S., Braun, B. L., et al. (2003), 'Marijuana use and injury events resulting in hospitalization', *Annals of Epidemiology* 13, pp. 230–7.

Gettman, J. (2000), *United States marijuana arrests, part two: racial differences in drug arrests*, National Organization for the Reform of Marijuana Laws, Washington, DC. Available at http://norml.org/index.cfm?Group_ID=5326.

Gieringer, D., St Laurent, J. and Goodrich, S. (2004), 'Cannabis vaporizer combines efficient delivery of THC with effective suppression of pyrolytic compounds', *Journal of Cannabis Therapeutics* 4, pp. 7–27.

Gorman, D. M. (1995), 'On the difference between statistical and practical significance in school-based drug abuse prevention', *Drugs: Education, Prevention & Policy* 2, pp. 275–83.

Gowing, L. R., Ali, R. L. and White, J. M. (2000), *Respiratory harms of smoked cannabis: DASC monograph 8*, Drug and Alcohol Services Council South Australia, Parkside, SA. Available at http://www.dassa.sa.gov.au/webdata/resources/files/MONOGRAPH8.pdf.

Greenwald, G. (2009), *Drug decriminalization in Portugal: lessons for creating fair and successful drug policies*, Cato Institute, Washington, DC.

Grier, S. and Bryant, C. A. (2005), 'Social marketing in public health', *Annual Review of Public Health* 26, pp. 319–39.

Grotenhermen, F. (2004), 'Cannabinoids for therapeutic use: designing systems to increase efficacy and reliability', *American Journal of Drug Delivery* 2, pp. 229–40.

Grotenhermen, F., Leson, G., Berghaus, G., et al. (2007), 'Developing limits for driving under cannabis', *Addiction* 102, pp. 1910–17.

Hall, W. D. (2006), 'Cannabis use and the mental health of young people', *Australian and New Zealand Journal of Psychiatry* 40, pp. 105–13.

Hall, W. D. (2006), 'The mental health risks of adolescent cannabis use', *PLoS Medicine* 3, pp. 159–62.

Hall, W. D. and Homel, R. (2007), 'Reducing cannabis-impaired driving: is there sufficient evidence for drug testing of drivers?', *Addiction* 102, pp. 1918–19.

Hall, W. D. and Lynskey, M. T. (2005), 'Is cannabis a gateway drug? Testing hypotheses about the relationship between cannabis use and the use of other illicit drugs', *Drug and Alcohol Review* 24, pp. 39–48.

Hall, W. D. and MacPhee, D. (2002), 'Cannabis use and cancer', *Addiction* 97, pp. 243–7.

Hall, W. D. and Pacula, R. L. (2003), *Cannabis use and dependence: public health and public policy*, Cambridge University Press, Cambridge, UK.

Hall, W. D. and Swift, W. (2000), 'The THC content of cannabis in Australia: evidence and implications', *Australian and New Zealand Journal of Public Health* 24, pp. 503–08.

Hall, W. D., Teesson, M., Lynskey, M. T. and Degenhardt, L. (1999), 'The 12-month prevalence of substance use and ICD-10 substance use disorders in Australian adults: findings from the National Survey of Mental Health and Well-being', *Addiction* 94, pp. 1541–50.

Hall, W. D., Degenhardt, L. and Patton, G. C. (2008a), 'Cannabis abuse and dependence', in Essau, C. A. (ed.), *Adolescent addiction: epidemiology, treatment and assessment*, Academic Press, London, pp. 117–48.

Hall, W. D., Degenhardt, L. and Sindicich, N. (2008b), 'Illicit drug use and the burden of disease', in Heggenhougen, K. and Quah, S. (eds), *International encyclopedia of public health*, Elsevier, Amsterdam, pp. 523–30.

Harkin, A., Anderson, P., Goos, P. (1997), *Smoking, drinking and drug taking in the European Region*, WHO Regional Office for Europe, Copenhagen.

Hazekamp, A., Ruhaak, R., Zuurman, L., van Gerven, J. and Verpoorte, R. (2006), 'Evaluation of a vaporizing device (Volcano) for the pulmonary administration of tetrahydrocannabinol', *Journal of Pharmaceutical Sciences* 95, pp. 1308–17.

Henquet, C., Krabbendam, L., Spauwen, J., et al. (2004), 'Prospective cohort study of cannabis use, predisposition for psychosis, and psychotic symptoms in young people', *BMJ* 330, p. 11.

Henstridge, J., Homel, R. and Mackay, P. (1997), *The long-term effects of random breath testing in four Australian states: a time series analysis*, Federal Office of Road Safety, Canberra. Available at http://www.infrastructure.gov.au/roads/safety/publications/1997/Alc_Random.aspx.

Hughes, C. E. and Stevens, A. (2007), *The effects of decriminalization of drug use in Portugal*, Briefing paper 14, The Beckley Foundation Drug Policy Program, London.

Human Rights Watch (2000), *Punishment and prejudice: Racial disparities in the war on drugs*, Human Rights Watch Report 12/2, New York. Available at http://www.hrw.org/legacy/reports/2000/usa/.

Iversen, L. (2007), *The science of marijuana*, Oxford University Press, Oxford.

Jeffery, D., Ley, A., McLaren, S. and Siegfried, N. (2004), 'Psychosocial treatment programmes for people with both severe mental illness and substance misuse', *Cochrane Database of Systematic Reviews 2000*, 2, CD001088.

Jones, A. W., Holmgren, A. and Kugelberg, F. C. (2008), 'Driving under the influence of cannabis: a 10-year study of age and gender differences in the concentrations of tetrahydrocannabinol in blood', *Addiction* 103, pp. 452–61.

Kaplan, J. (1970), *Marijuana: the new prohibition*, World Publishing Company, New York.

Kavanagh, D. J. (1995), 'An intervention for substance abuse in schizophrenia', *Behaviour Change* 12, pp. 20–30.

Laumon, B., Gadegbeku, B., Martin, J. L. and Biecheler, M. B. (2005), 'Cannabis intoxication and fatal road crashes in France: population based case-control study', *BMJ* 331, p. 1371.

Lehman, A. F., Herron, J. D., Schwartz, R. P. and Myers, C. P. (1993), 'Rehabilitation for adults with severe mental illness and substance use disorders: a clinical trial', *Journal of Nervous and Mental Disease* 181, pp. 86–90.

Lenton, S. (2000), 'Cannabis policy and the burden of proof: is it now beyond reasonable doubt that cannabis prohibition is not working?', *Drug and Alcohol Review* 19, pp. 95–100.

Lenton, S., Bennett, M. and Heale, P. (1999a), *The social impact of a minor cannabis offence under strict prohibition: the case of Western Australia*, National Centre for Research into the Prevention of Drug Abuse, Perth.

Lenton, S., Christie, P., Humeniuk, R., et al. (1999b), *Infringement versus conviction: the social impact of a minor cannabis offence under a civil penalties system and strict prohibition in two Australian states*, Commonwealth Department of Health and Aged Care, Canberra.

Llewellyn, C. D., Linklater, K., Bell, J., Johnson, N. W. and Warnakulasuriya, S. (2004), 'An analysis of risk factors for oral cancer in young people: a case-control study', *Oral Oncology* 40, pp. 304–13.

Lynskey, M. T. and Hall, W. D. (2000), 'The effects of adolescent cannabis use on educational attainment: a review', *Addiction* 96, pp. 433–43.

MacCoun, R. and Reuter, P. (1997), 'Interpreting Dutch cannabis policy: reasoning by analogy in the legalization debate', *Science* 278, pp. 47–52.

Macleod, J., Oakes, R., Copello, A., et al. (2004), 'Psychological and social sequelae of cannabis and other illicit drug use by young people: a systematic review of longitudinal, general population studies', *Lancet* 363, pp. 1579–88.

Mann, R. E., Stoduto, G., Macdonald, S. and Brands, B. (2008), 'Cannabis use and driving: implications for public health and transport policy', in Sznitman, S. R., Olsson, B., Room, R. (eds), *A cannabis reader: global issues and local experiences*, EMCDDA, Lisbon, pp. 173–98.

Marselos, M. and Karamanakos, P. (1999), 'Mutagenicity, developmental toxicity and carcinogeneity of cannabis', *Addiction Biology* 4, pp. 5–12.

Martin, G. and Copeland, J. (2008), 'The adolescent cannabis check-up: randomized trial of a brief intervention for young cannabis users', *Journal of Substance Abuse Treatment* 34, pp. 407–14.

Mehra, R., Moore, B. A., Crothers, K., Tetrault, J. and Fiellin, D. A. (2006), 'The association between marijuana smoking and lung cancer: a systematic review', *Archives of Internal Medicine* 166, pp. 1359–67.

Melamede, R. (2005), 'Harm reduction: the cannabis paradox', *Harm Reduction Journal* 2, p. 17.

Miller, W. R. and Sovereign, R. G. (1989), 'The check-up: a model for early intervention in addictive behaviors', in Leberg, T., Miller, W., Nathan, G. and Marlatt, G. (eds.), *Addictive behaviors: prevention and early intervention*, Swets and Zeitlinger, Amsterdam, pp. 219–31.

Moore, T. H., Zammit, S., Lingford-Hughes, A., et al. (2007), 'Cannabis use and risk of psychotic or affective mental health outcomes: a systematic review', *Lancet* 370, pp. 319–28.

Mueser, K. T., Bellack, A. S. and Blanchard, J. J. (1992), 'Comorbidity of schizophrenia and substance abuse: implications for treatment', *Journal of Consulting and Clinical Psychology* 60, pp. 845–56.

Mura, P., Kintz, P., Ludes, B., et al. (2003), 'Comparison of the prevalence of alcohol, cannabis and other drugs between 900 injured drivers and 900 control subjects: results of a French collaborative study', *Forensic Science International* 133, pp. 79–85.

Nordstrom, B. R. and Levin, F. R. (2007), 'Treatment of cannabis use disorders: a review of the literature', *American Journal of Addiction* 16, pp. 331–42.

Nutt, D., King, L., Saulsbury, W., Blakemore, C. (2007), 'Development of a rational scale to assess the harm of drugs of potential misuse', *Lancet* 369 (9566), pp. 1047–53.

Pacula, R. L., Chriqui, J. F. and King, J. (2004), *Marijuana decriminalization: what does it mean in the United States?*, Working Paper WR-126, RAND, Santa Monica. Available at http://www.rand.org/pubs/working_papers/WR126/.

Pakes, F. (2004), 'The politics of discontent: the emergence of a new criminal justice discourse in the Netherlands', *The Howard Journal* 43, pp. 284–98.

Patton, G. C., Coffey, C., Carlin, J. B., et al. (2002), 'Cannabis use and mental health in young people: cohort study', *BMJ* 325, pp. 1195–8.

Ramaekers, J. G., Berghaus, G., van Laar, M. and Drummer, O. H. (2004), 'Dose related risk of motor vehicle crashes after cannabis use', *Drug and Alcohol Dependence* 73, pp. 109–19.

Roffman, R. A. and Stephens, R. S. (eds) (2006), *Cannabis dependence: its nature, consequences and treatment*, Cambridge University Press, Cambridge, UK.

Room, R., Fischer, B., Hall, W. D., Lenton, S. and Reuter, P. (2008), *Cannabis policy: moving beyond stalemate*, The Global Cannabis Commission Report, Beckley Foundation, Oxford, UK. Available at http://www.beckleyfoundation.org/.

Rosenblatt, K. A., Daling, J. R., Chen, C., Sherman, K. J. and Schwartz, S. M. (2004), 'Marijuana use and risk of oral squamous cell carcinoma', *Cancer Research* 64, pp. 4049–54.

Saha, S., Chant, D., Welham, J. and McGrath, J. (2005), 'A systematic review of the prevalence of schizophrenia', *PLoS Medicine* 2, p. e141.

SAMHSA (2006), *Results from the 2005 National Survey on Drug Use and Health: Detailed tables. Prevalence estimates, standard errors, p values. Section 1.* Substance Abuse and Mental Health Administration, Office of Applied Studies, Rockville, MD. Available at http://www.oas.samhsa.gov.

Shand, F., Gates, J., Fawcett, J. and Mattick, R. (2003), *The treatment of alcohol problems: a review of the evidence*, Commonwealth Department of Health and Ageing, Canberra.

Sidney, S., Quesenberry, C. P., Jr., Friedman, G. D. and Tekawa, I. S. (1997), 'Marijuana use and cancer incidence (California, United States)', *Cancer Causes and Control* 8, pp. 722–8.

Single, E. W. (1989), 'The impact of marijuana decriminalization: an update', *Journal of Public Health Policy* 9, pp. 456–66.

Smart, R. G. and Ogborne, A. C. (2000), 'Drug use and drinking among students in 36 countries', *Addictive Behaviors* 25, pp. 455–60.

Solowij, N. (1998), *Cannabis and cognitive functioning*, Cambridge University Press, Cambridge, UK.

Stephens, R. S., Roffman, R. A., Copeland, J. and Swift, W. (2006), 'Cognitive behavioral and motivational enhancement treatments for cannabis dependence', in Roffman, R. A. and Stephens, R. S. (eds), *Cannabis dependence: its nature, consequences and treatment*, Cambridge University Press, Cambridge, UK, pp. 131–53.

Stephens, R. S., Roffman, R. A., Fearer, S. A., Williams, C. and Burke, R. S. (2007), 'The marijuana check-up: promoting change in ambivalent marijuana users', *Addiction* 102, pp. 947–57.

Swift, W., Copeland, J. and Lenton, S. (2000), 'Cannabis and harm reduction', *Drug and Alcohol Review* 19, pp. 101–12.

Tashkin, D. P. (1999), 'Effects of cannabis on the respiratory system', in Kalant, H., Corrigall, W., Hall, W. D. and Smart, R. (eds), *The health effects of cannabis*, Centre for Addiction and Mental Health, Toronto, pp. 311–45.

Tobler, N. S., Lessard, T., Marshall, D., Ochshorn, P. and Roona, M. (1999), 'Effectiveness of school-based drug prevention programs for marijuana use', *School Psychology International* 20, pp. 105–37.

Toumbourou, J., Williams, J., Waters, E. and Patton, G. (2004), 'What do we know about preventing drug-related harm through social developmental intervention with children and young people?', in Stockwell, T., Gruenewald, P., Toumbourou, J. and Loxley, W. (eds), *Preventing harmful substance use: the evidence base for policy and practice*, John Wiley & Sons Ltd, Chichester, pp. 87–100.

UNODC (United Nations Office on Drugs and Crime) (2006), *World drug report 2006. Volume 1: Analysis*, United Nations Office on Drugs and Crime, Vienna.

UNODC (2007), *World drug report 2007. Volume 1: Analysis*, United Nations Office on Drugs and Crime, Vienna.

van Os, J., Bak, M., Hanssen, M., et al. (2002), 'Cannabis use and psychosis: a longitudinal population-based study', *American Journal of Epidemiology* 156, pp. 319–27.

White, D. and Pitts, M. (1998), 'Educating young people about drugs: a systematic review', *Addiction* 93, pp. 1475–87.

Williams, J. (2004), 'The effects of price and policy on marijuana use: what can be learned from the Australian experience?' *Health Economics* 13, pp. 123–37.

Wodak, A., Reinarman, C. and Cohen, P. (2002), 'Cannabis control: costs outweigh benefits', *BMJ* 324, pp. 105–06.

Zammit, S., Allebeck, P., Andréasson, S., Lundberg, I. and Lewis, G. (2002), 'Self reported cannabis use as a risk factor for schizophrenia in Swedish conscripts of 1969: historical cohort study', *BMJ* 325, pp. 1199–201.

Zhang, Z. F., Morgenstern, H., Spitz, M. R., et al. (1999), 'Marijuana use and increased risk of squamous cell carcinoma of the head and neck', *Cancer Epidemiology, Biomarkers and Prevention* 8, pp. 1071–8.

Zimmer, L., Morgan, J. P. (1997), *Marijuana myths, marijuana facts: a review of the scientific evidence*, The Lindesmith Center, New York.

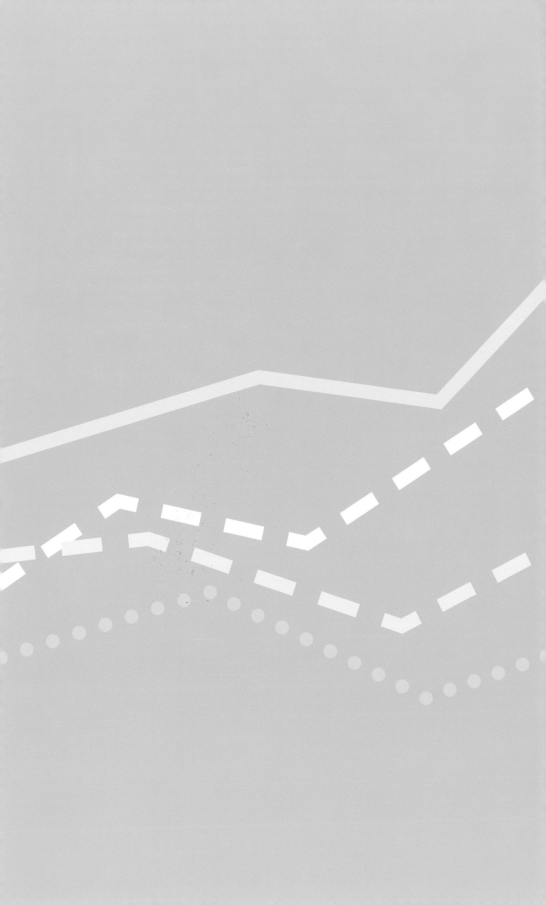

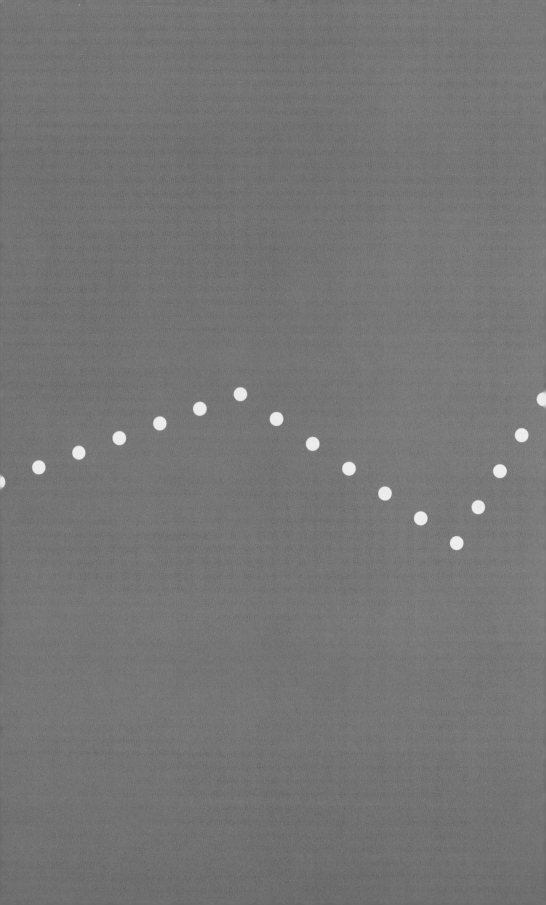

Chapter 9
Harm reduction policies for tobacco

Coral Gartner, Wayne Hall and Ann McNeill

Abstract

Tobacco smoking is the leading cause of preventable premature mortality and disability in European and other developed countries. This chapter first reviews strategies that (1) aim to reduce harm to non-smokers (public smoking bans and reduced ignition propensity cigarettes) and (2) aim to reduce harm to the smoker who is unable or unwilling to quit nicotine use, namely, regulating the harmfulness of cigarettes, and encouraging smokers to switch to less harmful nicotine products. The putative tobacco harm reduction products discussed include: modified tobacco cigarettes and cigarette-like devices, smokeless tobacco products and pharmaceutical nicotine products. The evidence for the harm reduction potential of each of these is discussed, as are adverse public health outcomes that may potentially arise from their promotion. The chapter concludes with a description of the most promising options for promoting tobacco harm reduction.

Keywords: smokeless tobacco, snus, reduced ignition propensity cigarettes, smoking bans, potential reduced exposure products, pharmaceutical nicotine.

Introduction

Tobacco can be smoked as cigarettes, in a pipe, or as cigars or used via non-smoked products such as chewing tobacco or oral and nasal snuff. Nicotine is the primary substance responsible for tobacco dependence but the majority of harm caused by tobacco use is not from nicotine but from the by-products of smoked tobacco (e.g. fine particulates, carcinogens, and noxious gases including carbon monoxide). Cigarettes are the most addictive and hazardous tobacco product, because cigarette smoke is readily drawn deep into the lungs where it is rapidly absorbed into the bloodstream and from which nicotine quickly reaches the brain (Benowitz, 2008).

In Europe, as in many regions of the world, the cigarette has become the dominant form of tobacco use over the past century (Berridge, 2007). The rise in the popularity of the cigarette was followed with a lag of several decades by increases in tobacco-caused diseases including cancers, pulmonary and cardiovascular diseases. By mid century tobacco smoking had become the leading cause of preventable premature mortality and disability in Europe and other developed countries. Cigarette smoking is currently responsible for around 730 000 deaths in the European Union (EU) each year (including 80 000 from passive smoking) (ASPECT Consortium, 2004).

Smoking prevalence has declined in most western European countries over the past 40 years, but prevalence remains high in many eastern European countries (ASPECT Consortium,

2004; WHO Regional Office for Europe, 2007). The disparities in smoking prevalence across Europe largely reflect differences in the intensity with which tobacco control policies have been implemented, such as increasing cigarette taxes, banning cigarette advertising, public mass media anti-smoking campaigns and restricting smoking in indoor public spaces (ASPECT Consortium, 2004; WHO Regional Office for Europe, 2003; WHO Regional Office for Europe, 2007).

Policies that encourage existing smokers to quit and discourage non-smokers from starting remain the most effective ways of reducing tobacco-related harm (World Bank, 2003). Nonetheless, even in countries that have most rigorously enforced these types of policies (Australia, the United States, Canada, the United Kingdom and Sweden), none have reduced overall smoking prevalence below one in six adults. Plausible projections show that more than 10 % of adults will be smoking in another 20 years if current rates of cessation and initiation continue (Gartner et al., 2009; Kemm, 2003; Mendez et al., 1998).

The persistence of smoking in a substantial minority of adults has prompted some to advocate tobacco harm reduction (THR) policies as an addition to conventional strategies that promote abstinence from tobacco. Harm reduction policies are generally those that 'attempt to prevent problems by targeting risky contexts or patterns of use, or by moderating the relation between use and problem outcomes, without necessarily affecting overall rates of use' (Toumbourou et al., 2007, pp. 1398–9). In the case of THR, this approach involves attempting to reduce the harmfulness of tobacco use without necessarily advocating cessation or abstinence, typically by advocating the use of much less harmful forms of tobacco or nicotine use.

Policies that reduce the harm to others

Public smoking bans

Non-smokers who are exposed to second-hand smoke (the emissions from the end of lit cigarettes and the exhaled smoke from a smoker) are at increased risk of many of the same diseases that affect smokers (US Department of Health and Human Services, 2006). Workers in smoky environments, such as bar staff, are particularly at risk due to their regular and prolonged exposure. Legislated bans on smoking in enclosed public spaces such as office buildings, restaurants, cafes, bars and clubs provide protection of employees and patrons and are the most widespread and non-controversial tobacco harm reduction policy. Research has shown that public smoking bans in countries like the United States and Australia have been effective in reducing exposure to second-hand smoke in these previously smoky environments (Hopkins et al., 2001). There is also evidence that these policies can provide immediate population health improvements, such as a reduction in the number of hospitalisations for acute coronary events (Pell et al., 2008).

A number of European countries have recently introduced indoor public smoking bans (for example, Republic of Ireland, United Kingdom), but many countries still do not have comprehensive smoking bans (Joossens and Raw, 2007). To be effective at reducing the exposure of non-smokers, these bans need to cover all enclosed areas and should also extend to outdoor areas that are serviced by waiting staff. Smoking bans also have the added benefit of increasing cessation in the smoking population by reducing the opportunities to smoke and contributing to the de-normalisation of smoking (Fichtenberg and Glantz, 2002).

Reduced ignition propensity (RIP) cigarettes

Fires started by cigarettes cause substantial damage to property and loss of life. Internal tobacco industry documents show that the industry knew how to reduce the ignition propensity of cigarettes many years ago (Gunja et al., 2002) by reducing tobacco density, paper porosity and cigarette circumference, eliminating burn additives and by increasing the length of filters (Chapman and Balmain, 2004). Legislation requiring cigarettes to meet RIP performance standards has now been implemented in 22 US states and Canada (Arnott and Berteletti, 2008). In 2007, the EU Member States endorsed plans to develop a mandatory standard to reduce the ignition propensity of cigarettes sold in the EU (Arnott and Berteletti, 2008; Commission of the European Communities, 2008). An evaluation of New York's RIP standard (implemented in 2004), showed that it substantially reduced the ignition propensity of cigarettes sold in that state, largely via 'paper banding', without increasing the toxicity of the emissions (Alpert et al., 2005). There is as yet no evidence that the introduction of RIP standards has reduced cigarette-related fires. Nevertheless, implementation of a RIP performance standard in Europe would not be costly to the public, would have very little risk of producing adverse outcomes and could reduce the number of fires caused by discarded cigarettes.

Policies that reduce harm to the smoker

The main putative tobacco harm reduction products in order of decreasing relative harmfulness are modified tobacco cigarettes and cigarette-like devices, smokeless tobacco (SLT) products and pharmaceutical nicotine (PN) products (Stratton et al., 2001).

Modified tobacco cigarettes and cigarette-like devices

Regulating the harmfulness of cigarette emissions

The tobacco industry began developing a 'safer' cigarette in response to the emerging evidence of the harm from cigarette smoking in the 1950s (Glantz et al., 1996). The first example was the filtered cigarette, followed by so-called light, low-tar and low-nicotine cigarettes in the 1980s (Stratton et al., 2001). These cigarette modifications, which consisted of the addition of tiny ventilation holes in the side of the filter to dilute the smoke with air drawn in through these holes, were popular with smokers; however, they did not reduce the health risks of smoking as smokers compensated by drawing harder on the cigarette, covering the filter ventilation holes and smoking the cigarettes down to a shorter butt length. Research later revealed that the cigarette manufacturers knew these were not genuine reduced harm products, but marketed them to reassure health-conscious smokers and discourage quitting (Glantz et al., 1996).

The World Health Organization's Study Group of Tobacco Product Regulation (TobReg) advocates mandatory maximum permissible levels of key toxicants in mainstream cigarette smoke (Burns et al., 2008) and the tobacco industry has developed and marketed cigarettes made with low nitrosamine tobacco and carbon filters, both of which are claimed to expose smokers to fewer toxins than regular cigarettes (Hatsukami et al., 2004; Rees et al., 2008). A major problem with this approach is that reductions in some toxins are often achieved by increasing others (King et al., 2007). Given that tobacco smoke contains more than 4 000 different chemicals, it will be difficult to achieve a substantial reduction in overall harmfulness (Stratton et al., 2001). Futhermore, there is no evidence that reducing or removing known toxins in cigarettes will produce observable reductions in smoking-related lung cancer (Pankow et al., 2007), yet publicity around mandating these changes may give consumers the impression that they do significantly reduce harm. Monitoring and enforcing a cigarette emissions standard will also require substantial laboratory and regulatory resources that may arguably be better used in other ways.

Cigarette-like devices

The tobacco industry has also marketed cigarette-like devices that aim to minimise tars and maximise nicotine by heating tobacco to produce an aerosol or vapour rather than smoke (for example, Eclipse, Premier, Accord and Heatbar) (Shiffman et al., 2002a; Stratton et al., 2001). Some of these products reduce emissions of one or more key toxins, but some studies report higher emissions of others (Breland et al., 2002; Breland et al., 2006; Fagerström et al., 2000; Stratton et al., 2001). Given the long latency of many tobacco-related diseases, it will take several decades before we know whether these products substantially reduce tobacco-related mortality and morbidity. Given these difficulties, we should arguably abandon attempts to reduce the harmfulness of cigarette emissions by modifying cigarettes or producing cigarette-like tobacco products in favour of harm reduction using non-smoked forms of tobacco and clean nicotine products (Stratton et al., 2001).

Smokeless tobacco (SLT) products

SLT products present greater opportunity for THR than smoked tobacco because there is no combustion/vaporisation and therefore no risk of respiratory disease, fire or passive smoking. SLT products include traditional chewing tobacco and snuff, and new products such as compressed tobacco lozenges, tobacco chewing gum and dissolvable strips (Hatsukami et al., 2007; Stepanov et al., 2006). Most policy attention has focused on a form of moist oral snuff used in Sweden, known as snus (see box on p. 262). It has much lower levels of tobacco-specific nitrosamines than snuffs marketed in the United States and elsewhere because it is produced by pasteurisation rather than fermentation (Hoffmann et al., 1995; Österdahl et al., 2004; Ramström, 2000). Levels of nitrosamines in Swedish snus have decreased over the past 20 or so years in response to the development of an industry standard (Hatsukami et al., 2007; Österdahl et al., 2004). The development of portion snus in the 1970s (tea-bag-like sachets of snus) has produced a more user-friendly version that has increased prevalence of snus use among Swedish men. The fact that until recently snus was taxed at a much lower rate than cigarettes may also have contributed to its increased popularity. Increased snus use by Swedish men has been accompanied by decreased cigarette smoking and tobacco-related disease mortality (Foulds et al., 2003; Ramström, 2003).

A major barrier to the adoption of this form of harm reduction is the ban on the sale of the least harmful smokeless tobacco products in many countries. In Australia and New Zealand, for example, oral snuff and chewing tobacco products cannot be sold (Commonwealth of Australia, 1974; Parliament of New Zealand, 1990). With the exception of Sweden, the same is true in all EU Member States, where the sale of these tobacco products is prohibited, although chewing tobacco and nasal snuff can be sold (European Court of Justice, 2004).

Pharmaceutical nicotine (PN)

PN products in the form of gum, patches, inhalers and sprays have been available for many years. A new PN product under development is an oral nicotine pouch that mimics portion snus (Fagerström and Jiménez-Ruiz, 2008). PN is generally a safe (except perhaps in pregnancy), modestly effective and cost-effective way to help smokers to quit (Bertram et al., 2007; Stead et al., 2008), or, potentially, also as a long-term alternative to cigarette smoking (Warner et al., 1997). These products have minimal risk of abuse, in part because of their design. The long-term use of PN appears to be safe, as no treated morbidity or mortality was observed in five years of follow-up of nicotine gum users (Murray et al., 1996). Long-term use of PN in ex-smokers may also help prevent relapse to smoking (Hajek et al., 2007; Medioni et al., 2005).

The major disadvantages of PN are that, like other smoking cessation aids (bupropion, varenicline), most smokers who use it do not succeed in quitting (Nides, 2008; Shiffman et al., 2002b), and it has not been taken up by smokers as an alternative to smoking despite its wide availability in many developed countries. This seems to be because these products have been engineered for smoking cessation, with the aim of minimising their abuse by delivering a lower nicotine dose at a slower speed to cigarettes. They are also not marketed as long-term alternatives to tobacco smoking. For these products to gain popularity, PN regulation would need to be relaxed to allow these products to be made more attractive to inveterate smokers.

Recreational nicotine products

The marketing of the 'e-cigarette', a device that looks like a standard tobacco cigarette but contains only nicotine in a carrier vapour, is a recent attempt to commercialise a recreational nicotine product. Its similarity to cigarettes has led most tobacco control advocates to refer to it as a cigarette-like device. The e-cigarette produces a propylene glycol vapour and has a glowing red tip to simulate a lit cigarette. The manufacturers have not marketed it as a smoking cessation aid and this has created regulatory barriers in some countries (for example, Australia and New Zealand) (National Drugs and Poisons Scheduling Committee, 2009; New Zealand Public Health Directorate, 2006). Some EU Member States have defined e-cigarettes as medical devices and require them to obtain a Confirmatory European (CE) mark before sale (e.g. Denmark, Austria) (Danish Medicines Agency, 2009; European Commission Health and Consumer Protection Directorate-General, 2008). A safety assessment of one brand of e-cigarette funded by the manufacturer suggests the product may be relatively safe (Laugesen, 2008; Laugesen et al., 2008), but there are no data on the patterns of use in smokers or uptake by non-smokers in countries where these products are sold, and there are no safety studies by groups that are independent of the industry.

There are claims in the popular media in the United Kingdom that the e-cigarette is being used in response to smoking bans in pubs and clubs (Sikora, 2007). Critics of the e-cigarette also argue that it maintains a visible smoking-like behaviour that may undermine the de-normalisation of smoking produced by public smoking bans (Chapman and Freeman, 2008). The substantial cost of the device and its replacement cartridges, the gimmicky nature of the smoke and glowing tip, and the regulatory hurdles in most countries will probably limit its use for THR (Arendt, 2008). However, more data is needed on whether smokers find these devices an acceptable substitute for smoking regular cigarettes.

The e-cigarette illustrates the inadequacy of current regulatory structures. Claims about aiding cessation would result in the e-cigarette being classified as a medicine and would require safety, quality and efficacy data before being marketed. If no such claims are made, the e-cigarette is likely to be regulated like tobacco cigarettes, and would then be subject to all the regulations that apply to tobacco products. Neither set of regulations are appropriate for e-cigarettes, the relative harmfulness of which is likely to fall somewhere between tobacco cigarettes and PN.

Will tobacco harm reduction products reduce harm to users?

There is no evidence that modified smoked tobacco products and cigarette-like devices substantially reduce harm. Experience with 'light' cigarettes also provides strong reasons for not allowing them to be promoted as THR products (Stratton et al., 2001; Warner, 2001). 'Light' cigarettes failed to reduce harm in smokers due to compensatory changes in the way they were smoked, such as inhaling more deeply, smoking a greater number of cigarettes and more of each cigarette, and blocking ventilation holes designed to dilute smoke exposure (Stratton et al., 2001). The mistaken image of a less harmful cigarette also provided reassurance to health-concerned smokers, which discouraged quitting. Similar compensatory changes, and/or 'risk swapping' by decreasing some toxins whilst increasing others, and false reassurance of safety, are likely to limit any benefits from THR products that involve the combustion or vaporisation of tobacco (e.g. Gray, 2004; Pierce, 2002; Stratton et al., 2001).

This argument does not apply to THR using PN and low nitrosamine SLT (LNSLT). The safety of PN is well established in the short to medium term with users having been followed for up to five years (Murray et al., 1996). PN may carry some residual health risks, such as an increased risk of cardiovascular disease arising from chronic nicotine intake, and adverse foetal outcomes if used in pregnancy, but these effects are small by comparison with those of cigarette smoking (Benowitz, 2000). Literature reviews of the health effects of SLT (Broadstock, 2007; Royal College of Physicians, 2007; SCENIHR, 2008) have concluded that some forms of SLT such as Swedish snus, which is low in nitrosamines, are significantly less harmful than smoking cigarettes. SLT use is not associated with respiratory diseases, including lung cancer and chronic obstructive pulmonary disease (COPD), but some potential health risks remain, namely oral and pancreatic cancer, cardiovascular disease and type 2 diabetes. Even so, these risks appear to be much lower than those of smoking. An expert panel estimated on the basis of the epidemiological literature that the overall risk of tobacco-related mortality in LNSLT users was 10 % of the risk of cigarette smokers (Levy et al., 2004). Epidemiological modelling of the aggregate health effects of quitting tobacco and switching from smoking to LNSLT suggest there is little difference in years of healthy life gained by those who quit tobacco and those who switch to LNSLT (Gartner et al., 2007b) (see box on p. 262).

Effects of tobacco harm reduction on aggregate harm

Whether THR produces a net benefit or harm depends on: the relative harmfulness of the THR product compared to regular cigarettes; how popular the THR product is among current smokers, ex-smokers and never smokers; and its effect on rates of smoking cessation and initiation. The risks of overall net harm are greatest for modified cigarettes and cigarette-like devices, because these produce the least reduction in risk and could discourage cessation in much the same way as 'light' cigarettes did.

Epidemiological modelling of the aggregate health effects of smoking and LNSLT use suggests that relaxations of bans on LNSLT use would only produce net harm if these products proved much more attractive to non-smokers than to smokers; led non-smokers to start to smoke; and/or maintained cigarette use in smokers by dual use rather than complete switching (Gartner et al., 2007a) (see box on p. 262). These putative effects of LNSLT have not been observed in Sweden and there are good reasons for thinking that they are unlikely to occur. As Kozlowski and colleagues (Kozlowski et al., 2001) have shown, PN would still produce a net population health gain, even if we made: (1) the most pessimistic assumptions about its residual health risks; and (2) we assumed that PN was used by the whole adult population (Kozlowski et al., 2001). A similar argument can be made for LNSLT.

Epidemiological modelling of the aggregate health effects of lifelong smoking, ex-smoking, switching to snus and lifelong snus use

Gartner et al (2007b) used multistate life tables and expert panel risk estimates to model the years of healthy life lost (YHLL) due to lifelong smoking, quitting tobacco use, switching from smoking to snus and lifelong snus use without smoking. The results showed that smokers who switched to snus would achieve health gains nearly as good as quitting all tobacco use. Men who switched from smoking to snus would lose 1.2–3.6 months of healthy life and women 1.2–4.8 months compared to smokers who quit tobacco altogether.

Figure 9.1: Years of healthy life lost by lifelong smoking, ex-smoking, switching to snus and lifelong snus use

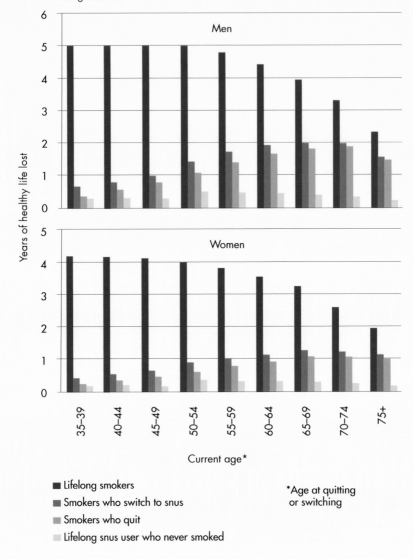

'Gateway' effects

There is no evidence that PN in its currently available forms encourages non-smokers to take up smoking (Gerlach et al., 2008; Klesges et al., 2003). This situation could change if PN was re-engineered to be more rapidly absorbed and produced higher blood nicotine, and if it were allowed to be marketed as a recreational nicotine product, like smoked tobacco. The current marketing of the e-cigarette in some countries may allow an assessment of the risks of more liberal regulation of the nicotine market, although the nicotine dose and delivery of currently marketed e-cigarettes may be too similar to existing PN cessation aids for a full assessment. The cost of the e-cigarette may also preclude its widescale uptake.

The Swedish experience

Snus is a traditional moist oral snuff used in Sweden. Snus use declined as cigarettes became popular. However, a marketing campaign that started in the 1970s reinvigorated the snus market and resulted in increased uptake among Swedish men, with as many Swedish men now using snus as smoking cigarettes (Ramström, 2000). The Swedish experience has been described as a natural experiment of tobacco harm reduction (Brandt, 2007; Henningfield and Fagerström, 2001) as the shift from cigarette smoking to snus use has occurred without the support of the Swedish health community.

Figure 9.2: Prevalence of daily smoking for men and women (ages 18–70 years) in Sweden 1976–2002 and prevalence of daily snus use for men (age 18–70 years) in Sweden 1976–2002

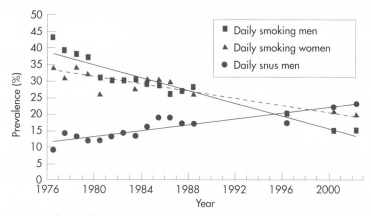

Source: Reproduced from Foulds et al., 2003.

The increase in snus use was accompanied by a decline in cigarette smoking from 40 % in 1976 to 15 % in 2002 (see Figure 9.2). Contrary to the gateway hypothesis, there were no increases in smoking among adolescent males, who were the heaviest users of snus. Instead, snus use appears to deter smoking initiation in young men and promote smoking cessation in older men (Foulds et al., 2003; Furberg et al., 2005; Ramström, 2000). Most critically, the increase in snus use was accompanied by a decline in lung cancer mortality and the absence of an increase in either cardiovascular mortality or head and neck cancers (Foulds et al., 2003). The plausibility of a causal relationship between increased snus use and these good health outcomes was strengthened by the absence of any similar changes in smoking prevalence or lung cancer mortality in Swedish women, who did not adopt snus at the same rate as men (Foulds et al., 2003).

Figure 9.3: Lung cancer incidence for men and women in Sweden and Norway 1960–99 for age-standardised rates per 100 000 inhabitants based upon census population in each country

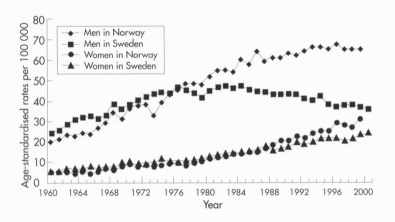

Source: Reproduced from Foulds et al., 2003.

Whether SLT serves as a gateway to smoking is a more contentious issue. The Swedish experience with snus contradicts the pessimistic view about the population impact of THR (Foulds et al., 2003) (see box on p. 263). The relationship between SLT use and smoking has been more varied in American studies. In some studies the same pattern has been reported as in Sweden (Ault et al., 2004; O'Connor et al., 2005). Other studies, however, have reported an apparent 'gateway' effect with young SLT users 'graduating' to smoking (Haddock et al., 2001). It is challenging to quantify how much smoking is attributable to prior SLT use because it is difficult to determine whether smokers who used SLT before cigarettes would have become smokers in the absence of SLT use. One analysis suggests that when the demographic and social factors associated with smoking initiation are taken into account, SLT does not appear to increase the uptake of smoking (Timberlake et al., 2009). In the United States, public health authorities may have also inadvertently encouraged SLT users to switch to cigarettes by claiming that the health risks of SLT are the same as those of smoking (Kozlowski and Edwards, 2005; Kozlowski and O'Connor, 2003; Waterbor et al., 2004).

'Dual use'

The use of PN to relieve nicotine withdrawal during periods of temporary abstinence is an approved use in some countries (for example, United Kingdom, Republic of Ireland, France, Austria, Denmark, Norway, Portugal, Brazil, Venezuela, New Zealand and Canada), as is its use to reduce smoking in preparation for quitting (ASH UK, 2008). Some studies have reported that users of PN often use it for purposes other than cessation (Hammond et al., 2008; Klesges et al., 2003). Such use does not appear to reduce quitting (Levy et al., 2007); indeed, such use may increase cessation in smokers who were not initially interested in quitting (Carpenter et al., 2004; Le Houezec and Sawe, 2003).

The tobacco industry has begun to market SLT for smokers to use when smoking is not permitted (Gartner et al., 2007a). This pattern of use could perpetuate smoking by reducing the incentive to quit provided by public smoking bans (Fichtenberg and Glantz, 2002). Alternatively, such use of SLT could lead some smokers to switch fully to SLT or even to quit tobacco use, as happens with PN. This pattern of short-term dual use as an intermediate step to full switching or quitting appears more common in Sweden than long-term dual use of SLT and cigarettes (Ramström and Foulds, 2006). It is a pattern that could be encouraged by a combination of policies, such as educating smokers about health risks, imposing differential tax rates on smoked tobacco and SLT products based on their relative harmfulness, and regulating the availability and accessibility of these products to favour SLT.

Ethical issues

Do public health practitioners have the ethical right to prevent smokers from being informed about THR products in order to reduce the possibility that THR may increase population nicotine use? Those who argue that smokers should not be told how to reduce their risks promote a paternalistic policy that sacrifices smokers' interests to the greater public good. Others argue that informing smokers about THR is an effective public health measure that properly respects their autonomy (Kozlowski, 2003; Kozlowski and Edwards, 2005; Waterbor et al., 2004).

Some opposition to THR reflects the belief that the goal of tobacco control policy should be the elimination of all nicotine use (for example, Pierce, 2002). Some opponents also argue that THR is morally wrong because it involves the long-term use of an addictive substance (Warner et al., 1997). These views contrast with the consequentialist ethical views of proponents who argue that the benefits of THR outweigh its harms (for example, Kozlowski, 2002).

The THR debate is complicated by the role of the tobacco industry whose interests conflict with those of public health. THR is seen as benefiting the tobacco industry by condoning continued tobacco use and thereby allowing the industry's continued existence (Bullen et al., 2006). Whilst the abolition of the tobacco industry would arguably be preferable, most THR proponents see this as an unrealistic goal, at least in the short to medium term (Hall and Gartner, 2009) and accept that enabling the tobacco industry to become part of the solution could accelerate change in the nicotine market over time.

Options for promoting tobacco harm reduction

Regulating the harmfulness of tobacco products

Mandating standards for RIP of cigarettes is unlikely to cause harm and may reduce cigarette-related fires. It is much less certain whether mandated maximum levels of key toxins in cigarette emissions will reduce aggregate harm because of the risk that any gains will be offset by compensatory smoking, higher levels of other toxins, and/or the impression of a significant reduction in harm. It will in any case take decades to assess. Mandated standards for toxins, such as tobacco-specific nitrosamines, in SLT should be less problematic to implement because the feasibility of this strategy has already been demonstrated (Österdahl et al., 2004; Stepanov et al., 2006) and, on Swedish experience, it is likely to minimise oral cancer risk.

Information about THR products

Harm reduction could be promoted through advising smokers to use less harmful products, such as LNSLT and PN. This could be done via product warning labels on cigarettes and less harmful tobacco and nicotine products that indicate the relative harmfulness of each product. This option is currently most relevant for non-EU countries and Sweden because of the sales ban on most of these products in EU Member States. Information provided by governments and health authorities could also clearly indicate the relative harms of each product, rather than misleadingly suggesting that all tobacco products are equally hazardous (Kozlowski, 2003; Kozlowski and O'Connor, 2003; Waterbor et al., 2004).

Regulation and promotion of THR products

Smokers who fail to quit after obtaining cessation assistance could be encouraged to use PN as a long-term alternative (Kozlowski, 2002; Kozlowski et al., 2003). This is one of the few THR strategies supported by the majority of US tobacco control advocates (Warner and Martin, 2003) and advocated by the Royal College of Physicians in the United Kingdom (Royal College of Physicians, 2007) and experts in the EU (ASPECT Consortium, 2004). It would probably have limited public health impact if it was aimed solely at high-risk smokers who failed to quit, because only a minority of these smokers seek help to quit, and probably few of whom find existing forms of PN attractive (Stratton et al., 2001; Warner et al., 1997).

In order to have a larger public health impact, THR requires as many smokers as possible to switch to either PN or LNSLT. The Swedish experience suggests that LNSLT may be more likely to achieve this goal than current forms of PN as more smokers in Sweden have switched to LNSLT than PN (Foulds et al., 2003; Ramström, 2000). This could change if regulators allowed more attractive forms of PN to be developed and marketed to smokers. In EU countries other than Sweden, consideration could be given to relaxing the sales ban on non-smoked, non-chewed oral tobacco products. More equal competition between cigarettes and less hazardous nicotine delivery devices could be achieved by making it harder to introduce new cigarette-like tobacco products and easier to introduce and promote the use of non-smoked THR products and recreational PN products (Stratton et al., 2001; Warner et al., 1997). Thought should be given to the regulation of products that fall between current PN products and cigarettes. The e-cigarette could provide a test case for developing a more flexible regulatory structure that works in favour of public health, by regulating nicotine-containing products according to criteria that consider the relative harmfulness of each product.

A graduated policy sequence

We believe that exploring the use of LNSLT for THR is the most promising route facing regulators at the moment. The development of faster-acting PN is likely to take some time and e-cigarettes are probably too similar to PN products. The following steps could be used to explore the public health potential of THR using LNSLT in those countries in which their production and sale is prohibited, such as the EU, Australia and New Zealand (Commonwealth of Australia, 1974; European Parliament and Council of the European Union, 2001; Parliament of New Zealand, 1990).

First, the utility of LNSLT for smoking cessation could be cautiously trialled among smokers who had failed to quit with the use of PN and other smoking cessation medications by encouraging them to switch to LNSLT rather than return to smoking. Evaluations of this approach would provide information on how attractive these products may be to inveterate smokers.

Second, relaxation of PN product regulation could encourage the use of existing PN for long-term substitution if smokers fail to stop, and enable the delivery of nicotine doses in ways more like SLT, thereby encouraging smokers who failed to quit smoking to use these products instead.

Third, if there was sufficient interest in switching to LNSLT among inveterate smokers, permitting restricted sale of LNSLT products to these smokers (e.g. from specialist tobacconists) could provide an alternative to continued smoking. Legislation could impose differential taxes to reflect the relative harmfulness.

Fourth, the impacts of the sale of these products on: population smoking cessation rates; all forms of tobacco use among youth; and tobacco industry marketing should be rigorously evaluated.

Conclusions

Public smoking bans and mandatory reduced ignition propensity standards for cigarettes are strategies that reduce tobacco-related harm to non-smokers and should be implemented as a priority. The most promising strategy for reducing harm to tobacco smokers is to encourage smokers who are unable or unwilling to quit to switch to pharmaceutical nicotine or low nitrosamine smokeless tobacco products. There is good support for this policy from epidemiological studies in Sweden. Modelling studies indicate that this would very substantially reduce the risks of tobacco use. Nonetheless, this remains a controversial policy because the view of some in the tobacco control community is that our policy goal should be elimination of all nicotine use. A major barrier to its implementation is that many states in the EU ban the sale of these products, and proposals to remove these bans have been opposed because of concerns that THR may increase the uptake of tobacco smoking and the harm that it causes.

References

Alpert, H. R., Carpenter, C., Connolly, G. N., Rees, V. and Wayne, G. F. (2005), *'Fire safer' cigarettes: the effect of the New York State Cigarette Fire Safety Standard on ignition propensity, smoke toxicity, and the consumer market. A preliminary report*, Harvard School of Public Health, Boston. Available at http://www.firesafecigarettes.org/assets/files/harvardstudy.pdf.

Arendt, P. (2008), 'One month of … electronic cigarettes', *Guardian*, 8 December, Comment and features, p. 17.

Arnott, D. and Berteletti, F. (2008), 'Europe: agreement on reducing cigarette fires', *Tobacco Control* 17, pp. 4–5.

ASH UK (2008), *Beyond Smoking Kills: protecting children, reducing inequalities*, Action on Smoking and Health, London. Available at www.ash.org.uk/beyondsmokingkills.

ASPECT Consortium (2004), *Tobacco or health in the European Union*, European Commission, Luxembourg. Available at http://ec.europa.eu/health/ph_determinants/life_style/Tobacco/Documents/tobacco_fr_en.pdf.

Ault, R. W., Ekelund, R. B., Jackson, J. D. and Saba, R. P. (2004), 'Smokeless tobacco, smoking cessation and harm reduction: an economic analysis', *Applied Economics* 36, pp. 17–29.

Benowitz, N. (2008), 'Clinical pharmacology of nicotine: implications for understanding, preventing, and treating tobacco addiction', *Clinical Pharmacology & Therapeutics* 83, pp. 531–41.

Benowitz, N. L. (2000), 'Nicotine toxicity', in Ferrence, R., Slade, J., Room, R. and Pope, M. (eds), *Nicotine and public health*, American Public Health Association, Washington, DC, pp. 65–76.

Berridge, V. (2007), *Marketing health: smoking and the discourse of public health in Britain, 1945–2000*, Oxford University Press, Oxford.

Bertram, M. Y., Lim, S. S., Wallace, A. L. and Vos, T. (2007), 'Costs and benefits of smoking cessation aids: making a case for public reimbursement of nicotine replacement therapy in Australia', *Tobacco Control* 16, pp. 255–60.

Brandt, A. (2007), *The cigarette century: the rise, fall, and deadly persistence of the product that defined America*, Basic Books, New York.

Breland, A. B., Evans, S. E., Buchhalter, A. R. and Eissenberg, T. (2002), 'Acute effects of AdvanceTM: a potential reduced exposure product for smokers', *Tobacco Control* 11, pp. 376–8.

Breland, A. B., Kleykamp, B. A. and Eissenberg, T. (2006), 'Clinical laboratory evaluation of potential reduced exposure products for smokers', *Nicotine & Tobacco Research* 8, pp. 727–38.

Broadstock, M. (2007), *Systematic review of the health effects of modified smokeless tobacco products, New Zealand Health Technology Assessment Report 10/1*, Department of Public Health and General Practice, Christchurch School of Medicine and Health Sciences, Christchurch. Available at http://nzhta.chmeds.ac.nz/publications/smokeless_tobacco.pdf.

Bullen, C., McRobbie, H., Thornley, S., Walker, N. and Whittaker, R. (2006), 'Working with what we have before getting into bed with the tobacco industry', *New Zealand Medical Journal* 119, p. U2139.

Burns, D. M., Dybing, E., Gray, N., et al. (2008), 'Mandated lowering of toxicants in cigarette smoke: a description of the World Health Organization TobReg proposal', *Tobacco Control* 17, pp. 132–41.

Carpenter, M. J., Hughes, J. R., Solomon, L. J. and Callas, P. W. (2004), 'Both smoking reduction with nicotine replacement therapy and motivational advice increase future cessation among smokers unmotivated to quit', *Journal of Consulting and Clinical Psychology* 72, pp. 371–81.

Chapman, S. and Balmain, A. (2004), *Reduced-ignition propensity cigarettes: a review of policy relevant information prepared for the Commonwealth Department of Health and Ageing*, Commonwealth of Australia, Canberra. Available at http://www.health.gov.au/internet/main/publishing.nsf/Content/health-pubhlth-publicat-document-smoking_rip.htm.

Chapman, S. and Freeman, B. (2008), 'Markers of the denormalisation of smoking and the tobacco industry', *Tobacco Control* 17, pp. 25–31.

Commission of the European Communities (2008), *Commission Decision of 25 March 2008 on the fire safety requirements to be met by European standards for cigarettes pursuant to Directive 2001/95/EC of the European Parliament and of the Council*, Official Journal of the European Union, Office for Official Publications of the European Communities, Luxembourg. Available at http://eur-lex.europa.eu/.

Commonwealth of Australia (1974), *Trade Practices Act No. 51 of 1974*, Attorney General's Department. Available at http://www.comlaw.gov.au/.

Danish Medicines Agency (2009), *Classification of electronic cigarettes, March 9 2009 (medicinal products)*, Lægemiddelstyrelsen, Copenhagen. Available at http://www.dkma.dk/1024/visUKLSArtikel.asp?artikelID=14819.

European Commission Health and Consumer Protection Directorate-General (2008), *Orientation note: electronic cigarettes and the EC legislation*, European Commission, Brussels. Available at http://ec.europa.eu/health/ph_determinants/life_style/Tobacco/Documents/orientation_0508_en.pdf.

European Court of Justice (2004), 'The Court declares the prohibition on tobacco products for oral use to be valid', press release No. 99/04, Judgments of the Court of Justice in Cases C-210/03 and C-434/02, European Court of Justice, Luxembourg. Available at http://curia.europa.eu/.

European Parliament and Council of the European Union (2001), *Directive 2001/37/EC of the European Parliament and of the Council of 5 June 2001 on the approximation of the laws, regulations and administrative provisions of the Member States concerning the manufacture, presentation and sale of tobacco products*, Official Journal of the European Union, Luxembourg. Available at http://eur-lex.europa.eu/.

Fagerström, K. O. and Jiménez-Ruiz, C. A. (2008), 'Pharmacological treatments for tobacco dependence', *European Respiratory Review* 17, pp. 192–8.

Fagerström, K. O., Hughes, J. R., Rasmussen, T. and Callas, P. W. (2000), 'Randomised trial investigating effect of a novel nicotine delivery device (Eclipse) and a nicotine oral inhaler on smoking behaviour, nicotine and carbon monoxide exposure, and motivation to quit', *Tobacco Control* 9, pp. 327–33.

Fichtenberg, C. M. and Glantz, S. A. (2002), 'Effect of smoke-free workplaces on smoking behaviour: systematic review', *British Medical Journal* 325, pp. 188–95.

Foulds, J., Ramström, L., Burke, M. and Fagerström, K. (2003), 'Effect of smokeless tobacco (snus) on smoking and public health in Sweden', *Tobacco Control* 12, pp. 349–59.

Furberg, H., Bulik, C. M., Lerman, C., et al. (2005), 'Is Swedish snus associated with smoking initiation or smoking cessation?' *Tobacco Control* 14, pp. 422–4.

Gartner, C. E., Hall, W. D., Chapman, S. and Freeman, B. (2007a), 'Should the health community promote smokeless tobacco (snus) as a harm reduction measure?', *PLoS Medicine* 4, pp. 1703–04.

Gartner, C. E., Hall, W. D., Vos, T., et al. (2007b), 'Assessment of Swedish snus for tobacco harm reduction: an epidemiological modelling study', *Lancet* 369, pp. 2010–14.

Gartner, C., Barendregt, J. and Hall, W. (2009), 'Predicting the future prevalence of cigarette smoking in Australia: how low can we go and by when?' *Tobacco Control* 18, pp. 183–9.

Gerlach, K. K., Rohay, J. M., Gitchell, J. G. and Shiffman, S. (2008), 'Use of nicotine replacement therapy among never smokers in the 1999–2006 National Health and Nutrition Examination Surveys', *Drug and Alcohol Dependence* 98, pp. 154–8.

Glantz, S. A., Slade, J., Bero, L. A., Hanauer, P. and Barnes, D. E. (eds) (1996), *The cigarette papers*, University of California Press, Berkeley.

Gray, N. (2004), 'The ethics of policies for the prevention of tobacco disease', *Acta Oncologica* 43, pp. 8–10.

Gunja, M., Wayne, G. F., Landman, A., Connelly, G. and McGuire, A. (2002), 'The case for fire safe cigarettes made through industry documents', *Tobacco Control* 11, pp. 346–53.

Haddock, C. K., Vander Weg, M., DeBon, M., et al. (2001), 'Evidence that smokeless tobacco use is a gateway for smoking initiation in young adult males', *Preventive Medicine* 32, pp. 262–7.

Hajek, P., McRobbie, H. and Gillison, F. (2007), 'Dependence potential of nicotine replacement treatments: effects of product type, patient characteristics, and cost to user', *Preventive Medicine* 44, pp. 230–4.

Hall, W. D. and Gartner, C. E. (2009), 'Supping with the devil? The role of law in promoting tobacco harm reduction using low nitrosamine smokeless tobacco products', *Public Health* 123, pp. 287–91.

Hammond, D., Reid, J. L., Driezen, P., et al. (2008), 'Smokers' use of nicotine replacement therapy for reasons other than stopping smoking: findings from the ITC Four Country Survey', *Addiction* 103, pp. 1696–703.

Hatsukami, D. K., Lemmonds, C., Zhang, Y., et al. (2004), 'Evaluation of carcinogen exposure in people who used "reduced exposure" tobacco products', *Journal of the National Cancer Institute* 96, pp. 844–52.

Hatsukami, D. K., Ebbert, J. O., Feuer, R. M., Stepanov, I. and Hecht, S. S. (2007), 'Changing smokeless tobacco products: new tobacco delivery systems', *American Journal of Preventive Medicine* 33, pp. S368–S78.

Henningfield, J. E. and Fagerström, K. O. (2001), 'Swedish match company, Swedish snus and public health: a harm reduction experiment in progress?', *Tobacco Control* 10, pp. 253–7.

Hoffmann, D., Djordjevic, M. V., Fan, J., et al. (1995), 'Five leading U.S. commercial brands of moist snuff in 1994: assessment of carcinogenic N-nitrosamines', *Journal of the National Cancer Institute* 87, pp. 1862–9.

Hopkins, D. P., Briss, P. A., Ricard, C. J., et al. (2001), 'Reviews of evidence regarding interventions to reduce tobacco use and exposure to environmental tobacco smoke', *American Journal of Preventive Medicine* 20, pp. 16–66.

Joossens, L. and Raw, M. (2007), *Progress in tobacco control in 30 European countries, 2005 to 2007*, Swiss Cancer League, Berne. Available at http://www.ensp.org/files/30_european_countries_text_final.pdf.

Kemm, J. (2003), 'A model to predict the results of changes in smoking behaviour on smoking prevalence', *Journal of Public Health Medicine* 25, pp. 318–24.

King, B., Borland, R. and Fowles, J. (2007), 'Mainstream smoke emissions of Australian and Canadian cigarettes', *Nicotine & Tobacco Research* 9, pp. 835–44.

Klesges, L. M., Johnson, K. C., Somes, G., Zbikowski, S. and Robinson, L. (2003), 'Use of nicotine replacement therapy in adolescent smokers and nonsmokers', *Archives of Pediatrics and Adolescent Medicine* 157, pp. 517–22.

Kozlowski, L. T. (2002), 'Harm reduction, public health, and human rights: smokers have a right to be informed of significant harm reduction options', *Nicotine & Tobacco Research* 4, pp. S55–S60.

Kozlowski, L. T. (2003), 'First, tell the truth: a dialogue on human rights, deception, and the use of smokeless tobacco as a substitute for cigarettes', *Tobacco Control* 12, pp. 34–6.

Kozlowski, L. T. and Edwards, B. Q. (2005), '"Not safe" is not enough: smokers have a right to know more than there is no safe tobacco product', *Tobacco Control* 14, pp. 113–117.

Kozlowski, L. T. and O'Connor, R. J. (2003), 'Apply federal research rules on deception to misleading health information: an example on smokeless tobacco and cigarettes', *Public Health Reports* 118, pp. 187–92.

Kozlowski, L. T., Strasser, A. A., Giovino, G. A., Erickson, P. A. and Terza, J. V. (2001), 'Applying the risk/use equilibrium: use medicinal nicotine now for harm reduction', *Tobacco Control* 10, pp. 201–03.

Kozlowski, L. T., O'Connor, R. J. and Quinio Edwards, B. (2003), 'Some practical points on harm reduction: what to tell your lawmaker and what to tell your brother about Swedish snus', *Tobacco Control* 12, pp. 372–3.

Laugesen, M. (2008), *Second safety report on the Ruyan® e-cigarette*, Health New Zealand Ltd, Christchurch. Available at http://www.healthnz.co.nz/2ndSafetyReport_9Apr08.pdf.

Laugesen, M., Thornley, S., McRobbie, H. and Bullen, C. (2008), *How safe is an e-cigarette? The results of independent chemical and microbiological analysis* (poster), SRNT 14th Annual Meeting, Society for Research on Nicotine and Tobacco, Portland, Oregon.

Le Houezec, J. and Sawe, U. (2003), 'Smoking reduction and temporary abstinence: new approaches for smoking cessation', *Journal des Maladies Vasculaires* 28, pp. 293–300.

Levy, D. T., Mumford, E. A., Cummings, K. M., et al. (2004), 'The relative risks of a low-nitrosamine smokeless tobacco product compared with smoking cigarettes: estimates of a panel of experts', *Cancer Epidemiology, Biomarkers and Prevention* 13, pp. 2035–42.

Levy, D. E., Thorndike, A. N., Biener, L. and Rigotti, N. A. (2007), 'Use of nicotine replacement therapy to reduce or delay smoking but not to quit: prevalence and association with subsequent cessation efforts', *Tobacco Control* 16, pp. 384–9.

Medioni, J., Berlin, I. and Mallet, A. (2005), 'Increased risk of relapse after stopping nicotine replacement therapies: a mathematical modelling approach', *Addiction* 100, pp. 247–54.

Mendez, D., Warner, K. E. and Courant, P. N. (1998), 'Has smoking cessation ceased? Expected trends in the prevalence of smoking in the United States', *American Journal of Epidemiology* 148, pp. 249–58.

Murray, R. P., Bailey, W. C., Daniels, K., et al. (1996), 'Safety of nicotine polacrilex gum used by 3,094 participants in the Lung Health Study. Lung Health Study Research Group', *Chest* 109, pp. 438–45.

National Drugs and Poisons Scheduling Committee (2009), *Standard for the uniform scheduling of drugs and poisons (SUSDP) No. 23*, Department of Health and Ageing, Commonwealth of Australia, Canberra. Available at http://www.comlaw.gov.au/.

New Zealand Public Health Directorate (2006), 'Classification of medicines notice, schedule 3, pharmacy-only medicines: nicotine', *New Zealand Gazette*, NZ Department of Internal Affairs, Wellington, p. 188.

Nides, M. (2008), 'Update on pharmacologic options for smoking cessation treatment', *American Journal of Medicine* 121, pp. S20–S31.

O'Connor, R. J., Kozlowski, L. T., Flaherty, B. P. and Edwards, B. Q. (2005), 'Most smokeless tobacco use does not cause cigarette smoking: results from the 2000 National Household Survey on Drug Abuse', *Addictive Behaviors* 30, pp. 325–36.

Österdahl, B. G., Jansson, C. and Paccou, A. (2004), 'Decreased levels of tobacco-specific N-nitrosamines in moist snuff on the Swedish market', *Journal of Agricultural and Food Chemistry* 52, pp. 5085–8.

Pankow, J. F., Watanabe, K. H., Toccalino PL, Luo, W. and Austin, D. F. (2007), 'Calcuated cancer risk for conventional and "potentially reduced exposure product" cigarettes', *Cancer Epidemiology, Biomarkers and Prevention* 16, pp. 584–92.

Parliament of New Zealand (1990), *Smoke-free environments act no. 108.* Available at http://www.legislation.govt.nz/act/public/1990/0108/latest/DLM223191.html?search=ts_act_smoke-free+environments&;sr=1.

Pell, J. P., Haw, S., Cobbe, S., et al. (2008), 'Smoke-free legislation and hospitalizations for acute coronary syndrome', *New England Journal of Medicine* 359, pp. 482–91.

Pierce, J. P. (2002), 'Harm reduction or harm maintenance?', *Nicotine and Tobacco Research* 4, pp. S53–S4.

Ramström, L. (2003), 'Snus: part of the problem or part of the solution?', *Addiction* 98, pp. 1198–9.

Ramström, L. M. (2000), 'Snuff: an alternative nicotine delivery system', in Ferrence, R., Slade, J., Room, R. and Pope, M. (eds), *Nicotine and public health*, American Public Health Association, Washington, DC.

Ramström, L. M. and Foulds, J. (2006), 'Role of snus in initiation and cessation of tobacco smoking in Sweden', *Tobacco Control* 15, pp. 210–4.

Rees, V. W., Wayne, G. F. and Connolly, G. N. (2008), 'Puffing style and human exposure minimally altered by switching to a carbon-filtered cigarette', *Cancer Epidemiology Biomarkers & Prevention* 17, p. 2995.

Royal College of Physicians (2007), *Harm reduction in nicotine addiction: helping people who can't quit. A report by the Tobacco Advisory Group of the Royal College of Physicians*, RCP, London. Available at http://www.rcplondon.ac.uk/.

SCENIHR (2008), *Health effects of smokeless tobacco products*, Scientific Committee on Emerging and Newly Identified Health Risks, European Commission, Brussels. Available at http://ec.europa.eu/health/ph_risk/committees/04_scenihr/docs/scenihr_o_013.pdf.

Shiffman, S., Gitchell, J. G., Warner, K. E., et al. (2002a), 'Tobacco harm reduction: conceptual structure and nomenclature for analysis and research', *Nicotine & Tobacco Research* 4, pp. S113–S129.

Shiffman, S., Rolf, C. N., Hellebusch, S. J., et al. (2002b), 'Real world efficacy of prescription and over-the-counter nicotine replacement therapy', *Addiction* 97, pp. 505–16.

Sikora, K. (2007), 'Electric cigarette beats pub smoking ban', *Daily Telegraph* 15 November. Available at http://www.news.com.au/story/0,23599,22762416-13762,00.html.

Stead, L. F., Perera, R., Bullen, C., Mant, D. and Lancaster, T. (2008), 'Nicotine replacement therapy for smoking cessation', *Cochrane Database of Systematic Reviews*, CD000146.

Stepanov, I., Jensen, J., Hatsukami, D. and Hecht, S. S. (2006), 'Tobacco-specific nitrosamines in new tobacco products', *Nicotine & Tobacco Research* 8, pp. 309–13.

Stratton, K., Shetty, P., Wallace, R. and Bondurant, S. (eds) (2001), *Clearing the smoke: assessing the science base for tobacco harm reduction*, National Academy Press, Washington, DC.

Timberlake, D. S., Huh, J. and Lakon, C. M. (2009), 'Use of propensity score matching in evaluating smokeless tobacco as a gateway to smoking', *Nicotine and Tobacco Research* 11, pp. 455–62.

Toumbourou, J. W., Stockwell, T., Neighbors, C., et al. (2007), 'Adolescent health 4: interventions to reduce harm associated with adolescent substance use', *Lancet* 369, pp. 1391–401.

US Department of Health and Human Services (2006), *The health consequences of involuntary exposure to tobacco smoke: a report of the Surgeon General*, U.S. Department of Health and Human Services, Centers for Disease Control and Prevention, National Center for Chronic Disease Prevention and Health Promotion, Office on Smoking and Health, Atlanta, GA. Available at http://www.surgeongeneral.gov/library/secondhandsmoke/.

Warner, K. E. (2001), 'Reducing harm to smokers: methods, their effectiveness and the role of policy', in Rabin, R. L. and Sugarman, S. D. (eds), *Regulating tobacco*, Oxford University Press, Oxford, pp. 111–42.

Warner, K. E. and Martin, E. G. (2003), 'The US tobacco control community's view of the future of tobacco harm reduction', *Tobacco Control* 12, pp. 383–90.

Warner, K. E., Slade, J. and Sweanor, D. T. (1997), 'The emerging market for long-term nicotine maintenance', *JAMA* 278, pp. 1087–92.

Waterbor, J. W., Adams, R. M., Robinson, J. M., Crabtree, F. G., Accortt, N. A. and Gilliland, M. J. (2004), 'Disparities between public health educational materials and the scientific evidence that smokeless tobacco use causes cancer', *Journal of Cancer Education* 19, pp. 17–28.

WHO Regional Office for Europe (2003), *WHO European country profiles on tobacco control*, World Health Organization, Copenhagen. Available at http://www.euro.who.int/tobaccofree/publications/publications.

WHO Regional Office for Europe (2007), *The European tobacco control report 2007*, World Health Organization, Copenhagen. Available at http://www.euro.who.int/tobaccofree/publications/publications.

World Bank (2003), *Tobacco control at a glance*, World Bank Group, Washington, DC. Available at http://go.worldbank.org/3HHPVQI020.

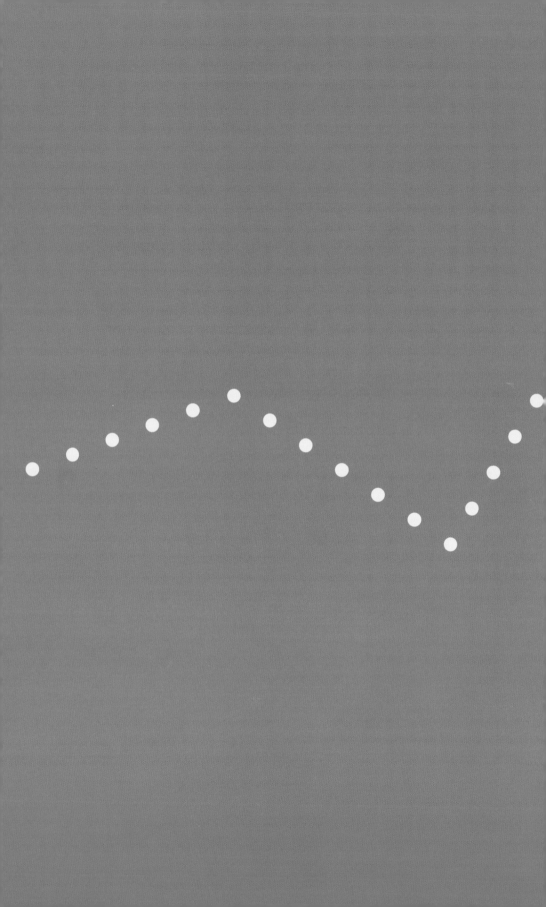

Chapter 10
Alcohol harm reduction in Europe

Rachel Herring, Betsy Thom, Franca Beccaria, Torsten Kolind and Jacek Moskalewicz

Abstract

This chapter provides an overview of harm reduction approaches to alcohol in Europe. First, definitions ascribed to alcohol harm reduction are outlined. Then, evaluated alcohol harm reduction interventions in European countries are described and the evidence for their effectiveness examined. These include multi-component programmes, improvements to the drinking environment, and initiatives to reduce the harms associated with drink-driving. Third, harm reduction activities that have been recorded and described but not yet evaluated are briefly outlined. These include 'grassroots' initiatives and more formal local initiatives. To conclude, the chapter raises questions about how alcohol harm reduction is defined and put into practice, the evidence-base that is available for policymakers, and how information is shared. It highlights the need to develop systems to facilitate knowledge transfer on alcohol harm reduction between researchers, policymakers and practitioners in Europe but stresses the importance of respecting local and cultural diversity in the development and implementation of harm reduction initiatives.

Keywords: alcohol, harm reduction, Europe, evaluation.

Introduction

The consumption of alcohol is an integral part of many European cultures and is embedded in a variety of social practices. Whilst drinking alcohol is, for the most part, a pleasurable experience often associated with relaxation and celebrations, there are a number of societal and health harms associated with its consumption. The European Union (EU) is the heaviest drinking region of the world (Anderson and Baumberg, 2006) and alcohol is linked to multiple health and social problems. Health-related conditions include cancer, injury, liver cirrhosis and cardiovascular disease; it is estimated that in the EU alcohol is responsible for 7.4 % of all disability and premature deaths (Anderson and Baumberg, 2006, p. 401). At a global level, it is estimated that 3.8 % of all deaths and 4.6 % of disability-adjusted life years are attributable to alcohol (Rehm et al., 2009, p. 2223). There is also a broad range of societal harms associated with alcohol consumption including crimes, violence, unemployment and absenteeism, which place a significant burden on societies and economies (WHO, 2008a)

A wide array of measures are employed by European countries to reduce the harms associated with alcohol. These include restrictions on availability, taxation, education campaigns, laws on drink-driving, and a range of formal and informal interventions commonly referred to as 'harm reduction' or 'risk reduction' measures. Yet the concept of harm reduction is contested — as is the usefulness of this approach — and there is very little rigorous evaluation of harm reduction projects or programmes, including in Europe.

This chapter begins with a brief overview of alcohol consumption and alcohol-related harms in Europe. This will be followed by an examination of what is meant by the term 'harm reduction' in relation to alcohol. It then considers harm reduction interventions that have been evaluated in European countries, also drawing upon the broader published literature, much of which is North American or Australasian. We briefly outline harm reduction activities that have been recorded and described but not yet evaluated. These include 'grass roots' initiatives and more formal local initiatives. In conclusion, we argue for a clarification of what is meant by the term 'alcohol harm reduction', and the creation of more effective systems for sharing information and collecting data, alongside research to examine the extent to which harm reduction is seen as an appropriate approach to reducing alcohol-related harms in the different countries of Europe.

Alcohol-related harm in Europe

The relationship between alcohol consumption and health and social outcomes is complex and multidimensional. Key factors include: volume of alcohol drunk over time; pattern of drinking (for example, occasional or regular drinking to intoxication); and drinking context (e.g. place, companions, occasion) (WHO, 2008a). The countries with the highest overall alcohol consumption in the world are in eastern Europe, around Russia, but other areas of Europe also have high overall consumption (WHO Europe region 11.9 litres per adult; Rehm et al., 2009, p. 2228). In all regions worldwide, including Europe, men consume more alcohol than women, and are more likely to die of alcohol-attributable causes, suffer from alcohol-attributable diseases and alcohol-use disorders (Rehm et al., 2009; Anderson and Baumberg, 2006). Europe has the highest proportion of alcohol-attributable net deaths and within Europe the highest proportion is for the countries of the former Soviet Union (Rehm et al., 2009, p. 2229). Alcohol is thought to be responsible for 12 % of male and 2 % of female deaths in Europe (Anderson and Baumberg 2006, p. 3), and 25 % of male youth mortality and 10 % of female youth mortality (Anderson and Baumberg 2006). The health impact of alcohol is seen over a wide range of conditions (see Table 10.1 for examples) and includes acute harms (e.g. accidents and injuries as a result of intoxication) and harms associated with longer-term consumption (e.g. cirrhosis).

Table 10.1: The impact of alcohol on health in Europe

Harm	Impact
Road traffic accidents	17 000 deaths per year (1 in 3 of all road traffic fatalities)
Homicides	2 000 (4 in 10 of all murders and manslaughters)
Accidental deaths	27 000 deaths
Suicide	10 000 deaths (1 in 6 of all suicides)
Cancer	50 000 deaths
Liver cirrhosis	45 000 deaths
Neuropsychiatric conditions	17 000 deaths
Depression	200 000 episodes
Alcohol dependence	23 million people in any one year (5 % men and 1 % women)

Source: Compiled from data in Anderson and Baumberg 2006, pp. 3 and 6).

Alcohol consumption can negatively impact on an individual's work, their relationships and studies (e.g. absenteeism, breakdown of relationships) and consequently on other people (e.g. families, colleagues) and society as a whole. At a societal level the harms associated with the consumption of alcohol include public nuisance (e.g. disturbance, fouling of the streets), public disorder (e.g. fights), drink-driving and criminal damage. The tangible costs of alcohol to the EU (that is, to the criminal justice system, health services, economic system) were estimated to be EUR 125 bn in 2003; this included EUR 59 bn in lost productivity due to absenteeism, unemployment and lost working years through premature death (Anderson and Baumberg, 2006, p. 11); the intangible costs of alcohol (which describe the value people place on suffering and lost life) to the EU were estimated to be EUR 270 bn in 2003 (Anderson and Baumberg, 2006, p. 11).

What is alcohol harm reduction?

Although in recent times the term 'harm reduction' has mostly been associated with the illicit drug field, alcohol harm reduction strategies have been used for centuries (Wodak, 2003; Nicholls, 2009). For instance, in England, the idea that those serving alcoholic beverages should be legally responsible for preventing customers from getting drunk can be traced back to James I's 1604 'Act to restrain the inordinate haunting and tipling of inns, alehouses and other victualling houses'; in practice the law was largely ignored, but it did establish an important principle (Nicholls, 2009, p. 11). Examples of similar formal and informal constraints on behaviour can be found in other European countries and, indeed, worldwide. In sixteenth century Poland an innkeeper was supposed to make sure that farmers had no dangerous objects with them in a pub, as they often became violent after drinking and then would try to use drunkenness as an excuse for their behaviour (Bysto , 1960). Thus, those who served alcohol combined their profit-oriented job with harm reduction. Women have often served as social control or harm reduction agents; in Patagonia, Indian Tehuelche young women, not yet of drinking age, collected all weapons, including knives and axes, prior to a drinking party to prevent severe injures in a case of alcohol-induced violence (Prochard, 1902).

Measures to ensure the safety of alcoholic beverages (that is, free from harmful adulteration or contamination, regulation of the alcohol content of drinks) are also long-standing and remain important. Austrian wine adulterated with diethylene glycol (found in antifreeze) to make it taste sweeter was withdrawn from sale across the world in the mid-1980s (Tagliabue, 1985). Regulation of the sale and size of containers of medicinal (pure) alcohol has reduced the harms associated with its consumption in Nordic countries (Lachenmeier et al., 2007). Research in Estonia (Lang et al., 2006) examining the composition of illegally produced (such as home-produced) and surrogate alcohol products (e.g. aftershave, fire lighting fuel) found high levels of alcohol by volume (up to 78.5 %) and various toxic substances (e.g. long chain alcohols). Moreover, it is likely that the consumption of surrogate alcohol and illegally produced alcohol contributes to the high mortality and morbidity associated with alcohol consumption in other countries in transition (see, for example, McKee et al., 2005; Leon et al., 2007 on Russia).

Harm reduction principles were central to the influential 'Gothenburg System', named after the Swedish city that first adopted the approach in 1865 (Pratt, 1907). Under Swedish law private companies could be established that were empowered to buy up the sprits trade in specific localities and run it on a not-for-profit basis, thus removing the financial incentive to sell large quantities of spirits. Managers whose salaries were not dependent on high sales of spirits (the law did not cover sales of beer or food) were employed to run the pubs. Although the effectiveness of the Gothenburg System in reducing excessive consumption was not entirely clear (Nicholls, 2009), it was an idea that attracted much interest and was adopted in other places, including Bergen, Norway. The Gothenburg system also inspired the system of 'disinterested management', established in late nineteenth century England, whereby companies were formed that bought up pubs and employed salaried managers; shareholders, in return for their investment, received a capped dividend on their investment. However, the impact of this scheme was limited by the small number of establishments run on these lines (Nicholls, 2009).

Whilst not a new idea, harm reduction was not particularly formulated as a concept for policy intervention until it came to prominence in the illicit drugs field in response to HIV/AIDS in conjunction with the spread of HIV through sexual intercourse and drug injecting (Stronach, 2003). There was a recognition that sexual abstinence and stopping injecting drugs was not a feasible option for many people, so realistic and pragmatic strategies were required that focused on managing the outcomes of behaviour rather than eliminating or changing the behaviour (Stronach, 2003). As Stockwell (2006) notes, what made harm reduction distinctive when it emerged in the drugs field was the practice of encouraging safer behaviour (e.g. not sharing injecting equipment and using condoms for sex) without necessarily reducing the occurrence of the behaviour (see, for example, Lenton and Single, 1998 and box below).

World Health Organization definition of harm reduction

In the context of alcohol or other drugs, describes policies or programmes that focus directly on reducing the harm resulting from the use of alcohol or drugs. The term is used particularly of policies or programmes that aim to reduce the harm without necessarily affecting the underlying drug use; examples includes needle/syringe exchanges to counteract needle-sharing among heroin users, and self-inflating airbags in automobiles to reduce injury in accidents, especially as a result of drinking-driving. Harm reduction strategies thus cover a wider range than the dichotomy of supply reduction and demand reduction.

(WHO, 1994)

With respect to alcohol, Robson and Marlatt (2006) have argued that the World Health Organization (WHO) has emphasised total population measures, such as restricting supply, almost to the point of discounting other approaches. However, the WHO are in the process of drafting a global strategy to reduce the harmful use of alcohol (to be considered by the World Health Assembly in May 2010) and harm reduction has been identified as one of nine possible strategy and policy element options (WHO, 2008a). At the same time, whilst acknowledging the positive contribution of harm reduction measures, the WHO note that the evidence base is not, as yet, as well established as that for regulating the availability and demand for alcohol (WHO, 2008a).

However, since the 1990s harm reduction has become increasing influential in the alcohol field; indeed Robson and Marlatt (2006, p. 255) contend that 'it is now, up to a point, the conventional wisdom'. So what is alcohol harm reduction? As is common with such terms it will depend on whom you ask or where you look. Stockwell (2006) has shown that the term is applied in many different ways, some of which rather push the boundaries of 'harm reduction'. For Stockwell, what distinguishes harm reduction from other approaches is that it does not require a reduction in use for effectiveness, rather it is about seeking to 'make the world safer for drunks' (2004, p. 51). On their website the International Harm Reduction Association (IHRA) state, 'Alcohol harm reduction can be broadly defined as measures that aim to reduce the negative consequences of drinking' (IHRA, n.d.), whilst Robson and Marlatt (2006, p. 255) suggest that the common feature of harm reduction interventions is that they do not aim at abstinence.

These broader definitions encompass interventions that do not attempt to reduce consumption, such as the provision of safety (shatterproof) glassware in drinking venues, 'wet' shelters, 'sobering up' stations, and which often focus on specific risk behaviours (e.g. drink-driving), particular risk groups (e.g. young people) and particular drinking contexts (e.g. clubs, bars). They also encompass interventions that implicitly or explicitly do aim to reduce alcohol consumption, for example server training, brief interventions and controlled drinking. But the labelling of approaches that aim to reduce alcohol use as 'harm reduction' has been challenged, with Stockwell (2004, 2006) arguing that such interventions would be better described as 'risk reduction' as they require the reduction of alcohol intake to less risky levels. Furthermore, a recent round-table discussion involving health professionals and non-governmental organisations about harmful alcohol use, concluded that: 'Brief interventions are not considered to constitute a harm reduction approach because they are intended to help people drink less' (WHO, 2008b, p. 8).

Stronach (2003, p. 31) identified five key elements that should underpin alcohol harm policies and interventions:

- Harm reduction is a complementary strategy that sits beside supply control and demand reduction.

- Its key focus is on outcomes rather than actual behaviours per se.

- It is realistic and recognises that alcohol will continue to be used extensively in many communities, and will continue to create problems for some individuals and some communities.

- Harm reduction is non-judgemental about the use of alcohol, but is focused on reducing the problems that arise.

- It is pragmatic — it does not seek to pursue policies or strategies that are unachievable or likely to create more harm than good.

Thus, within policy and research discourse, the notion of 'alcohol harm reduction', although influential, has not gone unchallenged or without controversy. Indeed, there has been a tendency, particularly within the media, to dismiss or even ridicule harm reduction approaches. Within the United Kingdom, recent harm reduction interventions, including handing out 'flip-flops' to women drinkers to prevent injuries caused by falling over in high heels or walking barefooted, have attracted negative headlines (Hope, 2008; Salked, 2008).

This lack of consensus can be reflected in the responses of service and policy providers across Europe. To capture how harm reduction is understood and how related strategies are implemented in practice in Europe, we conducted a brief survey of the 30 European Monitoring Centre for Drugs and Drug Addiction (EMCDDA) Heads of Focal Groups. We received responses from Austria, Belgium, Croatia, the Czech Republic, Cyprus, Estonia, Finland, Latvia, Netherlands, Norway, Portugal, Slovakia, Spain and Sweden.

We asked our survey informants what they understood by the term 'harm reduction'. The definitions they gave were anchored around the concept of limiting or reducing the negative health, social and economic consequences of alcohol consumption on both individuals and communities. A key idea was that harm reduction approaches do not seek to convince individuals to abstain or to introduce prohibition but rather take a 'pragmatic' approach to reducing harms associated with drinking.

Distinctions were made between harm reduction initiatives, which aimed to minimise harm once it has actually been caused, and risk reduction initiatives, which aimed to prevent harm being caused. Several respondents placed qualifiers; for example, the respondent from Norway did not classify 'responsible host' or educational campaigns as harm reduction measures. Similarly the Swedish respondent classified as 'harm reduction' only those measures that aimed to reduce harm that already exists to some extent.

Such variations were not unexpected but do highlight the fact that, whilst there might be a shared language, the meaning attributed to the term 'harm reduction' can differ from one European country to another. While the meaning of harm reduction varies by country, it is important that the measures used are based on evidence and focused on outcomes (WHO, 2008b, p. 14). Evidence, however, is scanty.

Reducing alcohol-related problems: the international evidence

According to findings from international research, the most effective interventions include alcohol taxes, restrictions on the availability of alcohol and measures to reduce drink-driving; interventions identified as the least effective include alcohol education, public awareness programmes and designated driver schemes and many of the 'harm reduction' approaches (Babor et al., 2003; Anderson, et al., 2009). Stockwell (2004, p. 49) argues that the most effective interventions to prevent alcohol-related harm require reduction in the amount of alcohol consumed on a single occasion but suggests that other measures can be employed alongside measures to reduce total population consumption.

There is some international evidence about 'what works' to reduce alcohol-related harm as defined in this chapter. The impact of screening and brief intervention (sometimes referred to as 'identification and brief advice'), particularly in primary care settings, in reducing harmful alcohol consumption has been extensively evidenced as effective (Babor et al., 2003; Kaner et al., 2007), although, as mentioned earlier, the inclusion of brief interventions as a harm reduction measure is contested.

Graham and Homel (2008, pp. 196–238) provide a useful overview of the problems of reducing alcohol-related aggression in and around pubs and clubs and review the evidence for prevention and harm reduction measures. As they report, only a small number of interventions have been evaluated with sufficient rigour to draw conclusions. They mention a large randomised controlled trial of the Safer Bars Programme (a 'stand-alone' programme in Ontario, Canada), which consists of a risk assessment component, a training component and a pamphlet outlining legal responsibilities, as having a modest but statistically significant effect on incidents of aggression. Police enforcement trials did not provide sufficient evidence to make recommendations but the Alcohol Linking Programme (Australia) indicated the success of using place of last drinks data as the basis for targeted enforcement. Community action models to implement local policy depend heavily on partnerships but have demonstrated some success. This approach, evaluated largely in North America, Australia, New Zealand and Scandinavia, has been described as 'any established process, priority, or structure that purposefully alters local social, economic or physical environments to reduce alcohol problems' (Holder 2004, p. 101); it is discussed more fully below.

In a comprehensive synthesis and assessment of the international evidence, Babor et al. (2003) offer a menu of interventions, which they have rated on four major criteria: evidence of effectiveness, breadth of research support, extent of testing across diverse countries and cultures, relative cost of the intervention in terms of time, resources and money. The assessment reflects a consensus view of the 15 expert authors. For illustration, Table 10.2 (adapted from Babor et al., 2003) shows ratings for two of the criteria: interventions that were rated on effectiveness from none (zero) to highest (three), and interventions rated on breadth of research support from none (zero) to highest (three). The table tells us, for example, that alcohol education in schools has five or more studies of effectiveness but that there is no good evidence of effectiveness. It clearly indicates that typical harm reduction measures such as warning labels on alcohol, designated driver schemes and voluntary codes of practice are judged as least effective, although, as illustrated in the second column, many harm reduction measures have few well-designed evaluation studies. However, increasing attention has been given to the potential of programmes of projects rather than stand-alone initiatives to achieve change. These 'multi-component' programmes, which include many of the harm reduction interventions rated as least successful, are discussed in the following sections.

Table 10.2: **What works in reducing alcohol problems?**		
Strategy or intervention	Effectiveness ([1])	Research support ([2])
Alcohol taxes	+ + +	+ + +
Minimum legal purchase age	+ + +	+ + +
Government monopoly of retail sales	+ + +	+ + +
Hours and days of sale restrictions	+ +	+ +
Restrictions on density of outlets	+ +	+ + +
Random breath testing	+ + +	+ +
Lowered limits of blood alcohol concentration (BAC)	+ + +	+ + +
Low BAC for young drivers	+ + +	+ +
Brief intervention for hazardous drinkers	+ +	+ + +
Designated drivers and ride services	0	+
Advertising bans	+	+
Voluntary controls of advertising by alcohol industry	0	+
Alcohol education in schools	0	+ + +
Alcohol education in colleges	0	+
Alcohol education targeting general public	0	+ + +
Warning labels	0	+
Voluntary codes of bar practice	0	+

Notes:

([1]) 0 = lack of effectiveness, + = evidence for limited effectiveness, ++ = evidence for moderate effectiveness, +++ = evidence for high effectiveness.

([2]) 0 = no well-designed study of effectiveness, + = only one study completed, ++ = from two to four studies completed, +++ = five or more studies completed.

Source: Adapted from Babor, T. F., et al. (2003, Table 16.1, pp. 264–6).

Harm reduction approaches to alcohol in Europe: evaluated initiatives

Although the focus of this section is on harm reduction initiatives that have been evaluated in a European context, we also draw on the broader literature. Table 10.3 provides a summary of the evaluated alcohol harm reduction interventions we have identified either from the European literature or from international sources. Many evaluated harm reduction interventions are part of multi-component community programmes designed to prevent and reduce alcohol-related harm, whilst others are 'stand alone' interventions delivered at the local or national level. First, the multi-component approach will be outlined, followed by an examination of harm reduction interventions under two broad themes: improving the drinking environment and reducing the harms associated with drink-driving. Interventions that form part of multi-component programmes are summarised in the box on p. 288 and some will be considered in more detail under the relevant theme. Although brief interventions are often regarded as harm reduction, this chapter will not consider brief interventions, in part because such classification has been contested (as noted above) and because an extensive literature already exists and has been reviewed elsewhere (Nilsen et al., 2008).

Table 10.3: Examples of evaluations of alcohol harm reduction initiatives in Europe: summaries

Name of project	Start date	Country	Goal, intervention and outcome measures	Main findings
'Restaurant intervention' — responsible beverage service (RBS), Stockholm Prevents Alcohol and Drug Problems (STAD)	1998	Sweden	Reduce over-serving and serving to minors. Reduce problems related to alcohol consumption in licensed premises, including violence. RBS, enforcement, partnership working. Test purchases. Police reported incidents of violence between 10pm–6am. Pre and post intervention measures, control area.	Statistically significant reduction in over-serving and serving to minors in both project and control area. Possible 'spill-over' effects from changes in alcohol policy in both areas. (Wallin et al., 2003a) 29 % reduction in police-reported violence (Wallin et al., 2003b)
'Restaurant intervention' — RBS, STAD	1998	Sweden	Calculate cost-effectiveness of 'restaurant intervention' from a societal perspective. Survey of victims of violence, costs, savings, quality adjusted life years (QALYS)	39 times higher savings than cost but caution needs to be exercised because of low response rate (35 %). (Månsdotter et al., 2007)
Alcohol and drug prevention in six municipalities	2003	Sweden	Reduce over-serving of alcohol to intoxicated individuals and sale of medium strength beer to those aged under 18. RBS, enforcement, partnership working. Six trial and six control municipalities.	No reduction in serving to intoxicated patrons in trial or controls. Harder for youths to be served in control areas but differences not significant. (SNIPH, 2008)
Local Alcohol Policy Project (PAKKA)	2004–08	Finland	Decrease under-age drinking, reduce heavy drinking occasion and related acute problems, develop a model for sustainable prevention structure at local level. RBS, enforcement, partnership working, public discussion. Two test communities and two control. Pre- and post-intervention measures	Outline of research and discussion of methods. (Holmila and Warpenius, 2007)

Table 10.3 (continued)

Name of project	Start date	Country	Goal, intervention and outcome measures	Main findings
Responsible Hosts Programme: Trondheim	2000	Norway	Reduce alcohol-related violence, over-serving and serving to minors. RBS. Pre- and post-intervention measures.	Low participation in RBS training (12 % of licensed premises) — intervention thus not fully exploited. No impact: no changes in police-reported violence in/around licensed premises, underage sales, over-serving or attitudes/perceptions of staff. (Baklien and Buvik, 2006)
Kirseberg project	1988	Sweden	Reduce alcohol consumption in the population and decrease the incidence of alcohol-related problems. Consumption measures, problem measures, survey of exposure to project.	Consumption declined in men but not women. Alcohol-related problems showed a statistically significant reduction for men, and a decline for binge drinkers, but no reduction among women. High awareness (67 %) of project. (Hanson et al., 2000)
Alcohol-interlock programme	1999	Sweden	To prevent drink-driving. Two programmes: driving while intoxicated (DWI) offenders (instead of licence revocation); and commercial drivers (buses/taxis/trucks). DWI: two-year programme, biomarkers/AUDIT. Control groups. Post-intervention measures. Commercial: Primary prevention. Blood alcohol concentration (BAC) tests.	DWI: Only 11 % of eligible DWI offenders participated. 60 % alcohol dependent/abusers. Reduced alcohol consumption during programme (Bjerre, 2005). Post-treatment (when compared to five year period prior to treatment) recidivism 60 % lower and police-recorded accidents 80 % lower. Control – accident reduction similar but not DWI recidivism (Bjerre and Thorsson, 2008). Commercial: Among 600 heavy vehicles, 0.19 % of all starts prevented as BAC >0.02 % (20 mg/dl), mostly at weekends or mornings. (Bjerre and Kostela, 2008)

Table 10.3 (continued)

Name of project	Start date	Country	Goal, intervention and outcome measures	Main findings
Reducing alcohol-related injury, violence and disorder in Glasgow city centre	2004	Scotland	Reduce alcohol-related injury, violence and disorder in the city centre. RBS, 'Best Bar None' (BBN), test purchasing. 'Nite Zone': transport/community safety improvements (e.g. relocation of bus stops, taxi wardens, extra CCTV with loudspeakers). Awareness raising (conference, radio campaigns and website, police custody cards).	Decrease (−9.7 %) in police-recorded crimes and decrease (−4.4 %) in ambulance incidents. Increase (+74.4 %) in police-recorded alcohol-related incidents, increase (+6.5 % in emergency department attendances. Nite Zone: decrease in road accidents (−11.4 %), violent crime (−19 %), serious assault (−4.4 %), robbery (−21.5 %). Awareness: >100 000 websites hits, >2 000 calls to radio station, 2 889 information packs supplied, 17 treatment referrals from 400 cards. (Mistral et al., 2007)
Multi-agency, community-based intervention to reduce excessive drinking in Cardiff city centre	2004	Wales	Reduce excessive drinking in the city centre. Improve regulation of licensed premises by feedback of individual risk assessments of premises and RBS. Awareness-raising. Community Safety Partnership focus on reducing crime and disorder. Test purchasing, police/National Health Service statistics, environmental audits.	Decrease (−25.7 %) in emergency department attendances, but increase (+33 %) in police-recorded crimes/incidents. = 9 % of city centre staff successfully trained. 30 % of premises failed test purchasing. Audits — minority heavily intoxicated, training targeted to problem premises, details of public litter. (Mistral et al., 2007)
'Route 50' Project, Birmingham	2005	England	Reduce alcohol-related harm in the community using a multi-component approach. Focus on licensed premises. Engage in partnership working. RBS, strict enforcement, awareness-raising — publicity campaigns and partnership working. Test purchasing, police statistics, survey.	Public place wounding decreased by −29.5 % within 800m of project area and more than neighbouring police area (−17.2 %) (but caution as numbers small). Signs that awareness raised — e.g. Pubwatch established and active, community forum on alcohol. Partnerships established and active (e.g. police, licensees, local government). (Mistral et al., 2007)

Table 10.3 (continued)

Name of project	Start date	Country	Goal, intervention and outcome measures	Main findings
The Ringsted Project	2001	Denmark	A controlled experiment in a provincial town, focusing on normative misperceptions/ exaggerated beliefs amongst Danish youth in relation to the use of tobacco, alcohol and drugs.	Statistically significant reduction in the use of alcohol and general risk behaviour. (Balvig et al., 2005)
'Caschiamoci'	2005	Italy	To prevent drink-driving: information campaign during a beer festival in Arezzo province in 2005. During the festival social and health workers offered information and the opportunity to measure BAC using alcohol tests.	More than 50 % of people who did the alcohol tests were positive (more than 0.5g/l BAC). (Ranieri et al., 2007)
'Questa sera chiamatemi Bob' — a designated driver campaign	2005	Italy (Piedmont)	To prevent drink-driving: social campaign on drink-driving (radio, poster, free cards, disco events with information and alcohol testing). Evaluation of the campaign: 1 451 questionnaires, 1 235 interviews, 1 focus group, 11 health worker diaries.	Positive evaluation of the campaign. Positive evaluation of information activities in the discos (10), both about methods (gadget, alcohol testing) and quality of information. Positive evaluation about security driving course award. Suggestion for future campaign. (Beccaria and Marchisio, 2006)

Multi-component programmes

Multi-component programmes involve the identification of alcohol-related problems at the local level and implementation of a programme of coordinated projects to tackle the problem, based on an integrative design where singular interventions run in combination with each other and/or are sequenced together over time; the identification, coordination and mobilisation of local agencies, stakeholders and community are key elements (Thom and Bayley, 2007). Furthermore, as Thom and Bayley (2007) note, evaluation is an integral part of multi-component programmes; both the overall programme and the individual projects within it should have clearly defined aims, objectives and measures of effectiveness. Another key element is that projects and the programme as a whole should have a strategic framework underpinned by a theoretical base.

The 'systems theory approach', which is closely associated with the work of Holder and colleagues in the United States (Holder, 1998), and the 'community action' approach have been particularly influential (see Thom and Bayley, 2007, pp. 35–9). The United States, Australia and New Zealand were at the forefront of the development of multi-component programmes in the alcohol field and influenced the establishment of such programmes in Europe (e.g. Holmila, 2001). Multi-component programmes have been conducted in Scandinavia, Italy, Poland and the United Kingdom (see box on p. 288 and Table 10.3) and have included a range of harm reduction projects. Whilst the specific targets of the multi-component programmes vary, the majority aim to influence community systems and change drinking norms, and most aim to mobilise local communities with the intention of securing sustainable, long-term change. For example, STAD (Stockholm prevents Alcohol and Drug problems), a multi-component community programme in Sweden that ran 1996–2006, included responsible beverage service training, community mobilisation and strict enforcement of alcohol laws (Wallin, 2004; Wallin et al., 2003a; Wallin et al., 2003b; Wallin et al., 2004; Månsdotter et al., 2007).

So, do multi-component programmes work? There is, as Thom and Bayley (2007) conclude, 'no simple answer' to this question. Whilst there is evidence from international research as to what is likely to work at a 'stand alone' level (see Table 10.2), what is less clear is how they work in combination or what kind of combinations may result in an effective multi-component programme. This is in part because of the expected synergistic effect of the components and also the possible cumulative effects over time; furthermore, it has not been possible to identify the contribution of particular components to programme outcomes as a whole (US Department of Health and Human Services, 2000). For example, educational and awareness-raising campaigns are often cited as ineffective in changing behaviour (see Table 10.2) but are seen as a crucial element of most multi-component programmes. Anderson and colleagues (2009) argue that although the evidence shows that information and education programmes do not reduce alcohol-related harm, they do play a key role in providing information and in increasing awareness of the need to place alcohol issues firmly on public and political agendas (Anderson, et al., 2009).

Examples of multi-component programmes in Europe

Name of project	Country	Start date
Aquarius South Birmingham Community Alcohol Action Project ('Route 50' project) (UKCAPP)	England	2004
Lahti Project	Finland	1992
Metropolitan Suburbs Project	Finland	1997
Local Alcohol Policy Project (PAKKA)	Finland	2004
Florence (Rifredi) Community Alcohol Action Project	Italy	1992
Florence (Scandici) Community Alcohol Action Project	Italy	1999
Drinking and driving related injuries, Florence	Italy	2004
Community Action Project, Malczyce	Poland	1994
Reducing alcohol-related injury, violence and disorder in the city centre: Glasgow (UKCAPP)	Scotland	2004
The Kiresberg Project (demonstration)	Sweden	1988
Kungsholmen Project	Sweden	1990
Stockholm Prevents Alcohol and Drug Problems (STAD)	Sweden	1996
Six Communities Project	Sweden	2003
Multi-agency, community-based intervention to reduce excessive drinking in Cardiff city centre ('Lion's Breath') (UKCAPP)	Wales	2004

Source: Adapted from Thom and Bayley, 2007, pp. 62–3.

Although evaluation is integral to multi-component programmes, in reality these evaluations are complex and it is not only difficult to untangle the effects of the interventions from each other, but also from other activities in the locality. In relation to the evaluation of the three projects in the United Kingdom Community Alcohol Prevention Programme (UKCAPP), Mistral et al. commented:

> The UKCAPP projects were part of a multi-faceted web of other local projects, partnerships, and interventions … The complexity of these partnerships meant that it was impossible to consider any UKCAPP project as a discrete set of interventions, clearly delineated in space, and time, the effects of which could be evaluated independently of other local activities.

> (Mistral et al., 2007, p. 86)

Another important issue highlighted by the UKCAPP evaluation was the inadequacy of statistical datasets, which meant that it was impossible to judge the effectiveness of interventions over time (Mistral et al., 2007). This was in part due to the different methods of data collection, analysis and retrieval used by police, ambulance service and emergency care departments, which made data validity hard to verify and comparison across sources or sites highly problematic (Mistral et al., 2007). In addition, local issues (e.g. timing of intervention, funding delays, getting agreement from all partners) can make systematic local evaluation challenging.

In summary, whilst some programmes have reported considerable successes (e.g. Community Trials Project, reported by Holder, 2000), others have yielded more mixed results, including the Lahti project in Finland (Holmilia, 1997), Kiresberg project (Hanson et al., 2000) and STAD (Wallin et al., 2003a) in Sweden. However, Thom and Bayley (2007) in their overview conclude that the evidence suggests that a multi-component approach has a greater chance of success than stand-alone projects.

Harm reduction interventions

Improving the drinking environment

Observational studies indicate that the drinking environment of licensed premises can impact on the risk of violence and injury. A lack of seating, loud music, overcrowding, unavailability of food are considered risk factors (Graham and Homel, 2008; Homel et al., 2001; Rehm et al., 2003). A variety of initiatives to improve the drinking environment have been implemented. These include server training, awards to well-managed licensed premises and the use of safety glassware (or plastic). A recent systematic review concluded that there was no reliable evidence that interventions such as these in the alcohol server setting are effective in preventing injuries (Ker and Chinnock, 2008). Nevertheless, we look at some of the research findings for each of these interventions in turn.

Server training

A number of European countries including Spain, United Kingdom, Ireland and the Netherlands have developed national responsible beverage service (RBS) training and accreditation schemes (EFRD website, 2009). Responsible beverage service is a key feature of many Scandinavian and United Kingdom multi-component programmes (see Table 10.3), with the aim of reducing sales to minors, over-serving and violence in and around licensed premises. These interventions usually involve formal training of staff and strict enforcement of existing alcohol laws; outcome measures include test purchasing and police statistics.

Results have been mixed. The STAD project in Sweden took a quasi-experimental approach with a control area, also located in central Stockholm, but not adjacent to the project area. In relation to both over-serving and serving to minors there was a statistically significant reduction in both the control and project areas, although in the project area the improvement in relation to over-serving was slightly higher (but not statistically significant) (Wallin et al., 2003a). Wallin et al. (2003a) note that during the time of research the Stockholm Licensing Board (which covers both areas) altered practices and policy, and this might be one explanation for why there were changes in alcohol service in both the project and the control area (i.e. spill-over effects).

In contrast, there was a reduction in violence only in the project area, with a 29 % reduction in police-reported violence in and around licensed premises (Wallin et al., 2003b). The authors put forward several explanations for this result. First, there were a greater number of large nightclubs in the project area and changes in practice in large establishments may have a greater impact than changes in smaller establishments. Second, it may be a synergy effect, with improved serving practices and increased enforcement combining to produce a positive effect (Wallin et al., 2003b; SNIPH, 2008). Although it did appear to be harder for youths to get served in the project site than the control, the differences were not statistically significant (SNIPH, 2008).

Other studies, for example in Trondheim, Norway, experienced a low uptake of the intervention, and not surprisingly no impact was observed (Baklien and Buvik, 2006). The 'Route 50' project in Birmingham, an area with no history of partnership working, faced similar challenges, but boosted uptake by providing incentives (e.g. waived the course fee) (Mistral et al., 2007). Whilst there were decreases in police-recorded statistics compared to the adjacent area, the number of crimes was low and thus no inferences could be safely drawn (Mistral et al., 2007).

Awards for management of premises

In 2003, as part of a broad, multi-agency programme to reduce alcohol-related crime and disorder in the city centre area, Manchester developed a scheme, called 'Best Bar None' (BBN), to identify and recognise the best-managed licensed premises in the area (Home Office, 2004) (see box on p. 291 for details). The scheme has since been rolled out nationally, but despite this BBN has yet to be fully evaluated. Although 'a detailed assessment' of the impact of BBN on reducing disorder is planned (Harrington, 2008), a small-scale evaluation concluded that there was 'a lack of credible evidence to suggest that the implementation of the BBN scheme in Croydon has specifically had an impact on the reduction of crime and disorder in the town centre on its own' (GOL, 2007, p. 2). Whilst acknowledging there were benefits for those who implemented the scheme, these benefits were difficult to measure and 'largely amount to perception rather than evidenced reality' (GOL, 2007, p. 2). The report recommended that if the BBN is to continue, then an agreed measuring tool (that is, set of indicators) is required, so that the impact of the schemes can be assessed and can provide credible evidence for other areas considering its implementation (GOL, 2007).

From pilot project to national scheme — Best Bar None

2003
BBN developed within Manchester's 'City Safe Scheme'.
Quickly adopted by other towns in the United Kingdom.

2007
Agreement reached between Greater Manchester Police, the Home Office and British Institute of Innkeeping (the professional body for the licensed retail sector), to develop the scheme nationally.

2008
Over 90 schemes in place (Harrington, 2008).

Features of the BBN scheme:

- *Involves*: partnership with the licensing industry, police, local and central government, health workers and other agencies.
- *Aims*: to make licensees and the public aware of safety levels within premises, and reduce alcohol-related crime and irresponsible drinking.
- *Sets*: national standards of good practice in the management of licensed premises.
- *Awards*: the best-managed licensed premises in an area — gold, sliver and bronze- represent the levels to which the premises are assessed as meeting the standards.

Premises gaining an award display a plaque.

Use of safety glassware

Research in the United Kingdom identified that bar glasses were being used as weapons to inflict injuries, in particular to the face (Shepherd et al., 1990b). Further research concluded that the use of toughened glass would reduce injuries (Shepherd et al., 1990a; Warburton and Shepherd, 2000). This research led to the replacement of ordinary glassware with toughened glassware in licensed premises and there is evidence from the British Crime Survey that this change resulted in a significant reduction of violent incidents involving the use of glasses or bottles as weapons (Shepherd, 2007). However, Shepherd (2007) notes that reductions in glass injury have not been sustained — probably because of the increased availability of bottled drinks and the use of poorly toughened glass. Despite repeated calls, there is, as yet, no manufacturing standard but the use of alternative materials, particularly plastics, is seen as a way forward.

In 2006, as part of its approach to reducing alcohol-related violence and disorder in the city centre, Glasgow city council banned the use of glassware (other than special 'safety' glass) from venues holding an entertainment licence — which in practice meant nightclubs (Forsyth, 2008). However, individual premises could apply for an exemption for champagne/wine glasses (Forsyth, 2008). The study, based on naturalistic observations and interviews, reported that exemptions to the ban had allowed some premises to continue to serve in glass vessels, and this resulted in injuries. Although disorder in all-plastic venues was observed, it incurred less injury risk and Forsyth (2008) concluded that the research demonstrated the potential of such policy to reduce the severity of alcohol-related violence in the night-time economy. Earlier initiatives, for example 'Crystal Clear' in Liverpool, aimed to remove glass from outdoor public places in the city centre in order to reduce glass injuries; a high-profile awareness campaign was mounted and action taken by bar and door staff to prevent glass being removed (Young and Hirschfield, 1999). The evaluation found that there was high recognition of the campaign and police and hospital data showed a reduction in glass injuries during the campaign (Young and Hirschfield, 1999).

Reducing the harms associated with drink-driving

Systematic reviews and meta-analyses have found that highly effective drink-driving policies include lowered blood alcohol concentration (BAC), unrestricted (random) breath testing, administrative licence suspension, and lower BAC levels and graduated licenses for novice drivers (Babor, et al., 2003; Anderson, et al., 2009). Less effective are designated driver schemes and school-based education schemes (Babor et al., 2003). We look at three examples — BAC measures, 'alcolocks' (or alcohol-interlocks, which are devices that prevent a motor vehicle from starting when a driver's BAC is elevated) and designated driver schemes.

BAC measures

All European countries place legal limits on the BAC of drivers and the 2001 European Commission Recommendation on the maximum permitted blood alcohol concentration (BAC) for drivers of motorized vehicles called for all Member States to adopt a BAC of 0.5 g/L, lowered to 0.2 g/L for novice, two-wheel, large vehicle or dangerous goods drivers; in addition, random breath testing was recommended so that everyone is checked every three years on average (Anderson, 2008). There are currently three Member States of the EU-27 that have a BAC limit of greater than 0.5 g/L (Ireland, Malta and the United Kingdom) (ETSC, 2008). There is evidence that the reduction in BAC limits supported by strict enforcement and publicity can reduce drink-driving at all BAC levels. For example, Switzerland reduced the legal BAC limit from 0.8 g/L to 0.5 g/L and introduced random breath testing in January 2005. The number of alcohol-related road deaths in 2005 reduced by 25 per cent and contributed to an overall 20 % reduction in the number of road deaths (ETSC, 2008).

Alcolocks

Alcolocks (or alcohol-interlocks) are devices that prevent a motor vehicle from starting when a driver's BAC is elevated. Sweden introduced two alcolock programmes in 1999, which have been evaluated. One programme involved commercial drivers (of taxis, lorries and buses); in 600 vehicles, 0.19 % of all starts were prevented by a BAC higher than the legal limit and lock point of 0.2 g/L, mostly during weekends and mornings (Bjerre and Kostela, 2008). Another was a voluntary two-year programme for drinking while intoxicated (DWI) offenders, which included regular medical monitoring designed to reduce alcohol use and was offered in lieu of having licence revoked for a year. There were two control groups; one group had revoked licences but did not have the opportunity to participate in an interlock programme, and the other comprised DWI offenders who had declined the opportunity to participate in the programme (Bjerre and Thorsson, 2008). Only 11 % of eligible drivers took part in the programme. The intervention group were significantly more likely to be re-licensed two and three years after the DWI offence than the control groups and also, according to Alcohol Use Disorder Identification Test (AUDIT) scores, had lower rates of harmful alcohol consumption. In the post-treatment period the rate of DWI recidivism was about 60 % lower, and the rate of police-reported traffic accidents about 80 % lower than during the years before the offence. Among the controls being re-licensed, a similar reduction in traffic accidents was observed but not in DWI recidivism. Bjerre and Thorsson (2008) conclude that these results suggest that the alcolock programme was more effective than the usual licence revocation and also that it was a useful tool in achieving lasting changes in the alcohol and drink-driving behaviour of DWI offenders. To date systematic reviews of research indicate that alcolocks are only effective whilst in situ (Willis et al., 2004; Anderson, 2008) and further work is required into what steps need to be taken to prevent recidivism and ensure behaviour changes are sustained.

Designated driver schemes

The designated driver concept was first initiated in Belgium in 1995, jointly by the (industry-funded) Belgian Road Safety Institute and Arnouldous (EFRD, 2007). Designated driver campaigns are currently running in 16 European countries (EFRD, 2009) and were co-financed by the European Commission for five years (ETSC, 2008). Table 10.3 provides a summary of an evaluated designated driver scheme in Italy (Beccaria and Marchisio, 2006). There is no universal definition of a 'designated driver', but the most common definition requires that the designated driver does not drink any alcohol, be assigned before alcohol consumption, and drive other group members to their homes (see Ditter et al., 2005). Other definitions adopt a risk and harm reduction strategy, in which the main goal is not necessarily abstinence, but to keep the designated driver's blood alcohol content (BAC) at less than the legal limit. The evidence is that although the BACs of designated drivers are generally lower than those of their passengers they are still often higher than the legal limit for drinking and driving. Furthermore, an increase in passenger alcohol consumption is often found when a designated driver is available. To date, no study has evaluated whether the use of designated drivers actually decreases alcohol-related motor vehicle injuries (Anderson, 2008). Anderson (2008) argues that existing designated driver campaigns should be evaluated for their impact in reducing drink-driving accidents and fatalities before financing and implementing any new campaigns.

Alcohol harm reduction in Europe: non-evaluated harm reduction initiatives

In this section, we look at examples of harm reduction initiatives that have been recorded and described in the literature but not thoroughly evaluated, and also at examples given by our key informants (see box below). Harm reduction initiatives often begin as practical responses to a problem rather than as a research question and thus are not usually formally evaluated, at least not in the first instance. Information about such initiatives at the local level is often difficult to come by. This indicates that there is a need for systematic pooling of information, particularly for dissemination of knowledge about smaller local or regional initiatives. One attempt at systematic collection of data is being promoted in the United Kingdom. The Hub of Commissioned Alcohol Projects and Policies (HubCAPP) is an online resource of local alcohol initiatives focused on reducing alcohol-related harms to health throughout England (www.hubcapp.org.uk) launched in 2008. The focus of HubCAPP is on identifying and sharing local and regional practice in relation to reducing alcohol harm, and it is constantly expanding. Although not exclusively a database of harm reduction initiatives, many of the projects can be classified as such, for example, the 'Route 50 Project' a multi-component, community-based initiative in Birmingham (Goodwin and McCabe, 2007).

Harm reduction initiatives: some examples that have been recorded and described

- 'Flip-flops' (simple flat shoes) given to women who are experiencing difficulties walking in high heels (to prevent injuries from falling over or from walking barefoot). United Kingdom towns including Torquay, Bognor, Rugby.
- Lollipops (sweets) given to people as they leave venues by door staff (to keep them quiet and to raise blood sugar so that they are more alert and less inclined to violence). United Kingdom towns including Southampton, Manchester, Guildford, London.
- Bubble blowers (which double as pens) handed out (focus on having fun blowing bubbles, reduce anti-social behaviour and violence). Bolton, United Kingdom.
- Parent volunteers known as natteravnene (Night Owls) walk the streets at night in distinctive yellow jackets. They do not intervene in the night life but believe that their presence can reduce trouble, fights and vandalism. They also hand out sweets, water, sandwiches and condoms. Denmark.
- First aid assistance provided for young people at open air drinking gatherings. Spain.
- Alcohol testing for drivers leaving a three-day music festival. Slovakia.
- SMS service — text what you have drunk and get back an estimate of BAC. Czech Republic.
- Parent-organised youth parties for 14- to 18-year-olds. Young people bring their own beverages and drink under the supervision of parents. Denmark.
- Public transport runs until the early morning at the weekends and provided free on New Year's Eve. Poland.
- Sobering up stations — safe places where intoxicated drinkers are taken to sober up (i.e. away from the cold and threats of violence). Poland, Czech Republic, Russia and other former Soviet nations.

Some of the non-evaluated initiatives can be described as 'grassroots' interventions, that is, they have been devised and initiated by lay people (e.g. parents, members of a local community) to reduce alcohol-related harm within the local community. For example, in provincial Denmark, parents have organised parties where young people drink alcohol under adult supervision, with the aim of reducing harmful drinking in unsupervised outdoor areas (Kolind and Elmeland, 2008). In similar vein, in Slovakia, in an attempt to supervise the behaviour of young people coming home from parties, pubs and discos, local people and police formed patrols to guide young people home safely and with minimal disturbance to the community. Grassroots initiatives are generally pragmatic and reactive and they may also be very specific to a time and place. However, if such initiatives appear to be 'successful' they may over time be subject to formal evaluation and also be implemented in other areas.

Other initiatives have been developed by agencies such as police, local government, health and welfare agencies, often working in partnership, and like the 'grassroots' initiatives they are aimed at reducing alcohol-related harm in the local area. Such initiatives are often innovative, for example, giving out 'goody bags' containing items including sweets, 'flip-flops' (simple flat shoes), water, condoms and information leaflets on alcohol and safer sex, as part of campaigns to reduce alcohol-related harm and disorder in town centres (*Chichester Observer*, 2008; Hope, 2008; Lewisham Drug and Alcohol Strategy Team, 2007). The innovative nature of these interventions generates media coverage, much of which is negative or cynical (e.g. Hope, 2008; Salkeld, 2008; Smith, 2008 — on bubble blowers, flip-flops and lollipops), and some groups (e.g. Taxpayers' Alliance, United Kingdom) dismiss these harm reduction measures as 'gimmicks' and a 'waste of money'.

Whilst most of these measures have been introduced relatively recently, other interventions have a longer history. For example, the first 'sobering up station' (záchytka) opened in Czechoslovakia (now the Czech Republic) in 1951. It provided a place for intoxicated people to sober up. It was a model that was soon adopted by other countries, including Poland which established sobering up stations following the decriminalisation of public drunkenness in 1956 (Moskalewicz and Wald,1987). Facilities that serve a similar function are dotted across Europe; for example Scotland has two 'designated places' (in Aberdeen and Inverness), which provide an alternative to custody for persons arrested for being drunk and incapable; they are monitored in a safe environment until fit to leave, and further help is available. There have been calls for a comprehensive system of 'designated places' to provide a safe place for intoxicated people to sober up and to divert them from the criminal justice and health systems (BBC, 2007).

There are a number of routes by which knowledge of successful interventions is spread, both informal and more formal, including identification, dissemination and awards for 'best practice' (e.g. by government agencies, interest groups), fact finding visits, web resources (e.g. HubCAPP in the United Kingdom), stakeholder networks and organisations (e.g. Global Alcohol Harm Reduction Network — GAHRA-Net). The Internet plays a key role in the exchange of information globally through websites, online publications, and virtual networks.

Policy and knowledge transfer can be aided by thorough evaluation of interventions. But whilst it is straightforward to find a description of a simple 'evaluation' of a particular intervention, as we have seen in the case of BBN, robust, comprehensive evaluation is often lacking. However, it is not merely a question of the evaluation of interventions. What works in provincial Denmark may not work in inner city Paris, and care needs to be taken not to simply 'cherry pick' interventions. Cultural and local contexts are important factors in transferring intervention models and are often ignored when apparently successful projects or programmes are 'rolled out'.

Conclusion

Current usage and definition of the concept of harm reduction derives from the drugs field rather than from the long history of formal and informal regulation of alcohol-related harm. The lack of consensus regarding the definition and a tendency to include within the definition initiatives that are contested as being 'prevention' and not really 'harm reduction', suggests both a risk that the adoption of a very broad definition may result in loss of meaning and usefulness of the concept for policy and practice and an opportunity to debate and clarify the concept and its application in differing national, local and cultural contexts. Apart from the distinction between measures that aim to reduce consumption, and measures that tackle only associated harms, approaches to reduce or minimise harm once it has happened (harm reduction) can be distinguished from risk reduction measures, which aim to prevent harm being caused in the first place. These nuances of meaning have important implications for the development of strategy, the adoption of specific projects and programmes, the evaluation of policies and initiatives and for the effectiveness outcomes researchers choose to measure. Although the evidence base for harm reduction approaches appears less solid than the evidence for measures to reduce consumption, there has been far less research and fewer evaluated studies of measures that address the harms without necessarily requiring lower consumption. This would be useful, both in designing locally appropriate multi-component programmes and in providing a 'menu' of evaluated initiatives to run alongside measures aimed at consumption levels.

It is also essential to establish the boundaries of inclusion in 'harm reduction' if more effective systems for information sharing and data collection in Europe are to be agreed. Information on harm reduction approaches — especially those that emerge from local or grassroots activity — is hard to come by. Descriptions on websites are often ephemeral, and this is a reflection also of the origins of harm reduction activity, which is frequently rooted in transient local concern and crises. As the crisis or concern recedes, the initiatives fade away. At the same time, most harm reduction activity appears to be semi-official (as opposed to grassroots or lay), emerging at regional or local levels from professional and local authority action. Sometimes a particular initiative catches the policy and public attention and is transferred from one area to another, based more on the perception of success rather than on any evaluation or formal assessment of effectiveness or of the appropriateness of transfer from one setting to another. The development of information sharing systems, nationally and possibly on a European scale, would be a step forward in providing the field with a more comprehensive overview of harm reduction measures, settings in which they have been implemented and with what results, and measures of effectiveness.

While harm reduction 'thinking' has joined the raft of policy strategies and local initiatives in most European countries, remarkably few initiatives have been fully described, let alone scientifically evaluated with any degree of rigour. This in itself may be one reason why assessments of effectiveness based on international research result in harm reduction measures being reported as less effective. However, before demanding conformity to 'gold standard' evaluation studies, it is worth considering the nature and uses of many harm reduction approaches. If, as appears to be the case, harm reduction requires flexibility and immediacy in its reaction to locally defined need, there is a case for arguing that descriptions of the approach and narratives of the implementation and perceived outcomes are more useful than formal (expensive) evaluation. Such narratives are largely missing and could be an important addition to information banks such as the United Kingdom's HubCAPP.

Evaluation and research findings are, of course, only one element in decisions to adopt or reject harm reduction as a legitimate goal for policy and in decisions about which initiatives are suitable for implementation nationally or locally. Success or failure of harm reduction initiatives can depend as much on media and public perceptions (as in the case of 'flip-flops') or on gaining the collaboration of stakeholders (as in the case of server training) or the willingness of volunteers (as in the Danish 'Night Owls' and the Danish parents' parties) as on the evaluated effectiveness of a particular strategy or activity. This is especially the case if the evaluations emerge from projects located in very different social, cultural and political systems. So questions arise as to what extent harm reduction is seen as an appropriate approach to reducing alcohol-related harms in the different countries of Europe. Is harm reduction the 'conventional wisdom' in Europe or are there countries where harm reduction is thought to be inappropriate to that particular country's cultural context and consumption patterns? These are questions that deserve further exploration. In the drive towards a Europe-wide planned approach to tackling alcohol-related harm, this overview of harm reduction approaches highlights the need to develop opportunities and systems to facilitate knowledge transfer on alcohol harm reduction between researchers, policymakers and practitioners in Europe, but stresses the importance of respecting local and cultural diversity in the development and implementation of harm reduction initiatives.

References

Anderson, P. (2008), *Reducing drinking and driving in Europe*, Deutsche Hauptstelle für Suchtfragen e.V. (DHS), Hamm.

Anderson, P. and Baumberg, B. (2006), *Alcohol in Europe: a public health perspective. A report for the European Commission*, Institute of Alcohol Studies, London. Available at http://ec.europa.eu/health-eu/doc/alcoholineu_content_en.pdf (accessed 20 July 2009).

Anderson, P., Chisholm, D. and Fuhr, D. (2009), 'Effectiveness and cost-effectiveness of policies and programmes to reduce the harm caused by alcohol', *Lancet* 373, pp. 2234–46.

Babor, T., Caetano, R., Casswell, S., et al. (2003), *Alcohol: no ordinary commodity*, Oxford University Press, Oxford.

Babor, T. F. (2008), *Evidence-based alcohol control policy: toward a public health approach*, Conference on Tobacco and Alcohol Control — Priority of Baltic Health Policy, Vilnius.

Baklien, B. and Buvik, K. V. (2006), *Evaluation of a responsible beverage service programme in Trondheim*, Sirus-Reports 4 (English summary), SIRUS, Oslo. Available at http://www.sirus.no/internett/alkohol/publication/310.html (accessed 20 January 2010).

Balvig, F., Holmberg, L. and Sørensen, A-S. (2005), *Ringstedforsøget. Livsstil og forebyggelse i lokalsamfundet* [The Ringsted project: lifestyle and prevention in the local community], Jurist-og Økonomiforbundets Forlag, København.

BBC (2007), *Profits 'to aid alcohol problems'*, BBC News 10 October 2007. Available at http://news.bbc.co.uk/1/hi/scotland/north_east/7036806.stm (accessed 16 July 2009).

Beccaria, F. and Marchisio, M. (2006), 'Progetto Bob. Vatutazione di una compagna di promozione del guidatore designato', *Dal fare al dire* 15 (2), pp. XII–XX.

Bjerre, B. (2005), 'Primary and secondary prevention of drink driving by the use of alcolock device and program: Swedish experiences', *Accident Analysis and Prevention* 37 (6), pp. 1145–52.

Bjerre, B. and Kostela, J. (2008), 'Primary prevention of drinking driving by the large-scale use of alcolocks in commercial vehicles', *Accident Analysis and Prevention* 40 (4), pp. 1294–9.

Bjerre, B. and Thorsson, U. (2008), 'Is an alcohol ignition interlock programme a useful tool for changing the alcohol and driving habits of drink-drivers?', *Accident Analysis and Prevention* 40 (1), pp. 267–73.

Bystoń, J. (1960), *Dzieje obyczajów w dawnej Polsce. Wiek XVI-XVII*. PIW, Warszawa.

Chichester Observer (2008), 'Police to hand out flip flops to clubbers in Bognor', 26 December.

Ditter, S. M., Elder, R. W., Shults, R. A., et al., (2005), 'Effectiveness of designated driver programs for reducing alcohol-impaired driving a systematic review', *American Journal of Preventative Medicine* 28 (5 Supplement), pp. 280–7.

EFRD (European Forum for Responsible Drinking) (2007), *Guidelines to develop designated driver campaigns*, EFRD, Brussels.

EFRD (2009), European Forum for Responsible Drinking website at www.efrd.org/main.html (accessed 9 March 2009).

ETSC (European Transport Safety Council) (2008), *Drink driving fact sheet*. Available at www.etsc.eu/documents/Fact_Sheet_DD.pdf (accessed 9 March 2009).

Forsyth, A. J. M. (2008), 'Banning glassware from nightclubs in Glasgow (Scotland): observed impacts, compliance and patrons' views', *Alcohol and Alcoholism* 43 (1), pp. 111–17.

Goodwin, P. and McCabe, A. (2007), *From loose, loose to win, win: Aquarius Route 50 project. Report to the AERC.* Available at: www.hubcapp.org.uk (accessed 9 March 2009).

GOL (Government Office for London) (2007), *Best Bar None Croydon review*, GOL, London. Available at http://ranzetta.typepad.com/Croydon_BBN_evaluation.doc (accessed 9 March 2009).

Graham, K. and Homel, R. (2008), *Raising the bar: preventing aggression in and around bars, pubs and clubs*, Willan Publishing, Cullompton.

Hanson, B. S., Larsson, S. and Rastram, L. (2000), 'Time trends in alcohol habits: results from the Kiresberg project in Malmo, Sweden', *Substance Use and Misuse* 35 (1 & 2), pp. 171–87.

Harrington, J. (2008), 'Sky's the limit for Best Bar None', *Morning Advertiser*, 16 June. Available at http://www.morningadvertiser.co.uk/news.ma/article/62912 (accessed 12 March).

Holder, H. D. (1998), *Alcohol and the community: a systems approach to prevention*, Cambridge University Press, Cambridge.

Holder, H. D. (2000), 'Community prevention of alcohol problems', *Addictive Behaviours* 25 (6), pp. 843–59.

Holder, H. D. (2004), 'Community action from an international perspective', in Müller, R. and Klingemann, H. (eds), *From science to action? 100 years later – alcohol policies revisited*, Kluwer Academic Publishers, Dordrecht, pp. 101–12.

Holmlia, M. (1997), *Community prevention of alcohol problems*, Macmillan Press, Basingstoke.

Holmlia, M. (2001), 'The changing field of preventing drug and alcohol problems in Finland: can community-based work be the solution?', *Contemporary Drug Problems* 28 (2), pp. 203–20.

Holmila, M. and Warpenius, K. (2007), 'A study on effectiveness of local alcohol policy: challenges and solutions in the PAKKA project', *Drugs: Education, Prevention and Policy* 14, pp. 529–41.

Home Office (2004), *Alcohol audits, strategies and initiatives: lessons from Crime and Disorder Reduction Partnerships*, Home Office Development and Practice Report 20,Home Office, London.

Homel, R., McIlwain, G. and Carvolth, R. (2001), 'Creating safer drinking environments', in Heather, N., Peters, T. and Stockwell, T. (eds), *International handbook of alcohol dependence and problems*, John Wiley & Sons Ltd, Chichester, pp 721–40.

Hope, C. (2008), 'Police give free goodie bags containing condoms, flip-flops and lollipops to drinkers', *Daily Telegraph*, 20 December. Available at www.telegraph.co.uk/news/newstopics/politics/lawandorder/3850898/Police-give-free-goodie-bags-containing-condoms-flip-flops-and-lollipops-to-drinkers.html (accessed 4 February 2009).

IHRA (International Harm Reduction Association) (n.d.), 'What is alcohol harm reduction?' Available at www.ihra.net/alcohol (accessed 4 February 2009).

Kaner, E. F. S., Dickinson, H. O., Beyer, F. R., et al. (2007), 'Effectiveness of brief alcohol interventions in primary care populations', Cochrane Database of Systematic Reviews 2007, Issue 2, Art. No.: CD004148. DOI: 10.1002/14651858.CD004148.pub3.

Ker, K. and Chinnock, P. (2008), 'Intervention in the alcohol server setting for preventing injuries', Cochrane Database of Systematic Reviews, Issue 3, Art No.: CD005244. DOI: 10.1002/14651858.CD005244.pub3.

Kolind, T. and Elmeland, K. (2008), 'New ways of socializing adolescents to public party-life in Denmark', in Olson, B. and Törrönen, J. (eds), *Painting the town red: pubs, restaurants and young adults' drinking cultures in the Nordic countries*, Vol. 51, NAD (Nordic Centre for Alcohol and Drug Research), Helsinki, pp. 191–219,

Lachenmeier, D., Rehm, J. and Gmel, G. (2007), 'Surrogate alcohol: where do we know and where do we go?', *Alcoholism: Clinical and Experimental Research* 31910, pp. 1613–27.

Lang, K., Väli, M., Szűcs, S., Ádány, R. and McKee, M. (2006), 'The composition of surrogate and illegal alcohol products in Estonia', *Alcohol and Alcoholism* 41 (4), pp. 446–50.

Lenton, S. and Single, E. (1998), 'The definition of harm reduction', *Drug and Alcohol Review*, 17 (2), pp. 213–19.

Leon, D. A., Saburova, L.,Tomkins, S., et al. (2007), 'Hazardous alcohol drinking and premature mortality in Russia: a population based case-control study', *Lancet* 369 (9578), pp. 2001–9.

Lewisham Drug and Alcohol Strategy Team (2007), *Don't binge and cringe evaluation: Lewisham 2007 anti-binge drinking festive campaign*. Available at www.alcoholpolicy.net/files/dont_binge_and_cringe_evaluation.pdf (accessed 4 February 2009).

Månsdotter, A. M., Rydberg, M. K., Wallin, E., Lindholm, L. A. and Andréasson, S. (2007), 'A cost-effectiveness analysis of alcohol prevention targeting licensed premises', *European Journal of Public Health* 17, pp. 618–23.

McKee, M., Suzcz, S, Sárváry, A., et al. (2005), 'The composition of surrogate alcohols consumed in Russia', *Alcoholism Clinical and Experimental Research* 29, pp. 1884–8.

Mistral, W., Velleman, R., Mastache, C. and Templeton, L. (2007), *UKCAPP: an evaluation of 3 UK Community Alcohol Prevention Programs. Report to the Alcohol Education and Research Council.* Available at www.aerc.org.uk/documents/pdfs/finalReports/AERC_FinalReport_0039.pdf (accessed 10 February 2009).

Moskalewicz, J. and Wald, I. (1987), 'From compulsory treatment to the obligation to undertake treatment: conceptual evolution in Poland', *Contemporary Drug Problems* Spring, pp. 39–51.

Nicholls, J. (2009), *The politics of alcohol: a history of the drink question in England*, Manchester University Press, Manchester.

Nilsen, P., Kaner, E. and Babor, T. F. (2008), 'Brief intervention, three decades on: an overview of research findings and strategies for more widespread implementation', *Nordic Studies on Alcohol and Drugs* 25 (6), pp. 453–67.

Pratt, E. A. (1907), *Licensing and temperance in Sweden, Norway and Denmark*, John Murray, London.

Prochard, H. (1902), 'Through the heart of Patagonia, London', quoted in Horton, D. (1943), 'The functions of alcohol in primitive societies: a cross-cultural study', *Quarterly Journal of Studies on Alcohol* 4.

Ranieri, F. et al. (2007), 'Prevenzione ad una festa della birra?', *S&P: Salute e Prevenzione: La Rassegna Italiana delle Tossicodipendenze* 22 (45), pp. 59–68.

Rehm, J., Room, R., Monteiro, M., et al. (2003), 'Alcohol as a risk factor for global burden of disease', *European Addiction Research* 9, pp. 157–64.

Rehm, J., Mathers, C., Popova, S., et al. (2009), 'Global burden of diseases and injury and economic cost attributable to alcohol use and alcohol-use disorders', *Lancet* 373, pp. 2223–32.

Robson, G. and Marlatt, G. A. (2006), 'Harm reduction and alcohol policy', *International Journal of Drug Policy* 17, pp. 255–7.

Salkeld, L. (2008), 'Flipping madness! Police offer free flip-flops to binge drinkers who keep falling over in heels', *Daily Mail*, 27 November. Available at www.dailymail.co.uk/newsarticle-1089919/Flipping-madness-Police-offer-free-flip-flops-binge-drinkers-falling-heels.html (accessed 4 February 2009).

Shepherd, J. (2007), 'Preventing violence — caring for victims', *Surgeon* 5 (2), 114–21.

Shepherd, J. P., Price, M. and Shenfine, P. (1990a), 'Glass abuse and urban licensed premises', *Journal of the Royal Society of Medicine* 83, pp. 276–7.

Shepherd, J. P., Shapland, M., Pearce, N. X. and Scully, C. (1990b), 'Pattern, severity and aetiology of injuries in victims of assault', *Journal of the Royal Society of Medicine* 83, pp. 75–8.

Smith, D. (2008), 'How to calm binge drinkers: get them all blowing bubbles', *Observer*, 30 November. Available at: www.guardian.co.uk/society/2008/nov/30/binge-drinking-bubbles (accessed 9 February 2009).

Stockwell, T. (2004), 'Harm reduction: the drugification of alcohol policies and the alcoholisation of drug policies', in Klingemann, H. and Müller, R. (eds), *From science to action? 100 years later — alcohol policies revisited*, Klewer Academic Publishers, Dordrecht, pp. 49–58.

Stockwell, T. (2006), 'Alcohol supply, demand, and harm reduction: what is the strongest cocktail?', *International Journal of Drug Policy* 17, pp. 269–77.

Stronach, B. (2003), 'Alcohol and harm reduction', in Buning, E., Gorgullo, M, Melcop, A. G. and O'Hare, P. (eds), *Alcohol and harm education: an innovative approach for countries in transition*, Amsterdam, ICAHRE, pp. 27–34.

SNIPH (Swedish National Institute of Public Health) (2008), *Alcohol prevention work in restaurant and medium-strength beer sales in six municipalities* (English summary), Stockholm: SNIPH. Available at www.fhi.se/en/Publications/Summaries/Analysis-of-alcohol-and-drug-prevention-work-in-six-municipalities/ (accessed 28 January 2009).

Tagliabue, J. (1985), 'Scandal over poisoned wine embitters village in Austria', *New York Times*, 2 August. Available at www.nytimes.com/1985/08/02/world/scandal-over-poisoned-wine-embitters-village-in-austria.html?sec=health (accessed 14 July 2009).

Thom, B. and Bayley, M. (2007), *Multi-component programmes: an approach to prevent and reduce alcohol-related harm*, Joseph Rowntree Foundation, York.

US Department of Health and Human Services (2000), *10th special report to the US Congress on alcohol & health*, US Department of Health and Human Services, National Institute on Alcohol and Alcoholism, Washington, DC.

Warburton, A. L. and Shepherd, J. P. (2000), 'Effectiveness of toughened glassware in terms of reducing injury in bars: a randomised controlled trial', *Injury Prevention*, pp. 36–40.

Wallin, E. (2004), *Responsible beverage service: effects of a community action project*, Karolinska Institutet, Stockholm.

Wallin, E., Norström, T. and Andréasson, S. (2003a), 'Effects of a community action project on responsible beverage service', *Nordic Studies on Alcohol and Drugs* (English supplement) 20, pp. 97–100.

Wallin, E., Norström, T. and Andréasson, S. (2003b), 'Alcohol prevention targeting licensed premises: a study of effects on violence', *Journal of Studies on Alcohol* 64, pp. 270–7.

Wallin, E., Lindewald, B. and Andréasson, S. (2004), 'Institutionalization of a community action program targeting licensed premises in Stockholm, Sweden', *Evaluation Review* 28 (5), pp. 396–419.

Willis, C., Lybrand, S. and Bellamy, N. (2004), 'Alcohol ignition interlock programmes for reducing drink driving recidivism' (Review), Cochrane Database of Systematic Reviews 2004, Issue 3, Art. No.: CD004168. DOI:10.1002/14651858.CD004168.pub2.

Wodak, A. (2003), 'Foreword', in Buning, E., Gorgullo, M., Melcop, A. G. and O'Hare, P. (eds), *Alcohol and harm education: an innovative approach for countries in transition*, ICAHRE, Amsterdam, pp. 1–4.

WHO (World Health Organization) (1994), Lexicon of drug and alcohol terms. Available at http://www.who.int/substance_abuse/terminology/who_lexicon/en/index.html (accessed 24 June 2009).

WHO (2008a), *Strategies to reduce the harmful use of alcohol: report by the Secretariat to the 61st World Health Assembly*, 20 March 2008, A61/13, World Health Organization, Geneva. Available at http://apps.who.int/gb/ebwha/pdf_files/A61/A61_13-en.pdf (accessed 24 June 2009).

WHO (2008b), *Report from a roundtable meeting with NGOS and health professionals on harmful use of alcohol, Geneva, 24 and 25 November*, World Health Organization, Geneva. Available at http://www.who.int/substance_abuse/activities/msbngoreport.pdf (accessed 24 June 2009).

Young, C. and Hirschfield, A. (1999), *Crystal clear: reducing glass related injury. An evaluation conducted on behalf of Safer Merseyside Partnership*, University of Liverpool, Liverpool.

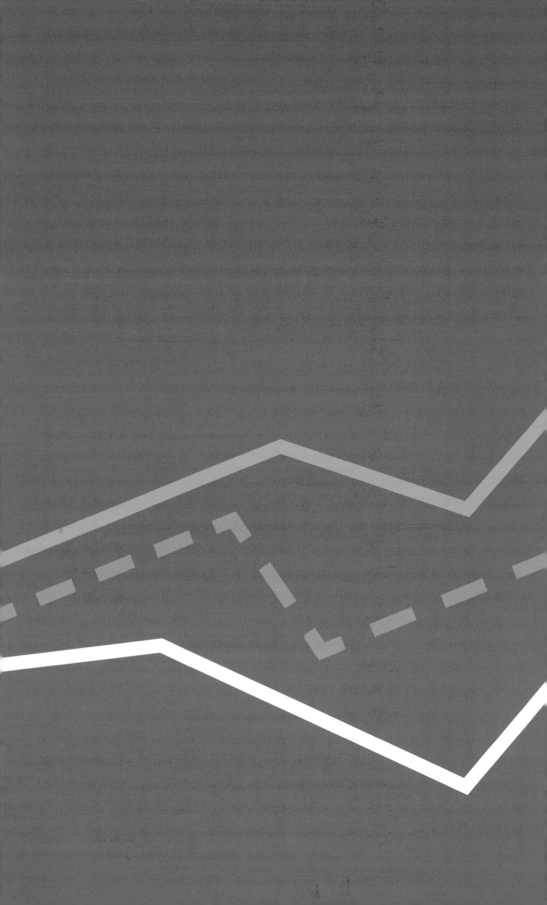

Challenges and innovations

PART III

Chapter 11

Drug consumption facilities in Europe and beyond

Dagmar Hedrich, Thomas Kerr and Françoise Dubois-Arber

Abstract

Drug consumption rooms (DCRs) are professionally supervised healthcare facilities where drug users can use drugs in safer and more hygienic conditions. Since 1986, more than 90 DCRs have been set up in Switzerland, the Netherlands, Germany, Spain, Luxembourg, Norway, Canada and Australia. Consumption rooms aim to establish contact with difficult-to-reach populations of drug users, provide an environment for more hygienic drug use, reduce morbidity and mortality risks associated with drug use — in particular street-based drug injecting — and promote drug users' access to other social, health and drug treatment services. They also aim to reduce public drug use and improve public amenity near urban drug markets. At times, their establishment has been controversial due to concerns that they may encourage drug use, delay treatment entry or aggravate problems of local drug markets. As with evaluations of other public health interventions, research on DCRs faces methodological challenges in taking account of the effects of broader local policy or ecological changes. Despite these limitations, research shows that the facilities reach their target population and provide immediate improvements through better hygiene and safety conditions for injectors. At the same time, the availability of safer injecting facilities does not increase levels of drug use or risky patterns of consumption, nor does it result in higher rates of local drug acquisition crime. There is consistent evidence that DCR use is associated with self-reported reductions in injecting risk behaviour such as syringe sharing, and in public drug use. Due to a lack of studies, as well as methodological problems such as isolating the effect from other interventions or low coverage of the risk population, evidence regarding DCRs — while encouraging — is insufficient for drawing conclusions with regard to their effectiveness in reducing HIV or hepatitis C virus (HCV) incidence. However, use of the facilities is associated with increased uptake of detoxification and treatment services. While there is suggestive evidence from modelling studies that they may contribute to reducing drug-related deaths at a city level where coverage is adequate, the review-level evidence of this effect is still insufficient. Taken in sum, the available evidence does not support the main concerns raised about this kind of intervention and points to generally positive impacts in terms of increasing drug users' access to health and social care, and reducing public drug use and associated nuisance.

Keywords: injecting drug use, drug consumption rooms, safer injecting facilities, open drug scenes, public nuisance, Europe.

Introduction

Drug consumption rooms (DCRs), also called safer injecting facilities, are professionally supervised healthcare facilities providing safer and more hygienic conditions for drug users to take drugs (Stöver, 2000). They comprise highly targeted services within wider networks of drug services. While they often operate from separate areas located in existing facilities for drug users or the homeless, some operate as stand-alone facilities.

DCRs arose in specific local contexts in response to problems posed by public drug use, especially by drug injecting in streets, railway stations or staircases of residential buildings, that persisted despite the availability of a variety of drug treatment, harm reduction and social services, and despite law enforcement efforts to disperse or contain public drug use. The rationale for the establishment of DCRs was to address public health and community problems associated with specific populations of drug users, especially injectors who consume in public or other high-risk situations.

These groups have important unmet healthcare needs and contribute to public order problems within local communities. A relationship between public injecting, elevated risk of viral infections and socio-economic deprivation, especially precarious housing or homelessness, has been long established by epidemiological research (for example, Latkin et al., 1994; Klee and Morris, 1995; Galea and Vlahov, 2002; Navarro and Leonard, 2004; Corneil et al., 2006). Risk factors exogenous to the individual, including multiple interacting physical, social and economic and policy factors, have been identified as constituting a broader 'risk environment' affecting the health of injection drug users (Rhodes, 2002; Rhodes et al., 2003). Qualitative research has shown that public injecting is associated with reduced options to maintain safety and hygiene, often related to an individual's fear of interruption, feelings of shame and hasty injection (Small et al., 2007; Rhodes et al., 2007).

DCRs aim to reduce high-risk and public drug use and to improve public amenity near urban drug markets, by providing a hygienic and regulated environment for drug use off the streets. They aim to create an acceptable situation for the public with regard to order and safety concerns that arise from open drug scenes. As pragmatic 'safer injecting environment' interventions, DCRs aim to minimise the likelihood of police and public interference and enable individual and community risk reduction practices to occur (Rhodes et al., 2006).

They further aim to reduce risk behaviour and improve health and social integration by: providing clean injecting equipment (needles, syringes, spoons, filters, wipes), good light, clean surfaces and sharps disposal; facilitating individually tailored health education, and promoting access to healthcare and drug treatment. House rules prohibit violent and threatening behaviour, alcohol use at the premises, drug dealing and the sharing of drugs and any injecting equipment, and define requirements regarding hygiene and injecting behaviour. Staff are trained to provide assistance and emergency care in cases of overdose or other adverse events but do not assist clients to inject (see Dolan et al., 2000; Kimber et al., 2005; Hedrich, 2004).

The first legally sanctioned DCR was established in Berne, Switzerland in 1986 (Hämmig, 1992). During the 1990s DCRs were set up in other Swiss cities, the Netherlands and Germany; and from 2000 they were set up in Spain, Norway, Luxembourg, Australia (Sydney) and Canada (Vancouver) (Stöver, 1991; Klee, 1991; Eastus, 2000; Zurhold et al., 2001; Parliament of New South Wales, 1998; Health Canada, 2002). By the beginning of 2009 there were 92 operational DCRs in 61 cities, including in 16 cities in Germany, 30 cities in the Netherlands and 8 cities in Switzerland.

In Europe, most DCRs are integrated components of local service networks offering a range of social and health services. In Norway, and in Sydney and Vancouver, they are scientific pilot projects, operating under legal exemptions, which focus on supervising drug consumption and providing referral to other services (MSIC Evaluation Committee, 2001; van Beek, 2003; Wood et al., 2003; Skretting and Olsen, 2008). While most target drug injectors, some cater for heroin and crack smokers (Willen, 2002; Spreyermann and Willen, 2003; Simmedinger and Vogt, 2008). In all cases, the drugs used are pre-obtained and prepared by the clients.

With objectives in public health and public order, DCRs operate within a triangle of individual and public health interests and the public order interests of local communities (Stöver, 2002). More than many other public services, they rely on acceptance by a wide range of key actors: drug users, communities, other health and social agencies, police and politicians.

The establishment of drug consumption rooms has led to some controversy and disagreement between the International Narcotics Control Board (INCB) and some UN Member States. This has centred on the interpretation of the international Drug Conventions, in particular in relation to the basic provision of the Conventions obliging States to limit the use of narcotic drugs strictly to medical and scientific purposes (INCB, 2008, p. 111).

This chapter does not address this debate; nor does it comment on the position of consumption rooms in respect of international drug control treaties. Its purpose is to summarise available evidence on the processes, outcomes and risks of DCRs, and also to identify key challenges for their development as mechanisms of harm reduction. Our review is structured according to the objectives of DCRs, as outlined in Table 11.1. The balance of priorities attributed to DCRs varies, with some placing greater emphasis on health goals, and others on public order. The main concerns expressed regarding the establishment of DCRs is that such facilities may promote initiation to drug injecting, conflict with treatment goals by encouraging users to continue injecting rather than enter treatment, and increase local drug dealing and drug-related crime by attracting users from other areas.

Table 11.1: Aims and objectives of drug consumption rooms

Aims	Outcome objectives	Indicators
1. Provide an environment for safer drug use	a) Reach and be accepted by target groups	Client profiles, service use patterns, client satisfaction
	b) Gain acceptability	Responses of local residents, businesses, police, politicians
	c) Establish conditions for safe, hygienic use	Various process indicators
2. Improve health status of target group	a) Improve risk-related behaviours	Street drug use, risk awareness, injection hygiene, borrowing/lending
	b) Reduce morbidity	Injection injuries, infectious disease transmission
	c) Reduce mortality	Overdose outcomes
	d) Improve access to healthcare and drug treatment	Treatment referral/uptake
3. Reduce public disorder	a) Reduce public drug use	Self-reported rates of public injecting, ethnographic observations of the burden of public injecting
	b) Improve public perceptions	Perceived nuisance, discarded syringes
	c) No increases in local drug-related crime	Crime statistics

Methods

Experimental study designs, and in particular the randomised controlled trial, are considered the gold standard for the generation of scientific level-1 evidence about the effects of treatments (Ashcroft et al., 1997). Maher and Salmon (2007) discuss this imperative with regard to the evaluation of the outcomes of DCRs, and conclude that 'the scientific, practical and ethical issues involved in applying this methodology to evaluating [such] complex public health interventions (…) mean that the likelihood of obtaining this level of evidence is negligible' (Maher and Salmon, 2007, p. 351f). To inform public health decision-making, the authors recommend the use of prospective observational studies (level 2 evidence) as a feasible alternative (Maher and Salmon, 2007).

There have been relatively few rigorous evaluations of DCRs, with evidence reviews relying primarily on analyses of descriptive data, cross-sectional survey data, and ecological indicators from a larger number of less sophisticated studies. This is especially the case in Europe, where DCRs emerged as a local service response with questions of evaluation arising subsequently. However, the Sydney and Vancouver facilities were established as scientific pilot studies, and thus incorporated more rigorous research designs (see below). The Vancouver study is so far the only DCR evaluation to have used an elaborate prospective cohort-based design (Wood et al., 2004a; Wood et al., 2006b).

As with any health service evaluation, a key methodological challenge is to establish causality. It is difficult to attribute observed effects to DCRs since: (a) most users use these facilities only for some consumption episodes and may otherwise continue to engage in risk behaviour (Dubois-Arber et al., 2008a); and (b) other factors (typically unmeasured) in the local environment influence levels of risk behaviour and public drug use, including policy or ecological changes such as those related to availability of substitution treatment and other harm reduction services, and changes in police operations or in the drug market (Maher and Dixon, 1999; Fischer et al., 2002; Hall and Kimber, 2005). If, as in the case of evaluating syringe exchange programmes, DCRs do succeed in attracting higher risk clients, then controlling for selection bias poses a further challenge (Wood et al., 2007a; Schechter et al., 1999).

Cross-sectional studies have limitations regarding their interpretation, as they provide a 'snapshot' of the outcome and the characteristics associated with it at a specific point in time (Bland, 2001). Repeated cross-sectional studies can be useful for tracking trends over time (see an example in box on p. 317).

The level to which coverage of the most risky consumptions can be achieved plays an important role in whether any impact of DCRs can be detected at community level (Kimber et al., 2008a). For instance, in Frankfurt, in 1994 and 1995, the capacity of three DCRs with 22 places and a total of 100 coordinated opening hours per week was insufficient to cover the demand of 300 to 400 highly problematic street injectors out of an estimated population of 6 000 to 8 000 drug users (Kemmesies, 1995). From 1996, when a fourth facility provided 13 additional places, opening hours were extended to a total of 300 per week and 4 000 injections were supervised each week. It was together with other measures and interventions, including shelters, day-centres and treatment programmes, that a visible reduction of public drug use in the city was achieved (Hedrich, 2004).

Further, population HIV (and perhaps HCV) incidence rates may be too low to identify intervention effects. As a result, most outcomes can reliably only be observed at individual, rather than at population level.

Review methods

The available evidence on DCRs was reviewed in 2004 (Hedrich, 2004), based mainly on research published during the 1990s in the languages of countries where DCRs were operating (German, Dutch, French and Spanish), and which were relatively inaccessible to the English-speaking world.

The present chapter draws on this review, on research reports resulting from the evaluations of a medically supervised injecting centre in Sydney (MSIC Evaluation Committee, 2003; NCHECR, 2005, 2006, 2007a, 2007b) and of a safer injecting facility in Vancouver (Expert Advisory Committee on Supervised Injection Site Research, 2008; BC Centre for Excellence in HIV/AIDS, 2004; Wood et al., 2006b), as well as on peer-reviewed research articles on DCR outcomes published between 2003 and 2009, and on other recent literature reviews

(Springer, 2003; Tyndall, 2003; Independent Working Group, 2006; Kerr et al., 2007a; Fischer and Allard, 2007).

Relevant English language articles were identified using Medline. Further sources, especially for the non-English scientific literature, which is under-represented in Medline, were identified by reviewing reference lists, searching by author names, or through direct contact with researchers in different countries.

Due to their scientific relevance, it is useful to note the research designs of the Sydney and Vancouver studies. The Sydney evaluation used an observational design (MSIC Evaluation Committee, 2001). The facility database provided data for process evaluation, including client utilisation, referrals, overdoses, and client and staff attitudes to the service. Serial cross-sectional studies were conducted to determine impact on individual health outcomes. Using ecological data, notifications of new infections and ambulance attendances at opioid-related overdose events were compared between the DCR locality and control localities. Recently, the Sydney evaluation incorporated a cohort-based element in its methodology, although only limited data are available from this cohort (NCHECR, 2007a; Kimber et al., 2008a).

The Vancouver evaluation used a prospective cohort design (Wood et al., 2004a). A randomly selected cohort of 1 000 users of the facility was monitored on a range of health indicators and potential impacts including risk behaviour surveys, venous blood samples to assess HIV and HCV incidence, overdose events, and health service use. For ethical reasons, participation in the research was optional, although over 95 % of those invited agreed to participate. The Vancouver evaluation's greatest strength was the existence of a community-recruited cohort of over 1 500 injectors, the Vancouver Injection Drug Users Study, which was initially recruited in 1996–97. This cohort consisted of individuals who did and did not use the safer injecting facility, and therefore allowed for control-based comparisons, as well as before and after analyses. As with the Sydney evaluation, the Vancouver design also included a facility database to track all key service events (referrals, overdose, drugs used), and data from both cohort studies were linked to a range of external databases (detoxification programme databases, hospital databases).

Both the Sydney and Vancouver research projects included local resident surveys, qualitative interviews with users, staff and key stakeholders, and standardised evaluations of public order changes (discarded syringes, perceived nuisance, and crime data).

Feasibility

Objective 1a: reach and be accepted by target group

In all countries, studies have shown that the profiles of clients contacted reflect the target groups and that DCRs generally succeed in attracting drug users who are at high risk of HIV infection and overdose, as well as those who are likely to inject drugs in public (Hedrich, 2004; Wood et al, 2005b; Simmedinger and Vogt, 2008; Dubois-Arber et al., 2008a, Scherbaum et al., 2009). In most of the recent studies, the majority of clients are male and over 30 years old with long histories of drug use. According to current data from Frankfurt, 4 520 individuals used the four local DCRs at least once in 2007. These clients have an average age of 34 years and are characterised by a high level of unemployment (65 %). Many suffer from drug use-related infectious diseases (HCV: 53 %; HIV: 5.9 %). A majority of DCR clients maintain regular contact with the local drug help system, and in particular make use of low-threshold agencies (89 %), but also of outpatient drug counselling facilities (36 %). More than half of clients (55 %) report being in medical treatment, which may include opioid maintenance treatment (Simmedinger and Vogt, 2008). Similar sociodemographic data are reported on 10 514 service users registered during the first seven years of operation at the Medically Supervised Injecting Centre (MSIC) in Sydney: their average age is 33 years, 74 % of service users are men, 61 % live mainly on social welfare benefits, and 24 % are homeless (van Beek, 2007). A comparison of socio-demographic profiles of DRC users in Zürich between 1997 and 2007 shows that current user populations are on average about a decade older, have an improved housing situation (6.7 % homeless in 2007, compared to 13.8 % in 1997), and commit fewer crimes to generate income (9.4 % in 2007, compared to 30 % in 1997) (Gautschi et al., 2008).

Retention and attendance rates at the Vancouver DCR also indicate that the facility is successful in gaining acceptance by its target group and that regular users of DCRs tend to be more marginalised, with various health and social problems, such as those related to unstable housing and public injecting (Wood et al., 2005b; Wood et al., 2006a). Client surveys conducted at several facilities also show high levels of satisfaction with staff and the services provided, as well as criticism of aspects such as opening hours (Benninghoff and Dubois-Arber, 2002; Poschadel et al., 2003; NCHECR, 2005, 2007b; Petrar et al., 2007).

Objective 1b: gain acceptability

Surveys and qualitative research on residents, local businesses, police and other key actors show mixed reactions to DCRs. On balance they are generally accepted by communities, albeit with reservations. Although some police tend to be more sceptical (Zurhold et al., 2003; Benninghoff et al., 2003; Zobel et al., 2003; BC Centre for Excellence in HIV/AIDS, 2004), there is also evidence that police in some settings are accepting of DCRs and actively refer drug users to them (DeBeck et al., 2008).

Objective 1c: establish conditions for safe, hygienic consumption

Process evaluations indicate that DCRs provide hygienic facilities, sterile injecting equipment, professional staffing and supervision, entrance criteria, safety rules, emergency procedures, safer injecting instruction and health education (Ronco et al., 1996a, 1996b; Linssen et al., 2001; Zurhold et al., 2001; Wolf et al., 2003; and Zobel and Dubois-Arber, 2004; Kimber et al., 2005). Studies also indicate that hygiene and safety are important reasons why clients use the facilities (Poschadel et al., 2003; Benninghoff et al., 2003). Despite millions of injections occurring at DCRs over the past 20 years, there have been no reported overdose fatalities (Poschadel et al., 2003; NCHECR, 2007b; Milloy et al., 2008; Expert Advisory Committee on Supervised Injection Site Research, 2008).

The Canadian research in particular shows that concerns that DCRs delay entry into treatment or even promote drug use are not substantiated. There were no observable increases nor decreases in drug use in the community, and no measurable increases in rates of relapse into injection drug use or initiation into injection drug use (Kerr et al., 2007b), stopping injection drug use, or seeking treatment (Stoltz et al, 2007; Kerr et al., 2005, 2006a; Wood et al., 2005a). Available evidence from Sydney (MSIC Evaluation Committee, 2003; NCHECR, 2007b) and Europe (Ronco et al., 1996b; Poschadel et al., 2003; Benninghoff et al., 2003) points to the same 'neutral' effect.

There are occasional reports of users making their first injection in a DCR (Benninghoff et al., 2003; Solai et al., 2005; Kerr et al., 2007b). Whether these would have occurred in the absence of the DCR is not known.

Conclusions on objective 1

DCRs reach and are accepted by their target populations, including marginalised street users and those at higher risk of infectious diseases or overdose (objective 1a). They are generally accepted by communities and key actors, or at least tolerated as the lesser of alternative evils (objective 1b). Further, they provide conditions, especially for regular clients, that improve hygiene and reduce exposure to health risks such as infectious diseases or overdoses (objective 1c). The risk that some users initiate injecting at DCRs is low and there is no evidence they increase levels of drug use or risky patterns of consumption. On the basis of available evidence, consumption rooms achieve their immediate objective of providing an environment away from the streets where high-risk or public drug users can consume their drugs more safely and hygienically, and they don't encourage drug use or injecting.

Impact on health outcomes

Objective 2a: reduce risk behaviours

The European Report on DCRs (Hedrich, 2004) identified 12 studies and one review of the impact of DCRs in the Netherlands, Germany and Switzerland on risk behaviours. Although subject to various methodological limitations, all European studies indicated positive effects. Staff also report positive changes in many clients' injecting hygiene. For example, several pre-post studies in the Netherlands showed increased knowledge of injecting hygiene and safer drug use among DCR users (Meijer et al., 2001; Linssen et al., 2001); cross-sectional surveys in Germany and in the Netherlands showed self-reported improvements by large proportions of DCR clients in injecting-related risk behaviour, injecting practices and hygiene since using a DCR (Jacob et al., 1999; Poschadel et al., 2003; van der Poel et al., 2003; Zurhold et al., 2001). Serial cross-sectional surveys in Switzerland showed decreases in the proportion of DCR clients reporting syringe sharing and sharing of other injecting equipment (Benninghoff et al., 2001, 2003; Benninghoff and Dubois-Arber, 2002; Solai et al., 2004) as well as increases in the proportion saying they would never accept used injecting equipment (Minder Nejedly and Bürki, 1999; Reyes Fuentes, 2003; Ronco et al., 1996a, 1996b). These earlier findings have been confirmed by Dubois-Arber et al., 2008b and by a more recent study from Spain that also reports reduced borrowing of used syringes among highly marginalised injecting drug users attending DCRs (Bravo et al., 2009).

Backstreet where public drug use takes place, Vancouver

Safer injecting facility, Vancouver

Source: M. J. Milloy for both photographs.

Outside Europe, these results have been replicated by studies in Sydney, where DCR clients were more likely than non-DCR clients to report using sterile syringes for all injections and less likely to report sharing injecting equipment, and where staff also reported improved hygiene and reduced sharing among DCR clients (MISC Evaluation Committee, 2003; NCHECR 2007a, 2007b). Likewise in Vancouver, a prospective cohort study of injecting drug users (IDUs) showed that syringe sharing decreased among DCR users but not among non-users of DCRs after the facility opened, and that the degree of reduction was associated with greater use of the facility (Kerr et al., 2005; Wood et al, 2005a; Stoltz et al., 2007). A recent meta-analysis shows highly similar effects of DCRs on the extent of syringe sharing across sites, with frequent DCR use being associated with a 70 % reduced likelihood of reporting syringe sharing (Milloy and Wood, 2009).

Collectively, these studies provide clear evidence that DCR use is associated with reduced self-reported and observed injecting risk behaviour, including the risk of overdose, and improvements in reported and observed injecting hygiene, especially among those who use the facilities consistently.

Objective 2b: reduce morbidity

Few studies report on injection-related injuries, although such injuries may represent a significant source of morbidity among people who inject drugs (Palepu et al., 2001; Salmon et al., 2009a). In Sydney, a small decrease in the frequency of injection-related problems over time was observed among DCR clients, including less bruising, scarring and abscesses (NCHECR, 2007b). In Vancouver, the risk of injecting-related bacterial infections decreased among DCR users, and the use of the facility was independently associated with other safe injection practices, including decreased reuse of syringes, increased use of sterile water and increased cleaning of injection sites with alcohol swabs (Stoltz et al., 2007). There is further evidence from qualitative studies undertaken in Vancouver of the potential impact of DCRs on reducing the incidence of soft tissue infections (Small et al., 2008; Krüsi et al., 2009) and of the advantages of nurse-delivered safer injection education in reaching IDUs most at risk for injection-related harm (Wood et al., 2008; Lloyd-Smith et al., 2009).

No conclusions can be drawn about the direct impact of DCRs on infectious disease incidence, owing to a lack of studies as well as methodological problems, such as isolating the effect of DCRs from other interventions (substitution treatment, needle exchange, outreach), low rates of HIV/HCV incidence, or low coverage of the risk population. For example, in Sydney, health authorities were notified of fewer newly diagnosed HCV, HIV and HBV infections in the DCRs' locality compared to other control localities (MSIC Evaluation Committee, 2003). However, no evidence was found that any changes in the number of notified cases were attributable to the DCR. Furthermore, the low incidence of HCV and HIV among IDUs in Australia made it unlikely that the number of cases would be sufficient to detect any statistically significant associations. Limited coverage of the facility was also unlikely to produce a detectable community impact on incidence.

Objective 2c: reduce mortality (overdoses)

There is some evidence of the impact of DCRs on mortality, but this evidence is mostly indirect and based on the outcome of emergencies occurring in the facilities (see box on p. 144). The majority of emergencies among users of DCRs involve heroin injection-related overdoses, with smaller proportions involving cocaine use. Emergency rates vary from 0.5 to 7 per 1 000 injections (see Hedrich, 2004, for Germany, Netherlands, Switzerland and Spain; Kerr et al., 2006b, for Vancouver; NCHECR, 2007b, for Syndey; and Skretting and Olsen, 2008, for Norway). As rapid intervention is available at DCRs, these events are less severe than overdoses occurring elsewhere, and fewer ambulance attendances or hospitalisations are needed (NCHCR, 2007b). In addition, DCRs located near open drug scenes may respond to overdoses in the immediate vicinity (Hedrich, 2004). None of the overdoses recorded at DCRs have resulted in death (the only known death at a DCR involved anaphylactic shock). Furthermore, by providing immediate intervention following the first signs of overdose, other impacts of non-fatal overdose-related events, including irreversible damage to the brain and other vital organs due to hypoxia, can also be prevented (van Beek et al., 2004; Hämmig and van Beek, 2005; NCHECR, 2007b).

Apart from potential fatalities prevented through supervised consumption among clients, there are several estimates of the impact of DCRs on drug deaths at population or city level. Based on utilisation data and expected mortality rates among the populations reached by DCRs, it has been estimated that these facilities helped prevent 10 deaths per year in Germany, and four per year in Sydney (Hedrich, 2004; MSIC Evaluation Committee, 2003). In a comparison of overdose death trends in the vicinity of the DCR with the rest of the region of New South Wales, no statistically significant impact of the Sydney facility on opioid-related deaths in Kings Cross was found. Due to an approximate 70 % decrease in overdose deaths following a heroin shortage in Australia, the researchers argue that the assessment of the impact may have been hampered by small sample sizes (NCHECR, 2007b, p. 29). In their simulation of the impact of the Vancouver DCR, Milloy and colleagues (2008) concluded that the facility may have prevented between 1.9 and 11.7 overdose deaths per year.

An ecologically based time-series analysis involving four German cities from 1990–2001 concluded that statistically significantly reductions in overdose fatalities were observed in Saarbrücken and Hannover six months after the opening of the DCR, and in Hamburg and Frankfurt after the opening of the third and fourth rooms respectively (Poschadel et al., 2003).

While it is impossible to ascertain how many emergencies would have occurred and been fatal in the absence of DCRs, epidemiological and clinical data suggest that immediate staff interventions at emergencies occurring at DCRs, where millions of drug consumptions have taken place under supervision, has reduced the impact of overdose-related events, such as morbidity and death. Where coverage and capacity are sufficient and opening hours appropriate, DCRs may contribute to reducing drug-related deaths at a city level.

Objective 2d: improve access to healthcare and drug treatment

There are large variations between countries regarding services offered on-site, which make comparisons difficult. Different policies towards accepting clients who are already in substitution treatment also affect treatment referral rates. Regarding referrals to treatment, only the Vancouver and Sydney studies measure actual uptake.

In most European DCRs a range of other services are usually delivered on-site alongside supervision of drug consumption. Low-threshold medical care and psychosocial counselling services are especially well used and contribute to the stabilisation and improvement of the somatic and psychological health of users (Linssen et al., 2001; Poschadel et al., 2003; Zurhold et al., 2001; van der Poel et al., 2003; Ronco et al., 1994). Clients are also referred to drug treatment or other care, though proportions vary and uptake rates are often unknown. For instance, in the survey of all German consumption rooms, over half of all clients reported having received a referral by DCR staff to other drug or social services at least once (Poschadel et al., 2003).

In both Vancouver and Sydney, use of the facility was associated with more exposure to safe injecting education and access to healthcare (Wood et al., 2006a, 2007b; van Beek, 2003; Tyndall et al., 2006; NCHECR, 2007a, 2007b; Kimber et al., 2008b). In Vancouver, a 30 % increased uptake of detoxification and subsequent addiction treatment were noted. For frequent attenders in particular, DCRs act as a link to the wider system of healthcare and facilitate entry to treatment: in Vancouver, entering a detoxification programme was more likely among IDUs who visited the facility at least weekly and among those who had contact with onsite addiction counsellors (Wood et al., 2007b).

The above results suggest that DCRs complement rather than conflict with treatment goals. In fact, with the exception of the initial years of DCR operation, current typical client populations at DCRs are in (or have successfully been brought into) contact with other harm reduction and treatment services, and many oscillate between those, or make parallel use of them. This reflects the complementary role of DCRs within a comprehensive drug policy approach, such as in Switzerland, where long-term behavioural trends and health-related impacts are documented (see box on p. 317).

Studies assessing the effectiveness of treatment consistently show that opioid maintenance treatment reduces the level of illicit opiate use and the frequency of injecting. Drug use and injecting may, however, still occur among clients in opioid maintenance, and clients in treatment may also use DCR facilities. For instance, during the first seven years of operation of the MSIC in Sydney, 13 % of all clients registering at the facility indicated that they were in methadone treatment (van Beek, 2007). Data from the first year of operation of the DCR in Geneva (2002) show that a majority (61.1 %) of users declared at the time of enrolment that they were in substitution treatment (Dubois-Arber, 2008a).

The question of whether clients in oral methadone treatment should use DCRs for injection is dealt with in different ways. In Germany, and Luxembourg, methadone clients are formally excluded from most consumption rooms. Elsewhere, however, the pragmatic view is taken that if methadone clients are going to inject anyway it is better that they do so in hygienic circumstances where there is also the opportunity for staff to talk with them.

Long-term behavioural trends and health-related impact of harm reduction facilities, including DCRs (Switzerland)

In 1993, 1994, 1996, 2000 and 2006 repeated national cross-sectional surveys were conducted among IDUs attending facilities that offer needle and syringe programmes, in order to measure trends in injecting behaviour (Dubois-Arber et al., 2008b). In 2006, half of these facilities (n=11) included a DCR.

Between 1993 and 2006, current injecting — in the last six months — decreased among those who had ever injected from 95.1 % to 74.2 %. The median number of injections in the last week also decreased from 14 to 7. The proportion of new injectors (first injection in the last two years) decreased from 18.7 % to 3.3 %. In 2006, most injecting events took place at home (56.4 %) or in a DCR (32.8 %). The type of drugs consumed in the last month showed a reduction in heroin, from 60.5 % of users in 1993 to 43.1 % in 2006, but an increase in cocaine users, from 23.7 % to 63.5 %. This may partly be related to an increasing proportion of IDUs on methadone treatment among the clients: 37.2 % in 1993, and 59.1 % in 2006. In 2006, about 10 % of IDUs had injected with a borrowed syringe in the last six months. This proportion has been quite stable since 1994, after a decrease between 1993 and 1994. Although more common, sharing of other injection equipment — spoons, filters and water — has decreased since 1996. Behavioural trends did not differ between IDUs recruited in facilities with or without a DCR.

During the same period (1993–2006), the national monitoring of injecting equipment showed a decrease from 2.2 millions to 1.6 million in syringes delivered in NSPs. New cases of HIV reported among IDUs decreased from 498 to 61, and notified acute cases of hepatitis C from 37 to 33. The number of IDUs receiving methadone treatment increased from around 12 000 to around 17 000, and drug-related deaths decreased from 353 to 193 (Gervasoni and Dubois-Arber, 2009).

This overall evolution cannot be attributed exclusively to the availability of NSPs and DCRs. However, it is posited that DCRs have contributed to the improvement in IDUs' health in Switzerland.

Conclusions on objective 2

DCRs help to improve the health status of the target population and contribute to reductions in high-risk injecting behaviour. There is evidence that when coverage and capacity are adequate, DCRs help to reduce overdose deaths. Available evidence does not allow conclusions to be drawn on whether or not they have specific, attributable impact on HIV and HCV infection rates, although fairly substantial reductions in HIV and HCV risk behaviour have been associated with DCR use. DCRs do increase access for specific 'hard-to reach' target populations of drug users to health, welfare and drug treatment services.

Impact on public order and crime outcomes

Objective 3a: reduce public drug use

Direct evidence of the impact of DCRs on levels of public drug use is limited and sometimes mixed. This is because of methodological limitations, restricted coverage, the difficulty of knowing how many facility-based injections would otherwise have occurred in public, and because other factors, such as police activity or changes in the drug market, also affect public drug use.

Studies in the Netherlands, Germany, Switzerland, Sydney and Vancouver showed lower levels of self-reported public drug use among clients (van der Poel et al., 2003; Zurhold et al., 2001; Poschadel et al., 2003; Benninghoff and Dubois-Arber, 2002; Stoltz et al., 2007; NCHECR, 2007b). However, it was not always possible to attribute this effect to DCRs (Zobel and Dubois-Arber, 2004). In Vancouver, the opening of the DCR was associated with a reduction of public injection, discarded syringes and drug-related litter (Wood et al., 2006a). In this instance, these effects were found independently of changes in police presence and weather patterns. In Sydney there was a reduction in public drug use among regular clients and reduced community visibility of injecting drug use (NCHECR, 2007b; Kimber et al., 2008b).

Among those who attended DCRs some report that they also continued to take their drugs in public places, when the DCR had insufficient space, was located away from drug purchase sites or when opening hours were restricted (Zurhold et al., 2001, 2003; Poschadel et al., 2003). Public injecting in some DCR localities may increase as a result of police actions to reduce drug markets in other areas (Benninghoff et al., 2003; Poschadel et al., 2003; Hedrich, 2004).

Objective 3b: improve public perceptions

Evidence related to public perceptions is also mixed. Several German, Swiss and Dutch studies have reported mostly acceptance of DCRs, at least as a preferable option to public use (Linssen et al., 2001; Zurhold et al., 2003; Zobel et al., 2003). In Vancouver, a survey among a random sample of 117 business owners located in the vicinity of the DCR found that 54 (46 %) were in favour of having a DCR, 23 were undecided and 40 were opposed to it. Businesses located further away from the facility showed less support (BC Centre for Excellence in HIV/AIDS, 2004). A five-year evaluation of the community perceptions of drug-related amenity before (year 2000) and after the opening of the Sydney DCR (surveys conducted in 2002 and 2005) among local residents and businesses found a significant decrease over time of those who reported recently witnessing public injection and improperly discarded syringes (Salmon et al., 2007) and that community attitudes tended to become more positive over time (Thein et al., 2005; MSIC Evaluation Committee, 2003). However, attributing these improvements to the DCR was complicated by a concurrent heroin shortage and rise in stimulant use. In Germany and Switzerland some DCRs have encountered strong opposition from local residents, which diminished with experience of the DCR in operation. Generally, fewer nuisance problems are reported in cities where a political consensus or cooperation between police and drugs services exists (Hedrich, 2004).

Effects on local crime

No increase in acquisitive crime has been observed after the opening of DCRs in the Netherlands and Switzerland (Linssen et al., 2001; Meijer et al., 2001; Spreyermann and Willen, 2003; Benninghoff et al., 2003).

The impact of the safer injecting facility in Vancouver on public disorder and drug-related crime has been studied extensively, including through follow-up studies comparing the situation before and after the opening of the facility (see box below). Furthermore, no evidence of negative impacts of the operation of the facility on community drug use patterns has been found (Kerr et al., 2006a).

The impact of the Vancouver DCR on crime, nuisance, safety and police referrals

The Vancouver DCR, known as 'Insite', is situated in a large open drug scene. The area is known for high levels of public injecting, drug dealing, and its open sex work market. Insite is open 18 hours a day, and includes 12 individual booths for injecting.

Insite has been evaluated to assess its potential impact on public order, crime, and its potential impact on policing practices. An early mixed methods analysis employed field counts of the number of individuals injecting in public, discarded syringes and other injecting litter, over an 18-week period (Wood et al., 2004c).

In multivariate regression analyses, the opening of Insite was associated with reductions in each measure of disorder after adjustment for police presence and rainfall. In two follow-up studies, use of Insite was also found to be associated with self-reported declines in public injecting (Stoltz et al., 2007; Petrar et al., 2007). Local crime statistics have been used to assess a potential association between the opening of Insite and drug-related crime (Wood et al., 2006c). In this before and after analysis, the opening of Insite was not associated with increases in drug trafficking, robbery/assault, or vehicle break-in charges. A recent study also sought to assess whether local police were referring drug users to Insite (DeBeck et al., 2008). Among 1 090 DCR clients enrolled in a prospective cohort study, 182 (16.7 %) individuals reported having ever been referred to the SIF by local police. At baseline, 22 (2.0 %) participants reported that they first learned of the SIF via police. In multivariate analyses, factors positively associated with being referred to the SIF by local police when injecting in public included engaging in sex work, daily cocaine injection, and unsafe syringe disposal. Collectively, these findings suggest that Insite has reduced public disorder, in particular public injecting, and has not exacerbated drug-related crime. Furthermore, Insite has provided a mechanism for police referral of individuals who engage in public injecting.

In Sydney, an evaluation of the crime statistics in the relevant neighbourhoods documented that operation of the MSIC DCR did not lead to increases in crime or social disturbance in its immediate vicinity. There was no evidence of any positive or negative impact on rates of drug-related crime, drug-related loitering, and no increase in the proportion of supply offences following the opening of the MSIC (NCHECR, 2007b; Freeman et al., 2005).

Most European reports show a similar picture. However, there have been reports from a few European facilities of increases in drug dealing around the facility (Geense, 1997; Zurhold et al., 2001), as well as aggressive incidents outside the premises, increases in petty crime and resentment from local residents (Kimber et al., 2005).

Conclusions on public order and crime outcomes

Consumption rooms can reduce the level of drug use in public. The extent to which this is achieved depends on their accessibility, opening hours and capacity. There is no evidence that the operation of consumption rooms leads to more acquisitive crime. There is small-scale drug dealing in the vicinity of many services, which is not surprising given their location. Nuisance is more likely when capacity or location of the facility does not meet local needs and waiting times are long. In some instances, these problems can be addressed by an adjustment of service capacity, aided by police cooperation and the involvement of the DCR in local order maintenance. However, facilities near illicit drug markets are not able to solve wider nuisance problems that result from these markets. Consumption rooms have greater impact where there is a political consensus that they are part of a comprehensive local strategy to respond to drug use-related problems that acknowledges public and individual health objectives as well as the need to maintain an acceptable situation with regard to order and safety in the community.

Challenges

The evidence reviewed in this chapter indicates that DCRs may contribute to reducing drug-related harms in settings where public drug use and injecting pose serious public health and social problems. For the future, these types of interventions face a number of challenges. The first set of challenges arises from changing patterns of drug use and drug using contexts and the new configurations of harms that these may imply. The second set of challenges concerns creating the environmental conditions that enable the reach and impact of existing DCRs and the development of new projects where there is a demonstrated need.

Targeting interventions in a changing world of drug use

Changing drug use situations present challenges for harm reduction interventions, calling for the capacity of responses to adapt rapidly to shifts in drug use, risks, target groups and needs (see also Hartnoll et al., 2010). Such changes may impact on: the prevalence or frequency of injecting; modes of drug administration (such as inhaling or smoking); patterns of drug use (for example, the injecting of crack cocaine, cocaine or amphetamine, or 'speedball'); and risk environments.

Operational data collected at European DCRs shows that there is a cumulative 'revolving door' client group of ageing injectors (Simmedinger and Vogt, 2008), but also that there are new groups of service users, in some cases young, for whom differentiated responses regarding safer use education are needed (Sozialdepartement der Stadt Zürich, 2008).

Additionally, increases in cocaine injecting observed in several European countries (EMCDDA, 2009) may imply increased frequency of injecting and associated health harms, including vein damage, bacterial and viral infections (see also Grund et al., 2010). The use of DCRs by clients in opioid maintenance treatment may also point to ineffective treatment regimes or to clients for whom methadone is unsuitable. In one case, a small subgroup (4 % of DCR clients) who mainly injected cocaine, were among the most frequent users of the facility, accounting for almost two-fifths of all injections observed in the year of study (2002) (Dubois-Arber et al., 2008a). Most of this group (65 %) were in methadone treatment at the time they had registered at the facility. Differentiated intervention emphasis should therefore be tailored to different and changing client needs, including through integrating referral and service delivery as part of a wider local system response to drug treatment and care (Dubois-Arber et al., 2008a). Studies also show that frequent DCR users may use the room as a place of socialisation and support (Benninghoff et al., 2003).

Most DCRs target drug injectors, with the exception of the Netherlands, where the majority of places are for smoking, reflecting the low proportion of injectors in the problem drug use population. Limited facilities for smoking have been added to some DCRs in Germany and Switzerland, and a room has been opened specifically for crack users in Frankfurt and for heroin smokers in Hamburg. Although smoking is generally seen as less risky than injecting, there may still be health risks, for example of transmitting HCV through sharing crack smoking paraphernalia (Fischer et al., 2008; Macías et al., 2008; Neaigus et al., 2007; Grund et al., 2010), as well as problems associated with public drug use. The expected benefits of implementing facilities for smoking at DCRs include contact with recent or younger users with the possibility of facilitating early treatment and reducing the risk of HCV infection.

Given the increased prevalence of both heroin smoking and the use of crack cocaine in a number of EU countries, assessment of the advantages and disadvantages of providing facilities for non-injectors, and the manner in which such services are best delivered merits further research.

The examples given above suggest that DCRs can play a wider and more proactive role than originally envisaged, in particular with regard to transmitting tailored health education messages to individual clients and to developing realistic prevention and safer use messages for the wider population of problem drug users. Because DCRs are for most clients not the main place of drug use (Dubois-Arber et al., 2008a; MSIC Evaluation Committee, 2003; Hedrich, 2004), learning to consume drugs safely in other contexts is an important individual outcome to be achieved. From this perspective, DCRs could be a basis from which to extend peer education and community-oriented projects to modify local risk environments (Pretil, 2007). In this regard, as frontline services, DCRs have the potential to constitute a sensitive and timely early warning system about drug use trends and effects of market changes (Degenhardt et al., 2008); they can help to gain in-depth knowledge of risky drug use practices and risk-increasing aspects of the local environment (Salmon et al., 2009a; 2009b).

Creating an enabling environment for intervention

Where DCRs are 'normative' as part of established harm reduction policy (Switzerland, Germany, the Netherlands, Luxembourg, Norway, parts of Spain), they are likely to continue and evolve. In this situation they face the challenges outlined above. In other countries, the situation is different. In some, there is a polarisation of public debate leading to the rejection of proposals, in others there is ambivalence resulting in a deadlock of new initiatives. The role of DCRs in the future has to be seen in the context of developments regarding public drug use and accessibility, as well as quality of drug treatment, including the existence of real reintegration options, funding and sustained political commitment.

If DCRs are to have an impact at community level it is necessary to provide sufficient capacity relative to the estimated size of the target population, to locate rooms on sites that are easily accessible, and to ensure that opening hours are long enough to meet demand, especially in the evenings and on weekends. Staffing and modus operandi are also important. Assessing the cost-effectiveness and impact of different service models at different levels of population coverage in different epidemiological settings is a key research question for the future.

In settings where there is a demonstrable need for DCRs, their development and the extent to which they can achieve their objectives is tempered by the broader social and policy context. A qualitative assessment of the literature suggests that DCRs can only be effective if they are:

- integrated into a wider public policy framework as part of a network of services aiming to reduce individual and social harms arising from problem drug use;
- based on consensus, support and active cooperation among key local actors, especially health, police, local authorities, local communities and consumers themselves;
- seen for what they are — specific services aiming to reduce problems of health and social harm involving particular high-risk populations of problematic drug users and addressing needs that other responses have failed to meet.

Conclusion

This chapter has focused on scientific evidence regarding whether DCRs, as a specific intervention, have achieved their stated objectives. Despite some limitations of the available evidence, the broad conclusion is that DCRs do bring benefits on specific aspects of individual and public health and social order without incurring serious risks. To achieve this, adequate coverage is essential, as is political support and consensus between key actors.

Expectations towards DCRs thus need to be realistic, as they cannot address all the key variables of drug-related harms. They do not change the fact that users buy their drugs in illicit markets, nor can they aim to change the drug market itself. They are, however, an effective public health intervention providing a 'safer environment' to reduce risks inherent in public drug use; they are unique in their capacity to develop individually tailored health education that achieves sustainable behavioural change among the most vulnerable populations; and the facilities provide clear benefits by increasing drug users' access to health and social care, and in reducing public drug use and associated nuisance.

DCRs — implications for practice

Drug consumption rooms can only be effective if they are:

- integrated into a wider public policy framework as part of a network of services aiming to reduce individual and social harms arising from problem drug use;
- based on consensus, support and active cooperation among key local actors, especially health, police, local authorities, local communities and consumers themselves;
- seen for what they are — specific services aiming to reduce problems of health and social harm involving particular high-risk populations of problematic drug users and addressing needs that other responses have failed to meet.

References

Ashcroft, R. E., Chadwick, D. W., Clark, S. R. L., et al. (1997), 'Implications of socio-cultural contexts for the ethics of clinical trials', *Health Technology Assessment* I (9). Available at http://www.hta.ac.uk/project/htapubs. asp (accessed 23 October 2009).

BC Centre for Excellence in HIV/AIDS (2004), *Evaluation of the supervised injection site: year one summary*, BC Centre for Excellence in HIV/AIDS, Vancouver. Available at http://www.vch.ca/sis/docs/sis_year_one_sept16. pdf (accessed 3 June 2009).

Benninghoff, F. and Dubois-Arber, F. (2002), *Résultats de l'étude de la clientèle du Cactus BIEL/BIENNE 2001*, Institut universitaire de médecine sociale et préventive, Lausanne.

Benninghoff, F., Geense, R. and Dubois-Arber, F. (2001), *Resultats de l'étude 'La clientèle des structures à bas seuil d'accessibilité en Suisse'*, Institut universitaire de médecine sociale et préventive, Lausanne.

Benninghoff, F., Solai, S., Huissoud, T. and Dubois-Arber, F. (2003), *Evaluation de Quai 9 'Espace d'acceuil et d'injection' à Genéve: période 12/2001–12/2000, Raisons de santé 103*, Institut universitaire de médecine sociale et préventive, Lausanne.

Bland, M. (2001), *An introduction to medical statistics*, 3rd edition, Oxford University Press, Oxford.

Bravo, M. J., Royuela, L., De la Fuente, L., et al. (2009), 'Use of supervised injection facilities and injection risk behaviours among young drug injectors', *Addiction* 104 (4), pp. 6124–9.

Corneil, T. A., Kuyper L. M., Shoveller, J., et al. (2006), 'Unstable housing, associated risk behaviour, and increased risk for HIV among injection drug users', *Health Place* 12, pp. 79–85.

DeBeck, K., Wood, E., Zhang, R., Tyndall, M., Montaner, J. and Kerr, T. (2008), 'Police and public health partnerships: evidence from the evaluation of Vancouver's supervised injection facility', *Substance Abuse Treatment Prevention Policy* 7 May, 3, p. 11 (DOI:10.1186/1747-597X-3-11).

Degenhardt, L., Roxburgh, A., van Beek, I., et al. (2008), 'The effects of the market withdrawal of temazepam gel capsules on benzodiazepine injecting in Sydney, Australia', *Drug and Alcohol Review* 27 (2), pp. 145–51.

Dolan, K., Kimber, J., Fry, C., et al. (2000), 'Drug consumption facilities in Europe and the establishment of supervised injecting centers in Australia', *Drug and Alcohol Review — Harm Reduction Digest* 10 (19), pp. 337–46.

Dubois-Arber, F., Benninghoff, F. and Jeannin, A. (2008a), 'Typology of injection profiles of clients of a supervised drug consumption facility in Geneva, Switzerland', *European Addiction Research* 14, pp. 1–10.

Dubois-Arber, F., Balthasar, H., Huissoud, T., et al. (2008b), 'Trends in drug consumption and risk of transmission of HIV and hepatitis C virus among injecting drug users in Switzerland, 1993–2006', *Eurosurveillance* 22 May, 13 (21).

Eastus, C. (2000), 'Die Entwicklung von Gesundheitsräumen in der Schweiz', *Akzeptanz -Zeitschrift für akzeptierende Drogenarbeit und humane Drogenpolitik* 8 (1), pp. 10–12.

EMCDDA (2009), *Annual report on the state of the drugs problem in the European Union, 2009*, European Monitoring Centre for Drugs and Drug Addiction, Lisbon.

Expert Advisory Committee on Supervised Injection Site Research (2008), *Vancouver's Insite service and other supervised injection sites: what has been learned from the research? Final report, 31 March 2008*, Health Canada, Ottawa, Ontario. Available at http://www.hc-sc.gc.ca/ahc-asc/pubs/_sites-lieux/insite/index-eng.php (accessed 3 June 2009).

Fischer, B. and Allard, C. (2007), *Feasibility study on 'supervised drug consumption' options in the City of Victoria*, Centre for Addictions Research of British Columbia (CARBC), University of Victoria, Victoria. Available at http://www.viha.ca/NR/rdonlyres/9C3846B7-4836-4F1C-8CE2-952273E3A439/0/carbc_feasibility_study.pdf (accessed 15 January 2010).

Fischer, B., Rehm, J., Kim, G. and Robins, A. (2002), 'Safer injecting facilities (SIFs) for injection drug users (IDUs) in Canada: a review and call for an evidence-focused pilot trial', *Canadian Journal of Public Health* 93 (5), pp. 336–8.

Fischer, B., Powis, J., Firestone Cruz, M., Rudzinski, K. and Rehm, J. (2008), 'Hepatitis C virus transmission among oral crack users: viral detection on crack paraphernalia', *European Journal of Gastroenterology & Hepatology* January, 20 (1), pp. 29–32.

Freeman, K., Jones, C. G., Weatherburn, D. J., et al. (2005), 'The impact of the Sydney MSIC on crime', *Drug and Alcohol Review* 24 (2), pp. 173–84.

Galea, S. and Vlahov, D. (2002), 'Social determinants and the health of drug users: socioeconomic status, homelessness, and incarceration', *Public Health Reports* 117 (Supplement 1), pp. S135–S145.

Gautschi, T., Hangartner, D. and Magnin, C. (2008), ‚Kontakt- und Anlaufstellen der Stadt Zürich. Eine Analyse der Bedürfnisse Ihrer Benützerinnen und Benützer', in Stadt Zürich — Sozialdepartement (ed.), „Ein Ort wo man sein kann". Die Zukunft der „Harm Reduction" am Beispiel der Kontakt- und Anlaufstellen der Stadt Zürich, Edition Sozialpraxis Nr.3, Zürich, pp. 13–57.

Geense, R. (1997), 'Evaluation of the federal measures to reduce problems related to drug use. To have or have not: that's the question. A qualitative study on four low-threshold needle exchange services for drug users in Switzerland', *Cah Rech Doc IUMSP*, no. 111.11, University of Social and Preventive Medicine, Prevention Programmes Evaluation Unit, Lausanne.

Gervasoni, J.-P. and Dubois-Arber, F. (2009), *Indicateurs de résultats du Promedro III, situation en 2008 : rapport final*, Raisons de santé 147, Institut universitaire de médecine sociale et préventive, Lausanne.

Grund, J.-P., Coffin, P., Jauffret-Roustide, M., et al. (2010), 'The fast and furious: cocaine, amphetamines and harm reduction', in European Monitoring Centre for Drugs and Drug Addiction (EMCDDA), *Harm reduction: evidence, impacts and challenges*, Rhodes, T. and Hedrich, D. (eds), Scientific Monograph Series No. 10, Publications Office of the European Union, Luxembourg.

Hämmig, R.B. (1992), 'The streetcorner agency with shooting room (Fixerstübli)', in O'Hare, P. A., Newcombe, R., Matthews, A., Buning E. C., and Drucker, E. (eds), *The reduction of drug related harm*, Routledge, London, pp. 181–5.

Hämmig, R. and van Beek, I. (2005), 'Supervised injecting rooms', in Pates, R., McBride, A. and Arnold, K. (eds), *Injecting illicit drugs*, Wiley-Blackwell, Chichester.

Hall, W. and Kimber, J. (2005), 'Being realistic about benefits of supervised injecting facilities', *Lancet* 23–29 July, 366 (9482), pp. 271–2.

Hartnoll, R., Gyarmathy, A. and Zabransky, T. (2010), 'Variations in problem drug use patterns and their implications for harm reduction', in European Monitoring Centre for Drugs and Drug Addiction (EMCDDA), *Harm reduction: evidence, impacts and challenges*, Rhodes, T. and Hedrich, D. (eds), Scientific Monograph Series No. 10, Publications Office of the European Union, Luxembourg.

Health Canada (2002), 'Application for an exemption under section 56 of the Controlled Drugs and Substances Act for a scientific purpose for a pilot supervised injection site research project: interim guidance document', Drug Strategy and Controlled Substances Programme, Healthy Environments and Consumer Safety Branch, Health Canada, Ottawa.

Hedrich, D. (2004), *European report on drug consumption rooms*, EMCDDA, Lisbon.

INCB (International Narcotics Control Board) (2008), *Report of the International Narcotics Control Board for 2007*, E/INCB/2007/1, United Nations, New York. Available at http://www.incb.org/incb/en/annual-report-2007.html (accessed 11 January 2010).

Independent Working Group (2006), *The report of the Independent Working Group on Drug Consumption Rooms*, Joseph Rowntree Foundation, York. Available at http://www.jrf.org.uk/publications/drug-consumption-rooms-summary-report-independent-working-group (accessed 3 June 2009).

Jacob, J., Rottmann, J. and Stöver, H. (1999), *Entstehung und Praxis eines Gesundheitsraumangebotes für Drogenkonsumierende. Abschlußbericht der einjährigen Evaluation des 'drop-in Fixpunkt' in Hannover*, Schriftenreihe Sucht- und Drogenforschung, Vol. 2., BIS-Verlag, Universität Oldenburg, Oldenburg.

Kemmesies, U. (1995), Szenebefragung 1995. *Die offene Drogenszene und das Gesundheitsraumangebot in Frankfurt am Main – ein erster Erfahrungsbericht*, Indro, Münster (English version: Kemmesies, U. (1999), *The open drug scene and the safe injection room offers in Frankfurt am Main 1995*, Indro, Münster). Available at http://www.indro-online.de/injection_room.htm (accessed 27 August 2009).

Kerr, T., Tyndall, M., Li, K., Montaner, J. and Wood, E. (2005), 'Safer injecting facility use and syringe sharing in IDUs', *Lancet* 23–29 July, 366 (9482), pp. 316–18.

Kerr, T., Stoltz, J. A., Tyndall, M., et al. (2006a), 'Impact of a medically supervised safer injection facility on community drug use patterns: a before and after study', *BMJ* 28 January, 332 (7535), pp. 220–2.

Kerr, T., Tyndall, M., Lai, C., Montaner, J. and Wood, E. (2006b), 'Drug-related overdoses within a medically supervised safer injection facility', *International Journal of Drug Policy* 17 (5), pp. 436–41.

Kerr, T., Kimber, J., Debeck, K. and Wood, E. (2007a), 'The role of safer injection facilities in the response to HIV/AIDS among injection drug users', *Current HIV/AIDS Reports* 4 (4), pp. 158–64.

Kerr, T., Tyndall, M. W., Zhang, R., et al. (2007b), 'Circumstances of first injection among illicit drug users accessing a medically supervised safer injection facility', *American Journal of Public Health* 97 (7), pp. 1228–30.

Kimber, J., Dolan, K., van Beek, I., Hedrich, D. and Zurhold, H. (2003a), 'Drug consumption facilities: an update since 2000', *Drug and Alcohol Review/Harm Reduction Digest* 21, 22 (2), pp. 227–33.

Kimber, J., MacDonald, M., van Beek, I., et al. (2003b), 'The Sydney Medically Supervised Injecting Centre: client characteristics and predictors of frequent attendance during the first 12 months of operation', *Journal of Drug Issues* 33, pp. 639–48.

Kimber, J., Dolan, K. and Wodak, A. (2005), 'Survey of drug consumption rooms: service delivery and perceived public health and amenity impact', *Drug and Alcohol Review* 24, pp. 21–4.

Kimber, J., Hickman, M., Degenhardt, L., Coulson, T., and van Beek, I. (2008a), 'Estimating the size and dynamics of an injecting drug user population and implications for health service coverage: comparison of indirect prevalence estimation methods', *Addiction* 103 (10), pp. 1604–13.

Kimber, J., Mattick, R. P., Kaldor, J., et al. (2008b), 'Process and predictors of treatment referral and uptake', *Drug and Alcohol Review* 27, pp. 602–12.

Kimber, J., Palmateer, N., Hutchinson, S., Hickman, M., Goldberg, D. and Rhodes, T. (2010), 'Harm reduction among injecting drug users: Evidence of effectiveness', in European Monitoring Centre for Drugs and Drug Addiction (EMCDDA) *Harm reduction: evidence, impacts and challenges*, Rhodes, T. and Hedrich, D. (eds), Scientific Monograph Series No. 10, Publications Office of the European Union, Luxembourg.

Klee, J. (ed.) (1991), *Akzeptanzorientierte Angebote in der Drogen- und AIDS-Selbsthilfe: Gesundheitsräume in der aktuellen Debatte*, Deutsche Aidshilfe (DAH), Berlin.

Klee, H. and Morris, J. (1995), 'Factors that characterize street injectors', *Addiction* 90 (6), pp. 837–41.

Krüsi, A., Small, W., Wood, E. and Kerr, T. (2009), 'An integrated supervised injecting program within a care facility for HIV-positive individuals: a qualitative evaluation', *AIDS Care* 21 (5), pp. 638–44.

Latkin C., Mandell, W, Vlahov, D., et al. (1994), 'My place, your place and no place: behaviour settings as a risk factor for HIV-related injection practices of drug users in Baltimore, Maryland', *American Journal of Community Psychology* 22, pp. 415–30.

Linssen, L., de Jong, W. and Wolf, J. (2001), *Gebruiksruimten. Een systematisch overzicht van de voorziening en de effecten ervan*. Series: Resultaten Scoren, Trimbos Instituut, Utrecht. Available at www.ggznederland.nl/scrivo/asset.php?id=306955 (accessed 3 June 2009).

Lloyd, C. and Hunt, N. (2007), 'Drug consumption rooms: an overdue extension to harm reduction policy in the UK?', *International Journal of Drug Policy* 18, pp. 5–7.

Lloyd-Smith, E., Wood, E., Zhang, R., et al. (2009), 'Determinants of cutaneous injection-related care at a supervised injecting facility', *Annals of Epidemiology* 19, pp. 404–09.

Maher, L. and Dixon, D. (1999), 'Policing and public health: harm minimization and law enforcement in a street-level drug market', *British Journal of Criminology* 39, pp. 488–512.

Maher, L. and Salmon, A. (2007), 'Supervised injecting facilities: how much evidence is enough?', *Drug and Alcohol Review* July 26 (4), pp. 351–3.

Macías, J., Palacios, R. B., Claro, E., et al. (2008), 'High prevalence of hepatitis C virus infection among noninjecting drug users: association with sharing the inhalation implements of crack, *Liver International* July, 28 (6), pp. 781–6.

McKnight, I., Maas, B., Wood, E., et al. (2007), 'Factors associated with public injecting among users of Vancouver's supervised injection facility', *American Journal of Drug and Alcohol Abuse* 33 (2), pp. 319–25.

Meijer, G., de Jong, A., Koeter, M. and Bieleman, B. (2001), *Gebruik van de straat. Evaluatie gebruiksruimnte Binnenstad-Zuid Groningen*, Amsterdam Institute for Addiction Research (AIAR)/Intraval, Amsterdam/Groningen. Abstract in Dutch available at http://blowkwartet.nl/default4597.html?back=1 (accessed 15 January 2010).

Milloy, M. J. and Wood, E. (2009), 'Emerging role of supervised injecting facilities in human immunodeficiency virus prevention', *Addiction* 104 (4), pp. 620–1.

Milloy, M. J., Kerr, T., Tyndall, M., Montaner, J. and Wood, E. (2008), 'Estimated drug overdose deaths averted by North America's first medically-supervised safer injection facility', *PLoS ONE* 3 (10), p. e3351.

Minder Nejedly, M and Bürki, C. M. (1999), 'Monitoring HIV risk behaviours in a street agency with injection room in Switzerland', dissertation, Medical Faculty of the University in Berne, Berne.

MSIC Evaluation Committee (2001), *Evaluation Protocol for the trial of a Medically Supervised Injecting Centre in Kings Cross*, NSW Parliament, Standing Committee on Social Issues, Sydney. Available at http://www.worldcat. org/oclc/223407460&referer=brief_results (accessed 23 October 2009).

MSIC Evaluation Committee (2003), *Final report of the evaluation of the Sydney Medically Supervised Injecting Centre*, Authors, Sydney. Available at http://www.druginfo.nsw.gov.au/__data/page/1229/NDARC_final_evaluation_report4.pdf (accessed 3 June 2009).

Navarro, C. and Leonard, L. (2004), 'Prevalence and factors related to public injecting in Ottawa, Canada: implications for the development of a trial safer injecting facility', *International Journal of Drug Policy*, 15, pp. 275–84.

NCHECR (National Centre in HIV Epidemiology and Clinical Research) (ed.) (2005), *Sydney Medically Supervised Injecting Centre evaluation report no. 1: operations and service delivery (November 2002 to December 2004)*, University of New South Wales, Sydney. Available at http://www.nchecr.unsw.edu.au/NCHECRweb.nsf/resources/Interim_eval_Rep1/$file/INT_EVAL_REP_+1_SYD_+MSIC.pdf (accessed 3 June 2009).

NCHECR (ed.) (2006), *Sydney Medically Supervised Injecting Centre evaluation report no. 2: evaluation of community attitudes towards the Sydney MSIC*, University of New South Wales, Sydney. Available at http://www.nchecr.unsw.edu.au/NCHECRweb.nsf/resources/Interim_eval_Rep1/$file/IntRep2SurveyMSICJul06.pdf (accessed 3 June 2009).

NCHECR (ed.) (2007a), *Sydney Medically Supervised Injecting Centre evaluation report no. 3: evaluation of client referral and health issues*, University of New South Wales, Sydney. Available at http://www.nchecr.unsw.edu.au/NCHECRweb.nsf/resources/Interim_eval_rep_2/$file/EvalRep4SMSIC.pdf (accessed 3 June 2009).

NCHECR (ed.) (2007b), *Sydney Medically Supervised Injecting Centre evaluation report no. 4: evaluation of service operation and overdose-related events*, National Centre in HIV Epidemiology and Clinical Research, University of New South Wales, Sydney. Available at http://www.nchecr.unsw.edu.au/NCHECRweb.nsf/resources/Interim_eval_rep_2/$file/EvalRep4SMSIC.pdf (accessed 3 June 2009).

Neaigus, A., Gyarmathy, V. A., Miller, M., et al. (2007), 'Sexual and other noninjecting risks for HBV and HCV seroconversions among noninjecting heroin users', *Journal of Infectious Diseases* 195 (7), pp. 1052–61.

Palepu, A., Tyndall, M. W., Leon, H., et al. (2001), 'Hospital utilization and costs in a cohort of injection drug users', *Canadian Medical Association Journal* 165, pp. 415–20.

Parliament of New South Wales (1998), *Joint Select Committee into Safe Injecting Rooms report on the establishment or trial of safe injecting rooms*, Parliament of New South Wales, Sydney. Available at http://www.parliament.nsw. gov.au/safeinjectingrooms (accessed 3 June 2009).

Petrar, S., Kerr, T., Tyndall, M. W., et al. (2007), 'Injection drug users' perceptions regarding use of a medically supervised safer injecting facility', *Addictive Behaviours* 32 (5), pp. 1088–93.

Pretil, X. S. (2007), 'En qué sentido deberían evolucionar las salas de consumo supervisado?' *Mesa redonda, ddz cdd*, October 2007, 144, p. 10.

Poschadel, S., Höger, R., Schnitzler, J. and Schreckenberger, J. (2003), *Evaluation der Arbeit der Drogenkonsumräume in der Bundesrepublik Deutschland: Endbericht im Auftrag des Bundesministeriums für Gesundheit*, Das Bundesministerium für Gesundheit und Soziale Sicherung (Schriftenreihe Bd 149), Nomos-Verlags-Gesellschaft, Baden-Baden.

Reyes Fuentes, V. C. (2003), '15 Jahre Fixerraum Bern. Auswirkungen auf soziale und medizinische Aspekte bei Drogenabhängigen', dissertation at the Medical Faculty of the University of Berne.

Rhodes, T. (2002), 'The "risk environment": a framework for understanding and reducing drug-related harm', *International Journal of Drug Policy* 13, pp. 85–94.

Rhodes, T., Lilly, R., Fernández, C., et al. (2003), 'Risk factors associated with drug use: importance of "risk environment"', *Drugs: education, prevention, and policy*, 10 (4), pp. 303–29.

Rhodes, T., Kimber, J., Small, W., et al. (2006), 'Public injecting and the need for "safer environment interventions" in the reduction of drug-related harm', *Addiction* 101, pp. 1384–93.

Rhodes, T., Watts, L., Davies, S., et al. (2007), 'Risk, shame and the public injector', *Social Science and Medicine* 65, pp. 572–85.

Ronco, C., Spuler, G., Coda, P. and Schöpfer, R. (1994), *Evaluation der Gassenzimmer I, II und III in Basel (full report)*, Institut für Sozial- und Präventivmedizin der Universität Basel, Basel.

Ronco, C., Spuler, G., Coda, P. and Schöpfer, R. (1996a), 'Evaluation der Gassenzimmer I, II und III in Basel [Evaluation of street facilities I, II and III in Basel]', *Sozial- und Präventivmedizin*, 41 (Supplement 1), pp. S58–S68. Abstract in English available at http://www.ncbi.nlm.nih.gov/pubmed/8693818.

Ronco, C., Spuhler, G. and Kaiser, R. (1996b), 'Evaluation des "Aufenthalts- und Betreuungsraums für Drogenabhängige" in Luzern [Evaluation of a stay and care center for drug addicts in Lucerne]', *Sozial- und Präventivmedizin*, 41 (Supplement 1), pp. S45–S57. Abstract in English available at http://www.ncbi.nlm.nih.gov/pubmed/8693816.

Salmon, A., Thein, R., Kimber, J., Kaldor, J. and Maher, L. (2007), 'Five years on: what are the community perceptions of drug-related public amenity following the establishment of the Sydney Medically Supervised Injecting Centre?', *International Journal of Drug Policy* 18 (1), pp. 46–53.

Salmon, A. M., Dwyer, R., Jauncey, M., et al. (2009a), 'Injecting-related injury and disease among clients of a supervised injecting facility', *Drug Alcohol Dependence* 101 (1–2), pp. 132–6.

Salmon, A. M., van Beek, I., Amin, J., Grulich, A. and Maher, L. (2009b), 'High HIV testing and low HIV prevalence among injecting drug users attending the Sydney Medically Supervised Injecting Centre', *Australian and New Zealand Journal of Public Health* 33 (3), pp. 280–3.

Schechter, M. T., Strathdee, S. A., Cornelisse, P. G., et al. (1999), 'Do needle exchange programmes increase the spread of HIV among injection drug users? An investigation of the Vancouver outbreak', *AIDS* 16 April, 13 (6), pp. F45–F51.

Scherbaum, N., Specka, M., Bombeck, J. and Marziniak, B. (2009), 'Drug consumption facility as part of a primary health care centre for problem drug users: which clients are attracted?', *International Journal of Drug Policy* 20 (5), pp. 447–9.

Simmedinger, R. and Vogt, I. (2008), *Auswertung der Frankfurter Konsumraumdokumentation 2007. Endbericht*, ISFF, Frankfurt am Main.

Skretting, A. and Olsen H. (2008), 'The Norwegian injection room trial: politics and controversies', *Nordic Studies on Alcohol and Drugs* 25 (4), pp. 269–83.

Small, W., Rhodes, T., Wood, E. and Kerr, T. (2007), 'Public injecting settings in Vancouver: physical environment, social context and risk', *International Journal of Drug Policy* 18, pp. 27–36.

Small, W., Wood, E., Lloyd-Smith, E., Tyndall, M. and Kerr, T. (2008), 'Accessing care for injection-related infections through a medically supervised injecting facility: a qualitative study', *Drug and Alcohol Dependence* 98 (1–2), pp. 159–62.

Solai, S., Benninghoff, B., Meystre-Agustoni, G., Jeannin, A. and Dubois-Arber, F. (2004), 'Evaluation de l'espace d'accueil et d'injection "Quai 9" à Genève: deuxième phase 2003', *Raisons de santé*, 102, Institut universitaire de médecine sociale et préventive, Lausanne. Available at http://www.iumsp.ch/Unites/uepp/files/Quai9GE_2.pdf (accessed 3 June 2009).

Solai, S., Dubois-Arber, F., Benninghoff, F. and Benaroyo, L. (2006), 'Ethical reflections emerging during the activity of a low threshold facility with supervised drug consumption room in Geneva, Switzerland', *International Journal of Drug Policy* 17 (1), pp. 17–22.

Sozialdepartement der Stadt Zürich (ed.) (2008), *„Ein Ort wo man sein kann". Die Zukunft der „Harm Reduction" am Beispiel der Kontakt- und Anlaufstellen der Stadt Zürich*, Edition Sozialpraxis Nr. 3, Zürich.

Spreyermann, C. and Willen, C. (2003), *Evaluationsbericht Öffnung der Kontakt- und Anlaufstellen für risikoärmere Konsumformen. Evaluation der Inhalationsräume der Kontakt- und Anlaufstellen Selnau und Seilergraben der Ambulanten Drogenhilfe Zürich*, Sfinx, Berne. Available at http://www.sfinx.ch/siteman/file/innovation/Evaluationsbericht.pdf (accessed 3 June 2009).

Springer, A. (2003), *Konsumräume. Expertise im Auftrag des Fonds Soziales Wien*, Ludwig-Boltzmann-Institut für Suchtforschung, Anton-Proksch-Institut, Wien. Available at http://www.api.or.at/lbi/pdf/040622_expertise_konsumraeume.pdf (accessed 3 June 2009).

Stoltz, J. A., Wood, E., Small, W., et al. (2007), 'Changes in injecting practices associated with the use of a medically supervised safer injection facility', *Journal of Public Health* 29 (1), pp. 35–9.

Stöver, H. (ed.) (1991), *Der tolerierte intravenöse Drogengebrauch in den Angeboten der Drogen- und AIDS-Hilfe. Ein Sammelband*, AIDS-Forum der Deutschen AIDS-Hilfe, Vol. VI, DAH, Berlin.

Stöver, H. (2000), 'Konsumräume als professionelles Angebot der Suchtkrankenhilfe - Internationale Konferenz zur Erarbeitung von Leitlinien', *Bundesgesundheitsblatt — Gesundheitsforschung — Gesundheitsschutz*, 43, pp. 290–2.

Stöver, H. (2002), 'Consumption rooms: a middle ground between health and public order concerns', *Journal of Drug Issues* 32 (2), pp. 597–606.

Thein, H. H., Kimber, J., Maher, L., MacDonald, M. and Kaldor, J. M. (2005), 'Public opinion towards supervised injecting centres and the Sydney Medically Supervised Injecting Centre', *International Journal of Drug Policy* 16 (4), pp. 275–80.

Tyndall, M. (2003), 'Impact of supervised injection facilities on community HIV levels: a public health perspective', *Expert Review of Anti-Infective Therapy* 1 (4), pp. 543–9.

Tyndall, M., Kerr, T., Zhang, R., et al. (2006), 'Attendance, drug use patterns and referrals made from North America's first supervised injection facility', *Drug and Alcohol Dependence* 83, pp. 193–8.

van Beek, I. (2003), 'The Sydney Medically Supervised Injecting Centre: a clinical model', *Journal of Drug Issues* 33, pp. 625–38.

van Beek, I. (2007), *The Medically Supervised Injecting Centre: the first 7 years*, Clinical Activity Data. Available at www.sydneymsic.com (MSIC_NDARC_07.ppt) (accessed 27 August 2009).

van Beek, I., Kimber, J., Dakin, A and Gilmour, S. (2004), 'The Sydney Medically Supervised Injecting Centre: reducing harm associated with heroin overdose', *Critical Public Health* 14 (4), pp. 391–406.

van der Poel, A., Barendregt, C. and van de Mheen, D. (2003), 'Drug consumption rooms in Rotterdam: an explorative description', *European Addiction Research*, 9, pp. 94–100.

Willen, C. (2002), *Evaluation Inhalationsraum. Pilotprojekt der Anlaufstelle Rötzmatt, Suchthilfe Region Olten (SHO)*, Sfinx, Berne. Available at http://www.sfinx.ch/html/portfolio_act.html (accessed 3 June 2009).

Wolf, J., Linssen, L. and de Graaf, I., assisted by van Dam, T. (2003), 'Drug consumption facilities in the Netherlands', *Journal of Drug Issues* 33, pp. 649–61.

Wood, E., Kerr, T., Spittal, P. M., et al. (2003), 'The potential public health and community impacts of safer injecting facilities: evidence from a cohort of injecting drug users', *Journal of Acquired Immune Deficiency Syndrome* 32 (1), pp. 2–8.

Wood, E., Kerr, T., Lloyd-Smith, E., et al. (2004a), 'Methodology for evaluating Insite: Canada's first medically supervised safer injection facility for injection drug users', *Harm Reduction Journal* 1 (1), p. 9. Available at http://www.harmreductionjournal.com/content/1/1/9 (accessed 3 June 2009).

Wood, E., Kerr, T., Montaner, J. S., et al. (2004b), 'Rationale for evaluating North America's first medically supervised safer-injecting facility', *Lancet Infectious Diseases* 4, pp. 301–06.

Wood, E., Kerr, T., Small, W., et al. (2004c), 'Changes in public order after the opening of a medically supervised safer injecting facility for illicit injection drug users', *Canadian Medical Association Journal*, 171 (7), pp. 731–4.

Wood, E., Tyndall, M. W., Stoltz J. A., et al. (2005a), 'Factors associated with syringe sharing among users of a medically supervised safer injecting facility', *American Journal of Infectious Diseases* 1 (1), pp. 50–4.

Wood, E., Tyndall, M.W., Li, K., et al. (2005b), 'Do supervised injecting facilities attract higher-risk injection drug users?', *American Journal of Preventive Medicine*, 29 (2), pp. 126–30.

Wood, E., Tyndall, M. W., Qui, Z., et al. (2006a), 'Service uptake and characteristics of injection drug users utilizing North America's first medically supervised safer injecting facility', *American Journal of Public Health*, 96, pp. 770–3.

Wood, E., Tyndall, M. W., Montaner, J. S. and Kerr, T. (2006b), 'Summary of findings from the evaluation of a pilot medically supervised safer injecting facility', *Canadian Medical Association Journal*, 175 (11), pp. 1399–404.

Wood, E., Tyndall, M. W., Lai, C., Montaner, J. S. and Kerr, T. (2006c), 'Impact of a medically supervised safer injecting facility on drug dealing and other drug-related crime', *Substance Abuse Treatment, Prevention, and Policy*, 1 (13). Published online 8 May 2006. DOI: 10.1186/1747-597X-1-13.

Wood, E., Lloyd-Smith, E., Li, K., et al. (2007a), 'Frequent needle exchange use and HIV incidence in Vancouver, Canada', *American Journal of Medicine* 120 (2), pp. 172–9.

Wood, E., Tyndall, M. W., Zhang, R., Montaner, J. S. and Kerr, T. (2007b), 'Rate of detoxification service use and its impact among a cohort of supervised injecting facility users', *Addiction* 102 (6), pp. 916–19.

Wood, R. A., Wood, E., Lai, C., et al. (2008), 'Nurse-delivered safer injection education among a cohort of injection drug users: evidence from the evaluation of Vancouver's supervised injection facility', *International Journal of Drug Policy* 19 (3), pp. 183–8.

Zobel, F. and Dubois-Arber, F. (2004), *Short appraisal of the role and usefulness of drug consumption facilities (DCF) in the reduction of drug-related problems in Switzerland: produced at the request of the Swiss Federal Office of Public Health*, Institut universitaire de médecine sociale et préventive, Lausanne. Available at http://www.bag.admin.ch/evaluation/01759/02066/02343/index.html?lang=en (accessed 3 June 2009).

Zobel, F., Thomas, R., Arnaud, S., et al. (2003), *Global evaluation of the Confederation's measures to reduce drug-related problems (ProMeDro): fourth synthesis report 1999–200*, Institut universitaire de médecine sociale et préventive, Lausanne. Available at http://www.iumsp.ch/Unites/uepp/files/tox4_en.pdf (accessed 3 June 2009).

Zurhold, H., Kreuzfeld, N., Degkwitz, P. and Verthein, U. (2001), *Drogenkonsumräume. Gesundheitsförderung und Minderung öffentlicher Belastungen in europäischen Grossstädten*, Lambertus, Freiburg.

Zurhold, H., Degkwitz, P., Verthein, U. and Haasen, C. (2003), 'Drug consumption rooms in Hamburg, Germany: evaluation of the effects on harm reduction and the reduction of public nuisance', *Journal of Drug Issues* 33, pp. 663–88.

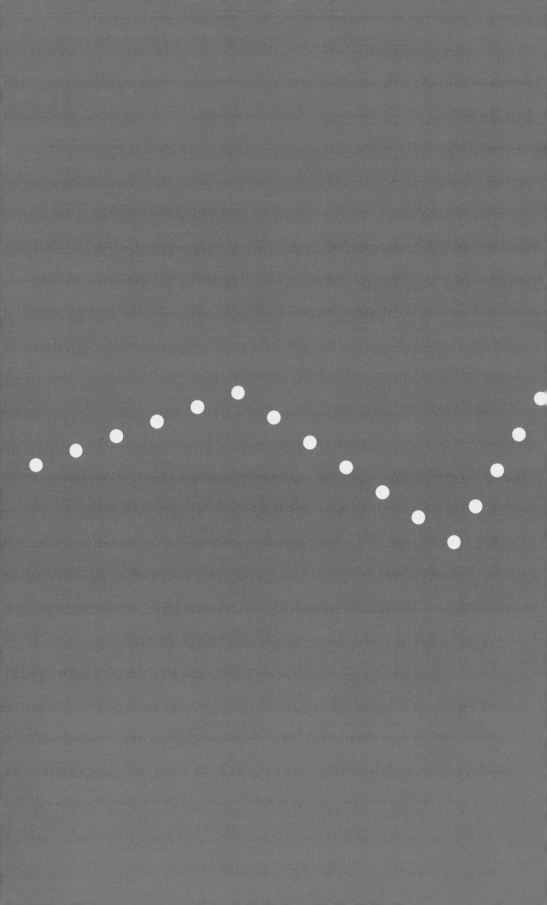

Chapter 12
User involvement and user organising in harm reduction

Neil Hunt, Eliot Albert and Virginia Montañés Sánchez

Abstract

Within Europe, the active involvement of drug users in services and activities that affect their lives can be traced back to the Netherlands in the 1970s, pre-dating the development of harm reduction in response to HIV/AIDS. This chapter distinguishes involvement approaches, which typically focus on improving treatment and care, from user-led initiatives, where objectives are determined more autonomously. The chapter describes differences in user involvement and organising with respect to the preferred drugs of different populations (heroin and cocaine, 'party drugs' and cannabis). We also highlight the different aims and methods of user involvement and user organising initiatives. These also illustrate differences that are shaped by: the drugs used; the context of their use; and national contrasts in patterns of use and harm. In addition to noting some of the practical challenges linked to user involvement/organising, we also note potential tensions, most notably regarding disputes about the extent to which drug prohibition is construed as a cause of harm, and its reform seen as a legitimate target for drug users' activism. Finally, we summarise available evidence of the impact of user involvement and organising. We conclude that harms can best be reduced where affected people participate meaningfully in decisions concerning the systems and services that shape their lives. This requires clear commitment at every level and will frequently need corresponding resources, if its full potential is to be realised.

Keywords: harm reduction, user involvement, user organising, user-led, empowerment.

Introduction

Across Europe, patterns of drug use and their corresponding burden of harms differ considerably (EMCDDA, 2008). Such variations in drug use have implications for harm reduction responses. Variations in patterns of drug use are shaped by geographical factors, such as the suitability of the climate for drug production, or trafficking and transit routes. But they are also shaped by social factors, as are harm reduction responses. These include: the cultural and ethnic context; national legislation; the policies of the prevailing government; the influence of organised religion; national traditions concerning the role of civil society; and the economic situation. Social contexts thus shape patterns of drug use and harm, as well as its reduction, including the role of user involvement and user organising. As Friedman has commented, 'the structures of drug scenes affect what users' groups can do and how they can function' (Friedman, 1996, p. 212).

Harm reduction is grounded within a public health model, which primarily aims to improve the health and well-being of drug users alongside reducing community and societal level harms (Newcombe, 1992). As such, a desire to make the services user-friendly (i.e. providing services that welcome and include drug users) and involving drug users is evident within formal definitions of harm reduction (Hunt et al., 2003) as well as within harm reduction practice. Yet the way that harm reduction is understood and translated into practice is variable, and this is reflected within drug user involvement and organising.

The geographical focus of this chapter is Europe. Nevertheless, some of the more relevant features of the international context are described. The main goal of the chapter is to describe and explain drug users' contributions to harm reduction, alongside the contrasting methods that comprise user involvement and organising. The constraints of a single, short chapter mean it is impossible to provide a comprehensive history of the drug user movement's contribution to harm reduction. Likewise, it is not feasible to provide a detailed, country-by-country account of all user involvement and organising. Some important features of this history are, nevertheless, included.

Within the drug user movement, there is ongoing debate about the language that should be used to refer to its participants. For example, some people readily describe themselves as 'addicts' or 'patients', whereas others resist such terms because of their implications regarding the legitimacy of medical power to shape their drug-using choices and the applicability of a disease model. Questions also arise as to who is a drug user and the role of non-drug-using supporters of drug user activists (Balian and White, 1998). While acknowledging the disputes surrounding these terms, we will largely use the terms 'user' or 'drug user', although even these terms are not without their critics.

History

The AIDS pandemic has clearly been a critical factor in the development of both the harm reduction movement and drug user organising (Crofts and Herkt, 1995; Zibbell, 2004). However, it is important to note that drug user activism does not relate purely to injecting, and it pre-dates the AIDS era. Theo van Dam credits Nico Adriaans as the founder and chairman of the first advocacy/activist group Rotterdam Junkie Union (RJB) in the Netherlands in 1977 (van Dam, 2008, p. 58). Around this time, van Dam and Daan van der Gouwe also started Landelijk Steunpunt Druggebruikers (LSD) to try to get the Dutch government to support users and user groups, reduce stigma and shape opinion around legalisation (Jezek, 2000; Tops, 2006; Museummouse, 2008). Initially, harm reduction was an offshoot of the drug users' movement, notably Dutch activists who established the world's first needle exchange programme, set up by the MDHG Belangenvereniging Druggebruikers (Interest Association for Drug Users) in 1984 (Tops, 2006).

Montañés Sánchez and Oomen define drug users' organisations as 'Organisations of users of prohibited drugs or organisations in which these people play an important role', and identify three types of organisations according to the profile of the users and the scene in which they use drugs: cannabis users; party drug users; and users of street drugs such as opiates and cocaine (Montañés Sánchez and Oomen, 2009, p. 213). Although our emphasis here is on user organising within the third group, we also include examples relating to cannabis users and 'party drugs'.

Drug user organising in Europe

Although there are publications that describe aspects of European drug users' activism, such as that of the Correlation Network (Bröring and Schatz 2008), accurately mapping the extent of drug users' organisations and their work is problematic. No survey has yet been undertaken across the whole of Europe using a consistent methodology. Any survey is also complicated because: activities are not necessarily publicly or well documented; some organisations have a short lifespan; and, stigma and the oppression of drug users mean that there are good reasons for organisations to avoid being too visible (Friedman, 1998). In addition, the work of some drug users is sometimes obscured, such as when drug user identities are not declared within services (Robbins, 2004). At the time of writing, the International Harm Reduction Association (IHRA) and the International Network of People who Use Drugs (INPUD) are developing a report describing the 'global state of drug user activism'. In time, this should provide a useful addition to what is currently known about the extent of drug user organisations.

Dolf Tops estimates that, at any one time, there are between 15 and 30 drug users' organisations in the Netherlands (Tops, 2006, p. 65). By 1994, such organisations existed in at least 11 European countries (Germany, the Netherlands, the United Kingdom, Norway, Denmark, Slovenia, France, Belgium, Italy, Lithuania and Spain) (Jürgens, 2008, p. 15).

In the Nordic countries, the first organisations for active drug users were formed during the 1990s in Denmark and Norway, and in Sweden in the early 2000s. In Finland, the first user-driven organisation was established in 2004. These drug user organisations were founded by heroin users, they are run by heroin users and users in maintenance treatment, and they also cater for active drug users, mainly heroin users (Anker et al., 2008, p. 18).

In France and Spain the first drug users' organisations started in the 1990s. Auto-support parmi les Usagers de Drogues (ASUD) was created in France in 1992 (Jürgens, 2008, p. 24). In 1996, the Spanish National Coordination for the Normalisation of Cannabis was born, largely comprising associations of cannabis users (Barriuso, 2003, p. 103); this developed into the Spanish Federation of Cannabis Associations (FAC, in Spanish) (Barriuso, 2007), and in 2003 the first national network of injecting drug users' organisations was created in Spain — the Spanish Nationwide Network of People Affected by Drugs and HIV (FAUDAS) (Pretel, 2007).

During 2003/4 the Central and Eastern European Harm Reduction Network (CEEHRN) assessed the needs of drug users' organisations across Central and Eastern Europe and Central Asia. Respondents came from 16 countries: Armenia, Belarus, Bulgaria, Croatia, Estonia, Georgia, Kazakhstan, Kyrgyzstan, Latvia, Lithuania, former Yugoslav Republic of Macedonia, Moldova, Poland, Romania, Russia, and Ukraine. They identified 41 organisations, of which 15 were for drug users in general, 19 were for people living with HIV/AIDS (PLWHA), and six were for HIV positive drug users (CEEHRN, 2004; Canadian HIV/AIDS Legal Network, 2008).

Contribution of international networks to promoting user involvement

Developments in Europe need to be understood in the context of global networks. These have been important for enabling drug users to share ideas, knowledge and skills internationally — both into and out of Europe — and to provide structures within which drug users have begun to work internationally to identify and address common concerns.

The IHRA is a global organisation that promotes harm reduction. It seeks to involve drug users in its meetings and processes and has provided opportunities for drug users to network internationally, which has facilitated the development of international drug user networks.

The International Drug Users Network (IDUN) was initiated in 1992 at IHRA's Melbourne conference and was, arguably, the first network of its kind. Representatives from Germany, the Netherlands and the United Kingdom were among the seven countries represented at the inaugural meeting (Byrne, 2000). IDUN aimed to support injecting drug users to exchange ideas, develop drug user groups, and set up needle exchanges. However, a lack of funding and competing national and local demands for members' time meant that the network proved hard to sustain.

The Internet has enabled an electronic network for international drug user organising to be created, and after the IHRA conference in Geneva in 1998 a network of activists began an international discussion list hosted by the American Drug Policy Foundation, called Drug Policy Foundation — Users (DPFU) (Efthimiou-Mordaunt, 2005). This functions as a loose network of activists and facilitates ongoing discussion between drug users internationally.

In 2005, frustration at the poor facilities for drug users at IHRA's Belfast conference was a catalyst for an invigorated international network and led to the inception of INPUD. This formed around a statement that was endorsed at IHRA's 2006 conference — 'The Vancouver declaration' (INPUD, 2006). Although this was the product of many activists' efforts, the initial process of transforming INPUD into a legal entity was undertaken by a working group including representatives from Asia, Europe, Latin America, North America and Oceania. This was initially facilitated by Grant McNally (United Kingdom) with technical assistance from Stijn Goossens (Belgium), who subsequently became INPUD's director. Financial support was provided from the United Kingdom's Department for International Development (DfID) through IHRA. INPUD's early phase was marked by problems concerning who was/was not a member and associated constitutional problems. A subsequent crisis meeting was held at IHRA's Barcelona conference in 2008, which led to a successful re-foundation General Meeting held in Copenhagen at the end of October 2008, where a Consensus Statement and a clearer infrastructure were both agreed. Since then, a representative from INPUD was invited to give a formal address as part of the United Kingdom delegation to the United Nations' Commission on Narcotic Drugs (CND) in April 2009 and several other members attended as part of various NGO delegations.

International drug user activists, Vienna 2009

The networks and structures described so far are global and have clear, historical connections to the harm reduction movement and some emphasis on injecting drug use. By contrast, the ENCOD (¹) (the European Coalition for Just and Effective Drug Policies) is a European network of 175 organisations and citizens affected by current drug policies, which also incorporates members with a more diverse range of concerns including all kinds of prohibited drugs. Created in 1994 by a group of European NGOs to work on drugs and development issues, it has become a drug policy reform network whose membership includes: drug users' organisations; harm reduction organisations; research groups; advocacy groups; and, individual members. Since its creation, ENCOD has advocated for drug policy changes at the European and UN level and for the participation of organisations and people affected by drugs/drug policies within the UN, the European Union and each country's government (ENCOD, 2006).

In 1998, a corresponding International Coalition of NGOs for Just and Effective Drug Policies (ICN) was founded by more than 200 organisations based on a 'Manifesto for just and effective drug policies', presented at that year's UN General Assembly Special Session on Drugs. Although less active than its European section (ENCOD), it appears to be the only formal international body where producers' and users' organisations can work together and pursue, among other things, the 'non-prosecution of drugs consumption while looking for means of regulation which are socially and culturally acceptable to those local populations involved, and the implementation of broad measures, including harm reduction, to prevent and treat the problematic consumption of drugs' (ICN, 1998). In 2004, ENCOD's General Assembly decided to adopt the title of the Manifesto in ENCOD's name, and signing it is one of the conditions of becoming a member.

(¹)   The acronym ENCOD stood initially for European NGO Council on Drugs.

In 2005, the network Correlation: European Network Social Inclusion and Health was initiated to address health inequalities among marginalised groups. It has an extensive number of partners and receives financial support from the European Commission and the Dutch Ministry of Health. Within their work, HIV and Hepatitis C are specific concerns; drug users are one of their priorities and harm reduction and peer support are among the areas where they aim to promote effective practice. Their website provides extensive access to publications and other resources relevant to user involvement and organising (Correlation, 2009).

Forms of drug user involvement and organising

Actively involving people in decisions about their personal treatment and service provision is probably the most basic way by which user involvement can be said to take place. The literature shows that 'user involvement' is sometimes used to refer to the extent to which someone is involved in determining their own treatment or care from a service (Fischer and Jenkins, 2007). There are also other relatively passive ways of 'involving' drug users, such as the use of suggestion boxes or asking people to rate their satisfaction with the service. Whatever the merits of those activities, the focus of this chapter is on more active forms of drug user involvement and organisation within harm reduction. At the outset, we draw a distinction between involvement and organising.

User involvement

Some groups are keen to involve drug users within the systems and structures that affect their lives. In practice, involvement typically means giving a degree of power to drug users in ways that are managed and circumscribed, for example some form of consultation with individuals or groups who are deemed to represent the drug using population. Including service users within staff recruitment would be an example of user involvement that can directly benefit both the drug user and the organisation (Foster et al., 2007). Organisations in the drugs field often attempt to motivate their service users to set up user groups — a process that the Australian drug user activist Jude Byrne has termed 'contrived spontaneity' (Byrne, 2000). Results seem highly variable; many fail or flounder, others thrive and may occasionally lay foundations for more autonomous organisations to develop.

User organising

Organising implies more autonomous organisation by drug users to work across self-determined agendas affecting their interests. It is more directly linked to the 'empowerment' of the affected population. The term 'user-led' denotes this principle, yet allows a role for professionals too. In Canada, the term 'user-driven' is used (personal correspondence, Walter Cavalieri, 2009). Bröring and Schatz use the term 'self-organisations of drug users' (Bröring and Schatz, 2008). Again, this suggests the central importance of independence and autonomy. For brevity, we will use the term 'user-led' to refer to organisations of this type.

User-led organisations often differ from treatment or care services, within which involvement is encouraged. Although interests frequently coincide regarding threats to health, user-led organisations may engage more actively with wider issues such as discrimination regarding their civil rights and the impact of legislation on their personal consumption choices. Methods may also differ; groups with more independence may be more prepared to use direct action to highlight an issue or effect change (Kerr et al., 2006).

In practice, these categories are often blurred. A drug user group that has been nurtured within a service as part of a process of involvement might reconstitute itself or progressively pursue a more independent, user-led agenda. Nevertheless, the distinction between systems that seek to consult or involve drug users in services, and those where power is asserted more directly in accordance with the concerns of drug users is an important one.

The 'JES network' — an example of user involvement in Germany (*Dirk Schäffer*)

Since its establishment in 1989, the JES network (Junkies, Ehemalige, Substituierte — Junkies, ex-users, substitution clients) users have been involved in its harm reduction initiatives at different levels.

An interesting and effective collaboration has existed for the past ten years between the 'AIDS Hilfe' NGO in Oldenburg and the local JES group, whose members provide safer use and safer sex education to prison inmates.

In some cities, such as Cologne, Bonn, Osnabrück, Braunschweig and Stuttgart, JES groups have become an integral part of the local network of drugs services and carry out important tasks, such as needle and syringe exchange.

The project 'JES-Seminars' is characterised by combining knowledge from self-help and acquired expertise. To promote the professionalism of activists in JES groups, the network conducts self-organised training sessions for users, in order to increase and expand the competencies of drug using people.

An impressive form of collaboration and cooperation between professional drugs service providers and user groups is in the preparation and implementation of a 'remembrance day' for deceased drug users, which has been held for over 10 years on 21 July in more than 40 cities in Germany. The event represents a great opportunity for users to discuss among themselves and with other citizens their vision for a progressive and liberal drug policy.

Of course, cooperation with the local drug services network is not always without problems. The role of JES as a component and at the same time critical counterpart of the drug system sometimes challenges the interests of aid agencies. However, in many cities successful collaboration between JES groups and the professional drugs help system has grown through mastering this challenge.

The particular strength of the JES self-help network lies in a specific approach to the problems of drug users, which has developed from personal experience, is orientated towards empowerment and aims at improving the skills of those seeking help. By developing and strengthening informal networks, new and qualitatively different resources and possibilities — beyond those accessible through the professional help system — can be opened up.

JES sees its offers of help and support, therefore, as a supplement to professional assistance and hence as increasing the effectiveness of such services. In this sense, JES offers of assistance are complementary rather than competing with the professional system of assistance.

Further reading: Schäffer and Hentschel (2004).

Aims and methods of intervention

In summarising the aims of user involvement and organising, several complications arise. Groups sometimes comprise loose associations, rather than being legally constituted organisations with a written statement of their aims. In some cases, aims also overlap or interact; for example, an aim of reducing stigma may affect an aim to improve treatment, or vice versa. This makes the production of any definitive list of aims problematic.

Aims relating to harm reduction that are readily identifiable within user involvement and organising include: responding to public health threats; improving the accessibility and quality of drug services; improving the accessibility and quality of other services to drug users; shaping and reforming drug policy; reducing stigma and increasing public understanding; improving the quality of life for drug users, their families and local communities; knowledge production; and drug law reform.

A recent typology of the methods used to achieve such aims derives from the categorisation of activities reported from an online, international survey of drug users' organisations, conducted in 2007 by the International Network of People Who Use Drugs (INPUD) in cooperation with the European Correlation Network (Goossens, 2008). Based on a sample of 38 organisations from 21 countries, Goossens grouped the activities into eleven major categories:

1. Advocacy and health/drug policymaking.
2. Peer support for people living with HIV/AIDS (PLWHA).
3. Peer support for drug users.
4. HIV and other blood-borne disease (BBD) education and prevention.
5. Issue/publish electronic and printed magazines and newsletters.
6. Producing other types of informational material.
7. Organise, conduct, moderate training, workshops, seminars, peer meetings.
8. Educational and peer support work in the party scene.
9. Run accommodation projects.
10. Drop-in centres with various services.
11. Raise public awareness about the main problems in the drug using community.

As with the classification of aims, some of these categories could easily be merged or subdivided, while others might be added. The review undertaken for this chapter suggests that additional categories of 'research' and 'user-driven market interventions' might also be added.

With the same reservations that apply to classifying aims, this list of methods is best viewed as provisional. It nevertheless provides a framework for some illustrative examples from the work of different organisations and activists across Europe. The criteria used to select the examples we provide included: geographical diversity;

innovative or leading practice; high quality; impact; and, inevitably, our greater personal knowledge of some examples.

Advocacy and health/drug policymaking

At the European level, ENCOD is the network with the longest experience of participating in consultation and dialogue, including: the Civil Society Forum on Drugs; conferences of the European Commission and its sections; hearings and conferences with the European Parliament; and submitting proposals to the European Commission (ENCOD, 2006). In 2007 INPUD also began to participate actively in the Civil Society Forum on Drugs, which was made possible through the allocation of seats for drug user representatives by IHRA and the Central and Eastern European Harm Reduction Network (CEEHRN). These are the only two participating organisations with drug users as open members.

An ENCOD study of drug users' organisations and drug policy dialogue found that most organisations had experience of dialogue and consultation with local and national authorities. These included one-off or time-limited formal meetings and, in some cases, more structured, ongoing participation (Montañés Sánchez and Oomen, 2009).

In Russia, where the context of drug user activism includes some of Europe's harshest policies and laws, drug users' advocacy contributed to the amendment of more than 200 articles of the Penal Code that had effects such as: decriminalising some possession offences; distinguishing manufacture for personal use and commercial distribution (unlike Western Europe, home production is common among drug users in Russia); and, abolished compulsory detention and treatment for the treatment of alcoholism and drug addiction (Canadian HIV/AIDS Legal Network, 2008).

The Alliance (originally the Methadone Alliance) is a user-led organisation in the United Kingdom, founded in 1998 by Bill Nelles and other supportive professionals. The Alliance provides advocacy for people receiving drug treatment with an aim to improve the quality and availability of treatment in the United Kingdom. It has trained advocates across most of England who mediate between services and drug users. The Alliance also trains other advocates and has contributed extensively to conferences, national consultations, guideline and policy development and other activities, such as steering groups for research projects.

Aupa'm (Spain) is an informal group of active/ex-drug users and professionals who meet at a weekly assembly to plan work focusing on increasing injecting drug users' inclusion as citizens in their community. It has an allied, NGO partner, Asaupam, whose members also includes active/ex-users and which manages the agreed projects. Asaupam has participated in the design and implementation of local community programmes in two cities of Catalonia, and manages and coordinates the local plans on drugs (including harm reduction, prevention and socio-labour incorporation) in three cities. Asaupam is one of many members of FAUDAS, a state federation of people affected by drugs or HIV/AIDS (personal communication, Carmen Romera and Xavier Pretel, 2009; FAUDAS, 2003).

Peer support for people living with HIV/AIDS

In Ukraine, the All Ukrainian Network of People Living with HIV is an umbrella organisation for eight Ukraine-based organisations with drug user members, within which peer support is one important activity (CEEHRN, 2004). It is also illustrative of the way organisations often pursue a range of aims using different methods, as they have also: made prominent national and international contributions to combating stigma and discrimination; campaigned for more humane and effective HIV/AIDS policies/treatment; and been influential in campaigns to pilot methadone and buprenorphine programmes and their subsequent expansion (Canadian HIV/AIDS Legal Network, 2008). In these respects they have also contributed to the areas of health/drug policymaking, discussed earlier, and to raising public awareness (discussed below).

Peer support for drug users

Peer support can be interpreted in numerous ways. Local support groups for specific concerns other than HIV, such as hepatitis C, are now common, as are Internet-based support groups. The impact of peer-driven interventions and peer-based groups has been noted with reference to Europe and Australia (Crofts and Herkt, 1995; Grund and de Bruin, 2007).

Within residential rehabilitation programmes that typically operate on some form of 'therapeutic community' model there is a tradition of involving ex-users to deliver programmes because they can sometimes relate to drug users in a way that professional staff cannot, and their presence demonstrates that a drug-free life can be achieved (Mold and Berridge, 2008).

In Italy, Pazienti Impazienti Cannabis (PIC — Cannabis Impatient Patients) provides a contrasting example (Barriuso, 2001). Starting in 2001, as a group for mutual self-help, its members include people who experience legal or economic problems associated with their use of cannabis as a medicine. Beyond providing mutual self-help its aims are to claim the rights of patients, and to promote cannabis as part of the botanical heritage of mankind along with other prohibited plants. As part of its pursuit of practical solutions for access to cannabis as medicine, they use methods including information provision and advocacy. Their work has included the clarification of procedures which patients have to follow regarding the importation of medicinal cannabis and cannabis-derived medicines (²), such as those produced by the Dutch Health Ministry, and their provision through pharmacies, subject to medical prescription. Under specific circumstances this is paid for by the local health system (Personal communication, Alessandra Viazzi, 2009).

HIV and other blood-borne diseases (BBD) education and prevention

According to Tops (Tops, 2006), the world's first needle exchange programme was started in Amsterdam in 1984 by the MDHG Belangenvereniging Druggebruikers (Interest Association

(²) The legal framework is Article 72 of DPR 309/90, Decree of the Ministry of Health 11/2/1997, Modalita' di importazione di specialita' medicinali registrate all'estero, (G.U. Serie Generale n. 72 del 27 marzo 1997), http://www.normativasanitaria.it/jsp/dettaglio.jsp?attoCompleto=si&id=20747 and D.Lgs 24 April 2006 n 72 paragraph 6.

for Drug Users). Many users' organisations across Europe now distribute syringes, other paraphernalia for sterile injecting, and condoms. These include most of the associations involved in the Spanish federation FAUDAS, some Akzept members in Germany, the Danish Drug User Union (BrugerForeningen or BF), and Blue Point in Budapest. Details vary considerably in the specific roles, extent and formality of these arrangements and whether organisations receive payment.

Issue/publish electronic and printed magazines and newsletters

Drug users' organisations produce publications in print and, increasingly, on the Internet. There are numerous examples, some very local and others that address national and international issues. Production standards, editorial quality, style and tone also vary considerably. Whereas some have a more mainstream harm reduction emphasis, focusing on risks, harms and their avoidance, others are more overtly politicised and celebrate positive features of a drug-using lifestyle. At IHRA's conference in 2008, a new international network was announced that aims to support drug user organisations with their own publishing projects — the Drum Alliance (IHRA, 2008).

Publications often operate on multiple levels: support; information provision; initiating or publicising campaigns to change policy, etc. In France, ASUD, a national drug users' organisation that has existed for 15 years, has published 39 editions of its magazine at the time of writing (Olivet, 2009). The magazine has a distinctly political edge, focusing on the marginalisation, discrimination and lack of rights faced by the majority of French drug users. ASUD has branches in most major French cities and regularly participates in or organises forms of direct action, such as the recent construction of a symbolic safe consumption room in its Paris office.

In England, *Black Poppy* (O'Mara, 2008) is a widely distributed 'drug users' health and lifestyle' magazine, founded and edited by Erin O'Mara. It includes health and harm reduction information alongside articles on cultural and historical aspects of drug use, user activism, personal stories and information about services. Individuals and many treatment agencies subscribe to the magazine and distribute it among their service users. Its prominence has also enabled its editor to present drug users' perspectives at parliamentary advisory committees and national radio, television and the press.

Producing other types of informational materials

Beyond harm reduction's early focus on HIV prevention among IDUs, users' organisations have produced a wide variety of information on: the effects, risks and reduction of harms from specific drugs; the prevention and management of specific hazards, such as overdose or hepatitis C; sexual risks and protection strategies for drug users in general, commercial sex workers or targeting gay drug users; legal rights if arrested; gaining access to welfare benefits; and the presence of contaminated batches of drugs. In addition to leaflets or posters, these are disseminated in a range of ways that overlap with the other activities we describe elsewhere.

Organising, conducting and moderating training, workshops and peer meetings

Activities in this area span highly structured training provision through to informal education within peer meetings. Training was one of the main activities reported among the 16 countries surveyed by the Central and East European Harm Reduction Network in 2004 (CEEHRN, 2004), and training, workshops, seminars and peer meetings with an educational component of some sort are an almost universal feature of groups' activity. Content is diverse, reflecting people's needs and concerns, such as: health, harm reduction and treatment information; explanation and skills development to increases users' capacity to influence local and national policy processes; and topics such as fund-raising and organisational management.

The Spanish Nationwide Network of People Affected by Drugs and HIV (FAUDAS) illustrates this work. Periodical seminars and formative courses for and, in some cases, by its member associations address topics such as computer skills, communication skills, fundraising, harm reduction or the development of harm reduction materials by and for users. There is also a permanent working group on gender and drugs focusing on the situation of female drug users and most member organisations implement local training for drug users on assorted harm reduction topics (Pretel, 2004).

Educational and peer support work in the party scene

The impact of ecstasy, alongside the wide range of other legal and illegal drugs used by party-goers, has triggered numerous peer-based initiatives across Europe that focus on the constantly evolving, free-party, festival and club-based electronic music scenes. Harm reduction activities include: creating and distributing information; providing or assisting in chill out areas; conducting drug checking; and, crisis intervention and support. A useful guide to peer-based work in this area comes from the Basics Network, which provides an online guide to organisations across Europe and an extensive downloadable library of information. At the time of writing, they list 22 organisations from 10 countries across Europe (BASICS, 2009).

Running accommodation projects

In Spain, Anydes and Comité Ciudadano Antisida de Ourense, both members of the Spanish Nationwide Network of People Affected by Drugs and HIV (FAUDAS), run what have been termed 'casa de acogida' (shelters), which are places where people who use drugs can stay for a certain time and get access to services.

Drop-in centres with various services

Drug users' organisations have been extensively involved in initiating, developing and delivering interventions at many levels. Goossens' (2008) category of 'drop-in centres with various services' reflects some of these but does not fully indicate the breadth of work that is undertaken.

Naloxone distribution

In Catalonia (Spain), Asaupam provide training courses for drug users on how to use naloxone to as part of efforts to reduce overdose deaths. As part of this, they distribute naloxone to the users participating in the training courses.

Methadone distribution

'Guerrilla' methadone distribution by users' organisations can be traced back to work in the 1980s by the Rotterdam Junkiebond, which led to improved formal methadone maintenance (Grund, n.d.). Today, various users' organisations within FAUDAS participate in the distribution of methadone at the local level (La Calle, Comité antisida de Ourense). This is done informally as, legally, the formal dispensing of methadone is only possible through health centres. In practice, one person from the association collects the drug in the health centre, and takes responsibility for dispensing it to the registered clients in their own premises.

Drug consumption rooms

In the role of 'experience experts', members of drug users' organisations have contributed to policies that underpin 'using rooms' (safer injecting rooms/drug consumption rooms) in the Netherlands (Tops, 2006). Elsewhere, users' groups have sometimes implemented clandestine and less formal users' rooms to provide their community with a more hygienic and safer place.

Drug dealing controls on quality and value for money

In the Netherlands, a users' group identified an inconsistency between providing hygienic equipment and space to users when the quality and purity of the substance they are using varied, with a potential for harm to arise. This led to the introduction of an 'in-house dealer' initiative to guarantee the availability and quality of the drug sold and ensure fair prices (Tops, 2006). In the United Kingdom, a peer-led group — The Crack Squad — introduced a 'dealer's charter' with similar aims (Carty, 2002).

Community reintegration

In Spain, almost all users' organisations have programmes assisting drug users in treatment programmes to access the labour market. One example is Engánchate al trabajo (Get hooked by work), run by two FAUDAS member organisations (Asaupam and Arpa ONG). Active drug users engage in community work such as repairing and maintaining urban spaces or taking care of public gardens. The programme's goals are to provide work experience, improve active users' quality of life and promote more responsible use of drugs. Participants set their own rules to organise and fulfil the work and solve the conflicts that can arise during the implementation. The programme is now in the process of external evaluation and a pilot programme will be implemented in other Spanish cities.

Raising public awareness about the main problems in the drug using community

Some of the earliest work in the Netherlands during the late 1970s was concerned with raising public awareness of problems experienced by drug users (Jezek, 2000), and from 1982 the Rotterdam Junkiebond presented an hour-long radio show on a popular national radio station every Friday evening (Grund, n.d.). We noted above the media work of Erin O'Mara (O'Mara, 2008), and in 2001 Mat Southwell produced a television programme 'Chemical Britannia', which was broadcast nationally by the BBC (Browne, 2001).

Such examples are numerous, but one further example seems especially worthy of mention. In a growing number of countries, users' groups hold an annual remembrance or memorial day for deceased drug users on 21 July (see also box on p. 339). This originated in Germany more than ten years ago when the mother of a heroin user who had recently died wanted to draw attention to the poor condition in which many drug users live. In Copenhagen, Denmark a similar event has been held for the last seven years and the United Kingdom also followed suit in 2008. In Australia, similar events are organised to coincide with 'International Drug Users' Day' on 1 November.

Often, remembrance events draw attention to issues that contribute to 'drug-related deaths', such as deficiencies in service provision, but also the impacts of drug prohibition. They also provide an opportunity for drug users to mark the deaths of friends; this is especially important as so often drug users die alone and their drug using friends are excluded from family burial services. In this respect the day can serve to raise the consciousness of the drug using community as a group. As an example, in Copenhagen, after many years of negotiations, the city council gave the Danish Drug Users' Union (BrugerForeningen) permission to install a permanent stone inscribed with the words 'In memory of dead drug users' beside a paradise apple tree. This site acts as a permanent place for users to remember lost friends. As drug policies have sometimes been described as a 'war on drugs', many in the user community regard these memorials as remembering those who have died as the unintended casualties of policies that have exacerbated rather than reduced harm.

User-driven market interventions

The Italian group PIC has already been discussed as a form of peer support for medical cannabis users, addressing availability and distribution. Initiatives to influence quality and value for money of drug purchases through dealers have also been mentioned. Since 2003, ENCOD and the Spanish Federation of Cannabis Associations (FAC) have proposed a much wider user-driven, market-level approach: a model for the production and distribution of cannabis for adults' personal use (ENCOD, 2007; Barriuso, 2007). ENCOD uses the Cannabis Social Club (CSC) model within the wider campaign 'Freedom to Farm', which seeks the decriminalisation of the three forbidden plants (opium poppy, coca leaves and cannabis). Originating in Spain, CSCs are non-profit associations whose members are adult cannabis users, most of whom use it recreationally but with others who do so medicinally. People who enter the club have to fulfil certain conditions in order to avoid the risk of selling or passing on to third persons or to minors. The CSC members organise a professional, collective cultivation of limited quantities of cannabis to cover the personal needs of their club members and the system is regulated by security and quality checks (Barriuso, 2003, 2005a, 2005b, 2007).

The first CSC started in Barcelona, Spain in 2001 (Barriuso, 2005a, p. 163), followed by others in Catalonia and Basque Country. Further clubs now operate in Spain and another in Belgium. According to Martin Barriuso, president of FAC, this system contributes to the reduction of both risk and harm, since:

> the uncertainty is often about the quality and possible adulteration of the product purchased on the black market. In a production system in closed circuit, the partner/s know the quality of what they consume, to which variety it belongs, how it has been cultivated, and so on. Furthermore, the association can serve as a point of advice and exchange of information, helping to create a new culture of use, which … is essential for true normalization.

> (Barriuso, 2005a, p. 165)

He also claims that this system prevents minors from accessing the substance and avoids the possibility of so-called 'cannabis tourism' (personal communication, 2009).

Research

Knowledge production, and its use, is often an explicit or implied aim of drug users' organisations. This production of knowledge on and by drug users reflects the approach taken by many other groups seeking civil liberties and human rights historically; notably, women's studies, black history, and queer studies. Much research is conducted on drug users. An increasing amount takes place with drug users. Research by drug users, who shape or decide the questions and methods used and are involved at every stage, is the most empowered position possible. Internationally, work by the Australian Injecting and Illicit Drug Users League (AIVL) has been at the forefront of discussions about the terms on which drug users are involved in research and their guidance is a valuable point of reference (AIVL, 2003).

ENCOD has made submissions and undertaken surveys that support drug users' roles, as members of civil society, to be participants in all aspects of policymaking that affects their lives — including research. The report *Green Pepper* was submitted as a response to the European Commission Green Paper on the Role of Civil Society in Drugs Policy in the European Union, with an historical analysis of the participation of drug users and their role in the drug policy debate at the European Union level (ENCOD, 2006). A recent survey on the participation of drug user organisations in the design of drug policies at local and European Level recommended ways to improve drugs users' participation and a proposal on how to structure the Civil Society Forum on Drugs of the European Commission (Montañés Sánchez and Oomen, 2009).

In the United Kingdom, a number of user activists with academic and other backgrounds have either initiated or been invited to be directly involved in research including: the causes and definitions of drug related deaths; the Randomised Injectable Opiate Treatment Trial (RIOTT); factors that promote and hinder successful user involvement in drug misuse treatment services; and user involvement in efforts to improve the quality of drug misuse services. There is also a drug user-run research and training company that only employs ex- or current drug users to undertake research on, and of benefit to, the drug using community (led by Mat Southwell).

Discussion

Although drug user involvement and organising seems increasingly widespread, we have noted some of the obstacles facing attempts to document it. Stigma, and the consequences of the criminalisation of drug use means that many drug users have reason to remain invisible (Robson and Bruce, 1997). The scarcity of resources to support activism itself means that archiving and preserving its history is often a subordinate concern, at best. Many key participants, such as Nico Adriaans, have died prematurely, taking personal knowledge of this history with them (Grund, n.d.). Nevertheless, one of the clearest messages is that drug users' organisations have multiple aims, and use many methods to engage with harm reduction; spanning mainstream public health work, through to efforts to amend drug control systems. Although there is ongoing debate about the place of drug law reform within harm reduction (see Reinarman, 2004), for many drug users' organisations drug prohibition is without doubt seen as a cause of drug-related harms. The pursuit of drug law reform with the aim of achieving some form of regulated drug market is therefore perceived as a legitimate harm reduction activity.

Besides bringing benefits, user involvement and organising are not without their challenges, including internal conflict (Kerr et al., 2006; Osborn and Small, 2006). Marginalised groups do not necessarily possess good knowledge of the way that systems they seek to influence work or the skills needed for establishing and operating their own organisations, especially early in the process. Expectations can also greatly exceed what is deliverable, although Crofts and Herkt suggest that these problems are no greater than those found within community development work with other disenfranchised groups (Crofts and Herkt, 1995).

Resources commonly fall short of needs, and in many countries funding for drug users' organising is not readily available. One indication of this comes from the CEEHRN needs assessment where drug user groups had noticeably less funding and had access to a smaller range of donors than people living with HIV/AIDS (CEEHRN, 2004).

The extent and nature of state support differs considerably across Europe. For example, England has seen a serious commitment to develop 'user involvement' through its National Treatment Agency (NTA). User involvement is expected at all levels within treatment systems and resources are provided to support it. Yet, this has produced tensions that have been noted elsewhere. For example, critics of the English system, such as the (now defunct) National Drug Users Development Agency (NDUDA), received little support. In just the same way, Crofts and Herkt have commented on the 'tension between the funding agencies (state and federal health departments) for AIDS prevention activities, and the community development agenda of the funded groups, which often includes criticism of the policies of the funding agencies, especially in relation to drug policy and enforcement' (Crofts and Herkt, 1995), and Byrne has referred to the problems that can follow groups that develop through 'contrived spontaneity' (Byrne, 2000).

Impacts

Setting aside any values-based arguments for thinking it right to properly include affected populations in the decisions and processes that shape their lives, policymakers or others may ask, what is the impact, outcome or benefit of involving drug users and their organisations in the reduction of drug-related harm? In an analysis of impacts within Europe, Grosso (Grosso, 2008) concludes that drug users' organisations have produced impacts through peer support in three areas:

- personal change, such as more prudent consumption and risk reduction;
- the social normalisation of drug use, by which they mean 'treating the phenomenon of drug use as any other socio-sanitary problem that society takes care of', and avoiding 'rigid and dichotomous interpretive categories that adopt binaries such as on/off, dependency/abstinence (where) drug use becomes identified totally with "hell" and abstinence with "salvation"', because 'scientific evidence has difficulty making headway with public opinion and consequently with the institutions that should support it and which instead remain paralysed by the generalized opinions of the people they represent'; and
- the modification of services, where drug users' organisations have 'managed to influence services and to make them — at least in part — closer to the needs of their clients, more receptive to their requirements and more contractual.'

The ENCOD survey on the participation of drug user organisations in the design of drug policies at local and European level also appraises the impacts of drug users' organisations on harm reduction as follows:

> Drug user organisations have contributed with methods to reduce harms and risks from their origin. Many of the programmes that are currently carried out by official state programmes (like drug testing, syringe exchange, opiate prescription, user rooms etc.), form part of claims that have surged from these organisations themselves, and in some cases, these programmes are being elaborated by drug user organisations, who have become more professional by converting themselves in service providers. This professionalization has helped to get rid of the stigma on drug users, demonstrating the fact that they can represent themselves.
>
> (Montañés Sánches and Oomen, 2009, p. 220)

In Canada, Thomas Kerr and his colleagues have described the development and impact of the Vancouver Area Network of Drug Users (VANDU), and concluded that:

> Through years of activism, advocacy, and public education, VANDU has repeatedly voiced the concerns of drugs users in public and political arenas. VANDU has also performed a critical public health function by providing care and support programmes that are responsive to immediate needs of their peers. This study indicates that greater efforts should be made to promote the formation of drug user organizations, and that health authorities and policy makers should explore novel methods for incorporating the activities of drug user organizations within existing public health, education, and policy making frameworks.
>
> (Kerr et al., 2006, p. 61)

In Australia, Crofts and Herkts' analysis of peer-based groups concluded that:

> IDUs have organized and, from that, they now successfully run a wide variety of programmes themselves. IDUs have had a real and often dominant influence on the development of policy in relation to harm reduction. User groups have run needle distribution and exchange programs that are among the best in the country; they have produced the most imaginative and appropriate educational material in this field; they have initiated and actively participated in research; they have provided structured access to informants for policy and program development; and have been active partners in this development. In general, this has been done with minimal funding and support, and often in an unsympathetic if not hostile environment. User groups have been agents of social change who have altered the landscape in relation to every aspect of our perception of injecting drug use in Australia.

(Crofts and Herkt, 1995, p. 614)

Finally, in the report *Nothing about us without us* (Canadian HIV/AIDS Legal Network, 2008), which focuses on the meaningful involvement of people who use illegal drugs in public health, the authors conclude:

> People living with HIV and people who use illegal drugs are central to the response to HIV/AIDS and HCV. There are ethical and human rights imperatives for involvement, but involvement is also required because it ensures a more effective public health response.

(Jürgens, 2008, p. 56)

Conclusion

Key messages

- The way that harm reduction is translated into practice is variable, and so is user involvement and user organising.
- User organising implies more autonomous organisation by drug users to work to self-determined agendas affecting their interests, whereas user involvement implies less autonomy.
- In Western Europe, the first drug user advocacy/activist group was the Rotterdam Junkie Union, founded in 1977 by Nico Adriaans.
- The aims and methods of user-led initiations are multiple and variable, and include: peer support; advocacy and lobbying for improved services and policies; provision of helping services; health promotion and user representation; and raising public awareness.
- User organising occurs in a climate of limited support and resources, yet has had a significant role in generating and sustaining harm reduction responses.
- Research and evaluation on the impacts of user involvement and organising is in its infancy, but is much needed, including through user-led research projects.

We have described the aims and methods evident within drug users' involvement and organising, and some evidence of its impact (see box on p. 339). For current and former drug users to make their full contribution to harm reduction an enabling environment is required, in which their capacity to contribute can develop. The challenges of achieving this in a context where having a drug user identity is, in effect, criminalised and certainly highly stigmatised, are hard to overstate. Nevertheless, there are two clear ways by which this can be directly helped.

First, any authority that is making decisions or shaping services that affect drug users' lives can introduce policies that promote or require the meaningful involvement of drug users at all relevant points, that is, from the very beginning of planning, through to monitoring and evaluation. This has implications at all levels of society, ranging from central government to local services. Most obviously, it relates to the planning and delivery of harm reduction and drug treatment services, but it also relates to the likes of research bodies, housing services, criminal justice services and so forth.

The second requirement is for the resources to support this and a corresponding readiness to alter systems in ways that enable drug users' participation. Becoming 'involved' often generates direct costs to the drug user, such as time and travel. It also implies the provision of the drug user's hard-won expertise. These costs should be fairly met. Likewise, systems need to be sensitive to ways they may need to adapt for this to occur successfully. At the same time, drug users need to recognise that accepting state or other official forms of funding/support may have a real impact on what they can or can't do, and the way that priorities for action may be affected.

In conclusion, we have tried to illustrate the need for a more nuanced appreciation of the contribution of drug user involvement and organising to harm reduction and its greater potential. In setting out many of its assorted aims and methods, we have also acknowledged that there are areas where consensus does not exist among drug users and within the harm reduction movement. Finally, we have highlighted ways that user involvement and organising can be nurtured, with an expectation that this will support wider efforts to reduce drug-related harms across Europe.

Acknowledgements

We would like to express our gratitude to all the people who have assisted us in different ways: Martín Barriuso (FAC, Spain), Jamie Bridge (IHRA, United Kingdom), Walter Cavalieri (Canada), Theo van Dam (Netherlands), Victor Feijoo (FAUDAS), Astrid Forschner (ENCOD/INPUD, Germany), Vito Georgievski (INPUD, Former Yugoslav Republic of Macedonia), Jean-Paul Grund (Netherlands), Joergen Kjaer (BFK, Denmark), Joaquín Laínez (FAUDAS, Spain), Willemijn Loss (MDHG, Netherlands), Joep Oomen (ENCOD), Xavier Pretel and Carmen Romera (FAUDAS, Spain), Jorge Roque (ENCOD, Portugal), Pepe Sánchez and Antonio Escobar (Federación ENLACE, Spain), Anya Sarang (Russia), Dirk Schäffer (JES, Germany), Iker Val (FAC, Spain) and Alessandra Viazzi (PIC, Italy). Any mistakes, omissions or errors are, nevertheless, entirely the responsibility of the authors.

References

AIVL (Australian Injecting and Illicit Drug Users League) (2003), *A national statement on ethical issues for research involving injecting/illicit drug users*, Australian Injecting and Illicit Drug Users League, Canberra.

Anker, J., Asmussen, V., Kouvonen, P. and Tops, D. (2008), 'Drug users and spaces for legitimate action', in Bröring, G. and Schatz, E. (eds), *Empowerment and self-organisations of drug users: experiences and lessons learnt*, Foundation Regenboog AMOC, Amsterdam.

Balian, R. and White, C. (1998), 'Defining the drug user', *International Journal of Drug Policy* 9, pp. 391–6.

Barriuso, M. (2001), 'La visión del movimiento asociativo cannábico', in Grup Igia (ed.), *Gestionando las drogas*, Publicaciones del Grup Igia, Barcelona, pp. 81–9.

Barriuso, M. (2003), 'La prohibición de drogas, el tabú moral a la desobediencia civil', in Arana, X., Husak, D. and Scheerer, S. (eds), *Globalización y drogas. Políticas sobre drogas, derechos humanos y reducción de riesgos*, Dykinson, Instituto Internacional de Sociología Jurídica de Oñati, Madrid, pp. 83–117.

Barriuso, M. (2005a) 'Propuesta de modelo legal para el cannabis en el Estado español', Eguzkilore. *Cuaderno del Instituto Vasco de Criminología* 19, pp. 151–68.

Barriuso, M. (2005b), 'Adiós al guetto: el discreto encanto de la normalidad', *Revista Española de drogodependencias* 30 (1–2), pp. 206–12.

Barriuso, M. (2007), 'Más allá de las excusas: hacia una regulación legal no prohibicionista para el cannabis', in Pantoja, L. (ed.), *Hablemos del cannabis. Avances en drogodependencias*, Universidad de Deusto, Bilbao, pp. 107–32.

BASICS (2009), 'Basics Network'. Available at http://www.basics-network.org/ (accessed 7 September 2009).

Bröring, G. and Schatz, E. (eds) (2008), *Empowerment and self-organisations of drug users: experiences and lessons learnt*, Foundation Regenboog AMOC, Amsterdam.

Browne, A. (2001), 'Heroin is safe and fun, says shock BBC show', *Guardian* 25 March. Available at http://www.guardian.co.uk/uk/2001/mar/25/drugsandalcohol.anthonybrowne (accessed 12 June 2009).

Byrne, J. (2000), 'Done to, done over, doing it for ourselves: the history of the drug users movement', *Black Poppy*. Available at http://www.blackpoppy.org.uk/blackpoppy/highlights_ourselves.htm (accessed 8 September 2009).

Canadian HIV/AIDS Legal Network, (2008), *'Nothing about us without us' — greater, meaningful involvement of people who use illegal drugs: a public health, ethical, and human rights imperative*, Eastern Europe and Central Asia Edition. Available at http://www.aidslaw.ca/publications/interfaces/downloadFile.php?ref=1351 (accessed 16 June 2009).

Carty, P. (2002), 'Caned and able', *Guardian*, 30 May 2002. Available at http://www.guardian.co.uk/lifeandstyle/2002/may/30/healthandwellbeing.health1 (accessed 12 June 2009).

CEEHRN (Central and Eastern European Harm Reduction Network) (2004), *Self-organization of drug users and people living with HIV/AIDS in Central and Eastern Europe and Central Asia: needs assessment report*, Central and Eastern European Harm Reduction Network, Vilnius.

Correlation (2009), 'Correlation: European network social inclusion and health'. Available at http://www.correlation-net.org (accessed 7 September 2009).

Crofts, N. and Herkt, D. (1995), 'A history of peer-based drug-user groups in Australia', *Journal of Drug Issues* 25, pp. 599–616.

Efthimiou-Mordaunt, A. (2005), 'Junkies in the house of the Lord', Masters Dissertation, Department of Social Policy and Planning, London School of Economics, London. Available at http://www.canadianharmreduction. com/readmore/Andrias+MSc+Dissertation.pdf (accessed 12 June 2009).

EMCDDA (2008), *Annual report 2008: the state of the drugs problem in Europe*, European Monitoring Centre for Drugs and Drug Addiction, Lisbon.

ENCOD (European Coalition for Just and Effective Drug Policies) (2006), *Green pepper: on the role of civil society in drug policy in the European Union*, European Commission, Antwerpen.

ENCOD (2007), *Cannabis social clubs*, Draft to the Project, ENCOD. Available at http://www.encod.org/info/ test.html (accessed 26 November 2009).

FAUDAS (2003) Website available at http://www.faudas.org (accessed 7 September 2009).

Fischer, J. and Jenkins, N. (2007), *Drug user involvement in treatment decisions*, Joseph Rowntree Foundation, York.

Foster, J., Tyrell, K., Cropper, V. and Hunt, N. (2007), 'Two case studies of user involvement in the recruitment of staff for drug services', *Drugs: Education, Prevention and Policy* 14, pp. 89–94.

Friedman, S. (1996), 'Theoretical bases for understanding drugs users' organizations', *International Journal of Drug Policy 7*, pp. 212–19.

Friedman, S. (1998), 'The political economy of drug-user scapegoating and the philosophy and politics of resistance', *Drugs: Education, Prevention, and Policy 5*, pp. 15–32.

Goossens, S. (2008), 'Drug user activism: an overview', in Bröring, G. and Schatz, E. (eds), *Empowerment and self-organisations of drug users: experiences and lessons learnt*, Foundation Regenboog AMOC, Amsterdam, pp. 117–24.

Grosso, L. (2008), 'Empowerment — models of good practice: heroin use and peer support. What lessons have been learnt?' in Bröring, G. and Schatz, E. (eds), *Empowerment and self-organisations of drug users: experiences and lessons learnt*, Foundation Regenboog AMOC, Amsterdam, pp. 41–55.

Grund, J. P. (n.d.), 'Letter for Nico'. Available at http://www.ibogaine.desk.nl/adriaans.html (accessed 30 May 2009).

Grund, J. P. and Bruin D. de (2007), *'Beyond HIV: the peer driven intervention and empowerment of vulnerable populations'*, Plenary presentation at Correlation Conference, Social Inclusion and Health – Crossing the Borders, Sofia, Bulgaria, 27–29 September.

Hunt, N., Ashton, M., Lenton, S., et al. (2003), 'A review of the evidence-base for harm reduction approaches to drug use', Forward Thinking on Drugs/Release, London. Available at http://www.ihra.net/Assets/23/1/ HIVTop50Documents11.pdf (accessed 12 June 2009).

ICN (1998), 'Manifesto for just and effective drug policies'. Available at http://www.encod.org/info/ MANIFESTO-FOR-JUST-AND-EFFECTIVE.html (accessed 13 January 2010).

IHRA (International Harm Reduction Association) (2008), '19th International Harm reduction Conference, Barcelona 2008. Daily update: 14th May 2008.' Available at http://www.ihra.net/Assets/134/1/2008_ DailyUpdate_Wednesday14thThursday15th.pdf (accessed 27 January 2010).

INPUD (International Network of People who Use Drugs) (2006) 'Why the world needs an international network of activists who use drugs', INPUD. Available at http://hardcoreharmreducer.be/VancouverDeclaration.html (accessed 27 January 2010).

Jezek, R. (2000), *Right to use: drug users and their representatives*, René de Milliano/LSD, Alkmaar.

Jürgens, R. (2008), 'Nothing about us without us' — greater, meaningful involvement of people who use illegal drugs: a public health, ethical, and human rights imperative, international edition, Canadian HIV/AIDS Legal Network, International HIV/AIDS Alliance, Open Society Institute, Toronto.

Kerr, T., Small, W., Peeace, W., et al. (2006), 'Harm reduction by a "user-run" organization: a case study of the Vancouver Area Network of Drug Users (VANDU)', International Journal of Drug Policy 17, pp. 61–9.

Mold, A. and Berridge, V. (2008), 'The rise of the user? Voluntary organizations, the state and illegal drugs in England since the 1960s', Drugs: Education, Prevention and Policy 15, 451–61.

Montañés Sánchez, V. and Oomen, J. (2009), Use of drugs and advocacy: a research into the participation of drug user organisations in the design of drug policies on a local and European level, Servicio Central de Publicaciones del Gobierno Vasco, Vitoria-Gasteiz.

Museummouse (2008), 'Harm reduction. Oh yea, it's history!', Cannabis Culture Forums. Available at http://forums.cannabisculture.com/forums/ubbthreads.php?ubb=showflat&Number=1436231 (accessed 12 June 2009).

Newcombe, R. (1992), 'The reduction of drug related harm: a conceptual framework for theory, practice and research', in O'Hare, P. (ed.), The reduction of drug related harm, Routledge, London.

O'Mara, E. (2008), Black Poppy. Available http://www.blackpoppy.org.uk/ (accessed 16 June 2009).

Olivet, F. (2009), ASUD website. Available at http://www.asud.org (accessed 16 June 2009).

Osborn, B. and Small, W. (2006), 'Speaking truth to power: the role of drug users in influencing municipal policy', International Journal of Drug Policy 17, pp. 70–2.

Pretel, X. (2004), 'FAUDAS, Federación Estatal de Asociaciones de Usuarios y grupos afines', XV Jornadas Andaluzas de Asociaciones de Drogodependencia y Sida. Federación Andaluza de Drogodependencias y Sida (ENLACE), Chiclana.

Pretel, X. (2007), 'FAUDAS: a process to develop formative, participation and advocacy skills in the community of people affected by drugs', Antiretroviral Treatment for Injecting Drug Users (ARV4IDUs) Seminar, Vilnius, Lithuania.

Reinarman, C. (2004), 'Public health and human rights: the virtues of ambiguity', International Journal of Drug Policy 15, 239–41.

Robbins, C. (2004), 'Secrets in the work place', MSc Dissertation, Imperial College, London.

Robson, P. and Bruce, M. (1997), 'A comparison of "visible" and "invisible" users of amphetamine, cocaine and heroin: two distinct populations?' Addiction 92 (12), pp. 1729–36.

Schäffer, D. and Hentschel, A. (2004), 'Förderung der Drogenselbsthilfe', in Klee, J. and Stöver, H. (eds), Drogen — HIV/AIDS — Hepatitis. Ein Handbuch, Deutsche AIDS-Hilfe, Berlin, pp. 40–52.

Tops, D. (2006), 'Stretching the limits of drug policies: an uneasy balancing act', in Anker, J., Asmussen, V., Kouvonen, P. and Tops , D. (eds), Drug users and spaces for legitimate action, Nordic Centre for Alcohol and Drug Research, Helsingfors.

van Dam, T. (2008), 'Users unite: a brief overview about the drug user movement', in Bröring, G. and Schatz E. (eds), Empowerment and self-organisations of drug users: experiences and lessons learnt, Foundation Regenboog AMOC, Amsterdam.

Zibbell, J. E. (2004), 'Can the lunatics actually take over the asylum? Reconfiguring subjectivity and neo-liberal governance in contemporary British drug treatment policy', International Journal of Drug Policy 15, pp. 56–65.

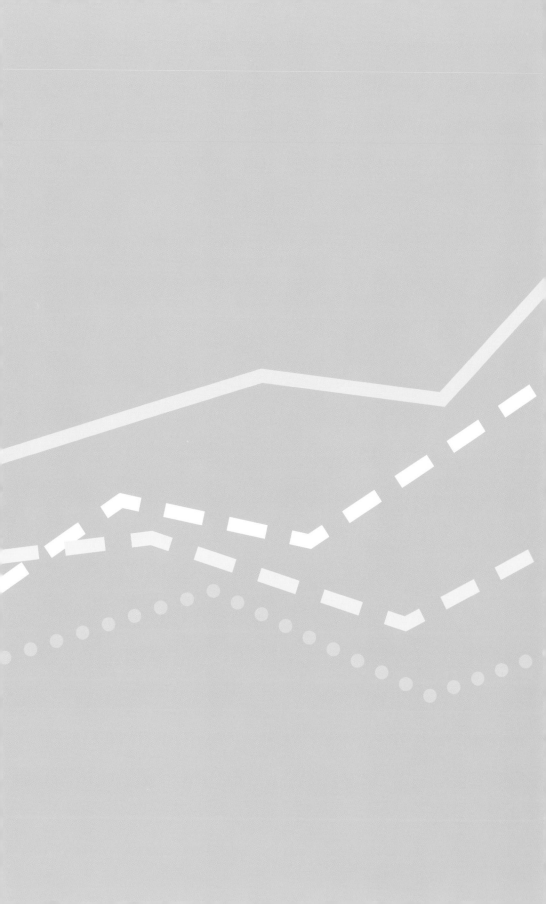

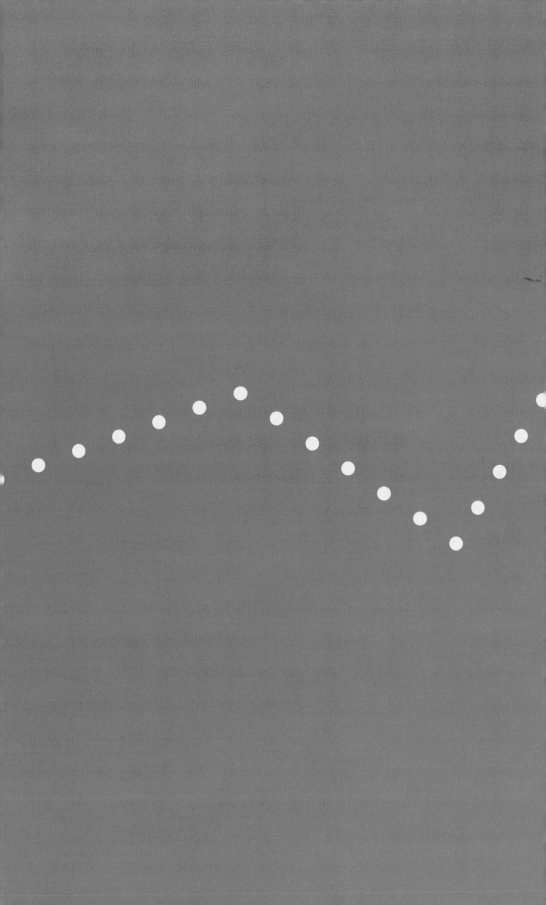

Chapter 13
Young people, recreational drug use and harm reduction

Adam Fletcher, Amador Calafat, Alessandro Pirona and Deborah Olszewski

Abstract

This chapter begins by reviewing the prevalence of recreational drug use and related adverse health outcomes among young people in European countries. It then employs a typological approach to review and discuss the current range of responses that aim to reduce the harms associated with young people's recreational drug use in Europe. These responses include: individually focused and group-based interventions (school-based drugs education and prevention, mass media campaigns, motivational interviewing, and youth development programmes) and 'settings-based approaches', which make changes to recreational settings, such as nightclubs, or institutional settings, such as schools, to address the social and environmental background of young people's drug use.

Keywords: young people, drug use, prevalence, harm, intervention, Europe.

Introduction

This chapter focuses primarily on young people's use of illegal drugs (rather than alcohol and tobacco use). However, the potential for harm is likely to be greatest when young people use both drugs and alcohol, and many of the interventions reviewed in this chapter are considered to be appropriate for reducing the harms associated with both drug and alcohol use. The chapter will begin by reviewing the prevalence of drug use among young people in Europe and the related adverse health and other harms. The appropriateness and likely effectiveness of different types of interventions that aim to reduce the harms associated with young people's recreational drug are then discussed. Harm reduction has traditionally focused on adult 'problem' drug users, particularly injecting drug users (see, for example, Ball, 2007, and Kimber et al., 2010), and neglected not only the harms associated with young people's recreational drug use but also how to reduce these harms.

This chapter considers young people's recreational drug use to be drug use that occurs for pleasure, typically with friends, in either formal recreational settings, such as nightclubs, and/ or informal settings, such as on the streets and in the home. This is thus a broader definition than the one applied in other EMCDDA publications, which often focus specifically on young people's drug use within a 'nightlife context' (e.g. EMCDDA, 2002). This chapter is primarily focused on young people aged 14–19, although some studies report on other age ranges (e.g. 14–24) and therefore at times it has been necessary to define 'young people' more broadly. Furthermore, data on prevalence and trends of drug use among young people often aim to provide an indication of overall levels of use and therefore do not always distinguish between recreational drug use and more problematic patterns of use.

Trends in young people's recreational drug use in Europe

The European School Survey Project on Alcohol and Other Drugs (ESPAD) and recent general population surveys have revealed lower prevalence of use of cannabis and other illicit drugs for European youth compared to youth in the United States (Hibell et al., 2004; Hibell et al., 2009; EMCDDA, 2009). However, these overall European-level data mask diversity within the EU in terms of young people's use of cannabis, 'club drugs', such as ecstasy and amphetamines, and cocaine.

Cannabis

The 2007 ESPAD data revealed that the highest lifetime prevalence of cannabis use among 15- to 16-year-old school students is in the Czech Republic (45 %), while Estonia, France, the Netherlands, Slovakia and the United Kingdom reported prevalence levels ranging from 26 % to 32 % (Hibell et al., 2009). Lifetime prevalence levels of cannabis use of between 13 % and 25 % are reported in 15 other countries. Less than 10 % of 15- to 16-year-old school students report cannabis use in Greece, Cyprus, Romania, Finland, Sweden and Norway.

Early onset of cannabis use has been associated with the development of more intensive and problematic forms of drug consumption later in life. In most of the 10 EU countries with relatively high prevalence of frequent use, between 5 % and 9 % of school students had initiated cannabis use at age 13 or younger. In addition, compared to the general population of students, cannabis users are more likely to use alcohol, tobacco and other illicit drugs (EMCDDA, 2009).

National survey data reported to the EMCDDA shows that in almost all EU countries cannabis use increased markedly during the 1990s, in particular among school students. By 2003, between 30–40 % of 15- to 34-year-olds reported 'lifetime use' of cannabis in seven countries, and more than 40 % of this age group reported ever having used cannabis in two other countries. However, data from the 2007 ESPAD surveys suggests that cannabis use is stabilising — and in some cases declining — among young people in Europe: of the 11 EU countries for which it is possible to analyse trends between 2002 and 2007, four countries showed overall decreases of 15 % or more in the proportion of 15- to 16-year-olds reporting cannabis use in the last year, and in four other countries the situation appears stable (Hibell et al., 2009; EMCDDA, 2009).

Ecstasy and amphetamines

It is estimated that 7.5 million young Europeans aged 15 to 34 (5.6 %) have ever tried ecstasy, with around 2 million (1.6 %) using it during the last year (EMCDDA, 2009). Estimates of prevalence are generally even higher among the subgroup of 15- to 24-year-olds, for whom lifetime prevalence ranges between 0.4–18.7 % in European countries (estimates fall between 2.1 % and 6.8 % in most European countries). Among 15- to 16-year-old students lifetime prevalence of ecstasy use ranges between 1 % and 7 % in countries surveyed in 2007 (EMCDDA, 2009).

Studies of recreational settings that are associated with drug use, such as dance events or music festivals, provide further evidence regarding young people's ecstasy and amphetamine use. Estimates of young people's drug use in these settings are typically high. However, comparisons between surveys can only be made with the utmost caution, as the age and gender distribution of survey respondents as well as variations in the setting may lead to observed differences. Studies conducted in recreational settings in 2007 in five EU countries (Belgium, Czech Republic, Latvia, Lithuania, Austria) reveal lifetime prevalence estimates of 15–71 % for ecstasy use and 17–68 % for amphetamines (EMCDDA, 2009). Much of party-going young people's drug use occurs on weekends and during holiday periods (EMCDDA, 2006b).

Figure 13.1: Proportion of 16- to 24-year-olds reporting use of the most prevalent drugs in the last year by frequency of nightclub visits

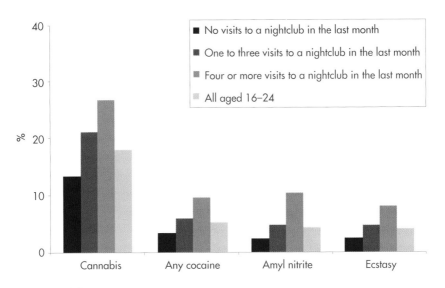

Source: Hoare and Flatley, 2008.

A further indication of the extent to which the use of these drugs may be concentrated among the young, club-going population can found in the 2007/8 British Crime Survey (Hoare and Flatley, 2008). The study found that those 16- to 24-year-olds who reported visiting a nightclub four or more times in the last month were more than three times as likely to have used ecstasy in the last year than those not attending nightclubs (2 % vs. 8 %) (Figure 13.1). In a French study that was carried out in 2004 and 2005 among 1 496 young people at 'electronic' music venues, 32 % of respondents reported ecstasy use and 13 % reported amphetamine use in the past month (Reynaud-Maurupt et al., 2007). Among specific sub-populations that self-identified as 'alternative', prevalence estimates for ecstasy and amphetamines were as high as 54 % and 29 %, respectively (Reynaud-Maurupt, 2007).

Cocaine

Although cocaine is the second most commonly used illicit drug in Europe after cannabis (EMCDDA, 2007), estimates of the prevalence of cocaine use among school students are very low. Lifetime prevalence of cocaine use among 15- to 16-year-old students in the ESPAD survey is between 1 % and 2 % in half of the 28 reporting countries, and in the rest it ranges between 3 % and 5 % (Hibell et al., 2009; EMCDDA, 2009).

Table 13.1: **Prevalence of cocaine use in the young adult population — summary of the data**

Age group	Time frame of use		
	Lifetime	Last year	Last month
15–34 years			
Estimated number of users in Europe	7.5 million	3 million	1 million
European average	5.6 %	2.2 %	0.8 %
Range	0.1–12.0 %	0.1–5.5 %	0.0–2.1 %
Lowest-prevalence countries	Romania (0.1 %) Lithuania (0.7 %) Malta (0.9 %) Greece (1.0 %)	Romania (0.1 %) Greece (0.2 %) Poland (0.3 %) Hungary, Czech Republic (0.4 %)	Estonia, Romania (0.0 %) Czech Republic, Greece, Poland (0.1 %)
Highest-prevalence countries	United Kingdom (12.0 %) Spain (11.8 %) Denmark (9.5 %) Ireland (8.2 %)	Spain (5.5 %) United Kingdom (4.5 %) Denmark (3.4 %) Ireland, Italy (3.1 %)	United Kingdom (2.1 %) Spain (1.9 %) Italy (1.2 %) Ireland (1.0 %)
15–24 years			
Estimated number of users in Europe	3 million	1.5 million	0.6 million
European average	4.4 %	2.2 %	0.9 %
Range	0.1–9.9 %	0.1–5.6 %	0.0–2.5 %
Lowest-prevalence countries	Romania (0.1 %) Greece (0.6 %) Lithuania (0.7 %) Malta, Poland (1.1 %)	Romania (0.1 %) Greece (0.2 %) Poland (0.3 %) Czech Republic (0.4 %)	Estonia, Romania (0.0 %) Greece (0.1 %) Czech Republic, Poland, Portugal (0.2 %)
Highest-prevalence countries	United Kingdom (9.9 %) Spain (9.3 %) Denmark (9.2 %) Ireland (7.0 %)	Denmark (5.6 %) Spain (5.4 %) United Kingdom (5.0 %) Ireland (3.8 %)	United Kingdom (2.5 %) Spain (1.7 %) Italy (1.2 %) Ireland (1.1 %)

Note: European prevalence estimates are based on weighted averages from the most recent national surveys conducted from 2001 to 2008 (mainly 2004–08), therefore they cannot be attached to a single year. The average prevalence for Europe was computed by a weighted average according to the population of the relevant age group in each country. In countries for which no information was available, the average EU prevalence was imputed. Population base is 133 million. The data summarised here are available under 'General population surveys' in the EMCDDA 2009 statistical bulletin. Source: EMCDDA, 2009.

Of the 4 million Europeans who used cocaine in the past year, around 3 million were young people and young adults (EMCDDA, 2009). The prevalence of past-year cocaine use among 15- to 24-year-olds is estimated to be 2.2 %, which translates to about 1.5 million cocaine users. In contrast to the prevalence estimates for cannabis or ecstasy use, which are highest among the 15 to 24 age group, measures of more recent cocaine use (last year and last month) are similar among the 15 to 24 and 25 to 34 age groups (see Table 13.1). Of the 11 countries for which it is possible to analyse trends in cocaine use between 2002 and 2007, the proportion of 15- to 34-year-olds reporting cocaine use in the last year increased by 15 % or more in five countries (Ireland, Italy, Latvia, Portugal, United Kingdom), remained stable in four (Germany, Spain, Slovakia, Finland) and only decreased in two countries (Hungary, Poland).

Cocaine use is also strongly associated with alcohol use. For example, the British Crime Survey 2007–08 found that among 16- to 24-year-olds who made nine or more visits to a pub in the last month, 13.5 % reported using cocaine in the last year, compared to 1.7 % among those who had not visited a pub (Hoare and Flatley, 2008). Visiting nightclubs was also associated with higher cocaine use, as nearly 10 % of the 16- to 24-year-olds who visited a club on four or more occasions during the last month reported using cocaine in the last year, compared to 3.3 % among those who had not visited a club (Hoare and Flatley, 2008). Studies conducted in nightlife settings also report higher prevalence of cocaine use among club-goers than among the general population (EMCDDA, 2007).

It is worth noting that alcohol is almost always the first drug with strong psychoactive and mind-altering effects used by young people, and its widespread availability makes it the main drug connected to poly-drug use among young adults, particularly in recreational settings. Other psychoactive substances commonly referred to as 'legal highs' are increasingly sold as alternatives to controlled drugs. In 2009, a snapshot study of 115 online shops located in 17 European countries showed that a range of herbal smoking products and 'party pills' containing legal alternatives to controlled drugs were being sold (EMCDDA, 2009).

Health and other harms

It is now widely acknowledged that recreational drug use can be an important source of status and recreation for young people (Henderson et al., 2007); it can not only facilitate a shared sense of group belonging and security (Fletcher et al., 2009a), but also a sense of being different from other groups of young people (Shildrick, 2002). However, as recreational drug use has increased among different sections of the youth population, so has evidence of drug-related harm and concerns about the consequences of adolescent drug use. Although the vast majority of this increase in drug use among young people has been attributed to the use of 'soft' drugs (e.g. cannabis and ecstasy), these substances still have health risks, especially for frequent users who are most at risk of harm.

Cannabis can cause short- and long-term health problems, such as nausea, anxiety, memory deficits, depression and respiratory problems (Hall and Solowij, 1998; MacLeod et al., 2004;

Solowij and Battisti, 2008; Hall and Fischer, 2010). Although more research is needed on the long-term effects of adolescent cannabis use on mental health, cannabis use is also thought to increase the risk of mental health problems, particularly among frequent users (Hall, 2006; Moore et al., 2007) and those with a predisposition for psychosis (Henquet et al., 2005). Regular cannabis users can also become dependent (Melrose et al., 2007).

The true extent of future mental health problems due to adolescent ecstasy use is unclear, but young ecstasy users may be at risk of depression in later life and there is evidence that ecstasy use may also impair cognitive functions relevant to learning (Parrott et al., 1998; Schilt et al., 2007). Dehydration, a more immediate risk for ecstasy users, can cause loss of consciousness, coma and even death. Furthermore, evidence from cohort studies suggests that early initiation and frequent use of 'soft' drugs may be a potential pathway to more problematic drug use in later life (Yamaguchi and Kandel, 1984; Lynskey et al., 2003; Ferguson et al., 2006).

Cocaine use can result in dependence and/or serious mental and physical health problems, such as depression, paranoia, and heart and respiratory problems (Emmett and Nice, 2006). Hence, although only a small minority of young people use cocaine (NatCen and NFER, 2007; Hibell et al., 2009), their numbers are increasing in some countries in Europe, posing an increasing public health issue.

In addition to presenting direct health risks, adolescent drug use is also associated with accidental injury, self-harm, suicide (Charlton et al., 1993; Beautrais et al., 1999; Thomas et al., 2007) and other 'problem' behaviours, such as unprotected sex, youth offending and traffic risk behaviours (Jessor et al., 1991; Home Office, 2002; Jayakody et al., 2005; Calafat et al., 2009). For example, a recent report by the United Kingdom Independent Advisory Group on Sexual Health and HIV (2007) has suggested that there are strong links between drug use, 'binge' drinking and sexual health risk, with similar trends in these risk behaviours. Furthermore, although the links between crime and heroin or cocaine dependence are well known, there is increasing evidence of links between teenage cannabis use and youth offending (e.g. Boreham et al., 2006). This is not to say that there is necessarily a direct causal relationship between adolescent drug use and social problems, but there is clear evidence that they cluster together among certain groups of young people.

A typology of interventions

There have been surprisingly few attempts to synthesise the evidence relating to interventions in European countries addressing young people's recreational drug use. Here we adopt a typological approach to describe and discuss responses that aim to reduce the harms associated with young people's recreational drug use. These include: (1) individually focused and group-based interventions — school-based drugs education and prevention, mass media campaigns, motivational interviewing and youth development programmes — and (2) 'settings-based approaches' which make changes to recreational settings, such as nightclubs, or institutional settings, such as schools, to address the social and environmental background of young people's drug use.

This is not an exhaustive list of interventions in Europe that target young people's recreational drug use. For example, we do not discuss interventions that are directed primarily at young people's parents rather than young people themselves (see Petrie et al., 2007 for a review of the evidence relating to current parenting programmes). Social policies that may impact on macro-social — or 'structural' — factors, such as youth cultures, poverty or social exclusion, that are also associated with young people's drug use, are also not discussed, because they rarely aim to specifically reduce the harms associated with recreational drug use. The decriminalisation of drugs, drug classification policies, and policies and enforcement to reduce the supply of illicit drugs and illicit sales of prescription drugs are also beyond the scope of this chapter.

Individual and group-based approaches

School-based drugs education and prevention

In Europe, schools provide universal access to young people under 16 and are widely recognised as a key site for drugs education and prevention interventions that aim to prevent or delay drug use and reduce the frequency of drug use during adolescence (Evans-Whipp et al., 2004). However, evidence from randomised controlled trials (RCTs) of classroom-based drugs education interventions aiming to improve knowledge, develop skills and modify peer norms suggest that the effect of these interventions on young people's drug-use behaviour are limited: a recent systematic review found that they can have positive effects but concluded that these are small, inconsistent and generally not sustained (Faggiano et al., 2005). In other words, drugs education may promote students' 'health literacy' but is not sufficient on its own for changing young people's behaviour or reducing drug-related harms.

Faggiano and colleagues (2005) found that school-based drugs education programmes based on a 'comprehensive social influence approach' and those that are delivered by other students (rather than teachers) appear to have the most positive effects — programme characteristics that were also associated with more positive effects in systematic reviews of alcohol education and smoking prevention interventions in schools (Foxcroft et al., 2002; Thomas and Perera, 2006). However, in reviewing the evidence for drug education programmes in schools, Cahill (2007) has highlighted the difficulties of implementing complex interventions such as peer-led programmes in school settings and suggested that caution is also required with normative education to ensure that adolescents receive appropriate messages.

A key challenge in Europe and elsewhere is therefore to pilot and further evaluate evidence-based school-based drugs education and prevention interventions (Faggiano and Vigna-Taglianti, 2008; Ringwalt et al., 2008). 'Unplugged' is an example of a European school-based programme that employs a comprehensive social influence model. It aims to reduce young people's substance use via 12 interactive sessions addressing topics such as decision-making, 'creative thinking', effective communication, relationship skills, self-awareness, empathy, coping skills and the risks associated with specific drugs (Van Der Kreeft et al., 2009). A recent cluster RCT of the 'Unplugged' programme in 170 schools across seven

European countries suggested that curricula based on such a comprehensive social-influence model are not only feasible to implement in schools in Europe, they may also reduce regular cannabis use and delay progression to daily smoking and episodes of drunkenness (Faggiano et al., 2008).

The ASSIST (A Stop Smoking in Schools Trial) programme in the United Kingdom provides an example of an effective peer-led health promotion intervention that is feasible to deliver in schools: a cluster RCT of the ASSIST programme involving 59 schools in Wales found a significant reduction in smoking among the intervention group, including among the most 'high risk' groups of students (Campbell et al., 2008). The programme uses network analysis to identify influential students and train them as peer supporters to 'diffuse' positive health messages throughout the school. Researchers at the Centre for Drug Misuse Research in Glasgow have recently piloted a peer-led drugs prevention programme based on the ASSIST programme in two secondary schools in Scotland; this study suggested that it is feasible to deliver cannabis and smoking education (CASE) together using this approach (Professor Mick Bloor, personal communication). However, further research is needed to examine the effects of this intervention on students' drug use and drug-related harms.

Mass media campaigns

Mass media campaigns have become a popular tool among health promoters seeking to inform young people about the risks associated with recreational drug use and/or seeking to encourage current users to reduce their use and minimise the risk of harm. These interventions, such as the recent United Kingdom FRANK advertising campaigns on the mental health problems associated with recreational cannabis use (http://www.talktofrank.com/cannabis.aspx), aim to increase the information available to young people and reframe issues relating to young people's recreational drug use on public health terms. These mass media campaigns to raise awareness about the effects of drug use in the United Kingdom have also been integrated with a 'credible, non-judgemental and reliable' online and telephone drugs advice and information service for young people and their parents (Home Office et al., 2006).

However, mass media campaigns that aim to reduce the harms associated with young people's recreational drug have rarely been evaluated to examine their effects on young people's behaviour, attitudes or intention to use drugs — and where they have, the findings have not always been positive. A national survey to evaluate the United States Anti-Drug Media Campaign suggested that mass media campaigns have little or no effect on changing attitudes once young people have initiated drug use (Orwin et al., 2006), and may even have harmful effects as those young people who were exposed to the adverts were more likely to report cannabis use or an intention to use cannabis (Hornik et al., 2008). Similar negative outcomes were reported in another large-scale evaluation of the Scottish cocaine campaign 'Know the score': two-fifths (41 %) of respondents said that the campaign made them more likely to find out more about cocaine and 12 % felt that the campaign had made them more likely to experiment with cocaine (Phillips and Kinver, 2007). A meta-analysis of evaluations of mass media campaigns to reduce smoking, drinking or drug use by Derzon and Lipsey (2002) found that campaigns featuring messages about resistance skills appeared to have the most harmful effects and were associated with significantly higher extent of substance use than observed in control communities.

Flay and colleagues (1980) have suggested that the key factors to change behaviour via mass media health promotion campaigns include: repetition of information over long time periods, via multiple sources and at different times (including 'prime' or high-exposure times). Mass media interventions also provide the opportunity to reach specific target groups within a short timeframe (HDA, 2004). However, population-level mass media campaigns require a significant financial investment (Hornik, 2002) and are competing in an increasingly crowded market with a range of other information available to young people (Randolph and Viswanath, 2004).

Brief interventions

Approaches based on early screening of young people's drug use and brief behaviour change interventions, such as motivational interviewing, have been rigorously evaluated in the United Kingdom and elsewhere (Tait and Hulse, 2003; Tevyaw and Monti, 2004). Developed by Miller and Rollnick, motivational interviewing has been defined as a 'client-centred, directive method for enhancing intrinsic motivation to change by exploring and resolving ambivalence' (Miller and Rollnick, 2002). Evidence suggests that it is feasible to deliver brief one-to-one interventions such as motivational interviewing to young drug-users in a wide range of settings, such as youth centres, further education colleges, general practitioners' surgeries and 'emergency rooms' (Gray et al., 2005; Martin et al., 2005; McCambridge et al., 2008), and where brief interventions employ motivational interviewing principles they have been found to be effective in reducing young people's drug use (Tait and Hulse, 2003; McCambridge and Strang, 2004; Tevyaw and Monti, 2004; Grenard et al., 2006).

Reviewing the evidence from trials of brief motivational interviewing interventions, Tevyaw and Monti (2004) found consistent evidence that this approach can 'result in decreases in substance-related negative consequences and problems, decrements in substance use and increased treatment engagement', and these effects appear to be greatest among young people who report the heaviest patterns of drug use and the least motivation to change prior to intervention. Researchers have also found evidence that as little as a 'single session' of motivational interviewing can significantly reduce cannabis use among heavy users and among those young people considered to be at 'high risk' of progressing to more problematic drug use (McCambridge and Strang, 2004).

However, the existing evidence suggests that, although brief interventions based on motivational interviewing can encourage young people to moderate their drug use in the short term, this approach is unlikely to have long-term effects on its own (McCambridge and Strang, 2005) and may therefore need to form part of a more holistic approach to harm reduction. Further research is also needed to examine the essential elements of motivational interviewing interventions and their effects on developmental transitions during adolescence (McCambridge and Strang, 2004; McCambridge et al., 2008). Furthermore, motivational interviewing is complex and requires practitioners to develop skills and experiences over time in order to deliver it proficiently. As such, it is likely to be difficult to replicate and evaluate existing intervention more widely across Europe at present while is there is limited capacity to deliver such interventions.

Youth development

Youth development programmes work with groups of teenagers and aim to promote their personal development, self-esteem, positive aspirations and good relationships with adults in order to reduce potentially harmful behaviours, such as drug use (Quinn, 1999). As well as enhancing young people's interests, skills and abilities, youth projects also have the potential to divert young people away from drug use through engaging them in more positive sources of recreation, and youth workers can provide credible health messages and signpost health services. There has been considerable interest from policymakers in youth development interventions as an alternative means of reducing young people's drug use. For example, in the United Kingdom youth work programmes targeted at socially disadvantaged and 'excluded' young people and other 'at-risk' groups have been supported by the Government, including new community-based youth development projects such as the Positive Futures initiative and the Young People's Development Programme (Department for Education and Skills, 2005).

Evaluations of youth development interventions targeted at vulnerable young people have shown mixed results: although some studies report that youth development interventions have had positive effects (Philliber et al., 2001; Michelsen et al., 2002), others suggest these interventions may be ineffective (Grossman and Sipe, 1992) or even harmful (Palinkas et al., 1996; Cho et al., 2005; Wiggins et al., 2009). It appears that involvement in such programmes may result in an increase in drug use where: young people are stigmatised (or 'labelled') via targeting, which further reduces their self-esteem and aspirations; and/or harmful social network effects arise through aggregating 'high risk' young people together, thus introducing young people to new drug-using peers (Bonell and Fletcher, 2008). For example, in a study examining an intervention for high-risk high school students (Cho et al., 2005), greater exposure to the programme predicted greater 'high-risk peer bonding' and more negative outcomes, including higher prevalence of cannabis and alcohol use (Sanchez et al., 2007).

Youth development approaches are therefore likely to be most appropriate and effective where they are delivered in universal settings to avoid the harmful 'labelling' and social network effects associated with targeting 'high risk' youth. In the United States, after-school and community-based youth development programmes promoting civic engagement and learning through the principle of 'serve and learn' — which involves voluntary service, reflection on this voluntary service though discussion groups, social development classes and learning support — have been found to be effective in reducing a wide range of risky behaviours including involvement with drugs and teenage pregnancy (Michelsen et al., 2002; Harden et al., 2009). Where youth workers aim to target 'high risk' groups of young people, 'detached', street-based services may be more appropriate in order to avoid the potentially harmful social network effects associated with aggregating these young people together in youth centres, although this needs further evaluation (Fletcher and Bonell, 2008). Examples of street-based youth projects include the Conversas de Rua programme in Lisbon (http://www.conversasderua.org/) and the 'Off the Streets' community youth initiative in Derry, Northern Ireland.

Settings-based approaches

Settings-based approaches to health promotion have their roots in the World Health Organization's (WHO) Health for All initiative and the Ottawa Charter for Health Promotion (WHO, 1986). The Ottawa Charter argued that health is influenced by where people 'learn, work, play and love', integrated new thinking about health promotion, and heralded the start of this new approach (Young, 2005). Key principles regarded as necessary to achieve the status of a 'health promoting setting' are the creation of a healthy environment and the integration of health promotion into the routine activities of the setting (Baric, 1993). Since the late 1980s, health promotion interventions have been widely established, which make changes to recreational 'settings', such as nightclubs, or institutional 'settings', such as schools, to address the social and environmental determinants of harmful drug use.

Interventions in recreational settings

Studies of young people in Europe who attend dance music events consistently report much higher prevalence of drug use than found in surveys of the general population (EMCDDA, 2006a). A 'Hegemonic Recreational Nightlife Model' has been used to understand how recreational drug use and the settings where this takes place now govern many young people's weekend entertainment and social networks, and can give 'meaning' to their lives through intensive participation (Calafat et al., 2003). The recreation industry thus not only supplies services but also contributes to defining entertainment and creating the conditions in which recreational drug use takes place. In turn, there is a wide range of risk behaviours associated with recreational drug use in this context (e.g. violence, sexual risk, traffic risk), and these have been found to be influenced by factors such as a 'permissive atmosphere' (Homel and Clark, 1994; Graham et al., 2006), overcrowding (Macintyre and Homel, 1997), overt sexual activity (Homel et al., 2004; Graham et al., 2006) and transport habits (Calafat et al., 2009).

A wide range of interventions now aim to change the physical context and/or the social and cultural norms of recreational settings to address the conditions and influences associated with the most 'habitual' contexts for young people's recreational drug use, such as nightlife settings and music festivals, and the potential harms arising from use in such contexts. For example, several organisations in Europe have launched safer nightlife guidelines. 'Safer dancing' guidelines, developed in the United Kingdom, have now become an important tool in this field. Other examples are the Safe Nightlife initiative in Holstebro, Denmark, and the London Drug Policy Forum's 'Dance Till Dawn Safely' initiative.

Safe-clubbing guidelines aim to reduce opportunities for drug-related problems to occur in these settings and include promoting the accessibility of free water, the immediate availability of first aid and outreach prevention work with young clubbers. Reports on the availability of such measures, in nightclubs with sufficiently large target populations for the intervention to be implemented, were collated by the EMCDDA in 2008 (EMCDDA, 2009). These reports highlighted the limited availability of simple measures to prevent or reduce health risks and drug use in European nightlife settings. For example, it was found that outreach prevention work was provided in the majority of dance clubs in only two out of 20 European countries (Slovenia and Lithuania), while free water was still not routinely available in nine of the 20 countries. Furthermore, while 12 countries now report having developed guidelines for nightlife venues, only the Netherlands, Slovenia, Sweden and the United Kingdom report that they are monitored and implemented.

The most widely implemented intervention in recreational settings is the responsible beverage service (RBS) guidelines to support staff and managers in harm reduction strategies. A recent systematic review, however, concluded that there is no reliable evidence that these interventions are effective in preventing injuries or other harms (Ker and Chinnock, 2008; see also Herring et al., 2010). Community-based approaches to responsible service may produce the largest and most significant effects. For example, Stockholm Prevents Alcohol and Drug Problems (STAD) is a community-based prevention programme that started in 1996 in Stockholm to promote community mobilisation, the training of bar staff in RBS and stricter enforcement of existing alcohol licensing and drug laws: an evaluation found a decrease in alcohol-related problems, increased refusal to serve minors and a 29 % reduction in assaults (Wallin and Andréasson, 2005). However, large-scale community-based interventions are likely to be expensive and need political commitment. Other factors may also limit compliance to responsible service, such as low pay, high staff turnover and a stressful working environment, and the efficacy of such interventions is therefore likely be greater when enforced as a statutory intervention (Ker and Chinnok, 2008; Wallin and Andréasson, 2005).

Promising interventions that need further evaluation are glassware bans in recreational settings (Forsyth, 2008) and the creation of collaborating guidelines between licensed premises and accident and emergency services (Wood et al., 2008). Some nightclubs in Europe have now incorporated a first aid service inside the premises, but we are not aware of any evaluations of their effectiveness. Further research and effective collaboration between health promoters, nightlife settings and the alcohol industry are likely to be crucial in reducing the harms associated with young people's recreational drug use. However, building relationships across these sectors is not straightforward. 'Codes of practice' with the potential of enforcement may be the most appropriate means to facilitate engagement across the sectors (Graham, 2000). At present, there seems to be a reluctance to enforce greater accountability through law enforcement. The Tackling Alcohol Related Street Crime (TASC) intervention in Cardiff provides an example of a broad and multifaceted intervention implemented largely by the police that produced reductions in violence at the relevant premises, although further research is needed to examine the feasibility of introducing police-led approaches in nightlife settings more generally (Maguire et al., 2003).

Finally, on-site pill testing in recreational settings has been a controversial issue for several years and appears to be steadily less common in Europe. The main arguments against pill testing are the limited capacity of on-site tests to accurately detect harmful substances and that, by permitting on-site pill testing, contradictory messages are being sent out about the risks related to both use and possession of controlled substances (EMCDDA, 2006b).

Whole-school interventions

Following the emergence of 'settings-based approaches' to health promotion, traditional classroom-based drugs education programmes have gradually been accompanied by additional strategies in schools that address more 'upstream' environmental, social and cultural determinants of young people's drug use, such as student disengagement and truancy. The origin of this new 'settings' approach to health promotion in schools is attributed to a WHO conference in 1989 which led to the publication of *The Healthy School* (Young and Williams, 1989). Following this report, 'whole-school' approaches have received continued support from international networks, such as the WHO, the European Network of Health Promoting Schools (ENHPS) and the International School Health Network (ISHN) (WHO, 1998; McCall et al., 2005).

Using cross-sectional survey data from 10 European countries, Canada and Australia, Nutbeam and colleagues (1993) found a consistent relationship between 'alienation' at secondary school and 'abusive behaviours', such as smoking, drinking and drug use, and warned that 'schools can damage your health'. Further analysis of this data suggested that students' perceptions of being treated fairly, school safety and teacher support were related to substance use (Samdal et al., 1998). Three recent systematic reviews of experimental studies of 'whole-school health promotion interventions', which make changes to schools' physical environment, governance and management, policies, and/or educational and pastoral practices, have found that these approaches appear to be 'promising' for reducing a wide range of 'risky' health behaviours among young people (Lister-Sharpe et al., 1999; Mukoma and Flisher, 2004; Fletcher et al., 2008). The review by Fletcher and colleagues found that changes to the school social environment that increase student participation, improve teacher–student relationships, promote a positive school ethos and reduce disengagement are associated with reduced drug use. The Gatehouse Project in Australia is one of the best-known examples (http://www.rch.org.au/gatehouseproject/).

Although various pathways may plausibly underlie school effects on drug use and drug-related harms, three potential pathways via which school effects on drug use may occur have been identified: peer-group sorting and drug use as a source of identity and bonding among students who are disconnected from the main institutional markers of status; students' desire to 'fit in' at schools perceived to be unsafe, and drug use facilitating this; and/or drug use as a strategy to manage anxieties about schoolwork and escape unhappiness at schools lacking effective social support systems (Fletcher et al., 2009b). This evidence further supports 'whole-school' interventions to reduce drug use through: recognising students' varied achievements and promoting a sense of belonging; reducing bullying and aggression; and providing additional social support for students.

Discussion

There is considerable data on the prevalence of recreational drug use among young people in European countries, and the related adverse health and other harms. However, much of this evidence regarding overall prevalence of young people's drug use is gained through school-based surveys and we cannot assume that patterns of drug use among young people who have low school attendance and young people who have been excluded from school will therefore be accurately captured in these surveys; there are also practical problems with collecting reliable self-report data about students' use of drugs in school-based surveys (McCambridge and Strang, 2006). Street-based surveys of young people, such as the Vancouver Youth Drug Reporting System (VCH, 2007), could therefore complement existing monitoring systems in Europe. Nonetheless, current European surveys that monitor prevalence and trends are well established and allow cross-national comparisons to be made regarding young people's drug use.

In response to public and political concerns about the harmful consequences of young people's drug use, a wide range of interventions have been implemented throughout Europe and elsewhere. There is no 'magic bullet', and harm reduction strategies in this context will need to encompass both universal and targeted strategies that seek to prevent or delay drug use, reduce the frequency of drug use during adolescence, and make changes to risk environments. Mass media campaigns may be politically important but appear to be largely ineffective (and occasionally counter-productive). If they are to continue to play a role in informing young people about the risks associated with recreational drug use, health promoters should design mass media campaigns in conjunction with young people and — although it is difficult to attribute changes in behaviour to mass media interventions — these campaigns should be subjected to pilot trials prior to 'roll-out'. Future mass media campaigns should also pay close attention to providing easy access to information via the Internet and telephone advice lines.

Based on the current evidence, school-based programmes show greater promise for preventing young people initiating drug use at a young age than mass media interventions. Comprehensive social influence models and peer-led programmes based on the 'diffusion of innovations' approach are the most promising approaches for drugs education and prevention in schools, and thus should be piloted and evaluated more widely in Europe. Interventions that promote a positive school ethos and reduce student disaffection and truancy are likely to be an effective complement to these drugs education and prevention interventions in schools. These school-level 'settings' interventions focusing on the more 'upstream' determinants of risk should also now be piloted and evaluated in Europe to examine their potential for harm reduction.

Motivational interviewing shows considerable promise in a wide range of settings, including among those young people with the heaviest patterns of drug use. However, motivational interviewing is resource-intensive and where there is insufficient investment this will impact on its potential for harm reduction. New training programmes in motivational interviewing should therefore be considered a priority in European countries, initially to build capacity for greater intervention in recreational contexts and among professionals working with high-risk young people.

Youth development approaches appear to be most appropriate and effective in addition to, rather than as an alternative to, school, such as after-school and school-holiday programmes promoting self-esteem, positive aspirations, supportive relationships and learning through the principle of 'serve and learn', which is based on volunteering in the local community. In addition, because of its focus on working with existing peer groups (and thus its ability to avoid the potentially harmful effects associated with centre-based youth projects), as well as its greater reach and flexibility, detached, street-based youth work may be the most appropriate and effective approach for targeting those young people deemed at 'high risk' of harm. These approaches should be the subject of further evaluation in Europe with high-risk groups.

Perhaps of greatest concern at present is the lack of agreement and guidance about what to do in recreational settings in Europe to reduce drug-related harm. There are few statutory policies governing the most 'habitual' contexts for young people's recreational drug use, such as nightlife settings and music festivals, or rigorous evaluations of interventions in such settings in Europe. Guidelines promoting the accessibility of free water, immediate availability of first aid and outreach services have been implemented with promising effects in some (but by no means all) European countries. These should be enforced through changing them into laws where possible and be accompanied by additional efforts to encourage responsible alcohol service and reduce other risky behaviours.

References

Ball, A. (2007), 'HIV, injecting drug use and harm reduction: a public health response', *Addiction* 102, pp. 684–90.

Baric, L. (1993), 'The settings approach: implications for policy and strategy', *Journal of the Institute of Health Education* 31, pp. 17–24.

Beautrais, A. L., Joyce, P. R. and Mulder, R. T. (1999), 'Cannabis abuse and serious suicide attempts', *Addiction*, 94, pp. 1155–64.

Bonell, C. and Fletcher, A. (2008), 'Addressing the wider determinants of problematic drug use: advantages of whole-population over targeted interventions', *International Journal of Drug Policy* 19, pp. 267–9.

Boreham, R., Fuller, E., Hills, A. and Pudney, S. (2006), *The arrestee survey annual report: Oct. 2003–Sept. 2004, England and Wales*, Home Office, London.

Cahill, H. W. (2007), 'Challenges in adopting evidence-based school drug education programmes', *Drug and Alcohol Review* 26, pp. 673–9.

Calafat, A., Fernandez, C., Juan, M., et al. (2003), *Enjoying nightlife in Europe: the role of moderation*, Irefrea, Palma de Mallorca.

Calafat, A., Blay, N., Juan, M., et al. (2009), 'Traffic risk behaviors at nightlife: drinking, taking drugs, driving, and use of public transport by young people', *Traffic Injury Prevention* 10, pp. 162–9.

Campbell, R., Starkey, F., Holliday, J., et al. (2008), 'An informal school-based peer-led intervention for smoking prevention in adolescence (ASSIST): a cluster randomised trial', *Lancet* 371, pp. 1595–602.

Charlton, J., Kelly, S. and Dunnell, K. (1993), 'Suicide deaths in England and Wales: trends in factors associated with suicide deaths', *Population Trends* 7, pp. 34–42.

Cho, H., Hallfors, D. D. and Sanchez, V. (2005), 'Evaluation of a high school peer group intervention for at-risk youth', *Journal of Abnormal Child Psychology* 33, pp. 363–74.

Department for Education and Skills (2005), *Every child matters: change for children, young people and drugs*, Her Majesty's Stationery Office, London.

Derzon, J. H. and Lipsey, M. W. (2002), 'A meta-analysis of the effectiveness of mass-communication for changing substance-use knowledge, attitudes and behaviour', in Crano, W. D. and Burgoon, M. (eds), *Mass media and drug prevention: classic and contemporary theories and research*, Lawrence Erlbaum Associates, Matwah.

Emmett, D. and Nice, G. (2006), *Understanding street drugs*, Jessica Kingsley Publishers, London.

EMCDDA (European Monitoring Centre for Drugs and Drug Addiction) (2002), *Recreational drug use: a key EU challenge*, Drugs in focus, European Monitoring Centre for Drugs and Drug Addiction, Lisbon.

EMCDDA (2006a), *Annual report 2006: the state of the drugs problem in Europe*, European Monitoring Centre for Drugs and Drug Addiction, Lisbon.

EMCDDA (2006b), *Developments in drug use within recreational settings*, European Monitoring Centre for Drugs and Drug Addiction, Lisbon.

EMCDDA (2007), *Cocaine and crack cocaine: a growing public health issue*, European Monitoring Centre for Drugs and Drug Addiction, Lisbon.

EMCDDA (2009), *Annual report 2009: the state of the drugs problem in Europe*, European Monitoring Centre for Drugs and Drug Addiction, Lisbon.

Evans-Whipp, T., Beyers, J. M., Lloyd, S., et al. (2004), 'A review of school drug polices and their impact on youth substance use', *Health Promotion International* 19, pp. 227–34.

Faggiano, F. and Vigna-Taglianti, F. D. (2008), 'Drugs, illicit — primary prevention strategies', *International Encyclopaedia of Public Health* 2, pp. 249–65.

Faggiano, F., Vigna-Taglianti, F. D., Versino, E., et al. (2005), 'School-based prevention for illegal drugs use', *Cochrane Database of Systematic Reviews* 2, Art. No. CD003020.

Faggiano, F., Galanti, M. R., Bohrn, K., et al. (2008), 'The effectiveness of a school-based substance abuse prevention program: EU–Dap cluster randomised controlled trial', *Preventive Medicine* 47, pp. 537–43.

Ferguson, D. M., Boden, J. M. and Horwood, L. J. (2006), 'Cannabis use and other illicit drug use: testing the cannabis gateway hypothesis', *Addiction* 101, pp. 556–69.

Flay, B. R., DiTecco, D. and Schlegel, R. P. (1980), 'Mass media in health promotion: an analysis extended information-processing model', *Health Education and Behavior* 7, pp. 127–47.

Fletcher, A. and Bonell, C. (2008), 'Detaching youth work to reduce drug and alcohol-related harm', *Public Policy Research* 15, pp. 217–23.

Fletcher, A., Bonell, C. and Hargreaves, J. (2008), 'School effects on young people's drug use: a systematic review of intervention and observational studies', *Journal of Adolescent Health* 42, pp. 209–20.

Fletcher, A., Bonell, C., Sorhaindo, A. and Rhodes, T. (2009a), 'Cannabis use and "safe" identities in an inner-city school risk environment', *International Journal of Drug Policy* 20, pp. 244–50.

Fletcher, A., Bonell, C., Sorhaindo, A. and Strange, V. (2009b), 'How might schools influence young people's drug use? Development of theory from qualitative case-study research', *Journal of Adolescent Health* 45, pp. 126–32.

Forsyth, A. J. M. (2008), 'Banning glassware from nightclubs in Glasgow (Scotland): observed impacts, compliance and patrons views', *Alcohol and Alcoholism* 43, pp. 111–17.

Foxcroft, D. R., Ireland, D., Lowe, G. and Breen, R. (2002), 'Primary prevention for alcohol misuse in young people', *Cochrane Database of Systematic Reviews* 3, Art. No. CD003024.

Graham, K. (2000), 'Preventive interventions for on-premise drinking: a promising but under researched area of prevention', *Contemporary Drug Problems* 27, pp. 593–668.

Graham, K., Bernards, S., Osgood, D. W. and Wells, S. (2006), 'Bad nights or bad bars? Multi-level analysis of environmental predictors of aggression in late-night large-capacity bars and clubs', *Addiction* 101, pp. 1569–80.

Gray, E., McCambridge, J. and Strang, J. (2005), 'The effectiveness of motivational interviewing delivered by youth workers in reducing drinking, cigarette and cannabis smoking among young people: quasi-experimental pilot study', *Alcohol and Alcoholism* 40, pp. 535–9.

Grenard, J. L., Ames, S. L., Pentz, M. A. and Sussman, S. (2006), 'Motivational interviewing with adolescents and young adults for drug-related problems', *International Journal of Adolescent Medicine and Health* 18, pp. 53–67.

Grossman, J. B. and Sipe, C. L. (1992), *Report on the long-term impacts (STEP program)*, Public/Private Ventures, Philadelphia.

Hall, W. (2006), 'The mental health risks of adolescent cannabis use', *PLoS Medicine* 3, p. e39.

Hall, W. and Fischer, B. (2010), 'Harm reduction policies for cannabis', in European Monitoring Centre for Drugs and Drug Addiction (EMCDDA), *Harm reduction: evidence, impacts and challenges*, Rhodes, T. and Hedrich, D. (eds), Scientific Monograph Series No. 10, Publications Office of the European Union, Luxembourg.

Hall, W. and Solowij, N. (1998), 'Adverse effects of cannabis', *Lancet* 352, pp. 1611–16.

Harden, A., Brunton, G., Fletcher, A. and Oakley, A. (2009), 'Teenage pregnancy and social disadvantage: systematic review integrating controlled trials and qualitative studies', *BMJ* 339, b4254.

HDA (Health Development Agency) (2004), *The effectiveness of public health campaigns*, Health Development Agency, London.

Henderson, S., Holland, J., McGrellis, S., Sharpe, S. and Thompson, R. (2007), *Inventing adulthoods: a biographical approach to youth transitions*, SAGE, London.

Henquet, C., Krabbendam, L., Spauwen, J., et al. (2005), 'Prospective cohort study of cannabis use, predisposition for psychosis, and psychotic symptoms in young people', *BMJ* 330, pp. 11–16.

Herring, R., Thom, B., Beccaria, F., Kolind, T. and Moskalewicz, J. (2010), 'Alcohol harm reduction in Europe', in European Monitoring Centre for Drugs and Drug Addiction (EMCDDA), *Harm reduction: evidence, impacts and challenges*, Rhodes, T. and Hedrich, D. (eds), Scientific Monograph Series No. 10, Publications Office of the European Union, Luxembourg.

Hibell, B., Anderson, B., Bjarnsson, T., et al. (2004), *The ESPAD report 2003: alcohol and other drug use among students in 35 countries*, The Swedish Council for Information on Alcohol and Other Drugs, Stockholm.

Hibell, B., Guttormsson, U., Ahlström, S., et al. (2009), *The 2007 ESPAD report: substance use among students in 35 European countries*, The Swedish Council for Information on Alcohol and Other Drugs, Stockholm.

Hoare, J. and Flatley, J. (2008), *Drug misuse declared: findings from the 2007/08 British Crime Survey*, Her Majesty's Stationery Office, London.

Home Office (2002), *Updated national drugs strategy*, Her Majesty's Stationery Office, London.

Home Office, Department of Health, Department for Education and Skills (2006), *FRANK review*, Her Majesty's Stationery Office, London.

Homel, R. and Clark, J. (1994), 'The prediction and prevention of violence in pubs and clubs', *Crime Prevention Studies* 3, pp. 1–46.

Homel, R., Carvolth, R., Hauritz, M., McIlwain, G. and Teague, R. (2004), 'Making licensed venues safer for patrons: what environmental factors should be the focus of interventions?', *Drug and Alcohol Review* 23, pp. 19–29.

Hornik, R. (2002), 'Public health communication: making sense of contradictory evidence', in Hornik, R., *Public health communication: evidence for behavior change*, Erlbaum, Mahwah.

Hornik, R., Jacobsohn, L., Orwin, R., Piesse, A., and Kalton, G. (2008), 'Effects of the National Youth Anti-Drug Media Campaign on youths', *American Journal of Public Health* 98, pp. 2229–36.

Independent Advisory Group on Sexual Health and HIV (2007), *Sex, drugs, alcohol and young people: a review of the impact drugs and alcohol has on the sexual behaviour of young people*, Department of Health, London.

Jayakody, A., Sinha, S., Curtis, K., et al. (2005), *Smoking, drinking, drug use, mental health and sexual behaviour in young people in East London*, Department of Health/Teenage Pregnancy Unit, London.

Jessor, R., Donovan, J. E. and Costa, F. M. (1991), *Beyond adolescence: problem behaviour and young adult development*, Cambridge University Press, Cambridge.

Ker, K. and Chinnock, P. (2008), 'Interventions in the alcohol server setting for preventing injuries', *Cochrane Database of Systematic Reviews* 3, Art. No. CD005244.

Kimber, J., Palmateer, N., Hutchinson, S., et al. (2010), 'Harm reduction among injecting drug users: evidence of effectiveness', in European Monitoring Centre for Drugs and Drug Addiction (EMCDDA), *Harm reduction: evidence, impacts and challenges*, Rhodes, T. and Hedrich, D. (eds), Scientific Monograph Series No. 10, Publications Office of the European Union, Luxembourg.

Lister-Sharp, D., Chapman, S., Stewart-Brown, S. and Sowden, A. (1999), 'Health promoting schools and health promotion in schools: two systematic reviews', *Health Technology Assessment* 3 (22), pp. 1–207.

Lynskey, M. T., Heath, A. C., Bucholz, K. K., et al. (2003), 'Escalation of drug use in early onset cannabis users vs co-twin controls', *JAMA* 289, pp. 427–33.

McCall, D. S., Rootman, I. and Bayley, D. (2005), 'International school health network: an informal network for advocacy and knowledge exchange', *Promotion and Exchange* 12, pp. 173–7.

McCambridge, J. and Strang, J. (2004), 'The efficacy of single-session motivational interviewing in reducing drug consumption and perceptions of drug-related risk and harm among young people', *Addiction* 99, pp. 39–52.

McCambridge, J. and Strang, J. (2005), 'Deterioration over time in effect of motivational interviewing in reducing drug consumption and related risk among young people', *Addiction* 100, pp. 470–8.

McCambridge, J. and Strang, J. (2006), 'The reliability of drug use collected in the classroom: what is the problem, why does it matter and how should it be approached?', *Drug and Alcohol Review* 25, pp. 413–18.

McCambridge, J., Slym, R. L. and Strang, J. (2008), 'Randomized controlled trial of motivational interviewing compared with drug information and advice for early information among young cannabis users', *Addiction* 103, pp. 1819–20.

Macintyre, S. and Homel, R. (1997), 'Danger on the dance floor: a study of interior design, crowding and aggression in nightclubs', in Homel, R. (ed.) *Policing for prevention: reducing crime, public intoxication and injury*, Criminal Justice Press, New York.

MacLeod, J., Oakes, R., Oppenkowski, T., et al. (2004), 'How strong is the evidence that illicit drug use by young people is an important cause of psychological or social harm? Methodological and policy implications of a systematic review of longitudinal, general population studies', *Lancet* 363, pp. 1579–88.

Maguire, M., Morgan, R. and Nettleton, H. (2003), *Reducing alcohol-related violence and disorder: an evaluation of the 'TASC' project*, Home Office, London.

Martin, G., Copeland, J. and Swift, W. (2005), 'The adolescent cannabis check-up: feasibility of a brief intervention for cannabis users', *Journal of Substance Abuse Treatment* 29, pp. 207–13.

Melrose, M., Turner, P., Pitts, J. and Barrett, D. (2007), *The impact of heavy cannabis use on young people: vulnerability and youth transitions*, Joseph Rowntree Foundation, York.

Michelsen, E., Zaff, J. F. and Hair, E. C. (2002), *A civic engagement program and youth development: a synthesis*, Child Trends, Edna McConnell Clark Foundation, New York.

Miller, W. R. and Rollnick, S. (2002), *Motivational interviewing: preparing people for change*, Guildford Press, London.

Moore, T. H. M., Zammit, S., Lingford-Hughes, A., et al. (2007), 'Cannabis use and risk of psychotic or affective mental health outcomes: a systematic review', *Lancet* 370, pp. 319–28.

Mukoma, W. and Flisher, A. J. (2004), 'Evaluations of health promoting schools: a review of nine studies', *Health Promotion International* 19, pp. 357–68.

NatCen and NFER (2007), *Smoking, drinking and drug use among young people in England in 2006: headline figure*, NHS Information Centre, London.

Nutbeam, D., Smith, C., Moore, L. and Bauman, A. (1993), 'Warning! Schools can damage your health: alienation from school and its impact on health behaviour', *Journal of Paediatric and Child Health* 29, pp. S25–S30.

Orwin, R., Cadell, D., Chu, A., et al. (2006), *Evaluation of the National Youth Anti-Drug Media Campaign*, NIDA, Rockville.

Palinkas, L. A., Atkins, C. J., Miller, C. and Ferreira, D. (1996), 'Social skills training for drug prevention in high-risk female adolescents', *Preventive Medicine* 25, pp. 692–701.

Parrott, A. C., Lees, A., Garnham, N. J., Jones, M. and Wesnes, K. (1998), 'Cognitive performance in recreational users of MDMA or "ecstasy": evidence for memory deficits', *Journal of Psychopharmacology* 12, pp. 79–83.

Petrie, J., Bunn, F. and Byrne, G. (2007), 'Parenting programmes for preventing tobacco, alcohol or drugs misuse in children <18: a systematic review', *Health Education Research* 22, pp. 177–91.

Philliber, S., Williams, K., Herrling, S. and West, E. (2001), 'Preventing pregnancy and improving health care access among teenagers: an evaluation of the Children's Aid Society-Carrera Program', *Perspectives on Sexual and Reproductive Health* 34, pp. 244–51.

Phillips, R. and Kinver, A. (2007), *Know the score: cocaine wave 4 — 2006/07 post-campaign evaluation*, Scottish Executive Research Group, Edinburgh.

Quinn, J. (1999), 'Where need meets opportunity: youth development programs for early teens', *The Future of Children* 9, pp. 96–116.

Randolph, W. and Viswanath, K. (2004), 'Lessons learned from public health mass media campaigns: marketing health in a crowded media world', *Annual Review of Public Health* 25, pp. 419–37.

Reynaud-Maurupt, C., Chaker, S., Claverie, O., et al. (2007), *A Pratiques et opinions liées aux usages des substances psychoactives dans l'espace festif «musiques électroniques»*, TRENDS, Observatoire Français des Drogues et des Toxicodependences.

Ringwalt, C., Vincus, A. A., Hanley, S., et al. (2008), 'The prevalence of evidence-based drug use prevention curricula in U.S. middle schools in 2005', *Prevention Science* 9, pp. 276–87.

Samdal, O., Nutbeam, D., Wold, B. and Kannas, L. (1998), 'Achieving health and educational goals through school: a study of the importance of the school climate and the student's satisfaction with school', Health Education Research: Theory and Practice 13, pp. 383–97.

Sánchez, V., Steckler, A., Nitirat, P., et al. (2007), 'Fidelity of implementation in a treatment effectiveness trial of Reconnecting Youth', Health Education Research 22, pp. 95–107.

Schilt, T., Maartje, M., de Win, M. L., et al. (2007), 'Cognition in novice ecstasy users with minimal exposure to other dugs: a prospective cohort study', Archives of General Psychiatry 64, pp. 728–36.

Shildrick, T. (2002), 'Young people, illicit drug use and the question of normalization', Journal of Youth Studies 5, pp. 35–48.

Solowij, N. and Battisti, R. (2008), 'The chronic effects of cannabis on memory in human: a review', Current Drug Abuse Reviews 1, pp. 81–98.

Tait, R. J. and Hulse, G. K. (2003), 'A systematic review of the effectiveness of brief interventions with substance using adolescents by type of drug', Drug and Alcohol Review 22, pp. 337–46.

Tevyaw, T. O. and Monti, P. M. (2004), 'Motivational enhancement and other brief interventions for adolescent substance use: foundations, applications and evaluations', Addiction 99, pp. 63–75.

Thomas, J., Kavanagh, J., Tucker, H., et al. (2007), Accidental injury, risk-taking behaviour and the social circumstances in which young people (aged 12–24) live: a systematic review, EPPI-Centre, London.

Thomas, R. E. and Perera, R. (2006), 'School-based programmes for preventing smoking', Cochrane Database of Systematic Reviews 3, Art. No. CD001293.

Van Der Kreeft, P., Wiborg, G., Galanti, M. R., et al. (2009), '"Unplugged": a new European school programme against substance abuse', Drugs: education, prevention and policy 16, pp. 167–81.

VCH (Vancouver Coastal Health) (2007), 2006 Vancouver youth drug reporting system: first results, Vancouver Coastal Health Authority, Vancouver.

Wallin, E. and Andréasson, S. (2005), 'Effects of a community action program on problems related to alcohol consumption at licensed premises', in Stockwell, T., Gruenewald, P. J., Toumbourou, J. W. and Loxley, W. (eds) Preventing harmful substance use: the evidence base for policy and practice, John Wiley, West Sussex.

Wiggins, M., Bonell, C., Sawtell, M., et al. (2009), 'Health outcomes of a youth-development programme in England: prospective matched comparison study', British Medical Journal 339, pp. 2534–43.

Wood, D. W., Greene, S. L., Alldus, G., et al. (2008), 'Improvement in the pre-hospital care of recreational drug users through the development of club specific ambulance referral guidelines', Substance Abuse Treatment, Prevention and Policy 3, p. 14.

WHO (World Health Organization) (1986), The Ottawa Charter for Health Promotion, World Health Organization, Copenhagen.

WHO (1998), HEALTH21: an introduction to the Health For All policy framework for the WHO European Region (European Health for All Series No. 5), World Health Organization, Copenhagen.

Yamaguchi, K. and Kandel, D. B. (1984), 'Patterns of drug use from adolescence to young adulthood: predictors of progression', American Journal of Public Health 74, pp. 673–81.

Young, I. (2005), 'Health promotion in schools: a historical perspective', Promotion and Education 12, pp. 112–17.

Young, I. and Williams, T. (1989), The healthy school, Scottish Health Education Group, Edinburgh.

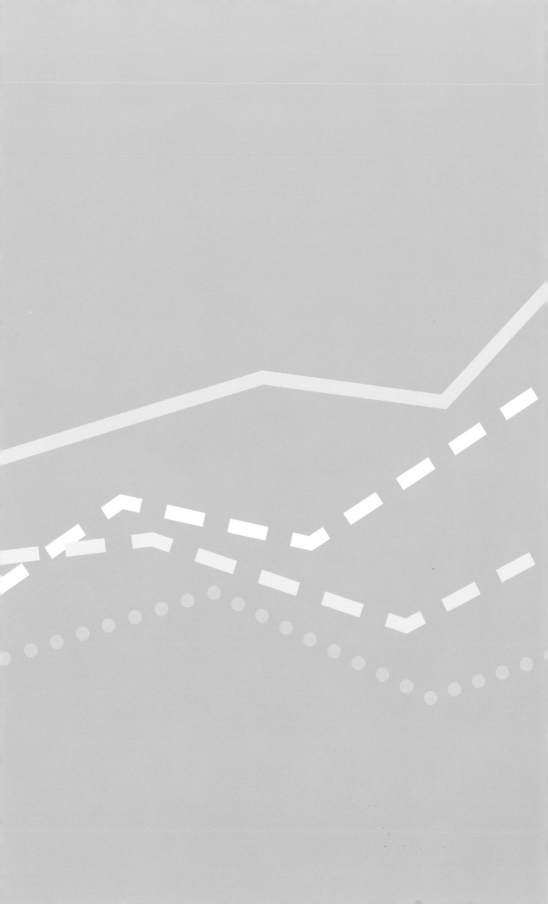

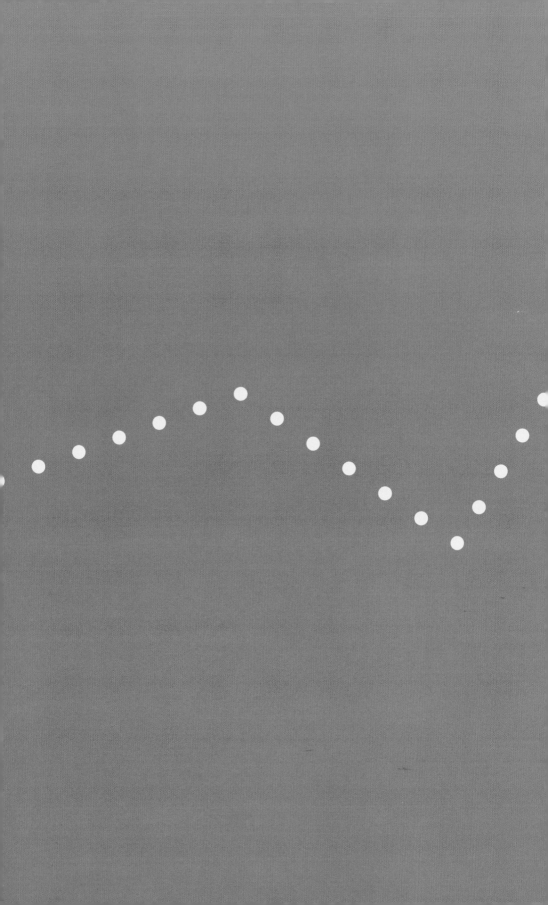

Chapter 14
Criminal justice approaches to harm reduction in Europe

Alex Stevens, Heino Stöver and Cinzia Brentari

Abstract

This chapter reviews the spread of harm reduction services in European criminal justice systems, and their evaluation. It begins with a discussion of the tensions and contradictions inherent in providing harm reduction services (which may accept continued drug use) in criminal justice settings (that do not). It then draws on research carried out for the Connections project, for its predecessor the European Network on Drug and Infections Prevention in Prisons and on the information gathered by the European Monitoring Centre for Drugs and Drug Addiction. It examines services such as needle and syringe exchange, opiate substitution and distribution of condoms and disinfectants in prisons. It also examines harm reduction services that have been developed in the context of police custody, and in the attempt to provide through-care and aftercare to drug users who pass through the criminal justice system. The chapter concludes that the tensions between harm reduction and criminal justice aims can be overcome in providing effective services to reduce drug-related harms.

Keywords: criminal justice systems, harm reduction, prison, decriminalisation, syringe exchange, opioid substitution treatment, arrest-referral.

Introduction

Harm reduction is often seen as conflicting with the use of law enforcement to reduce drug use, but there are ways in which policies and practice can develop in order to reduce harms related to drugs within the criminal justice system. The principle of harm reduction may also be applied to law enforcement itself. Drug prohibition can inadvertently increase the harmfulness of drug use as it means that users rely on illicit forms of supply and consume drugs of unknown purity and quality in a risky manner. It also creates artificially high prices, which stimulate acquisitive crime and facilitate corruption and violence. Given that drug markets cannot be eliminated, but may operate in ways that are more or less socially harmful, the key questions for law enforcement become: what sort of markets do we least dislike and how can we adjust the control mix so as to push markets in the least harmful direction? In this chapter, we leave aside more detailed discussion of the wider impact of drug law enforcement or criminalisation on societal levels of drug-related harm. We focus instead on the provision of services that aim to reduce harms done to drug users within the criminal justice system.

Many of the people who are caught up in the criminal justice system are highly exposed to drug-related harms (EMCDDA, 2009a; Singleton et al., 1997; Stöver, 2001; Rotily et al.,

2001; Møller et al., 2007; Stöver et al., 2008a; Dolan et al., 2007). These people do not lose their right to adequate and effective healthcare when they enter the criminal justice system (Carter and Hall, 2010). The ideal criminal justice system would therefore protect their health by offering the full range of healthcare approaches. Some European systems have been moving closer, in various ways, to achieving this, and we describe some of these developments in this chapter. We will examine how measures such as opioid substitution treatment (OST), needle and syringe exchange, and the provision of disinfectants and condoms have worked in prison contexts. We will look at issues of through-care and aftercare and we will explore how processes that follow arrest can divert drug users into treatment. Before looking at specific harm reduction measures we provide a short discussion of the inherent tensions between controlling drugs through the criminal law and efforts to reduce harms to drug users.

Tensions between law enforcement and harm reduction

There are at least two contradictions that hinder the effort to reduce harm through the criminal justice system. The first is the fact that criminal justice systems themselves produce harms. Of course, the criminal justice system also produces benefits to the extent that it protects people from crime and insecurity. But arrests, fines, community penalties, imprisonment and parole all infringe on individual freedoms and pleasures. The special pains of imprisonment have been a particular focus of criminological research (Sykes 1958; Mathiesen, 2006). The idea that these pains are justified by the need to reduce crime is challenged by the lack of evidence for the effectiveness of imprisonment, the most painful form of criminal justice intervention currently used in Europe (Tonry, 2004; Gendreau et al., 1999). It is well known, for example, that there is little relationship between imprisonment and crime rates (Kovandzic and Vieraitis, 2006; Reiner, 2000). Countries do not use prison as a direct, rational measure to reduce crime. Rather, they choose — through a complex process of ideological, moral, political and juridical negotiation — the level of pain that they are willing to inflict on their citizens (Christie 1982). If we choose the level of harm that we inflict, we can also choose to reduce it.

The second contradiction in pursuing harm reduction in the criminal justice system is that between the pursuit of abstinence and the acknowledgement of continuing drug use. Countries are obliged, through the UN drug conventions, to prohibit and to penalise the possession of certain substances. The criminal justice system is the process that puts these obligations into practice. It is very difficult for the same system to acknowledge that the people under its control continue to defy the law. Until the mid-1990s, for example, it was common for prison governors to deny that drug use was going on within their walls (Duke, 2003). More recently, it has been suggested by Phillip Bean (2008) that treatment agencies working with the criminal justice system should expect to subordinate their aims to those of the criminal justice agencies. Harm reduction approaches have traditionally been developed to meet the needs of people who continue to use illicit drugs, and therefore do not fit with the prescription that people under penal control should abstain. Some parts of the criminal justice system and some countries appear to negotiate this conflict more easily than others. This may be due to the different perceptions of the ideal goal of abstinence. Within the prison system, for example, abstinence has a relatively high value, because it fits with the prison's goal of incapacitating the prisoner from committing further crimes (e.g. drug purchase and possession). Probation services, with a greater focus on rehabilitation and relatively less control of the person's behaviour, seem to have less emphasis on absolute abstention, at least in Europe. In the United States, drug use while on probation often leads to imprisonment. It is more often tolerated in European probation systems, as long as no other offences are committed (Stevens, forthcoming).

So how do we deal with these contradictions? First, it seems axiomatic that the best way to reduce the amount of drug-related harm that occurs inside the criminal justice system is to reduce the number of drug users who enter it. Drug users cannot cause harm (or be harmed) in criminal justice settings if they are not actually in these settings. The number of drug users in criminal justice settings can be reduced through decriminalisation of drugs, which means that no drug users enter the criminal justice system for possession offences (though decriminalisation of drugs would not necessarily reduce the number of drug users who enter the system for other offences, which could be reduced by developing diversion or alternative sanctions) (Stevens, forthcoming). Different European countries have tried various forms of decriminalisation. They include the Netherlands' expedient non-prosecution of cannabis supply at the retail level, as well as the non-criminal offences of personal drug use in the Czech Republic, Estonia, Italy, Spain and suspension of prosecution of personal use offences in Germany and Austria.

The most comprehensive process of decriminalisation so far has occurred in Portugal. From July 2001 people who are found by the Portuguese police to be in possession of fewer than ten days' personal supply of any drug have not been arrested, though the drug is still confiscated. They have instead been referred to regional drug dissuasion committees, which have the option of imposing warnings, fines, administrative sanctions (such as taking away driving or firearms licences), or — in the case of dependent users — referring them to treatment. Since decriminalisation, and the simultaneous expansion of prevention, treatment and harm reduction services, there have been dramatic reductions in drug-related deaths and HIV. Rates of drug use seem to have fallen among children, but risen slightly in adults, in line with pan-European trends. The respective roles of decriminalisation and the simultaneous expansion of drug treatment in producing these changes can be debated (IDT, 2007; IDT, 2005; Hughes and Stevens, 2007; Greenwald, 2009). But Figure 14.1 shows clearly that decriminalisation reduced the use of imprisonment for drug offences and led to an overall reduction in the prison population (IDT, 2006, Table 62). This reduction has also been accompanied by substantial reductions in the number of people using drugs and living with HIV within Portuguese prisons (Torres et al., 2009).

The second contradiction is just a more extreme form of the long-standing argument that harm reduction conflicts with the goal — still subscribed to by all UN members (ECOSOC, 2009) — of eliminating illicit drug use. Over time, there has been a gradual acceptance that harm reduction measures do not prevent people from achieving abstinence, but rather protect the health of people who will continue to use drugs, whether or not they have the means to protect their health. This acceptance has been supported by decades of evaluative research on harm reduction measures outside the criminal justice system, including opiate substitution treatment (using methadone, buprenorphine or heroin itself) and needle and syringe exchange programmes (Hunt, 2003; Ritter and Cameron, 2005; Tilson et al., 2007; Kimber et al., 2010). As evidence develops on the use of such measures within the criminal justice system, we could expect that resistance to harm reduction within the criminal justice system will also subside. But we should not be too optimistic. The negotiations at the high level segment of the Commission on Narcotic Drugs in Vienna in March 2009 showed that resistance to harm reduction remains strong, even outside the criminal justice system. A glimmer of hope from that meeting can be perceived, if we look hard enough, in the commitment to provide treatment and 'related support services ... on a non-discriminatory basis, including in detention facilities' (ECOSOC, 2009).

Figure 14.1: Number of prisoners under sentence for drug and other offences in Portugal, 1997–2005

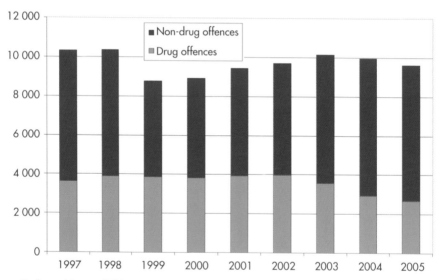

Source: Hughes and Stevens, 2007.

Harm reduction in the criminal justice system

Our exploration of existing harm reduction services in criminal justice systems starts in the place where drug-related harms of the criminal justice system are most acute: prisons.

In a report on the implementation of the European Council Recommendation (of 18 June 2003 (¹)) on the prevention and reduction of health-related harm associated with drug

(¹) http://europa.eu.int/eur-lex/pri/en/oj/dat/2003/l_165/l_16520030703en00310033.pdf

dependence (²) it was stated that a policy to provide drug users in prisons with services that are similar to those available to drug users outside prisons exists in 20 EU Member States and was about to be introduced in four countries (van der Gouwe et al., 2006). However, recent European monitoring data show that that the implementation of harm reduction programmes is quite heterogeneous in European prisons (EMCDDA, 2009a). Availability and accessibility of many key harm reduction measures in prisons lag far behind the availability and accessibility of these interventions in the community outside prisons (EMCDDA, 2009b).

Illustrating this gap most vividly is the provision — or lack thereof — of needle and syringe programmes (NSP), currently only implemented in five EU countries (EMCDDA, 2009c). The availability of opioid substitution treatment (OST) in prisons is low compared to the level of OST provision in the community in most European countries (EMCDDA, 2009d; see Figure 14.2). These findings support an earlier statement from the European Commission that:

> Harm reduction interventions in prisons within the European Union are still not in accordance with the principle of equivalence adopted by UN General Assembly, UNAIDS/WHO and UNODC, which calls for equivalence between health services and care (including harm reduction) inside prison and those available to society outside prison. Therefore, it is important for the countries to adapt prison-based harm reduction activities to meet the needs of drug users and staff in prisons and improve access to services.
>
> (European Commission, 2007, conclusion 5).

These findings also echo a 2008 WHO Regional Office for Europe report that monitored State progress in achieving Dublin Declaration goals. The Dublin Declaration commits the signatory States to take 33 specific actions — and in some cases meet specific targets — to address the HIV prevention, care, treatment and support situation across the region. The report found that, of the 53 signatory countries, condoms were available in prisons in only 18, syringe exchange programmes available in six and substitution treatment available in 17 (Matic et al., 2008). A more recent review (in 2009) by the International Harm Reduction Association (IHRA) found the situation has only marginally improved, with nine countries (out of 46) in Europe and Central Asia having syringe exchange in prisons and 28 substitution treatment (Cook, 2009; see also Cook et al., 2010).

Calls for an urgent and comprehensive response to addressing health risks within prison settings, including harm reduction measures (WHO Regional Office for Europe, 2005) are not new, and have been highlighted in international reports and policy documents spanning two decades (Parliamentary Assembly of the Council of Europe, 1988; UNODC et al., 2006; WHO, 1993; Matic et al., 2008). However, despite existing recommendations, guidelines and commitments made by governments and many others (Lines, 2008), only very few countries within the European region have come close to achieving the goals set out (Cook, 2009).

There are four key harm reduction tools for the prison setting. We describe each of these, including an example of best practice, below.

(²) http://ec.europa.eu/health/ph_determinants/life_style/drug/drug_rec_en.htm

Figure 14.2: Provision of substitution/maintenance treatment (OST) in the community and availability of OST programmes in the prison system in 2007 in the EU (expert rating)

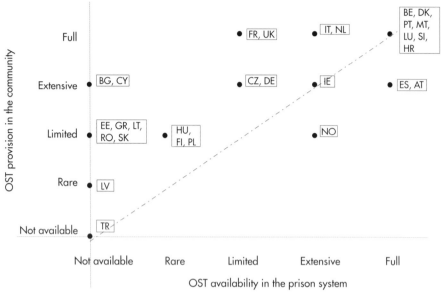

Notes:

This figure is available at: http://www.emcdda.europa.eu/stats09/hsrfig2.

Comments:

Data were not available for Sweden.

Rating scales:

Prison: expert rating of the availability of OST programmes in prisons in the country (and does not reflect level of OST provision in prison):

- Full: substitution/maintenance treatment exists in nearly all prisons.
- Extensive: exists in a majority of prisons but not in nearly all of them.
- Limited: exists in more than a few prisons but not in a majority of them.
- Rare: exists in just a few prisons.

Community: expert rating of the level of provision of OST in the community, in relation to the needs of target group problem opioid users:

- Full: nearly all problem opioid users (POUs) in need would obtain OST.
- Extensive: a majority but not nearly all POUs in need would obtain OST.
- Limited: more than a few but not a majority of POUs in need would obtain OST.
- Rare: just a few POUs in need would obtain OST.

Sources: EMCDDA, 2009d. Structured questionnaire on 'treatment programmes' (SQ27/P1), submitted by NFPs in 2008. Data for Malta is from DG Health and Consumer Protection, 'Final report on prevention, treatment, and harm reduction services in prison, on reintegration services on release from prison and methods to monitor/analyse drug use among prisoners', SANCO/2006/C4/02.

Needle and syringe exchange programmes in prisons

A position paper of the United Nations system identifies NSP as one component of 'a comprehensive package for HIV prevention among drug abusers' (Commission on Narcotic Drugs, 2002). In prisons, NSPs have been operating successfully for more than 15 years. A meta-analysis (based on 11 evaluations of the implementation of prison-based NSPs) revealed that none of the fears often associated with planned NSPs occurred in any project: syringe distribution was followed neither by an increase in drug intake nor in administration by injection. Syringes were not misused as weapons against staff or other prisoners, and disposal of used syringes was uncomplicated. Sharing of syringes among drug users disappeared almost completely or was apparent in very few cases. These studies demonstrate both the feasibility, safety and efficacy of harm reduction including NSP in prison settings (Meyenberg et al., 1999; Stöver and Nelles 2003).

At present, NSPs have been established in prisons in nine countries worldwide (Lines et al., 2006), including six countries in Europe. Coverage of the national prison systems is, however, variable. In Spain, implementation of needle and syringe exchange is authorised in all prisons (see box below) and in 2006, programmes existed in 37 prisons (Acín García, 2008). In Switzerland, NSPs are available in eight of 120 prisons, and in Germany, Luxembourg, Romania and Portugal such programmes operate in one or two prisons. Other countries, including the United Kingdom (Scotland), are considering the implementation of pilot projects (EMCDDA, 2009a; Lines et al., 2006). A review published in 2007 stated:

> Prison NSPs have been implemented in both men's and women's prisons, in institutions of varying sizes, in both civilian and military systems, in institutions that house prisoners in individual cells and those that house them in barracks, in institutions with different security ratings, and in different forms of custody (remand and sentenced, open and closed).
>
> (Stöver et al., 2009, p. 83)

Prison-based needle and syringe exchange programmes in Spain

Spanish prisons implement needle and syringe programmes (NSPs) via negotiated protocols and frameworks based on consensus among all actors involved. Following the positive experience of pilot projects, the Spanish government made a commitment to expand availability, and in March 2001 the parliament approved a green paper recommending NSPs in all prisons. This was followed by a directive, in June 2001, from the Directorate General for Prisons requiring all prisons to implement NSPs. In October, there was a further similar directive from the Subdirectorate General for Prison Health setting January 2002 as the target. In March 2002, the Ministry of the Interior and the Ministry of Health and Consumer Affairs jointly published guidelines, policies, and procedures, and training and evaluation materials, for the national implementation of prison-based NSPs. With these guidelines, every prison elaborates its own NSPs. In order to implement, follow up and evaluate the programme:

- a Commission is created, with the Director and vice directors (including sanitary vice director) and representatives of security staff of the prison, as well as representatives of the Drug Dependence and AIDS Regional Programmes;
- the needs of the prisoners and their patterns of drug use are assessed;
- the protocol for the NSP is developed; the attitudes of prisoners and staff are assessed;
- the implementation strategies are identified; and the evaluation designed.

(Stöver et al., 2007)

The Ministry of Labour and Social Security endorsed this process with additional guidance on reducing potential harm to prison staff (Ministry of Labour and Social Security, 2002).

Opioid substitution treatment

While opioid substitution treatment (OST) has become standard practice in community drug treatment services in many European countries (EMCDDA, 2009a), the implementation of OST in custodial settings in most European countries is still lagging behind the availability and quality of the treatment provision in the community (Kastelic et al., 2008; EMCDDA, 2009d).

Studies have indicated that OST initiated in the community is most likely to be discontinued in prisons (Stöver et al., 2004; Stöver et al., 2006; Michel, 2005; Michel and Maguet, 2003). This often leads to relapse both inside prisons and immediately after release, often with severe consequences, as indicated by high mortality rates after release from prisons (Singelton et al., 2003). Many studies have also shown the benefits of OST for the health and social stabilisation of opioid-dependent individuals passing through the prison system (Stallwitz and Stöver 2007; Larney and Dolan, 2009).

Substitution treatment has been widely recognised as an effective treatment for opioid dependence in the general community (Dolan et al., 1998; Farrell et al., 2001; Larney and Dolan, 2009; UNODC et al., 2006) and as having crime reducing effects (Lind et al., 2005). Despite this and the fact that methadone and buprenorphine have been added to the WHO model list of essential medicines (WHO, 2005), it remains controversial for prisons, particularly in Eastern European countries where substitution treatment also only exists on a low level in the community (van der Gouwe et al., 2006). Nevertheless, experience has clearly shown the benefits of this treatment in prisons (WHO et al., 2007; Heimer et al., 2005; Stöver et al., 2008b; Stöver and Michels, 2010).

In countries that provide OST in prisons, it is most commonly used for short-term detoxification, and less frequently as a maintenance treatment (Kastelic et al., 2008). In some countries, such as Austria, England (see box on p. 387) and Spain, substitution treatment is provided as standard therapy to many prisoners who began treatment in the community and are deemed likely to continue it after release (Stöveret al., 2004). In others it is either not available in prisons at all, although legally possible (Estonia and Lithuania), or only provided in very rare cases (Sweden). OST treatment that has been started in the community cannot legally be continued in prisons in Slovakia, Latvia, Cyprus and Greece. New substitution treatments cannot be initiated in Slovakia, Latvia, Cyprus, Greece, Portugal, Finland and Estonia (EMCDDA, 2009a).

Acknowledgement that the benefits of substitution treatment in the community might also apply to the prison setting has taken years. The sources of the controversy — and the slow and patchy manner of the intervention's implementation thus far — can be traced first to the prisons' general failure to provide adequate healthcare, with limited resources for populations with high concentrations of poor physical and mental health (Møller et al., 2007; Bertrand and Niveau, 2006). Second, due to the parallel prison healthcare system (separate to the national health services in most countries), responsibility for a prisoner's medical treatment is often transferred to healthcare providers only after that prisoner has been released. Third, the ethos of coercion and incapacitation manifests itself in a strict abstinence-based approach to drug use. Therefore, while opioid-dependent individuals in the community may be treated as patients and receive substitution treatment, in prison they continue to be treated as prisoners who are supposed to remain drug free. This double standard leads to frequent interruptions in treatment and inconsistency in dosages, especially as many opioid users spend substantial periods of time incarcerated.

Opioid substitution treatment (OST) in England

The number of methadone maintenance (OST) treatments started in prisons in England has increased from 700 in 2003 ([1]) to 19 450 for the year 2008. All 130 adult prisons in the country are now funded to provide OST. Approximately 26 000 treatments are anticipated for 2009, rising to 39 000 for the year 2010 (Marteau and Stöver, 2010).

Figure 14.3: Methadone maintenance treatments in prisons in England

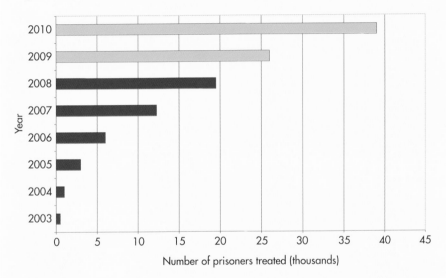

The massive expansion of OST in prisons is the result of: a shift of responsibility for prison healthcare from the Home Office to the National Health Service; political and professional leadership and investment; and a strong investment in training and education of staff in prisons. With these efforts, the number of patients in prison-based OST has been increased substantially over the past two years (Stöver et al., 2008b).

This example shows that the Integrated Drug Treatment System (IDTS) has been welcomed by a large section of the health and criminal justice community. It has also helped the British government to avoid repeated litigation by drug users who have been denied the appropriate treatment (in the past, the government has had to settle cases on this) (Radcliffe and Stevens, 2008; Marteau and Stöver, 2010). A large research programme will evaluate the process and outcomes of the IDTS.

([1]) Refers to the fiscal year 2003–04 which runs from 1 March 2003 until end February 2004. All dates cited in this box follow this pattern.

Evidence shows that methadone maintenance treatment (MMT, the most studied form of pharmacological drug treatment) can reduce risk behaviour in penal institutions, such as reduced frequency of illicit drug use in prison and reduced involvement in the prison drug trade (Dolan et al., 1998; Kimber et al., 2010). Studies have also demonstrated that methadone maintenance treatment provision in a prison healthcare setting can be effective in reducing heroin use, drug injection and syringe sharing among incarcerated heroin users (Stöver and Marteau, 2010). A sufficiently high dosage also seems to be important for improving retention rate, which helps in the provision of additional healthcare services (Dolan et al., 2002).

There is evidence that continued MMT in prison has a beneficial impact on transferring prisoners into drug treatment after release. The initiation of MMT in prisons also contributes to a significant reduction in serious drug charges and in behaviour related to activities in the drug subculture. Offenders participating in MMT also had lower readmission rates and were readmitted at a slower rate than non-MMT patients. For example, a 2001 evaluative study of the methadone programme of the Correctional Service of Canada (CSC) concluded that participation in methadone programmes had positive post-release outcomes. The study found that opiate users accessing MMT during their incarceration were less likely to be readmitted to prison following their release — and were less likely to have committed new offences — than were those not accessing methadone. These findings have been supported by a more recent randomised trial from the United States. It showed that prisoners who started methadone treatment before release and continued after it were significantly more likely to stay away from illicit drugs in the first year after release. Their outcomes were better than those achieved by similar prisoners who received only counselling in the prison, than if they were transferred to methadone programmes on release (Kinlock et al. 2009; Stöver and Marteau 2010; Stöver and Michels, 2010).

Studies have shown that prison staff tend to support the introduction of OST to a higher degree than they support other harm reduction measures, such as syringe exchange (Allen, 2001). Greater knowledge of substitution programmes is directly associated with more positive attitudes towards it (McMillan and Lapham, 2005). This suggests that training for staff on all levels may decrease resistance to substitution programmes and contribute to patient-oriented, confidential and ethical service delivery. Institutional constraints can also be overcome by highlighting the benefits of a substitution programme for the prison itself (Stöver and Marteau, 2010).

Provision of bleach and disinfectants

Many prison systems have adopted programmes that provide disinfectants such as bleach to prisoners who inject drugs, as a means to clean injecting equipment before re-using it (see box on p. 389). According to UNAIDS in 1997, the provision of full-strength bleach to prisoners as a measure had been successfully adopted in prisons in Europe, Australia, Africa, and Central America (UNAIDS, 1997). The WHO further reported that concerns that bleach might be used as a weapon proved unfounded, and that this has not happened in any prison where bleach distribution has been tried (WHO, 2007).

However, disinfection with bleach as a means of HIV prevention is of varying efficiency, and therefore regarded only as a secondary strategy to syringe exchange programmes (WHO, 2005). The effectiveness of disinfection procedures is also largely dependent upon the method used. Before 1993, guidelines for syringe cleaning stipulated a method known as the '2x2x2' method. This method involved flushing injecting equipment twice with water, twice with bleach and twice with water. Research in 1993 raised doubts about the effectiveness of this method in the decontamination of used injecting equipment, and recommended new cleaning guidelines where injecting equipment should be soaked in fresh full-strength bleach (5 % sodium hypochlorite) for a minimum of 30 seconds (Shapshank et al., 1993).

All of these developments further complicate the effective use of bleach and disinfectants in prison settings, where fear of detection by prison staff and lack of time often means that hygienic preparation of equipment and drug use happens quickly, and that prisoners will often not take the time to practise optimal disinfection techniques (WHO, 2005). Furthermore, bleach is effective in killing the HIV virus, but may be less effective for the hepatitis C virus.

Training drug users to clean syringes with bleach may provide the user with false reassurance regarding the risk of re-using injecting equipment. Despite these limitations, provision of disinfectants to prisoners remains an important option to reduce the risk of HIV transmission, particularly where access to sterile syringes is not available. The Royal College of General Practitioners concluded that '[o]n current evidence it would be difficult to support a policy of not distributing bleach' (2007, p. 13).

By August 2001, bleach was provided in 11 of 23 pre-expansion EU prison systems (Stöver et al., 2004). Disinfectants are also made available to prisoners in Canada, England and Wales, Iran, Kyrgyzstan, Moldova, Turkmenistan, Switzerland, and some parts of the Russian Federation.

Provision of bleach in Austrian prisons

In all 28 Austrian prisons, anonymous access (in most parts of the prison system) to disinfectants in order to avoid the transmission of blood-borne viruses (BBV) via sharing of needles and equipment is provided. The Austrian Ministry of Justice stated in several orders ('Erlass') that beside condoms, the disinfectant Betaisadona should be made available freely and anonymously in all prisons. The primary purpose is the cleaning of injection equipment and the treatment of injection punctures. In this context the target group are not only drug users but also those prisoners involved in tattooing. Implementation, however, is varied, with limited staff resources being a factor.

Provision of condoms, dental dams, and water-based lubricants

Many prisons globally provide condoms to prisoners as part of their institutional health and STI prevention policies. This is in keeping with the recommendation of the WHO Guidelines, 'Since penetrative sexual intercourse occurs in prison, even when prohibited, condoms should be made available to prisoners throughout their period of detention. They should also be made available prior to any form of leave or release' (WHO, 1993).

Multiple barriers exist to the use of condoms in many prisons, and there is often poor knowledge among prisoners of sexual risk behaviour and risk reduction (MacDonald, 2005; Todts et al., 1997; UNODC et al., 2006). These barriers include prison rape, the social stigma attached to homosexuality and same-sex activities, and insufficient privacy to enable safer sex. Furthermore, condoms, dental dams, and water-based lubricants are often theoretically available but often not easily and discreetly accessible, at least not available on a 24-hour basis. Prisoners may be reluctant to access safer sex measures for fear of identifying themselves as engaging in such activities.

Evidence suggests that the provision of condoms is feasible in a wide range of prison settings (WHO et al., 2007). No prison system enabling condom distribution has reversed this policy, and none have reported security problems or any major negative consequences. Research also demonstrates the importance of identifying the factors shaping resistance among stakeholders and prison officials to introducing harm reduction measures in custodial settings, including condom distribution (Jürgens et al., 2009; Stöver et al., 2007). The orientation of ministries of justice, public opinion, and prison system financial constraints are all factors shaping staff acceptance or resistance to implementing harm reduction, and it is important to develop tailor-made strategies to address these (Marteau and Stöver 2010; Stöver et al., 2009).

Through-care and aftercare

Prison may be the place where drug-related harms are most visible and acute, but the vast majority of prisoners will one day be released. According to Williamson (Williamson, 2006) the major challenge for prison healthcare is:

> to enable continuity of care, within, between, on admission and upon release. Using the prisoner journey from pre-arrest to post release as a template it will be possible for local health and social care, and criminal justice communities to better plan continuity of health and social care, alternatives to imprisonment and long term support services.

> (Williamson, 2006, p.5)

Several studies have shown that effective and rapid access to aftercare for drug-using prisoners is essential to maintain gains made in prison-based treatment (e.g. Zurhold et al., 2005; Inciardi et al., 1997; Department of Health/National Offender Management Service, 2009). Prisoners are marginalised in society and tend to fall into the gaps between care systems and structures, which find it hard to deal with multiple needs. Care should be taken to overcome this tendency. From previous studies on recidivism following in-prison treatment (e.g. Inciardi et al., 1997), maintaining therapeutic relationships initiated in the prison into the post-release period would be likely to reduce recidivism and improve health outcomes. Prisons can be places of relative safety and health promotion for prisoners. Many people slip back into less healthy habits when they leave this structured environment. The box on p. 391 gives an example of a promising programme that seeks to avoid this danger.

The 'Through the Gates' service

Many prisoners, including a high proportion of those with drug problems, leave prison with no home to go to. This increases the likelihood that they will continue risky patterns of drug use and offending. In response to this problem, the St Giles Trust (a non-governmental organisation based in London) set up the 'Through the Gates' service. This service employs a team of caseworkers (half of whom are themselves ex-offenders) to work with individual prisoners. The caseworkers go to meet prisoners before they are released in order to assess their housing and other needs. They then meet the prisoner at the gate of the prison on the day of their release. The worker accompanies the client to initial meetings with the housing service, with probation officers and, when necessary, drug treatment services. In the first year of this service, 70 % of the homeless clients it worked with were successfully placed in temporary or permanent accommodation. Probation officers reported that the service dramatically increased the chances of successful resettlement. Some clients reported that it was the first time that they had been helped to step off the repetitive treadmill of imprisonment, drug use and crime.

The following conclusions were drawn by a multi-country survey of key informants on aftercare programmes for drug-using prisoners in several European countries (Fox, 2000):

- Aftercare for drug-using prisoners significantly decreases recidivism and relapse rates and saves lives.

- Interagency cooperation is essential for effective aftercare. Prisons, probation services, drug treatment agencies and health, employment and social welfare services must join up to meet the varied needs of drug-using offenders.

- Short-sentence prisoners are the most poorly placed to receive aftercare and most likely to re-offend. These prisoners need to be fast-tracked into release planning and encouraged into treatment.

- Ex-prisoners need choice in aftercare. One size does not fit all in drug treatment.

- Aftercare that starts in the last phase of a sentence appears to increase motivation and uptake.

- In aftercare, housing and employment should be partnered with treatment programmes. Unemployed and homeless ex-prisoners are most likely to relapse and re-offend.

- Drug treatment workers must have access to prisoners during their sentence to encourage participation in treatment and to plan release.

As the mortality risks due to overdose are most critical in the first week after release (Singleton et al., 2003; Farrell and Marsden, 2008), all harm reduction measures to prevent overdose or drug-related infections should be available and accessible.

Earlier stages of the criminal justice system

As with prisons and through-care, the practice and policy of the police with regard to harm reduction varies throughout Europe, dependent on different legal backgrounds. What can be found all over Europe is a high level of formal or informal discretion (EMCDDA, 2002). The police on the street can simply turn a blind eye towards illicit behaviour, or the official strategy of the police might pro-actively support harm reduction. The basis for these choices is a growing awareness of the adverse effects of control and custody with regard to the health of drug users and thus an increasing acknowledgment of all forms of support, assistance, counselling and treatment for this target group.

The introduction of policing practices that are more open to harm reduction interventions can contribute substantially to reducing some of the negative consequences of police patrolling, such as a reluctance to carry syringes and unsafe disposal, hurried and unsafe preparation of injection, and the potential for police attention to deter drug users from going to treatment centres (MacDonald et al., 2008). The availability of an injection location that is safe from police interference is a significant harm reduction measure (Kerr et al., 2008). Drug consumption rooms are an interesting model of accepting an unlawful behaviour (possession and consumption of drugs) for the sake of the health of the drug users. In most countries where they operate, these facilities are not only tolerated, but also demanded and supported by the police, who also facilitate their use (DeBeck et al., 2008). Furthermore, the police mostly see drug consumption rooms as a 'win–win' situation, as they spend less of their time dealing with users, and therefore have more resources available to target dealers. In addition, drug consumption is no longer taking place in the local area and causing public nuisance, but is taking place under hygienic and less visible circumstances (Stöver, 2002; Hedrich et al., 2010). The success of drug consumption rooms depends on the police agreeing not to target drug users within and around them.

There are other examples in Europe of structured combinations of harm reduction and crime prevention approaches. Arrest referral programmes, which first appeared in the United Kingdom in the 1980s and were expanded at national level by the Home Office Circular in 1999, are an example of a criminal justice-based programme that can introduce drug users to treatment and harm reduction services (Seeling et al., 2001). Arrest referral places specially trained substance use assessment workers in police stations to counsel and refer drug-using arrestees who voluntarily request assistance with their drug-related problems. Arrest referral schemes provide an access point for new entrants to services. Data from the national monitoring programme in England and Wales showed that half (51 %) of all those screened by an arrest referral worker had never accessed specialist drug treatment services (Sondhi et al., 2002). This implies that arrest referral is successful in contacting problem drug-using offenders at an earlier point than they might have otherwise considered using services. Outcomes of the arrest referral schemes included consistent reductions in drug use and offending behaviour among problem drug-using offenders who have been engaged in the scheme (Sondhi et al., 2002).

However, arrest referral often suffers from low rates of retention, with large proportions of the contacted drug users not going on to contact services (Edmunds et al., 1998). In England and Wales, the Drug Intervention Programme was supplemented by a system of case management of drug-using offenders and, since 2005, testing on arrest and required assessments in order to address this problem. These latter measures enable the police to require a person arrested for any one of a specific list of offences to undergo a drug test. If the test is positive for cocaine or heroin, the person can then be ordered to attend an assessment with a drug treatment worker. The effect of these measures has not been evaluated. They have brought more drug users into treatment assessments, but many of them have been recreational users of cocaine who see no need to enter treatment.

At the stage of arrest, many drug users face risks associated with the seizure of their injecting equipment, as this increases the risks of syringe sharing the next time they use drugs. The provision of syringe exchange within police custody could reduce this risk. The revised 2007 ACPO Drug Strategy for Scotland, as well as reaffirming the support of police forces for harm reduction interventions, also acknowledges the role of the introduction of syringe exchange schemes in custody suites. As MacDonald et al. (2008) have stated:

> Research has demonstrated that the police can have a role in harm reduction provision, without necessarily compromising their legal and moral values. For example, they can encourage users in detention to make use of local needle exchange sites and provide information on their location, and they can use discretion in not arresting users at such sites, while consulting with the community on the need for such methods.

> (MacDonald et al., 2008, p. 6)

Early interventions have been implemented in many European states to avoid the negative impact of both continuous untreated drug addiction and conviction and possibly incarceration. 'FreD goes net' is a European network of such early intervention projects, which are diverting young drug users from police to counselling agencies to avoid adverse effects of the criminal justice system (LWL, 2009).

In a number of European countries legislation expands the options available to the courts for the diversion of drug-related offenders away from the criminal justice system to treatment, or for court-mandated treatment to form part of a sentence (EMCDDA, n.d.). Although data on usage of these options remain rare (European Commission, 2008), it seems they have historically been under-used (Turnbull and Webster, 1997). Few have been formally evaluated (Hough et al., 2003). Those that have been evaluated have tended to show that treatment that is entered through the legal system can be as effective as when people enter through other modes (McSweeney et al., 2007; Stevens et al., 2005). The under-exploitation of opportunities to divert drug users from the criminal justice system through alternative measures to imprisonment remains a major problem — particularly in new Member States of the European Union — which demands further investigation and action. In Cyprus in 2008, for example, a law had existed since 1992 that enabled drug-using offenders to be diverted into treatment, but no suitable treatments were in place and so the law was not used (Fotsiou, 2008).

Conclusion

The evidence and examples provided in this chapter have shown that it is possible to negotiate the tensions between law enforcement and harm reduction. Services have been successfully implemented that have reduced the harms experienced by drug users in the criminal justice system. However, implementation in many countries remains at the level of discussion, or small pilot projects. It is rare that countries actually practice the principle of equivalence between services inside and outside prisons to which they have signed up. And the chances of rapid extension of harm reduction in criminal justice systems may seem to be low, given the current scale of economic uncertainty and strains on the public purse.

Nevertheless, given the frequent contact between drug users and criminal justice systems, and ongoing epidemics of blood-borne viruses linked to problem drug use, there is an urgent need for harm reduction services to be scaled-up. Reducing the numbers of drug users in prison will be the least costly means of increasing the proportion of prisoners who have access to harm reduction. It would reduce demand for drug services in prison and would free up resources to spend on harm reduction and other services, assuming that these resources are not diverted away from working with drug users.

Additional challenges remain. These include the need to develop and expand services for non-opiate users (such as methamphetamine users in parts of Eastern Europe, and cocaine/crack users in the United Kingdom; see Decorte, 2008; Hartnoll et al., 2010), as well as the challenge of involving drug users themselves in the design and delivery of harm reduction services (see Hunt et al., 2010), which are especially severe when those drug users are subject to the criminal justice system.

All elements of the criminal justice system have roles to play in the reduction of drug-related harm, including police officers, prosecutors, courts, prisons, probation services and non-governmental organisations that work with offenders. Harm reduction is a challenge for law enforcement, and law enforcement is a challenge for harm reduction. The contradictions between the aims of these two approaches cannot be wished away. However, we can protect both public health and individual rights to healthcare by acknowledging these tensions and finding ways to move beyond them to provide high-quality harm reduction services to all who need them.

Acknowledgements

The authors' gratitude goes to the various reviewers of this chapter who helped us to improve it and to the EMCDDA for providing useful information.

References

Acín García, E. J. (2008), 'Un enfoque global sobre la prevención y el control del VIH en las prisiones de España', Secretaría General de instituciones Penitenciarias, Ministerio del Interior, Gobierno de España, presentation at the Internacional Harm Reduction Conference, Bangkok 2008.

Allen, A-M. (2001), Drug-related knowledge and attitudes of prison officers in Dublin prisons, Thesis submitted for the degree of M.Sc. in Community Health, Department of Community Health and General Practice, Trinity College, Dublin, October.

Allwright, S., Bradley, F., Long, J., et al. (2000), 'Prevalence of antibodies to hepatitis B, hepatitis C, and HIV and risk factors in Irish prisoners: results of a national cross sectional survey', *British Medical Journal* 321 (7253), pp. 78–82.

Bean, P. (2008), *Drugs and crime*, 3rd edition, Willan Publishing, Cullompton.

Bertrand, D. and Niveau, G. (eds) (2006), *Médecine, santé et prison*, Editions Medecine & Hygiene, Chene-Bourg.

Bravo, M. J., de la Fuente, L., Pulido, J., et al. (2009), 'Spanish HIV/AIDS epidemic among IDUs and the policy response from an historical perspective', Presentation at the 5th European Conference on Clinical and Social Research on AIDS and Drugs, Vilnius, 28–30 April 2009.

Carter, A. and Hall, W. (2010, in press), 'The rights of individuals treated for drug, alcohol and tobacco addiction', in Dudley, M., Silove, D. and Gale, F. (eds) (2010), *Mental health and human rights*, Oxford University Press, Oxford.

Caulkins, J. P. and Reuter, P. (2009), 'Towards a harm-reduction approach to enforcement', *Safer Communities* 8 (1), pp. 9–23.

Christie, N. (1982), *Limits to pain*, Martin Robertson, Oxford.

Cook, C. (2009), *Harm reduction policy and practice worldwide: an overview of national support for harm reduction in policy and practice*, International Harm Reduction Association, Victoria and London. Available at http://www.ihra.net/HRWorldwide.

Cook, C., Bridge, J. and Stimson, G. V. (2010), 'The diffusion of harm reduction in Europe and beyond', in European Monitoring Centre for Drugs and Drug Addiction (EMCDDA), *Harm reduction: evidence, impacts and challenges*, Rhodes, T. and Hedrich, D. (eds), Scientific Monograph Series No. 10, Publications Office of the European Union, Luxembourg.

Commission on Narcotic Drugs (2002), *Preventing the transmission of HIV among drug abusers: a position paper of the United Nations system, endorsed on behalf of ACC by the High-Level Committee on Programme (HLCP) at its first regular session of 2001, Vienna, 26–27 February 2001*, document E/CN.7/2002/CRP.5 for participants at the Forty-fifth session, Vienna, 11–15 March 2002. Available at http://www.cicad.oas.org/en/Resources/UNHIVaids.pdf.

Crawley, D. (2007), *Good practice in prison health*, Department of Health, London.

DeBeck, K., Wood, E., Zhang, R., et al. (2008), 'Police and public health partnerships: evidence from the evaluation of Vancouver's supervised injection facility', *Substance Abuse Treatment Prevention Policy* May, 7 (3), p. 11. DOI: 10.1186/1747-597X-3-11.

Decorte, T. (2008), 'Problems, needs and service provision related to stimulant use in European prisons', *International Journal of Prisoner Health* 3 (1), pp. 29–42. Available at http://dx.doi.org/10.1080/17449200601149122.

Department of Health/National Offender Management Service (2009), *Guidance notes: prison health performance and quality indicators*, Department of Health, London. Available at http://www.hpa.nhs.uk/web/HPAwebFile/HPAweb_C/1232006593707.

Dolan, K. and Wodak, A. (1999), 'HIV transmission in a prison system in an Australian State', *Medical Journal of Australia* 171 (1), pp. 14–17.

Dolan, K. A., Wodak, A. D. and Hall, W. D. (1998), 'Methadone maintenance treatment reduces heroin injection in New South Wales prisons', *Drug and Alcohol Review* June, 17 (2), pp. 153–8.

Dolan, K., Shearer, J., White, B. and Wodak, A. (2002), *A randomised controlled trial of methadone maintenance treatment in NSW prisons*, National Drug and Alcohol Research Centre, Sydney.

Dolan, K., Khoei, E. M., Brentari, C. and Stevens, A. (2007) *Prisons and drugs: a global review of incarceration, drug use and drug services. Report 12. Discussion paper*, The Beckley Foundation, Oxford. Available at http://kar.kent.ac.uk/13324/.

Dorn, N. and South, N. (1990), 'Drug markets and law enforcement', *British Journal of Criminology* 30 (2), pp. 171–88.

Dublin Declaration on HIV/AIDS in Prisons in Europe and Central Asia (2004), *Prison health is public health*, Irish Penal Reform Trust, Dublin.

Duke, K. (2003), *Drugs, prisons and policy-making*, Palgrave, Basingstoke.

ECOSOC (United Nations Economic and Social Council) (2009), *Political declaration and plan of action on international cooperation towards an integrated and balanced strategy to counter the world drug problem*, United Nations, Vienna.

Edmunds, M., May, T., Hearnden, I. and Hough, M. (1998), *Arrest referral: emerging lessons from research*, Home Office, London.

EMCDDA (European Monitoring Centre for Drugs and Drug Addiction) (n.d.), *Treatment as an alternative to prosecution or imprisonment for adults*, ELDD Topic overview, European Monitoring Centre for Drugs and Drug Addiction, Lisbon. Available at http://eldd.emcdda.europa.eu/html.cfm/index13223EN.html (accessed 3 December 2009).

EMCDDA (2002), *Prosecution of drug users in Europe: varying pathways to similar objectives*, Insights series number 5, European Monitoring Centre for Drugs and Drug Addiction, Lisbon. Available at http://www.emcdda.europa.eu/html.cfm/index33988EN.html.

EMCDDA (2005), *Alternatives to imprisonment: targeting offending problem drug users in the EU*, Selected issue, European Monitoring Centre for Drugs and Drug Addiction, Lisbon. Available at http://www.emcdda.europa.eu/html.cfm/index34889EN.html.

EMCDDA (2009a), *Annual report 2009: the state of the drugs problem in Europe*, European Monitoring Centre for Drugs and Drug Addiction, Lisbon. Available at http://www.emcdda.europa.eu/publications/annual-report/2009.

EMCDDA (2009b), Statistical bulletin 2009, Table HSR-7: availability and level of provision of selected health responses to prisoners in 26 EU countries, Norway and Turkey (expert ratings), European Monitoring Centre for Drugs and Drug Addiction, Lisbon. Available at http://www.emcdda.europa.eu/stats09/hsrtab7.

EMCDDA (2009c), Statistical bulletin 2009, Table HSR-4: year of introduction of needle and syringe programmes and types of programmes (NSP) available in 2007, European Monitoring Centre for Drugs and Drug Addiction, Lisbon. Available at http://www.emcdda.europa.eu/stats09/hsrtab4.

EMCDDA (2009d), Statistical bulletin 2009, Figure HSR-2: provision of substitution/maintenance treatment (OST) in the community and availability of OST programmes in the prison system in 2007 (expert rating), European Monitoring Centre for Drugs and Drug Addiction, Lisbon. Available at http://www.emcdda.europa.eu/stats09/hsrfig2.

European Commission (2007), 'Report from the Commission to the European Parliament and the Council on the implementation of the Council Recommendation of 18 June 2003 on the prevention and reduction of health-related harm associated with drug dependence', COM (2007) 199 final. Available at http://eur-lex.europa.eu/LexUriServ/site/en/com/2007/com2007_0199en01.pdf.

European Commission (2008), *Commission staff working document: accompanying document to the communication from the Commission to the Council and the European Parliament on an EU drugs action plan 2009–2012. Report of the final evaluation of the EU drugs action plan (2005–2008),* COM(2008) 567, SEC(2008) 2455, SEC(2008) 2454, European Community, Brussels. Available at http://eur-lex.europa.eu/SECMonth.do?year=2008&month=09.

Farrell, M. and Marsden, J. (2008), 'Acute risk of drug-related death among newly released prisoners in England and Wales', *Addiction* February 103 (2), pp. 251–5.

Farrell, M., Gowing, L. R., Marsden, J. and Ali, R. L. (2001), 'Substitution treatment for opioid dependence: a review of the evidence and the impact', in Council of Europe (ed.), *Development and improvement of substitution programmes: proceedings of a seminar organized by the Cooperation Group to combat Drug Abuse and Illicit Trafficking in Drugs (Pompidou Group)*, Strasbourg, France, 8–9 October 2001, pp. 27–54.

Fazel, S., Bains, P. and Doll, H. (2006), 'Substance abuse and dependence in prisoners: a systematic review', *Addiction* 101 (2), pp. 181–91.

Fotsiou, N. (2008), Personal communication, Cyprus Anti-Drugs Council, Nicosia.

Fox, A. (2000), *Prisoners' aftercare in Europe: a four countries study*, European Network of Drug and HIV/AIDS Services in Prison (ENDHASP), Cranstoun Drug Services, London.

Gendreau, P., Goggin, C. and Cullen, F. T. (1999), *The effects of prison sentences on recidivism*, Solicitor General Canada, Public Works and Government Services Canada, Ottawa. Available at http://www.prisonpolicy.org/scans/gendreau.pdf.

Greenwald, G. (2009), *Drug decriminalization in Portugal: lessons for creating fair and successful drug policies*, Cato Institute, Washington, DC. Available at http://www.cato.org/pub_display.php?pub_id=10080.

Hagan, H. (2003), 'The relevance of attributable risk measures to HIV prevention planning', *AIDS* 17, pp. 911–13.

Hartnoll, R., Gyarmarthy, A. and Zabransky, T. (2010), 'Variations in problem drug use patterns and their implications for harm reduction', in European Monitoring Centre for Drugs and Drug Addiction (EMCDDA), *Harm reduction: evidence, impacts and challenges*, Rhodes, T. and Hedrich, D. (eds), Scientific Monograph Series No. 10, Publications Office of the European Union, Luxembourg.

Hassim, A. (2006), 'The "5 star" prison hotel: the right of access to ARV treatment for HIV positive prisoners in South Africa', *International Journal of Prisoner Health* 2 (3), pp. 157–72.

Hedrich, D. (2004), *European report on drug consumption rooms*, European Monitoring Centre for Drugs and Drug Addiction, Lisbon. Available at http://www.emcdda.europa.eu/html.cfm/index54125EN.html.

Hedrich, D., Kerr, T. and Dubois-Arber, F. (2010), 'Drug consumption facilities in Europe and beyond', in European Monitoring Centre for Drugs and Drug Addiction (EMCDDA), *Harm reduction: evidence, impacts and challenges*, Rhodes, T. and Hedrich, D. (eds), Scientific Monograph Series No. 10, Publications Office of the European Union, Luxembourg.

Heimer, R., Catania, H., Zambrano, J. A., et al. (2005), 'Methadone maintenance in a men's prison in Puerto Rico: a pilot program', *Journal of Correctional Health Care, The Official Journal of the National Commission on Correctional Health Care* 11 (3), pp. 295–306.

Hough, M., Clancy, A., McSweeney, T. and Turnbull, P. J. (2003), 'The impact of drug treatment and testing orders on offending: two year reconviction results', *Home Office Research Findings* No. 184, Home Office, London.

Hughes, C. and Stevens, A. (2007), *The effects of the decriminalization of drug use in Portugal*, Beckley Foundation, Oxford. Available at http://www.idpc.net/php-bin/documents/BFDPP_BP_14_EffectsOfDecriminalisation_EN.pdf.pdf.

Hunt, N. (2003), *A review of the evidence-base for harm reduction approaches to drug use*, Forward Thinking on Drugs, London. Available at http://www.iprt.ie/contents/1328.

Hunt, N., Albert, E. and Montañés Sánchez, V. (2010), 'User involvement and user organising in harm reduction', in European Monitoring Centre for Drugs and Drug Addiction (EMCDDA), *Harm reduction: evidence, impacts and challenges*, Rhodes, T. and Hedrich, D. (eds), Scientific Monograph Series No. 10, Publications Office of the European Union, Luxembourg.

IDT (Instituto da Droga e da Toxicodependência) (2005), *Relatório anual 2004 — A situação do país em matéria de drogas e toxicodependências. Volume I - Informação estatística*, Instituto da Droga e da Toxicodependência, Lisbon. Available at http://www.idt.pt.

IDT (2006), *Relatório anual 2005 — A situação do país em matéria de drogas e toxicodependências. Volume I - Informação estatística*, Instituto da Droga e da Toxicodependência, Lisbon. Available at http://www.idt.pt.

IDT (2007), *Portugal: new developments, trends and in-depth information on selected issues: 2006 National report (2005 data) to the EMCDDA by the Reitox National Focal Point*, Instituto da Droga e da Toxicodependência, Lisbon. Available at http://www.idt.pt.

Inciardi, J. A., Martin, S. S., Butzin, C. A., Hooper, R. M. and Harrison, L. D. (1997), 'An effective model of prison-based treatment for drug-involved offenders', *Journal of Drug Issues*, 27 (2), pp. 261–78.

Jürgens, R., Ball, A. and Verster, A. (2009), 'Interventions to reduce HIV transmission related to injecting drug use in prison', *Lancet Infectious Diseases* 9, pp. 57–66.

Kastelic, A., Pont, J. and Stöver, H. (2008), *Opioid substitution treatment in custodial settings: a practical guide*, BIS-Verlag, Oldenburg. Available at http://www.unodc.org/documents/baltics/OST%20in%20Custodial%20Settings.pdf.

Keppler, K., Nolte, F. and Stöver, H. (1996), 'Übertragungen von Infektionskrankheiten im Strafvollzug — Ergebnisse einer Untersuchung in der JVA für Frauen in Vechta [Transmission of infectious diseases in prison: results of a study in the prison for women in Vechta]', *Sucht* 42 (2), pp. 98–107. Available at http://www.neuland.com/index.php?s=sxt&s2=inh&s3=1996204.

Kerr, T., Macpherson, D. and Wood, E. (2008), 'Establishing North America's first safer injection facility: lessons from the Vancouver experience', in Stevens, A. (ed.), *Crossing frontiers: international developments in the treatment of drug dependence*, Pavilion Publishing, Brighton, pp. 109–29.

Kimber, J., Palmateer, N., Hutchinson, S., et al. (2010), 'Harm reduction among injecting drug users: evidence of effectiveness', in European Monitoring Centre for Drugs and Drug Addiction (EMCDDA), *Harm reduction: evidence, impacts and challenges*, Rhodes, T. and Hedrich, D. (eds), Scientific Monograph Series No. 10, Publications Office of the European Union, Luxembourg.

Kinlock, T. W., Gordon, M. S., Schwartz, R. P., Fitzgerald, T. T. and O'Grady, K. E. (2009), 'A randomized clinical trial of methadone maintenance for prisoners: results at 12 months postrelease', *Journal of Substance Abuse Treatment* 37, pp. 277–85

Kovandzic, T. V. and Vieraitis, L. M. (2006), 'The effect of county-level prison population growth on crime rates', *Criminology and Public Policy* 5 (2), pp. 213–44.

Larney, S. and Dolan, K. (2009), 'A literature review of international implementation of opioid substitution treatment in prisons: equivalence of care?', *European Addiction Research* 15, pp. 107–12.

Lind, B., Chen, S., Weatherburn, D. and Mattick, R. (2005), 'The effectiveness of methadone maintenance treatment in controlling crime: an Australian aggregate-level analysis', *British Journal of Criminology* 45 (2), pp. 201–11.

Lines, R. (2008), 'The right to health of prisoners in international human rights law', *International Journal of Prisoner Health* 4 (1), pp. 3–53.

Lines, R., Jürgens, R., Betteridge, G., et al. (2006), *Prison needle exchange: lessons from a comprehensive review of international evidence and experience*, 2nd edition, Canadian HIV/AIDS Legal Network, Toronto. Available at http://www.aidslaw.ca/publications/publicationsdocEN.php?ref=184.

LWL (Landschaftsverband Westfalen-Lippe) (2009), *Fred goes net: Early intervention for young drug users*, Landschaftsverband Westfalen-Lippe, Münster. Available at http://www.lwl.org/LWL/Jugend/lwl_ks/Projekte_KS1/Fgn-english/.

MacCoun, R. J. and Reuter, P. (2001), *Drug war heresies: learning from other vices, times, and places*, Cambridge University Press, Cambridge.

MacDonald, M. (2005), *A study of health care provision, existing drug services and strategies operating in prisons in ten countries from central and eastern Europe*, Heuni, Helsinki. Available at http://www.heuni.fi/12542.htm.

MacDonald, M., Atherton, S., Berto, D., et al. (2008), *Service provision for detainees with problematic drug and alcohol use in police detention: a comparative study of selected countries in the European Union*, Paper No. 27, European Institute for Crime Prevention and Control, affiliated with the United Nations (HEUNI), Helsinki.

McMillan, G. P. and Lapham, S. C. (2005), 'Staff perspectives on methadone maintenance therapy (MMT) in a large southwestern jail', *Addiction Research and Theory* 13 (1), pp. 53–63.

McSweeney, T., Stevens, A., Hunt, N. and Turnbull, P. (2007), 'Twisting arms or a helping hand? Assessing the impact of "coerced" and comparable "voluntary" drug treatment options', *British Journal of Criminology* 47 (3), pp. 470–90.

Marteau, D. and Stöver, H. (2010, in press), 'The introduction of the prisons "Integrated Drug Treatment System (IDTS)" in England', *International Journal of Prisoner Health*.

Mathiesen, T. (2006), *Prison on trial*, 3rd edition, Waterside Press, Winchester.

Matic, S., Lazarus, J. V., Nielsen, S. and Laukamm-Josten, U. (eds) (2008), *Progress on implementing the Dublin Declaration on Partnership to Fight HIV/AIDS in Europe and Central Asia*, WHO Regional Office for Europe, Copenhagen. Available at http://www.euro.who.int/document/e92606.pdf.

Meyenberg, R., Stöver, H., Jacob, J. and Pospeschill, M. (1999), *Infektionsprophylaxe im Niedersächsischen Justizvollzug — Abschlußbericht*, BIS-Verlag, Oldenburg.

Michel, L. (2005), 'Substitutive treatments for major opionic dependance adapted to prison life', *Information Psychiatrique* 81 (5), pp. 417–22.

Michel, L. and Maguet, O. (2003), *L'organisation des soins en matière de traitements de substitution en milieu carcéral, Rapport pour la Commisssion nationale consultative des traitements de substitution*, Centre Régional d'Information et de Prévention du Sida Ile-de-France, Paris.

Michel, L., Carrieri, P. and Wodak, A. (2008), 'Harm reduction and equity of access to care for French prisoners: a review', *Harm Reduction Journal* 5, p. 17. DOI: 10.1186/1477-7517-5-17.

Ministry of Labour and Social Security (2002), *Instruction 101/2002 of the Directorate General on Labour Inspection and Social Security on criteria of action in connection with the implementation in a number of prisons of the needle exchange program for injecting drug users, 23*. August 2002, Ministry of Labour and Social Security, Madrid.

Møller, L, Stöver, H., Jürgens, R., Gatherer, A. and Nikogosian, H. (eds) (2007), *Health in prisons: a WHO guide to the essentials in prison health*, WHO Regional Office for Europe, Copenhagen.

Offender Health Research Network (2009), Website. Available at http://www.ohrn.nhs.uk (accessed 19 August 2009).

Parliamentary Assembly of the Council of Europe (1988), *Recommendation 1080 on a co-ordinated European health policy to prevent the spread of AIDS in prison*, Council of Europe, Strasbourg. Available at http://assembly. coe.int/documents/AdoptedText/ta88/erec1080.htm.

Pont, J. (2008), 'Ethics in research involving prisoners', *International Journal of Prisoner Health* 4 (4), pp. 184–97.

Radcliffe, P. and Stevens, A. (2008), 'Are drug treatment services only for "thieving junkie scumbags"? Drug users and the management of stigmatised identities', *Social Science and Medicine* 67 (7), pp. 1065–73.

Reiner, R. (2000), 'Crime and control in Britain', *Sociology: The Journal of the British Sociological Association*, 34 (1), pp. 71–94.

Ritter, A. and Cameron, J. (2005), *Monograph no. 06: a systematic review of harm reduction*, DPMP Monograph Series, Turning Point Alcohol and Drug Centre. Fitzroy.

Rolles, S. and Kushlick, D. (2004), *After the war on drugs*, Transform, Bristol.

Rotily, M., Weilandt, C., Bird, S. M., et al. (2001), 'Surveillance of HIV infection and related risk behaviour in European prisons: A multicentre pilot study', *European Journal of Public Health* 11 (3), 243–50.

Royal College of General Practitioners (2007), *Guidance for the prevention, testing, treatment and management of hepatitis C in primary care*, Royal College of General Practitioners, London. Available at http://www.smmgp.org. uk/download/guidance/guidance003.pdf.

Seeling, C., King, C., Metcalfe, E., Tober, G. and Bates, S. (2001), 'Arrest referral: a proactive multi-agency approach', *Drugs: Education, Prevention and Policy* 8, pp. 327–33.

Shapshank, P., McCoy, C., Rivers, J. , et al. (1993), 'Inactivation of Human Immunodeficiency Virus-1 at short time intervals using undiluted bleach', *Journal of Acquired Immune Deficiency Syndromes* 6, pp. 218–19.

Singleton, N., Meltzer, H. and Gatward, R. (1997), *Psychiatric morbidity among prisoners: summary report*, National Statistics, London. Available at http://www.statistics.gov.uk/downloads/theme_health/Prisoners_ PsycMorb.pdf.

Singleton, N., Pendry, E., Taylor, C., Farrell, M. and Marsden, J. (2003), 'Drug-related mortality among newly released offenders', *Findings 187*, Home Office, London. Available at http://www.homeoffice.gov.uk/rds/pdfs2/ r187.pdf.

Sondhi, A., O'Shea, J. and Williams, T. (2002), 'Arrest referral: emerging findings from the national monitoring and evaluation programme', *DPAS Briefing Paper 18*, Home Office Drug Prevention Advisory Service, London.

Stallwitz, A. and Stöver, H. (2007), 'The impact of substitution treatment in prisons: a literature review', *International Journal of Drug Policy* 18, pp. 464–74.

Stevens, A. (2008), 'Alternatives to what? Drug treatment alternatives as a response to prison expansion and overcrowding', Presentation at the 2nd Annual Conference of the International Society for the Study of Drug Policy, 3–4 April 2008, Lisbon.

Stevens, A. (forthcoming), 'Treatment sentences for drug users: contexts, mechanisms and outcomes', in Hucklesby, A. and Wincup, E. (eds), *Drug interventions and criminal justice*, Milton Keynes.

Stevens, A., Berto, D., Heckmann, W., et al. (2005), 'Quasi-compulsory treatment of drug dependent offenders: an international literature review', *Substance Use and Misuse* 40, pp. 269–83.

Stevens, A., Bewley-Taylor, D. and Dreyfus, P. (2009), *Drug markets and urban violence: can tackling one reduce the other?*, Beckley Foundation, Oxford.

Stöver, H. (1994), 'Infektionsprophylaxe im Strafvollzug', in Stöver, H. (ed.), *Infektionsprophylaxe im Strafvollzug. Eine Übersicht über Theorie und Praxis (Vol. XIV)*, Deutsche AIDS-Hilfe, Berlin, pp. 13–40.

Stöver, H. (2001), *An overview study: assistance to drug users in European Union prisons*, EMCDDA, Lisbon.

Stöver, H. (2002), 'Consumption rooms: a middle ground between health and public order concern', *Journal of Drug Issues* 32 (2), pp. 597–606.

Stöver, H. (ed.) (2008), *Evaluation of national responses to HIV/AIDS in prison settings in Estonia: evaluation carried out on behalf of the UNODC Regional project 'HIV/AIDS prevention and care among injecting drug users and in prison settings in Estonia, Latvia and Lithuania'*, UNODC, New York. Available at http://www.unodc.org/documents/baltics/Report_Evaluation_Prisons_2008_Estonia.pdf.

Stöver, H. and Marteau, D. (2010, in press), 'Scaling-up of opioid substitution treatment in custodial settings: evidence and experiences', *International Journal of Prisoner Health*.

Stöver, H. and Michels, I. I. (2010, in press), 'Drug use and opioid substitution treatment for prisoners', *Addiction*.

Stöver, H., and Nelles, J. (2003), '10 years of experience with needle and syringe exchange programmes in European prisons: a review of different evaluation studies', *International Journal of Drug Policy*, 14 (5–6), 437–44.

Stöver, H., Hennebel, L. and Casselman, J. (2004), *Substitution treatment in European prisons: a study of policies and practices of substitution treatment in prisons in 18 European countries*, Cranstoun Drug Services, London.

Stöver, H., Casselman, J. and Hennebel, L. (2006), 'Substitution treatment in European prisons: a study of policies and practices in 18 European countries', *International Journal of Prisoner Health* 2 (1), pp. 3–12.

Stöver, H., MacDonald, M. and Atherton, S. (2007), *Harm reduction for drug users in European prisons*, BIS-Verlag, Oldenburg.

Stöver, H., Weilandt, C., Zurhold, H., Hartwig, C. and Thane, K. (2008a), *Final report on prevention, treatment, and harm reduction services in prison, on reintegration services on release from prison and methods to monitor/analyse drug use among prisoners (Drug policy and harm reduction, SANCO/2006/C4/02)*, European Commission, Directorate – General for Health and Consumers. Available at http://ec.europa.eu/health/ph_determinants/life_style/drug/documents/drug_frep1.pdf .

Stöver, H., Weilandt, C., Huisman, A., et al. (2008b), *Reduction of drug-related crime in prison: the impact of opioid substitution treatment on the manageability of opioid dependent prisoners*, BISDRO, University of Bremen, Bremen.

Stöver, H., Lines, R. and Thane, K. (2009), 'Harm reduction in European prisons: looking for champions and ways to put evidence-based approaches into practice', in Demetrovics, Z., Fountain, J. and Kraus, L. (eds) *Old and new policies, theories, research methods and drug users across Europe*, European Society for Social Drug Research (ESSD), pp. 34–49. Available at http://www.essd-research.eu/en/publications.html.

Sykes, G. M. (1958), *The society of captives*, Princeton University Press, Princeton, NJ.

Taylor, A., Goldberg, D., Emslie, J., et al. (1995), 'Outbreak of HIV infection in a Scottish prison', *British Medical Journal* 310 (6975), pp. 289–92.

Tilson, H., Aramrattana, A., Bozzette, S., et al. (2007), *Preventing HIV infection among injecting drug users in high risk countries: an assessment of the evidence*, Institute of Medicine, Washington, DC. Available at http://www.nap.edu/catalog.php?record_id=11731.

Todts, S., Fonck, R., Colebunders, R., et al. (1997), 'Tuberculosis, HIV hepatitis B and risk behaviour in a Belgian prison', *Archives of Public Health* 55, pp. 87–97.

Tonry, M. (2004), *Punishment and politics: evidence and emulation in the making of English crime control policy*, Willan Publishing, Cullompton.

Torres, A. C., Maciel, D., Sousa, D. and Cruz, R. (2009), *Drogas e Prisões — Portugal 2007*, CIES/ISCTE, Lisbon.

Turnbull, P. J. and Webster, R. (1997), *Demand reduction activities in the criminal justice system in the European Union, Final Report*, EMCDDA, Lisbon.

UNAIDS (Joint United Nations Programme on HIV/AIDS) (1997), *Prisons and AIDS: UNAIDS technical update*, UNAIDS Best Practice Collection, United Nations, Geneva.

UNODC (United Nations Office on Drugs and Crime) and UNAIDS (2008), *Women and HIV in prison settings*, United Nations, Geneva/Vienna.

UNODC, WHO and UNAIDS (2006), *HIV/AIDS prevention, care, treatment and support in prison settings: a framework for an effective national response*, United Nations Office on Drugs and Crime, World Health Organization and the Joint United Nations Programme on HIV/AIDS, Vienna and New York.

van der Gouwe, D., Gallà, M., van Gageldonk, A., et al. (2006), *Prevention and reduction of health-related harm associated with drug dependence: an inventory of policies, evidence and practices in the EU relevant to the implementation of the Council Recommendation of 18 June 2003. Synthesis report*, Contract nr. SI2.397049, Trimbos Instituut, Utrecht. Available at http://ec.europa.eu/health/ph_determinants/life_style/drug/documents/drug_report_en.pdf.

WHO (World Health Organization) (1993), *WHO guidelines on HIV infection and AIDS in prisons*, WHO, Geneva.

WHO (2005), *Effectiveness of drug dependence treatment in preventing HIV among injecting drug users*, Evidence for action technical papers, WHO, Geneva.

WHO (2007), *Effectiveness of interventions to manage HIV in prisons: needle and syringe programmes and bleach and decontamination strategies*, Evidence for action technical papers, WHO, Geneva.

WHO (2005), *WHO model list of essential medicines, 14th revision (March 2005)*, WHO, Geneva. Available at http://www.who.int/medicines/publications/essentialmedicines/en/index.html.

WHO Regional Office for Europe (2005), *Status paper on prisons, drugs and harm reduction*, WHO Office for Europe, Copenhagen.

WHO Regional Office for Europe (2007), 'WHO health in prisons project', *Newsletter* December, WHO Office for Europe, Copenhagen. Available at http://www.euro.who.int/Document/HIPP/WHO_HIPP-Newsletter-dec07.pdf.

WHO, UNAIDS and UNODC (2007), *Effectiveness of interventions to manage HIV in prisons: provision of condoms and other measures to decrease sexual transmission*, Evidence for action technical papers, World Health Organization, Geneva.

Williamson, M. (2006), *Improving the health and social outcomes of people recently released from prisons in the UK: a perspective from primary care*, The Sainsbury Centre for Mental Health, London. Available at http://www.scmh.org.uk/pdfs/scmh_health_care_after_prison.pdf.

Zurhold, H., Haasen, C. and Stöver, H. (2005), *Female drug users in European prisons: a European study of prison policies, prison drug services and the women's perspectives*, BIS-Verlag, Oldenburg.

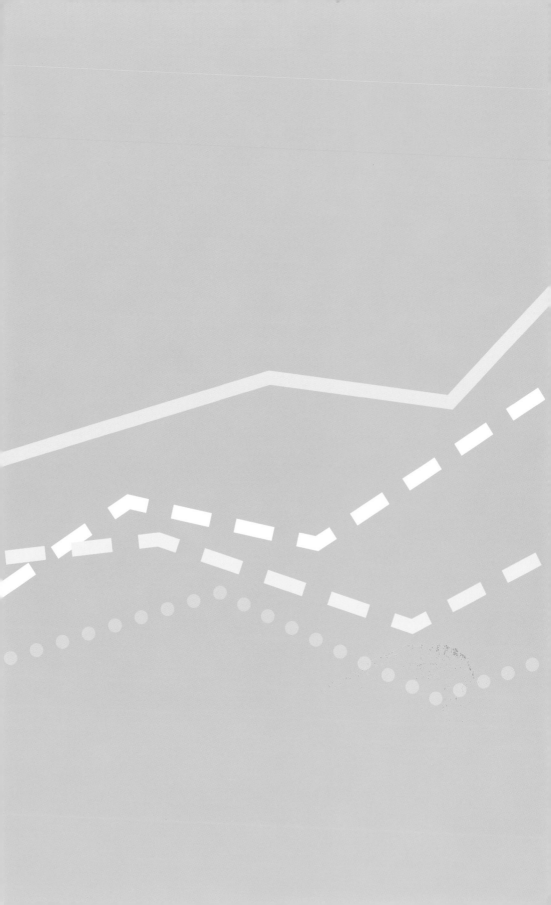

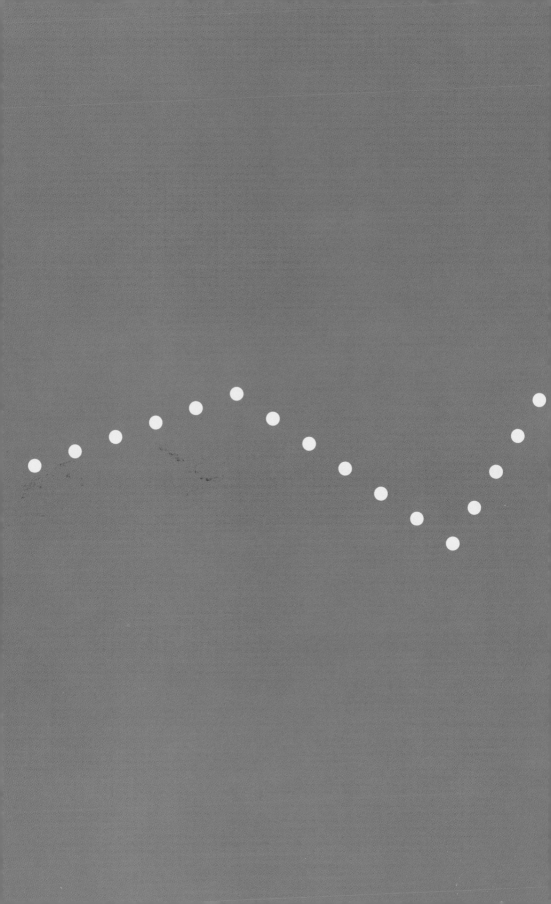

Chapter 15
Variations in problem drug use patterns and their implications for harm reduction

Richard Hartnoll, Anna Gyarmathy and Tomas Zabransky

Abstract

This chapter describes the diversity of problem drug use patterns across Europe, the different harms that may arise, and the implications for harm reduction responses. Harm reduction developed in response to concern about heroin injecting in the 1980s in western Europe. Since then, other patterns of problem drug use have increased and the geographical context has expanded. While heroin continues to present challenges, the problematic use of stimulants such as (meth-)amphetamine or cocaine, of other opioids such as home-made opiates or synthetic opiates, and of multiple drug combinations calls for innovative responses. These responses need to be flexible and based on consensus and cooperation between key actors, in particular from the health, social and law enforcement sectors.

Keywords: problem drug use, Europe, harm reduction, drug use patterns, responses.

Introduction

Historically, harm reduction has been heroin-focused and driven by concern over the risks of injecting. However, patterns of problem drug use vary widely across the European region. Different patterns of use can have different impacts on the burden of drug-related harms. The aim of this chapter is to highlight this diversity and to discuss the implications for harm reduction priorities and interventions.

The chapter does not provide an overview of drug use patterns in Europe but focuses on selected key themes together with illustrative case studies to underline the importance of innovative harm reduction responses that are adapted to the particular harms that different drug use patterns may incur. The emphasis is on health-related harms. For reasons of space, social harms such as drug-related crime or public order, though important, are not covered.

The Annual reports of the EMCDDA provide information on the broad differences in problem drug use ([1]) observed across Europe.

- Historically (from the 1970s/1980s) there has been a predominance of heroin in western and southern European countries compared to amphetamines in northern countries and home-made opiates and/or misuse of medicines in central and eastern Europe (Hartnoll, 2003).

([1]) Problem drug use is defined by the EMCDDA as 'injecting drug use or long-duration/regular use of opioids, cocaine and/or amphetamines'. This definition is currently being reviewed in the context of changes in the drug situation in recent years.

- More recently (1990s to early 2000s) there has been an increase in heroin/opiates in eastern and central countries compared to stabilisation or some decreases in western and southern countries; after 2003, there are signs of heroin increasing again.

- Also, more recently, there has been a significant increase in cocaine as the predominant stimulant in south and west Europe compared to amphetamines in northern, central and eastern countries.

- There has been a continuing high level of injecting (whether opioids or stimulants) in northern, central and eastern countries compared to relatively lower levels of injecting, together with increases in smoking or sniffing, in south and west Europe.

Some exceptions to this general picture are described later in this chapter. In all countries, multiple drug use, especially of opiates and stimulants, often together with heavy alcohol use or pharmaceuticals such as benzodiazepines, is common amongst problem drug users. Unless otherwise referenced, information on patterns of problem drug use in the EU is based on the Annual reports of the EMCDDA and national reports from the Reitox network of focal points in Member States.

Amphetamine and methamphetamine

While heroin and more recently cocaine have been the main drugs of concern in many European countries, in parts of northern and central Europe amphetamine use has been important among problem drug users for many years, either as a primary drug or in combination with opiates (Sweden, Finland, Norway, Czech Republic). Over recent years, relatively high levels of amphetamine injecting have also been reported from other countries around the Baltic, as well as from Slovakia and Hungary. Some problematic use is reported from other northern and north-western countries, though only the United Kingdom reports a substantial proportion of injectors. The drugs involved are mainly amphetamines (amphetamine sulphate powder, or in some cases tablets). Methamphetamine, which is more potent than amphetamine, is not common in European Union (EU) countries, with the notable exception of pervitin in the Czech Republic and, quite recently, Slovakia (EMCDDA, 2008; Griffiths et al., 2008). Reports of smoking crystal methamphetamine are rare in Europe (in contrast to the United States).

In the Czech Republic, methamphetamine has been the primary problem drug since the 1970s (see Case study 15.1). Recently, substantial increases have occurred in neighbouring Slovakia. In addition, increased availability and use of methamphetamine is reported from countries where amphetamine use has traditionally been prevalent (Norway, Sweden, Finland). For example, in Norway methamphetamine has been increasingly found in blood samples from arrested drivers (21 % in 2007 compared to 10 % in 2003) while the trend for amphetamine appears to be declining (SIRUS, 2008). Latvia, Lithuania and Hungary also report some increases.

Important levels of injecting home-made liquid forms of methamphetamine ('vint') or methcathinone ('jeff' or 'boltushka') (²), derived from ephedrine or pseudoephedrine, are reported in parts of Russia, Ukraine and other former Soviet Union countries (Grund et al.,

(²) Methamphetamine is produced by reduction of (pseudo)ephedrine, while methcathinone is produced by oxidation. The latter is a simpler process though methcathinone is less potent than methamphetamine.

2009). The (pseudo)ephedrine is usually extracted from common prescription medicines or over-the-counter cold preparations.

Legal restrictions on the sale of ephedrine-containing medicaments have led to the development of alternative methods of producing stimulant-type drugs. For example, a recent study in Odessa, Ukraine describes young drug users injecting home-made drugs containing cathinone, a weaker, shorter-lasting stimulant obtained by mixing freely available medications containing phenylpropanolamine with vinegar and potassium permanganate (Chintalova-Dallas et al., 2009). However, Czech customs report seizures of larger shipments of pure pseudo/ephedrine thought to originate in Balkan and/or in former Soviet countries. This may signal a renewed interest of criminal groups in the Czech pervitin market following failed attempts to control it in the late 1990s and early 2000s (Zabransky, 2009).

With some exceptions (e.g. the Czech Republic or Sweden) data on drug users in treatment facilities may underestimate the extent of problem use of amphetamines, and of stimulants in general, perhaps because of limited treatment options for amphetamines or because users may not have, or may not perceive, a need for treatment. For example, in Finland the estimated prevalence of problem use of amphetamines in 2005 was four times that of opiates. Despite that, opiates were the most common primary drug for which treatment was sought (Stakes, 2008).

Risks, harms, protective factors

Evidence on the risks and harms of injecting (meth)amphetamine, relative to heroin or other opioids, is variable, with different studies showing different results (see also Grund et al., 2010). For example some studies have shown lower HIV prevalence among amphetamine users, despite high levels of risk behaviour (e.g. Käll and Olin, 1990; Talu et al., 2010), while others report similar or higher HIV rates (e.g. Shaboltas et al., 2006; Zeziulin et al., 2008). It is likely that differences in risk behaviours and rates of infection reflect differences in the populations involved, in the contexts of use, and in the forms in which the drugs are prepared and used more than they reflect the specific substance per se. It has also been suggested that opiate-mediated immuno-suppression increases the likelihood of HIV infection in opioid compared to amphetamine users (Vallejo et al., 2004).

For example, a study of stimulant injectors in Ukraine (Booth et al., 2008) found a lower prevalence of HIV among stimulant users compared to opiate users in some cities and the reverse in others. Furthermore, despite an overall lower HIV prevalence, stimulant injectors showed higher risk scores on composite measures of both injection and sex risk. Since stimulant injectors were younger with shorter injecting histories, the study concluded that without intervention HIV was likely to increase among stimulant injectors.

Studies also suggest that the type of drug injected is associated with different profiles of risk behaviour. For example Kruse et al. (2009) report that risks specific to stimulant-only users were related to direct syringe sharing (sharing needles and rinse water) while risks specific to heroin users were related to sharing drugs while preparing for injection (front/backloading, sharing cotton and cookers). These differences only became apparent when geographical clustering by neighbourhood was included. The authors suggest that attention to neighbourhood differences might improve the impact of interventions for injectors of different drugs.

The frequency and intensity of injecting are also important aspects of infection risk (Colfax and Shoptow, 2005; Braine et al., 2005). For example, in a cohort study of predominantly heroin injectors in St Petersburg, frequent psychostimulant use was the main factor associated with HIV seroconversion (Koslov et al., 2006).

In settings where amphetamines are used in small, private groups, or on an intermittent or binge basis rather than daily, user groups may display lower levels of marginalisation and lower levels of risk behaviours than is often found among heroin using populations (see Case Study 15.1). In other populations of amphetamine users, health risks remain high, for example where use is associated with social exclusion, marginalised lifestyles, working in the sex industry, or imprisonment (March et al., 2006).

There is consistent evidence of increased sexual risk behaviour among (meth)amphetamine users, both injectors (Booth et al., 2008; Molitor et al., 1999; Käll and Nilsonne, 1995; Klee, 2006) and non-injectors (Molitor et al., 1998).

Overdose deaths appear to be relatively uncommon (EMCDDA, 2009a), in part because amphetamines are not central nervous system depressants and the range between effective and deadly dose is wider than with opiates. However overdoses can be more difficult to manage since there is no equivalent to naloxone that might be distributed to street workers or users — the only option is rapid, sophisticated medical help to deal with the threat of acute heart failure (personal communication, T. Zabransky).

The form of the drug preparation is also important regarding the risk of injection-related complications. Thus home-based methods of preparing central nervous system stimulants leave traces of chemicals such as phosphorus, permanganate or sulphuric acid. The additives may cause damage to blood vessels and liver (Pavlenko, 2008) or neurological damage and, in the case of permanganate, irreversible Parkinson-like symptoms (de Bie et al., 2007).

Implications

If, as appears to be the case in Finland (see above, Stakes, 2008), amphetamine injectors are less likely than their opiate-using counterparts to contact services, then greater emphasis is needed on outreach and peer education approaches targeted at amphetamine-using networks and groups. This is especially important where the populations involved are young. The high levels of sexual risk behaviour associated with methamphetamine use mean that sexual risk education needs to be addressed systematically in service development and delivery, not only in services targeting sex workers, and to go beyond providing condoms (Corski and Booth, 2008).

The current lack of an equivalent low-cost and effective treatment such as substitution treatment for opiate addiction implies that higher priority should be given to developing treatments for stimulant users. Several studies are underway in this regard (Elkashef et al., 2008).

In developing responses it may be useful to consider whether distinct approaches or services might encourage stimulant users to seek help. Thus opening hours could take account of more socially integrated users with regular jobs, or the locations and images projected of services could be more discrete in order to overcome barriers such as perceptions that drug services are for heroin addicts or 'junkies'. The distribution of hard gelatine capsules for pervitin users described in Case study 15.1 is another example of a specific, targeted intervention.

At the level of policy, several studies have noted that efforts to suppress home-production of amphetamine-type stimulants may have paradoxical adverse consequences in terms of users turning to potentially more risky patterns of drug production and consumption, or in terms of production becoming more professionally organised, leading to an expansion in the market (Grund et al., 2009; Chintalova-Dallas et al., 2009; see also Case study 15.1). This implies a need for discussions between those responsible for different aspects of drug policy.

Case study 15.1: Methamphetamine (pervitin) injecting in the Czech Republic

In contrast to other EU countries, the major drug used by problem drug users in the Czech Republic is crystal methamphetamine, locally known as pervitin ([3]). The predominance of pervitin has persisted from the early 1970s to the present.

Hard gelatine capsules

Quite recently, a remarkable harm reduction intervention specifically for pervitin users was introduced in the Czech Republic and is quickly spreading through the country.

Distribution of empty hard gelatine capsules was introduced in 2006 in South Moravia (personal communication, B. Janiková). The inspiration for providing capsules was the practice of some methamphetamine users of swallowing the drug in a bolus, wrapped in paper or a plastic bag, when they were experiencing severe problems with injecting due to injured veins. In English, this is nicknamed 'parachuting' (Hendrickson et al., 2006).

According to the only Czech study to date (Škařupová et al., 2009) in 2008 almost 29 000 capsules were distributed by at least 17 harm reduction organisations in different parts of the country ([4]). A further 20 facilities plan to introduce capsule distribution shortly. Drug users usually fill the capsules with pervitin powder before swallowing, though some report using liquid pervitin (dissolved powder) after failed attempts to inject.

The study reports that drug users perceive the effects of 'piko' used in this way as comparable in intensity to injecting the same amount of the drug. Administered rectally, the onset is perceived as even more intense. Oral use in capsule form reduces the intolerably bitter taste of methamphetamine and, compared to intravenous administration, has an exiguous onset of effect. The study identified that in addition to drug users switching to capsules from injecting, other groups were successfully targeted: sniffers looking for enhanced drug experience, and relatively stable, employed injecting drug users (IDUs) wishing to reduce injecting at work in order to avoid discovery.

---

[3] Originally a German label name for industrially produced methamphetamine. Commonly known as 'piko' (pronounced as 'pee-koh') in the Czech drug subculture.
[4] This is quite low compared to approximately 4 500 000 needles and hypodermic sets distributed by Czech needle and syringe programmes (NSPs) in the same year, and another 1 500 000 needles and sets sold to drug users by pharmacies in 2007 (Mravčík, et al., 2008).

Overall, providing hard gelatine capsules is perceived as a successful harm reduction intervention, averting risks of injecting (and sniffing) pervitin. However, professionals are concerned that titration of dosages can be difficult for inexperienced users, and that gastric ulcers may develop after long-term daily oral use of methamphetamine. Further studies are needed.

Drug markets and harm reduction

Many drug-related harms arise more from the characteristics of drug markets than from drug use per se (e.g. MacCoun and Reuter, 2001; Join Together, 2007). A specific aspect of pervitin in the Czech Republic is its mode of production. Most of what is consumed is locally produced and distributed in very small quantities (Mravčik et al., 2008). The producers ('cooks') use simple tools, freely available industrial chemicals and pseudoephedrine extracted from anti-cough medications that until recently were readily available from pharmacies. Production and subsequent use usually occurs in small groups of three to eight people who share the logistics of production [5]. There is little communication between these groups in terms of drug distribution and, most importantly, in terms of use (Miovský et al., 2007) — an aspect that probably contributes to the very low prevalence of HIV (<0.01 %) and hepatitis C (HCV (<35 %) among Czech users of pervitin. Finally, the atomised Czech pervitin market is comparatively non-violent since 'turf fights' associated with criminalised drug distribution are rare, and recruitment of new drug users is low due to the social seclusion of the 'squads'.

However, this relatively low-harm ('balanced' in economic terms) situation could rapidly change if small production patterns were destroyed — for example by restricting pseudoephedrine-containing medications to prescription only or by a complete ban [6]. Disrupting the 'balanced' drug market could well result in increased violence and health harms (e.g. Goldstein, 1989; Rasmussen et al., 1993; Rasmussen and Benson, 1997). The transition from atomised drug production and use into a 'standard' pyramidal drug market with marketing driven by high monetary profits could have long-term negative consequences.

Harms resulting from unintended consequences of drug policies — especially legal and law enforcement interventions — represent an area of harm reduction that needs to be further explored and the room for manoeuvre assessed.

The other important issue in terms of reducing the harms of homemade drugs is the production process and quality of the final product. For the Czech 'cooks', it is imperative to evaporate the final methamphetamine liquid into crystals and to share only the powder between the squad (Grund et al., 2009). From the public health point of view, sharing powder (that is subsequently dissolved and injected by each individual) is, compared to communal sharing of the liquid, substantially less risky in terms of disseminating blood borne diseases within the group.

[5] Procuring the pseudoephedrine-containing pharmaceuticals and other chemicals, providing the house or apartment for preparing the drug, sharing the necessary know-how.
[6] Both options were recently discussed by the Czech decision makers together with less severe forms of regulation such as electronic ID registration of buyers of pseudoephedrine products.

Cocaine and crack

In western and southern Europe the predominant stimulant is cocaine rather than amphetamines, though there are large differences in the extent of problematic use, with high rates reported from Italy, Spain, the Netherlands and the United Kingdom. Different sub-groups of problem cocaine users can be distinguished (EMCDDA, 2007).

One common pattern among socially integrated groups involves escalating use of cocaine, mainly by snorting, alongside heavy alcohol consumption, cannabis, benzodiazepines and, less commonly, heroin. In other groups, cocaine is more closely associated with heroin use as either a primary or secondary drug. Cocaine-injecting is mostly reported among heroin injectors (including clients of methadone programmes who were primary heroin injectors before entering treatment). In countries where heroin is mostly smoked rather than injected then cocaine is mainly either snorted or smoked. Crack appears to be mostly restricted to areas of some large cities and, as in the United States and Canada, is concentrated among more marginalised groups of heroin users, sex workers and certain minorities (Fischer et al., 2006). As shown in Case study 15.2, in the United Kingdom crack use appears to be more prevalent and widespread than in the rest of Europe, though still concentrated in major cities, especially London (GLADA, 2004) and other large metropolitan centres. While crack is usually smoked, the injection of crack in crack-heroin speedballs has been reported from several cities in the United Kingdom (Rhodes et al., 2007) and in a few cases from Dublin (Connolly et al., 2008).

As with amphetamines, cocaine-related problems may be less visible in services, especially in drug treatment, partly because of limited treatment options (no equivalent to methadone or buprenorphine), partly because of the more socially integrated profile of many primary cocaine users. This is reflected in long lag-times reported between first cocaine use and first treatment demand (9–12 years). Despite this, countries such as Spain, Italy or the Netherlands report relatively high numbers of cocaine users entering treatment. In Spain and the Netherlands, cocaine is more prevalent than heroin in treatment demand data (EMCDDA, 2009a). In Spain, the number of cocaine-related incidents seen in hospital emergency departments exceeds those for heroin or other drugs (Ministerio de Sanidad y Consumo, 2007).

Risks, harms, protective factors

Injecting cocaine, whether as a primary drug or in addition to heroin or methadone, involves more frequent injection than other drugs, including (meth)amphetamine, because of cocaine's shorter duration of action. This high frequency of injecting may carry higher risks of infections related to injecting (Tyndall et al., 2003; Chaisson et al., 1989; van Beek et al., 1994). The compulsive nature of crack use combined with user profiles also implies higher-risk use patterns (Edlin et al.; 1994, McCoy et al., 2004; van Beek et al., 2001). The use of both powder cocaine and crack is also linked to health risks such as medical emergencies and cardiovascular problems (Egred and Davis, 2005; Pozner et al., 2005). Smoking crack cocaine involves particular risks and harms, including mouth ulcers and the potential for transmission of HCV via sharing of crack pipes (Tortu et al., 2004; Fischer et al., 2008; Neaigus et al., 2007). The possibility that crack smoking methods might constitute risk factors for HIV infection had been suggested in the mid-1990s (Porter et al., 1994). Crack use is also associated with increased sexual risk behaviours (Booth et al., 2000). Cocaine injecting or crack use can also adversely affect opiate substitution treatment outcomes (Williamson et al., 2006).

Snorting cocaine, though less risky than injecting in terms of mortality or transmission of infectious diseases through sharing paraphernalia, also has risks, including dependence, damage to nasal membranes or escalating financial problems among heavy users (Smith et al., 2002; Grund et al., 2010). Sexual risk behaviours are also relevant. For example, a study comparing young cocaine users with young heroin users in three Spanish cities found that cocaine users were less marginalised, reported much lower levels of injecting or borrowing syringes, and were much less likely to be HIV or HCV positive than heroin users. However, cocaine users reported higher levels of unprotected sex with occasional partners, and higher rates of sniffing through tubes used by more than 10 persons (Brugal et al., 2009).

Implications

Problem cocaine users may be harder to reach than users of opiates. Socially integrated users may be slow to acknowledge problems and may not perceive drug services for 'junkies' as relevant to them. This implies the need for different approaches and messages for socially integrated users, for example as tried in Italy (Ministerio della Salute, 2007) and Ireland. The Irish pilot project suggested that cocaine users' reluctance to approach heroin-oriented programmes could be reduced through separate access during evenings, or immediately before and after the weekend (Horgan, 2007). However, the social networks and economic resources of more socially integrated users may also enable them to resolve problems without contacting services (Cohen and Sas, 1993; Decorte, 2000), though users do not consider recovery to be easy (Cunningham, 2000).

Highly marginalised heroin/cocaine/crack users may also be reluctant to contact regular treatment or harm reduction services, or may lead such chaotic lives that services are unable (or unwilling) to attract or retain them in treatment or facilitate reductions in risk behaviour (Prinzleve et al., 2004). This has several implications.

Intensive, targeted outreach projects are needed to access and deliver treatment or harm reduction interventions to such populations. Examples are found in the Netherlands and Ireland (Henskens et al., 2008; Connolly et al., 2008). The high-frequency injection needs of cocaine users have important implications for the number and manner of distribution of syringes/needles by NSPs, the capacity and opening hours for consumption rooms, and the type of health education and prevention messages (e.g. regarding syringe re-use). Crack use implies reviewing needs regarding provision of relevant paraphernalia and information on the risks associated with using and sharing crack pipes. For example, in several Canadian cities 'safer crack use kits' are distributed (Haydon and Fischer, 2005; Boyd et al., 2008; O'Byrne and Holmes, 2008). The distribution of materials for crack or heroin smoking or freebasing — such as aluminium foil and straws or crack pipes — takes place in low-threshold centres in Austria, Belgium, the Czech Republic, France, Luxembourg and Spain (EMCDDA national reports, 2008). An evaluation of the impact of distributing crack-smoking equipment at the needle exchange programme in Ottawa found that not only did infection-related risk behaviours associated with crack smoking diminish, but that there was also a shift from injecting to smoking the drug (Leonard et al., 2008).

Cocaine-injecting methadone clients may be seen as a group for whom substitution treatment is not working effectively (Williamson et al., 2006; Tyndall et al., 2003; Booth et al., 2003; Audit Commission, 2002). This points to the need to reinforce links between treatment, harm reduction sectors and the wider care system (e.g. joint case management of individual cases) and to the need to improve the quality of treatment services. Marginalisation, serious physical and mental health problems and the acute effects of crack such as paranoia and aggression impose special demands on staff and imply specific strategies for training staff as well as for contacting and delivering services to crack users.

Case study 15.2: The diffusion of crack-based speedball injection in the United Kingdom

Whereas only 1 % of heroin injectors in London reported crack injecting in 1990, over 50 % regularly did so by 2003, usually as part of a crack-heroin 'speedball' (Rhodes et al., 2006). In some metropolitan centres of the United Kingdom, such as Bristol and Manchester, over 70 % of injectors regularly inject crack-heroin speedball (Health Protection Agency et al., 2006). Patterns of injection in some United Kingdom cities have changed dramatically over the last decade. There is an emerging culture of crack-based speedball injection among many injectors that is quite distinct from injecting opiates alone, and almost unique to the United Kingdom (Rhodes et al., 2007).

In the United Kingdom, the odds of having HCV infection are elevated among injectors of crack and crack-based speedball (Hickman et al., 2007). The regular injection of crack-heroin speedball also appears linked to increased vein damage, including abscesses and bacterial infections. Qualitative research links such vein damage to 'missed hits' related to the local anaesthetic action of crack, the excess use of citric in the preparation of speedball injections, 'flushing' when making a hit, and the interplay of homelessness and crack injecting (Rhodes et al., 2007). Importantly, various data sources in the United Kingdom link speedball injection with shifts towards groin (femoral vein) injection, articulated by speedball injectors as an 'acceptable risk' and not merely as a 'last resort' in the face of increased vein deterioration (Rhodes et al., 2007). Surveys show that almost half (45 %) of injectors in England report groin injecting in the last month, with crack injectors significantly more likely than opiate-only injectors to inject into their femoral vein (Rhodes et al., 2006; Hickman et al., 2007). Groin injection may persist despite awareness of increased health risks and medical complications. Groin injectors are more likely to report open wounds at their injection sites and to have had deep vein thrombosis.

This emphasises an urgent need to review how harm reduction services respond in relation to vein care. Shifts to crack-based speedball and groin injection highlight a need for interventions to consider how to promote safer speedball injecting alongside emphasising basic vein care and injecting hygiene. Interventions also need to focus on preventing transitions towards groin and crack injection among users of heroin.

Opiates and opioids

Over the past decade or so, heroin injecting appears to have decreased, at least to some extent, in many western European countries, and its use by other routes, notably smoking or chasing ([7]), has increased. This is especially notable in the Netherlands, Spain and Denmark, and to a lesser extent in some other countries such as Ireland, Portugal, Germany and the United Kingdom. Sniffing heroin has increased in countries such as Austria, France and Greece. In some areas, this has led to decreases in demand on needle and syringe programmes.

However, despite the trend towards smoking or sniffing in some countries, there are large differences between countries, and injecting remains the predominant route of administration of opiates in most of the newer Member States as well as in some older members such as Finland, Italy and Luxembourg. Even in countries where injecting has decreased, important proportions of heroin users still inject and new groups of injectors continue to emerge. In France, for example, where injecting had decreased substantially in earlier years, increased injecting has been reported since 2005 among some groups of young people (Cadet-Taïrou et al., 2008; CEIP de Marseille, 2006). In Italy, the estimated incidence rate of new heroin use has not decreased over this decade and injecting remains the most common route of administration despite some increases in heroin smoking (Drug Policy Department, 2008). This is in marked contrast to Spain, where estimated incidence of new heroin use has dropped sharply, especially regarding use by injection (Sánchez-Niubò et al., 2009).

Although public and professional attention is often focused on recent trends, the legacy of the past may impose heavy burdens on current services. In many western European countries, the aftermath of the heroin 'epidemics' of the 1980s/90s and the heritage of two decades of harm reduction can be seen in cumulative populations of ageing addicts, especially in substitution programmes, with increasing needs for care, chronic health problems, co-morbidity, unemployment, and service dependency (EMCDDA, 2010b).

Heroin is not the only illicit opiate used in Europe. Market conditions sometimes limit or interrupt the availability of heroin leading to the use of a variety of other opiates or synthetic opioids.

Injecting home-produced liquid opiates has been observed in many central and eastern European countries since the 1980s (e.g. Poland, the Baltic States, Hungary, Czech Republic, Slovakia) (Grund, 2005). Since the disintegration of the Soviet Union and the opening up of previously closed economies, drug markets have also changed and heroin has become the predominant opiate. However, in parts of Russia, Ukraine, Belarus,

([7]) Technically, smoking and chasing are not the same. Smoking is mixing heroin with, for example, tobacco or marijuana, or both, and smoking it in cigarettes. Chasing is inhaling the evaporated fumes of heroin from a metal foil that is heated from underneath. In many studies and sources of data, however, these are not distinguished. In this chapter, the term 'smoking' is used in a generic sense to cover both meanings. With smoking, combustion occurs at high temperatures (about 1 000°C), which destroys many organic substances. With chasing, vaporisation occurs at lower temperatures (about 200°C), resulting in much lower levels of destruction.

Moldava and other former Soviet Union countries, as well as in the Baltic States, injecting liquid opiates remain an important component of problem drug use patterns (Grund, 2001; Abdala et al., 2006).

Since 1985 there has been a substantial expansion of methadone substitution treatment across the EU (Hedrich et al., 2008). This expansion has been accompanied by the emergence of an illicit market in diverted or stolen methadone. This is reflected, for example, in increasing mentions of methadone in fatal overdose cases, often in combination with other drugs or alcohol (EMCDDA, 2008). Methadone tablets are also sometimes crushed and injected.

In recent years the use of buprenorphine for substitution treatment has grown as an alternative to methadone. Initially implemented on a large scale in France (OFDT, 2003; Canarelli and Coquelin, 2009), other countries have also introduced it, and by 2007 buprenorphine accounted for 20 % of substitution treatment in the EU (Hedrich et al., 2008). Alongside this therapeutic use illicit markets have also developed, with the tablets often being crushed for snorting or injecting (Roux et al., 2008; Cadet-Taïrou et al., 2008).

For example, since 2000 the injection of buprenorphine tablets (which are intended for oral administration) has become an increasingly important pattern of problem use in Finland (Aalto et al., 2007) and in 2007 was reported as primary drug by a third of clients entering treatment (Stakes, 2008). Counselling centres report similar patterns among their clients, with buprenorphine often used in combination with amphetamines. Buprenorphine is also the most commonly reported substance found in drug-induced deaths (Alho et al., 2007). In both treatment and mortality data buprenorphine has almost entirely replaced heroin as the main problem opiate. Buprenorphine-naloxone and buprenorpine alone account for over half of the substitution treatment provided in Croatia, Cyprus, Finland, France, Latvia and Sweden (EMCDDA, 2009d).

Combined buprenorphine-naloxone tablets were introduced in 2006 in an attempt to reduce the risks of misuse, particularly by injection, and increased controls on prescribing were imposed in countries such as France. Despite this, buprenorphine remains available on the illicit market in many countries through diversion, theft from pharmacies or importation. Apart from Finland and France, these include the Czech Republic (Mravčík et al., 2008), Sweden (Hakansson et al., 2007) and Georgia (Otiashvili et al., 2009).

The illicit use of fentanyl ([8]), as well as overdose deaths, has been reported in parts of the United States since the 1980s (Henderson, 1988). Since 2002, following a heroin shortage, fentanyl powder, marketed as 'China White' or 'White Persian', has become the most widely used drug along with amphetamine among injecting drug users in Estonia (Talu et al., 2008). Some availability and use of fentanyl has also been reported from Finland, Lithuania and Sweden (EMCDDA, 2008) as well as from Russia and Belarus (Lelevich et al., 2008).

([8]) Fentanyl is a potent synthetic opioid widely used in surgery for anaesthesia and analgesia, and sometimes to manage chronic pain. In medical use it is administered via injection, transdermal patch or as a lozenge.

Risks, harms, protective factors

The different patterns of opiate use outlined above affect the balance of risks and harms. Relative to injecting, smoking (or sniffing) heroin carries lower risks in terms of injection-related damage, transmission of infections and overdose, though health risks remain including, of course, dependence. However, new groups of users and injectors noted above may emerge among populations who have not been exposed to harm reduction messages and interventions like the previous generation, putting them at higher risk of harms such as HIV/HCV or overdose.

Regarding chronic heroin users, there is a risk that the scenario of growing populations of institutionalised users with a low quality of life will be repeated in countries currently expanding substitution programmes. This may reflect a diminished (political) priority for old heroin users who become seen as less 'attractive'.

The injecting of home-produced opiates, which are found largely in countries bordering the EU, brings its own risks, as described in Case study 15.3.

Case study 15.3: Health risks of drugs purchased in liquid vs. solid form

In most of western and central Europe, drugs that are injected are purchased almost exclusively in powder form, whereas in most of the Baltic States, while drugs in powder form are also available for street purchase, a large proportion of IDUs inject home-made opiates purchased in liquid form (EMCDDA, 2008). The types of drugs injected by injecting drug users have several implications for harm reduction. Issues of concern are syringe type and related infection probability, drug injecting hygiene, and sharing of other injecting equipment.

Different types of syringes may be used for injecting different types of drugs. Drugs purchased in powder form (such as heroin) are most often injected using one-piece syringes, while drugs purchased in liquid form (such as 'shirka' or 'kompot') are nearly always injected using two-piece syringes (Gyarmathy et al., 2009b). The one-piece syringe, also called the low dead-space syringe, has minimal dead space between the needle and the depressed plunger, and has a very small, thin needle (Grund and Stern, 1991; Zule et al., 1997; Zule et al., 2002; Zule and Bobashev, 2009; Gyarmathy et al., 2009b). The two-piece syringe, also called the high dead-space syringe, has a detachable needle, and the syringe is attached to a hollow hub at the end of the needle. When the plunger of a two-piece syringe is completely depressed, there is still considerable space between the syringe and the needle. Two-piece syringes have larger, thicker needles. The larger space in the two-piece syringe enables it to hold more blood than the one-piece syringe, and studies have shown that those IDUs that inject with two-piece syringes are more likely to be infected with HIV (Zule et al., 1997; Zule et al., 2002; Zule and Bobashev, 2009), and possibly with HCV (Gyarmathy et al., 2009b). In addition, there is an indication that thorough cleaning of one-piece syringes may reduce the probability of HCV infection in low HCV-prevalence populations where syringe sharing is uncommon (Gyarmathy et al., 2009b), although this association has yet to be confirmed in longitudinal studies. The harm reduction implication of this is that in countries where drug users inject (almost) exclusively drugs purchased in powder form, syringe exchange programmes should offer only one-piece syringes, and in countries where both liquid and powder drugs are available for street purchase, syringe exchange programmes should offer both types of syringes. Providing drug users who inject drugs purchased in powder form with one-piece instead of two-piece syringes will have implications of reduced HIV and possibly HCV infection prevalence on the population level.

Infection prevalence is not the only harm reduction implication of one- and two-piece syringes and drugs purchased in powder vs. liquid form. Another aspect is drug injecting hygiene and infections related to lack of hygiene. As two-piece syringes have larger needles than one-piece syringes, injecting wounds caused by them are also larger. This may lead to more infections and abscesses among IDUs who use two-piece syringes. Furthermore, injecting liquid drugs usually involves purchasing the drugs in a large syringe and sharing the content of the large syringe with other drug injectors by means of syringe-mediated drug sharing (Jose et al., 1993; Grund et al., 1996). Drug users cannot be sure whether the syringes that they purchased that were pre-loaded with the liquid drug, or the other syringes used for syringe mediated drug sharing, are sterile or not. This constitutes a risk of drug-related infections for all drug users injecting the liquid drug. Furthermore, as drugs sold in liquid form are produced and sold under very unhygienic circumstances (J. Kulsiene, personal communication), there is a heightened risk of infections related to hygiene, such as, for example, hepatitis A (Perevoscikovs et al., 2009; O'Donovan et al., 2001). Lastly, the reason why injectors of drugs purchased in liquid form use two-piece syringes is that these liquid drugs have a lot of floating larger particles (J. Kulsiene, personal communication), and the thin needles of one-piece syringes get clogged with the particles. The combination of larger puncture wounds by two-piece syringes, unhygienic drug preparation and distribution practices, and large floating particles in the drugs may explain the larger sized and more common abscesses, skin lesions and skin infections among IDUs in Baltic countries compared to IDUs in western and central European countries (V. A. Gyarmathy, unpublished ethnographic findings). Harm reduction efforts in countries where drugs are sold in liquid form should also address injecting hygiene, provide filters and teach IDUs how to use and dispose of them properly, and teach users how to treat abscesses and infected injecting wounds.

Sharing injecting equipment other than syringes (e.g. filters and cookers) may also be associated with infection with drug-related infectious diseases (Hagan et al., 2001). In populations with low HCV and HIV prevalence where mostly sterile syringes are used by IDUs, no such association was found (Gyarmathy et al., 2009a). When two-piece syringes are used to inject liquid drugs in populations where syringes are often re-used, sharing other injecting equipment may also be a source of infection risk. Harm reduction efforts in such populations may include promoting the use of non-injectable sterile syringes for drug distribution.

Crushing and injecting buprenorphine tablets is linked to higher health risks than heroin in terms of vein and tissue damage, endocarditis and limb amputations, since it is difficult to grind the tablets finely enough (Mravčík et al., 2007; Partanen et al., 2009). Similar risks may arise from injecting other pharmaceutical products intended for oral administration, such as crushed methadone tablets.

The risks arising from the high potency and rapid onset of action of fentanyl is reflected in mortality data, with 117 fatal fentanyl overdoses reported in Estonia in 2005–06 (Ojanperä et al., 2008). Furthermore, fentanyl injectors reported higher-risk behaviours and were three times more likely to be HIV positive compared to amphetamine injectors (Talu et al., 2010).

Implications

The increase in the smoking of heroin may imply a greater need for facilities for heroin smokers at drug consumption rooms and for interventions that may discourage smokers from starting to inject (Hedrich et al., 2010). It has also prompted interventions to encourage injectors to reduce risks by switching to smoking. For example, a study at four needle and syringe programmes in the United Kingdom suggested that distributing foil packs to attendees can be a useful means of engaging clients in discussions of ways to reduce injecting risks and can reduce injecting in settings where there is a pre-established culture of heroin chasing (Pizzey and Hunt, 2008).

For countries with existing populations of older, long-term users, there is the need for more dignified options and 'normalised' conditions for living, in line with efforts to improve quality of life for elderly or handicapped elderly people in general (e.g. protected housing), or discussions on the changing role of drug consumption rooms in Switzerland (Sozialdepartement der Stadt Zürich, 2008).

For countries dealing with more recent 'epidemics' it would be valuable to anticipate the longer-term consequences of implementing harm reduction programmes that are concerned with keeping people alive and reducing infectious diseases and other harms now. This might include emphasising the importance of linking programmes to social reintegration options, education, training or work schemes in order to reduce the number of long-term 'institutionalised' users in the future.

The injection of synthetic opioids such as buprenorphine or methadone raises a general issue about the formulation of drugs used in substitution treatment (the composition of tablets, syrup, gel, etc.) and how to reduce the likelihood of them being injected, or at the very least how to reduce the risks if they are injected. For example, in the Czech Republic increasing number of doctors are asking for injectable buprenorphine, which they believe is better than injectable methadone because of a much lower risk of overdose, but at the same time they want to prevent disorders arising from particles that corrode the endothelium in blood vessels and heart (T. Zabransky, personal communication).

Heroin prescription therapy, which has existed in the United Kingdom since the early twentieth century (Bean, 1974), is becoming increasingly accepted in several European countries following clinical trials in different countries (EMCDDA, 2009c). For example, in recent years it has become an established treatment programme in Germany, the Netherlands and Switzerland. In clinical trials, heroin prescription has been shown to be highly effective among IDUs who are resistant to other forms of treatment, such as methadone. Not only are there higher rates of treatment retention among heroin patients than among methadone clients, but they also have higher proportions of improved mental health, decreased use of illicit drugs, and reductions in criminality (Frick et al., 2006; Drucker, 2001; Rehm et al., 2001; Hartnoll et al., 1980).

Discussion: cross-cutting issues

Multiple drug use

Among problem drug users multiple drug use is the norm. While users may have a preferred or primary drug, 'pure' users of only one type of drug are relatively uncommon. Separating users into categories such as amphetamine-type stimulants, cocaine, opiates, is thus somewhat artificial. Common combinations include stimulant and opiate (e.g. 'speedball' — cocaine and heroin, 'Czech speedball' — methamphetamine and buprenorphine) or stimulant and sedative (cocaine and alcohol and benzodiazepines). Injection drug use raises particular concerns whatever drugs are involved. Some combinations are especially associated with elevated health risks, for example opiate and alcohol (overdose) or heroin and cocaine injecting (infectious diseases) (Best et al., 2000). Other patterns of problem drug use (not covered in this chapter) that are reported by some treatment centres and counselling services for young people include heavy use of various combinations of cannabis, ecstasy, amphetamines, alcohol and benzodiazepines.

While those working in drug services are aware that problem drug use often involves multiple substances, it is possible that this is not fully appreciated by policymakers, the media or the public who tend to focus on 'the drug of the moment', with the implicit accompanying assumption that previous drug use patterns are now less important. The diversity of multiple drug use patterns, including the role of legal drugs such as benzodiazepines and alcohol, reinforces the importance of ongoing information exchange between researchers, practitioners and the political level.

Individual and public health harms

As noted at the beginning of this chapter, harm reduction evolved as a reaction to harms arising from heroin injecting. The substantial expansion of harm reduction policies and responses observed in the EU since the mid-1980s, especially substitution treatment and needle and syringe programmes, has been a major pillar of policies to reduce risk behaviours and contain serious harms such as HIV infection and overdose deaths. At the end of the 2000s, where do harm reduction responses stand in relation to the diversity of problem drug use patterns described in this chapter?

The incidence of new cases of HIV among injecting drug users is low or declining in many countries, but still relatively high in some countries including Portugal, Estonia and Latvia, and very high in Russia and Ukraine. In central European countries HIV prevalence remains low or relatively low, despite high levels in some neighbouring countries. However, some as yet small increases in incidence are observed in a few countries (e.g. Bulgaria, Sweden), and ongoing transmission among young injectors is reported in several localities, for example in France, Spain, Estonia, Lithuania and Poland. Risk behaviours too, though reduced, are still reported from many countries (EMCDDA, 2009a).

HCV prevalence among IDUs is high or relatively high in many European countries, even in some with low HIV levels. High rates of infection found among samples of new IDUs in several countries suggest that incidence also continues at significant levels (EMCDDA, 2010). Tuberculosis (including drug-resistant strains) is re-emerging as a potentially serious health threat (Deiss et al., 2009).

Drug overdose deaths in the EU as a whole decreased somewhat from a peak around 2000, though recent years show some increases (Vicente et al., 2008). However, trends, both long-term and short-term vary considerably between countries (EMCDDA, 2008).

That acute drug deaths have not continued to decrease overall in the EU might be thought puzzling in view of the trend of reduced injecting in many countries, and the introduction or expansion of substitution treatment and other harm reduction measures. Possible reasons include:

- The capacity and coverage of treatment and harm reduction services, including substitution treatment, have not yet reached a threshold in enough countries to maintain an observable impact (in terms of continued decreases) at population level.
- The high risk of overdose after release from prison (Seaman et al., 1998; Farrell and Marsden, 2008) or at the end of treatment (Davoli et al., 2007), which together could account for 15–25 % of all acute drug-related deaths, has not been adequately addressed.
- Increases in the use of high-risk drug combinations have counteracted the positive impact of other changes.
- Ageing and health deterioration of long-term users may increase the risk that opiate overdoses are fatal (Darke et al., 2006).
- Increased availability of heroin reflects increasing opium production in Afghanistan (following shortages in 2001–03) and has contributed to renewed rises in heroin use and more deaths.

It is also possible that without increased levels of substitution treatment and other interventions, overdose deaths would have been higher.

Apart from overdoses, other drug-related deaths continue to occur, for example among older users due to multiple morbidity, HCV and alcohol liver damage (McDonald et al., 2009). An increasing number of deaths due to AIDS among IDUs are reported from a few countries, for example Latvia and Estonia where a high proportion of IDUs are unaware of their HIV status, raising questions about policies regarding access to both testing and treatment (Abel-Ollo et al., 2009).

Thus, despite some success in containing and reducing individual and public health harms, harm reduction responses face a variety of challenges in terms of continuing risk behaviours and changing drug use patterns.

New drug injecting populations and local increases in HIV incidence underline the importance of continuing preventive and educational measures regarding HIV. In some newer Member States and countries bordering the EU this remains a major public health challenge.

It is recognised that HIV preventive measures are not adequate for HCV and that additional efforts are required. Examples given in this chapter reinforce the conclusion that not all risk behaviours regarding sharing of injecting equipment or other paraphernalia are dealt with adequately, for example specific practices such as syringe mediated drug sharing (Grund et al., 1996), syringe types (Gyarmathya et al., 2009a; Zule and Bobashev, 2009) straws or crack pipes (Haydon and Fischer, 2005).

Other health measures to reduce harms associated with infectious diseases include hepatitis B vaccination, hepatitis C treatment, and TB prevention (especially in high-risk environments, e.g. prisons).

Regarding deaths, a range of measures has been used in various countries, including pre-release counselling for prisoners, overdose prevention education for drug injectors or take-home naloxone (Strang et al, 2008; EMCDDA, 2009b). With all these measures, as with those seeking to prevent HIV/HCV, coverage of the relevant high-risk populations is critical, as is the need for evidence on the effectiveness of possible interventions.

Health harms such as vein and other tissue damage associated with injecting crushed tablets or home-made drugs, groin injection of crack/heroin, or smoking of crack in home-made metal pipes point to the continuing importance of delivering health and hygiene education in difficult contexts to often-marginalised populations.

Mental health harms associated with problem drug use present a further challenge to harm reduction responses in the future. It is well established that there is extensive psychiatric co-morbidity among clients with diagnoses of drug dependency (EMCDDA, 2004). Harm reduction interventions have tended to focus on somatic health harms such as infectious diseases, but are increasingly confronted by mental health and behavioural disturbances, in some contexts including violence, accentuated by heavy stimulant use. Prisons are another setting where mental health and drug use problems are especially severe (e.g. Hannon et al., 2000). It is unrealistic to expect frontline services to offer more than prophylactic assistance regarding drug-related harms to clients with serious mental health problems. It makes more sense to establish links and procedures such as joint case management with specialised mental health services.

Injecting and transitions to or from other routes

The majority of serious drug-related health harms arise from injecting. The shift towards other routes of administration observed in some countries is not incompatible with continuing levels of high risk. Many factors affect the preferred route of administration, for example the form and purity of a drug on the market (Bravo et al., 2003), or cultural attitudes and taboos about injecting. These can change.

The implications are that it is important to avoid complacency because trends suggest decreasing injecting. It does not mean that current, younger non-injectors will not inject in the future. Prevention of transitions to injecting, and encouragement of transitions to other routes among injectors should be a priority for those unwilling or unable to cease drug use altogether.

Several examples of interventions to encourage transitions from injecting to less harmful routes of administration have been noted in this chapter, including the distribution of foil packs for heroin chasing, safer crack use kits for crack cocaine smoking, and hard gelatine capsules for oral or rectal use of pervitin. In all of these examples, non-injecting drug users were also attracted to the services, suggesting possibilities for an expanded role for interventions such as needle and syringe programmes. The design and development of harm reduction interventions would benefit from the inclusion of qualitative/anthropological methods that take account of the perspectives of users themselves.

Geography, persistence and change

Geographical differences and changes in drug use reflect many dimensions: long-standing historical and cultural patterns; recent developments in politics, economy and youth cultures; drug markets and trafficking routes; drug policies, enforcement policies, prescribing policies.

Changes can be rapid, for example the emergence of the use of fentanyl in Estonia following reduced opium production in Afghanistan and a subsequent heroin shortage in the early 2000s. However, the specific nature of such changes is hard to predict, for example the same shortage of heroin appears to have been associated with increased injection of buprenorphine tablets in nearby Finland. In other situations, for example in Australia, a heroin shortage was associated with increases in benzodiazepine use and injection of stimulants (cocaine in New South Wales where a cocaine market already existed, methamphetamine in other states) (Topp et al., 2003; Degenhardt et al., 2005). In the Australian example, heroin injection diminished, especially among younger users, and fatal and non-fatal heroin overdoses decreased by between 40–85 %, but incidents of psychosis and violence attributed to stimulant use increased, as did requests for treatment of stimulant-related problems (Degenhardt et al., 2004). It is also hard to anticipate where rapid change will occur, or not. Thus explosive HIV epidemics have been observed over the last decade in the Baltic States (Uusküla et al., 2008), Russia and other former Soviet Union countries (Rhodes et al., 2002; Grund, 2001), but not in other areas of central Europe, despite high levels of risk behaviour among injectors.

Diffusion to neighbouring areas can also occur. For example, since 2000 the use of pervitin (methamphetamine) spread from the Czech Republic to Slovakia, but otherwise evidence of the diffusion of pervitin is more limited. Some pervitin is reported in border areas in Germany (Pfeiffer-Gerschel et al., 2008), among some sub-populations in Hungary (Griffiths et al., 2008) and Austria (VWS, 2008). An increase in methamphetamine in Nordic and Baltic countries appears to be associated with trafficking from Lithuania, not with export from Slovakia or the Czech Republic (EMCDDA–Europol, 2009). The increase in imported heroin observed in many newer Member States could be seen as a logical concomitant of EU membership and the harmonisation of markets in general, of which the drug market is a special case.

At the same time there is also continuity in differences, for example methamphetamine in the Czech Republic and amphetamine in Nordic countries. The predominance of cocaine as the main stimulant in southern and western Europe compared to amphetamines in northern and central Europe is another example. Sustained differences are also found within countries or even within cities (personal experience of author).

While it is feasible to monitor long-term trends through instruments such as those used by the EMCDDA, it is more difficult to identify rapidly emerging problems in time to react appropriately. The French TREND scheme provides one model (OFDT, 2007). Ethnographic and quantitative data are collected through a network of local co-ordination groups in seven cities, focusing on population groups with high drug use prevalence.

Contexts: implications for harm reduction

Many of the studies cited in this monograph make clear that problem drug use and drug-related harms are often closely associated with social dislocation and social exclusion and with factors such as unemployment, unstable living conditions, minority status, imprisonment, sex work, migration. Social exclusion and stigma are key contextual factors that exert a powerful influence on patterns of problem drug use and often hinder attempts to implement effective harm reduction measures. Attitudes towards human rights and problem drug users are a key element influencing how far harm reduction policies can be implemented. It is possible that this situation is further exacerbated by recession and economic crisis. A further dimension related to implementation of harm reduction policies concerns the importance of understanding the contexts, priorities and needs of problem drug users themselves when designing interventions.

It may be difficult for those working at the local level in specific areas of drug policy or service provision to change the broader structural context referred to above. However, it may be more feasible to influence local situational factors and risk environments. Studies focusing on micro-environmental factors are starting to provide insight into how local injecting environments and risk behaviours can be highly sensitive to public health, law enforcement and policing policies (Rhodes, 2002). In particular, policing practices can have a considerable effect on injecting behaviours and health harms at both individual and group level as well as a detrimental impact on the coverage and effectiveness of interventions such as needle exchange (Maher and Dixon, 1999; Wood et al., 2002). For example, Rhodes and colleagues report that police practices in Russia can encourage a fear of arrest, fine or detention among drug users that leads to reluctance to carry needles and syringes and in turn to paraphernalia sharing at points of drug sale (Rhodes et al., 2003). The implications of these studies point clearly to the importance of including law enforcement agencies in local harm reduction policies.

Conclusion

The specific implications of the variety of drug use patterns and health harms described in this chapter depend on local circumstances, but the broader message, especially to policymakers and service managers, is that changing conditions on the illicit market as well as the form and conditions in which substitute drugs are prescribed can have considerable impacts on local drug use patterns. Similarly, the balance within drug policies, especially in terms of policing approaches vis-à-vis treatment and harm reduction responses, can influence the risk environments in which drug use occurs. Local responses thus not only need to be flexible and adjust to changing needs, but also need to be based on consensus and cooperation between key actors. The rate at which risky drug use patterns can change suggests that brief rapid needs assessments and monitoring is needed to target information and health education at new user groups, and to identify new drug use patterns, risks and risk situations.

References

For EMCDDA annual reports and other publications, see www.emcdda.europa.eu. For national reports to the EMCDDA, see www.emcdda.europa.eu/publications/national-reports.

Aalto, M., Halme, J., Visapaa, J. P., and Salaspuro, M. (2007), 'Buprenorphine misuse in Finland', *Substance Use and Misuse* 42, pp. 1027–8.

Abdala, N., Grund, J-P., Tolstov, Y., Kozlov, A. and Heimer, R. (2006), 'Can home-made injectable opiates contribute to the HIV epidemic among injection drug users in the countries of the former Soviet Union?', *Addiction* 101, pp. 731–7.

Abel-Ollo, K., Rahu, M., Rajaleid, K., et al. (2009), 'Knowledge of HIV serostatus and risk behaviour among injecting drug users in Estonia', *AIDS Care*, 21, pp. 851–7.

Alho, H., Sinclair, D., Vuori, E. and Holopainen, A. (2007), 'Abuse liability of buprenorphine-naloxone tablets in untreated IV drug users', *Drug and Alcohol Dependence* 88, pp. 75–8.

Audit Commission (2002), *Changing habits: the commissioning and management of community drug treatment services for adults*, Audit Commission, London.

Bean, P. (1974), *The social control of drugs*, Martin Robertson, London.

Best, D., Man, L-H., Zador, D., et al. (2000), 'Overdosing on opiates. Part I: causes', *Drug and Alcohol Findings*, 4, pp. 4–21.

Booth, R., Kwiatkowski, C. and Chitwood, D. (2000), 'Sex-related HIV risk behaviors: differential risks among injection drug users, crack smokers, and injection drug users who smoke crack', *Drug and Alcohol Dependence* 58, pp. 219–26.

Booth, R., Corsi, K. and Mikulich, S. (2003), 'Improving entry to methadone maintenance among out-of-treatment injection drug users', *Journal of Substance Abuse Treatment* 24, pp. 305–11.

Booth, R., Lehman, W., Kwiatowski, C., et al. (2008), 'Stimulant injectors in Ukraine: the next wave of the epidemic', *AIDS and Behaviour* 12, pp. 652–61.

Boyd, S., Johnson, J. and Moffat, B. (2008), 'Opportunities to learn and barriers to change: crack cocaine use in the Downtown Eastside of Vancouver', *Harm Reduction Journal* 5, p. 34.

Braine, N., Des Jarlais, D., Gikdbkattm C., et al. (2005), 'HIV risk behaviour among amphetamine injectors at US syringe exchange programs', *AIDS Education and Prevention* 17, pp. 515–24.

Bravo, M., Barrio, G., de la Fuente, L., et al. (2003), 'Reasons for selecting an initial route of heroin administration and for subsequent transitions during a severe HIV epidemic', *Addiction* 98, pp. 749–60.

Brugal, T., Pulido, J., Toro, C., et al. (2009), 'Injecting, sexual risk behaviours and HIV infection in young cocaine and heroin users in Spain', *European Addiction Research* 15, pp. 171–8.

Cadet-Taïrou, A., Gandilhon, M., Toufik, A. and Evrard, I. (2008), 'Eighth national report from the TREND system', *Tendances* 58, OFDT, Paris.

Canarelli, T. and Coquelin, A. (2009), 'Données récentes relatives aux traitements de substitution aux opiacés', *Tendances* 65, OFDT, Paris.

Carrieri, M., Amass, L., Lucas, G., et al. (2006), 'Buprenorphine use: the international experience', *Clinical Infectious Diseases* 43, pp. S197–S215.

CEIP (Centre d'évaluation et d'information sur la phamacodépendance) de Marseille (2006), *OPPIDUM, résultats de l'enquête 17 (octobre 2005)*, AFSSAPS, Saint-Denis.

Chaisson, R., Bachetti, P., Osmond, D., et al. (1989), 'Cocaine use and HIV infection in IDUs in San Francisco', *Journal of the American Medical Association* 261, pp. 652–61.

Chintalova-Dallas, R., Case, P., Kitsenko, N. and Lazzarini, Z. (2009), 'A home-made amphetamine-type stimulant and HIV risk in Odessa, Ukraine', *International Journal of Drug Policy* 20, pp. 347–51.

Cohen, P. and Sas, A. (1993), *Ten years of cocaine: a follow-up study of 64 cocaine users in Amsterdam*, Department of Human Geography, University of Amsterdam, Amsterdam. Available at www.cedro-uva.org/lib/cohen.ten.pdf.

Colfax, G. and Shoptow, S. (2005), 'The methamphetamine epidemic: implications for HIV prevention and treatment', *Current HIV/AIDS Reports* 2, pp. 194–9.

Connolly, J., Foran, S., Donovan, A., Carew, A. and Long, J. (2008), *Crack cocaine in the Dublin region: an evidence base for a Dublin crack cocaine strategy*, HRB Research Series 6, Health Research Board, Dublin. Available at http://www.hrb.ie/uploads/tx_hrbpublications/HRB_Research_Series_6.pdf.

Corski, K. and Booth, R. (2008), 'HIV sex risk behaviours among heterosexual methamphetamine users: literature review from 2000 to present', *Current Drug Abuse Reviews* 1, pp. 292–6.

Cunningham, J. (2000), 'Remissions from drug dependence: is treatment a prerequisite?', *Drug and Alcohol Dependence*, 59, pp. 211–13.

Darke, S., Degenhardt, L. and Mattick, R. (2006), *Mortality amongst illicit drug users: epidemiology, causes and intervention*, Cambridge University Press, Cambridge.

Davoli, M., Bargagli, A., Perucci, C., et al. (2007), 'Risk of fatal overdose during and after specialised drug treatment: the VEdeTTE study, a national multi-site prospective cohort study', *Addiction* 102, pp. 1954–9.

de Bie, R., Gladstone, R., Strafella, A., Ko, J. and Lang, A. (2007), 'Manganese-induced Parkinsonism associated with methcathinone (ephedrone) abuse', *Archives of Neurology*, 64, pp. 886–9.

Decorte, T. (2000), *The taming of cocaine: cocaine use in European and American cities*, VUB University Press, Brussels.

Degenhardt, L., Day, C. and Hall, W. (eds) (2004), *The causes, course and consequences of the heroin shortage in Australia*, NDLERF Monograph 3, National Drug Law Enforcement Research Fund, Commonwealth of Australia. Available at http://www.ndlerf.gov.au/pub/Monograph_03.pdf.

Degenhardt, L., Day, C., Dieze, P., et al. (2005), 'Effects of a sustained heroin shortage in three Australian States', *Addiction*, 100, pp. 908–20.

Deiss, R., Rodwell, T. and Garfein, R. (2009), 'Tuberculosis and illicit drug use: review and update', *Clinical Infectious Diseases* 48, pp. 72–82.

Drucker, E. (2001), 'Injectable heroin substitution treatment for opioid dependency', *Lancet* 27 October, 358, p. 1385.

Drug Policy Department (2008), *2008 national report to the EMCDDA on the drug situation in Italy,* Presidency of the Council of Ministers, Rome.

Edlin, B., Irwin, K., Faruque, S., et al. (1994), 'Intersecting epidemics: crack cocaine use and HIV infection among inner-city young adults', *New England Journal of Medicine* 331, pp. 1422–7.

Egred, M. and Davis, G. (2005), 'Cocaine and the heart', *Postgraduate Medical Journal* 81, pp. 568–71.

Elkashef, A., Vocci, F., Hanson, G., et al. (2008), 'Pharmacotherapy of methamphetamine addiction: an update', *Substance Abuse* 29, pp. 31–49. See also EMCDDA Annual Report 2009.

EMCDDA (European Monitoring Centre for Drugs and Drug Addiction) (2004), *Co-morbidity,* Selected issue, European Monitoring Centre for Drugs and Drug Addiction, Lisbon.

EMCDDA (2007), *Cocaine and crack cocaine: a growing public health issue,* Selected issue, European Monitoring Centre for Drugs and Drug Addiction, Lisbon.

EMCDDA (2008), *Annual Report 2008: the state of the drugs problem in Europe,* European Monitoring Centre for Drugs and Drug Addiction, Lisbon.

EMCDDA (2009a), *Annual report 2009: the state of the drugs problem in Europe,* European Monitoring Centre for Drugs and Drug Addiction, Lisbon.

EMCDDA (2009b), Tables HSR-7 and HSR-8, Statistical bulletin. Available at http://www.emcdda.europa.eu/stats09/hsrtab7 and http://www.emcdda.europa.eu/stats09/hsrtab8.

EMCDDA (2009c), Table HSR-1, Statistical bulletin. Available at http://www.emcdda.europa.eu/stats09/hsrtab1.

EMCDDA (2009d), Table HSR-3, part ii, Statistical bulletin, Available at http://www.emcdda.europa.eu/stats09/hsrtab3b.

EMCDDA (2010a), *Trends in injecting drug use in Europe,* Selected issue, European Monitoring Centre for Drugs and Drug Addiction, Lisbon.

EMCDDA (2010b), *Ageing drug users,* Selected issue, Publications Office of the European Union, Luxembourg, forthcoming.

EMCDDA–Europol (2009), *Methamphetamine: a European Union perspective in the global context,* EMCDDA–Europol joint publications 1, Office for Official Publications of the European Communities, Luxembourg.

Farrell, M. and Marsden, J. (2008), 'Acute risk of drug-related death among newly released prisoners in England and Wales', *Addiction* 103, pp. 256–7.

Fischer, B., Rehm, J., Patra, J., et al. (2006), 'Crack across Canada: comparing crack users and crack non-users in a Canadian multi-city cohort of illicit opioid users', *Addiction* 101, pp. 1760–70.

Fischer, B., Powis, J., Cruz, M., Rudzinski, K. and Rehm, J. (2008), 'Hepatitis C virus transmission among oral crack users: viral detection on crack paraphernalia', *European Journal of Gastroenterology and Hepatology* 20, pp. 29–32.

Frick, U., Rehm, J., Kovacic, S., Ammann, J. and Uchtenhagen, A. (2006), 'A prospective cohort study on orally administered heroin substitution for severely addicted opioid users', *Addiction* 101, pp. 1631–9.

GLADA (Greater London Alcohol and Drug Alliance) (2004), *An evidence base for the London crack cocaine strategy*, Greater London Authority, London.

Goldstein, P. (1989), 'Drugs and violent crimes', in Weiner, N. and Wolfgang, M. (eds), *Pathways to criminal violence*, Sage Publications, Newbury Park, CA.

Griffiths, P., Mravcik, V., Lopez, D. and Klempova, D. (2008), 'Quite a lot of smoke but very limited fire: the use of methamphetamine in Europe', *Drug and Alcohol Review* 27, pp. 236–42.

Grund, J-P. (2001), 'A candle lit from both sides: the epidemic of HIV infection in central and eastern Europe', in McElrath, K. (ed.), *HIV and AIDS: a global view*, Greenwood Press, Wesport, Ct.

Grund, J-P. (2005), 'The eye of the needle: an ethno-epidemiological analysis of injecting drug use', in Pates, R., McBride, A. and Arnold, K. (eds), *Injecting illicit drugs*, Addiction Press, Blackwell, Oxford, pp. 11–32.

Grund, J-P. and Stern, L. (1991), 'Residual blood in syringes: size and type of syringe are important', *AIDS* 5, pp. 1532–3.

Grund, J-P., Friedman, S., Stern, L., et al. (1996), 'Syringe-mediated drug sharing among injecting drug users: patterns, social context, and implications for transmission of blood-borne pathogens', *Social Science and Medicine* 42, pp. 691–703.

Grund, J-P., Zabransky, T., Irvin, K. and Heimer, R. (2009), 'Stimulant use in central and eastern Europe: how recent social history shaped current drug consumption patterns', in Pates, R. and Riley, D. (eds), *Interventions for amphetamine misuse*, Wiley Blackwell, Oxford.

Grund, J-P., Coffin, P., Jauffret-Roustide, M., et al. (2010), 'The fast and furious: cocaine, amphetamines and harm reduction', in European Monitoring Centre for Drugs and Drug Addiction (EMCDDA), *Harm reduction: evidence, impacts and challenges*, Rhodes, T. and Hedrich, D. (eds), Scientific Monograph Series No. 10, Publications Office of the European Union, Luxembourg.

Gyarmathy, A., Neaigus, A., Mitchell, M. and Ujhelyi, E. (2009a), 'The association of syringe type and syringe cleaning with HCV infection among IDUs in Budapest, Hungary', *Drug and Alcohol Dependence* 100, pp. 240–7.

Gyarmathy, A., Li, N., Tobin, K., et al. (2009b), 'Correlates of unsafe injecting among injecting drug users in St Petersburg, Russia', *European Addiction Research* 15, pp. 163–70.

Hagan, H., Thiede, H., Weiss, N., et al. (2001), 'Sharing of drug preparation equipment as a risk factor for hepatitis C', *American Journal of Public Health* 91, pp. 42–6.

Hakansson, A., Medvedeo, A., Andersson, M. and Berglund, M. (2007), 'Buprenorphine misuse among heroin and amphetamine users in Malmo, Sweden: purpose of misuse and route of administration', *European Addiction Research* 13, pp. 207–15.

Hannon, F., Kelleher, C., Friel, S., et al. (2000), *General healthcare study of the Irish prison populations*, National University of Ireland, Galway.

Hartnoll, R. (2003) 'Overview of the drugs situation in the CEECs: situation and responses', in EMCDDA, *The state of the drugs problem in the acceding and candidate countries to the European Union*, European Monitoring Centre for Drugs and Drug Addiction, Lisbon, pp. 13–33.

Hartnoll, R., Mitcheson, M., Battersby, A., et al. (1980), 'Evaluation of heroin maintenance in a controlled trial', *Archives of General Psychiatry*, 37, pp. 877–84.

Haydon, E. and Fischer, B. (2005), 'Crack use as a public health problem in Canada: call for an evaluation of "safer crack use kits"', *Canadian Journal of Public Health* 96, pp. 185–8.

Health Protection Agency, Health Protection Scotland, National Public Health Service for Wales and Centre for Research on Drugs and Health Behaviour (2006), *Shooting up: infections among injecting drug users in the United Kingdom 2005*, Health Protection Agency, London.

Hedrich, D., Pirona, A. and Wiessing, L. (2008), 'From margin to mainstream: the evolution of harm reduction responses to problem drug use in Europe', *Drugs: Education, Prevention and Policy* 15, pp. 503–17.

Hedrich, D., Kerr, T. and Dubois-Arber, F. (2010), 'Drug consumption facilities in Europe and beyond', in European Monitoring Centre for Drugs and Drug Addiction (EMCDDA), *Harm reduction: evidence, impacts and challenges*, Rhodes, T. and Hedrich, D. (eds), Scientific Monograph Series No. 10, Publications Office of the European Union, Luxembourg.

Henderson, G. (1988), 'Designer drugs: past history and future prospects', *Journal of Forensic Science*, 33, pp. 569–75.

Hendrickson, R., Horowitz, Z., Norton, R. and Notenboom, H. (2006), '"Parachuting" meth: a novel delivery method for methamphetamine and delayed-onset toxicity from "body stuffing"', *Clinical Toxicology* 44, pp. 379–82.

Henskens, R., Garretsen, H., Bongers, I., Van Dijk, A. and Sturmans, F. (2008), 'Effectiveness of an outreach treatment program for inner city crack abusers: compliance, outcome and client satisfaction', *Substance Use and Misuse*, 43, pp. 1464–75.

Hickman, M., Hope, V., McDonald, T., et al. (2007), 'HCV prevalence and injecting risk behaviour in multiple sites in England in 2004', *Journal of Viral Hepatitis*, 14, pp. 645–52.

Horgan, J. (2007), *An overview of cocaine use in Ireland*, National Advisory Committee on Drugs and National Drugs Strategy Team, Dublin.

Join Together (2007), 'Oregon's tough meth laws may have unintended consequences', *In the News*. Available at http://www.jointogether.org/news/headlines/inthenews/2007/oregons-tough-meth.html (accessed 15 June 2009).

Jose, B., Friedman, S., Neaigus, A., et al. (1993), 'Syringe-mediated drug sharing (backloading): a new risk factor for HIV among injecting drug users', *AIDS 7*, pp. 1653–60.

Käll, K. and Nilsonne, A. (1995), 'Preference for sex on amphetamine: a marker for HIV risk behaviour among male intravenous amphetamine users in Stockholm', *AIDS Care 7*, pp. 171–88.

Käll, K. and Olin, R. (1990), 'HIV status and changes in risk behaviour among intravenous drug users in Stockholm', *AIDS 4*, pp. 153–7.

Klee, H. (2006), 'HIV risks for women injectors: heroin and amphetamines compared', *Addiction* 88, pp. 1055–62.

Koslov, A., Shaboltas, A., Toussova, O., et al. (2006), 'HIV incidence and factors associated with HIV acquisition among injection drug users in St. Petersburg, Russia', *AIDS* 20, pp. 901–06.

Kruse, G., Barbour, R., Heimer, R., et al. (2009), 'Drug choice, spatial distribution, HIV risk, and prevalence among injection drug users in St. Petersburg, Russia', *Harm Reduction Journal* 6 (22). Available at http://www.ncbi.nlm.nih.gov/pmc/articles/PMC2731096/.

Lelevich, V., Vintskaya, A., Lelevich, S., et al. (2008), *Annual report: Republic of Belarus drug abuse and illicit drugs trafficking in 2007*, BUMAD Programme, Minsk.

Leonard, L., DeRubeis, E., Pelude, L., et al. (2008), '"I inject less as I have easier access to pipes": injecting, and sharing of crack-smoking materials, decline as safer crack-smoking resources are distributed', *International Journal of Drug Policy* 19, pp. 255–64.

MacCoun, R. and Reuter, P. (2001), *Drug war heresies: learning from other vices, times, and places*, Cambridge University Press, Cambridge and New York.

McCoy, C., Shenghan, L., Metsch, L., Messiah, S. and Zhao, W. (2004), 'Injection drug use and crack cocaine smoking: independent and dual risk behaviours for HIV infection', *Annals of Epidemiology* 14, pp. 535–42.

McDonald, S., Hutchinson, S., Bird, S., et al. (2009), 'A population-based record linkage study of mortality in hepatitis C-diagnosed persons with or without HIV coinfection in Scotland', *Statistical Methods in Medical Research* 18, pp. 271–83.

Maher, L. and Dixon, D. (1999), 'Policing and public health: law enforcement and harm minimisation in a street-level drug market', *British Journal of Criminology* 39, pp. 488–511.

March, J., Oviedo-Joekes, E. and Romero, M. (2006), 'Drugs and social exclusion in ten European cities', *European Addiction Research* 12, pp. 33–41.

Ministerio de Sanidad y Consumo (2007), *2007 National Report to the EMCDDA*, Ministerio de Sanidad y Consumo, Spain.

Ministero della Salute (2007), *Proposta di Progetto Nazionale Cocaina, Dipartimento delle Dipendenze*, Regione Lombardia, Italia. Available at http://www.indipendenze.org/sx_canale/dettaglio.asp?sez=Cocaina&id_sezione=1&id_subSez=110&id_articolo=1397.

Miovský, M. (2007), 'Changing patterns of drug use in the Czech Republic during the post-communist era: a qualitative study', *Journal of Drug Issues* 37, pp. 73–102.

Molitor, F., Truax, S., Ruiz, J., et al. (1998), 'Association of methamphetamine use during sex with risky sexual behaviours and HIV injection among non-injection drug users', *Western Journal of Medicine* 168, pp. 93–7.

Molitor, F., Ruiz, J., Flynn, N., et al. (1999), 'Methamphetamine use and sexual and injection risk behaviors among out-of-treatment injection drug users', *American Journal of Drug and Alcohol Abuse* 25, pp. 475–93.

Mravčík, V., Chomynová, P., Orlíková, B., et al. (2008), *Výroční zpráva o stavu ve věcech drog v České republice v roce 2007* [The Czech Republic: drug situation 2007], Úřad vlády ČR, Praha [Office of the Czech Government, Prague].

Neaigus, A., Gyarmathy, A., Zhao, M., et al. (2007), 'Sexual and other noninjection risks for HBV and HCV seroconversions among noninjecting heroin users', *Journal of Infectious Diseases* 195 (7), pp. 1052–61.

O'Byrne, P. and Holmes, D. (2008), 'Evaluating crack pipe distribution in Canada: a systems change case study', *Addiction Research and Theory* 16, pp. 181–92.

O'Donovan, D., Cooke, R., Joce, R., et al. (2001), 'An outbreak of hepatitis A amongst injecting drug users', *Epidemiology and Infection* 127, pp. 469–73.

OFDT (2003), *Substitution aux opiacés en France, synthèse des informations disponibles de 1996 à 2001 en France*, OFDT, Paris.

OFDT (2007), *2007 national report to the EMCDDA on the drug situation in France*, OFDT, Paris.

Ojanperä, I., Gergov, M., Liiv, M., Riijokoja, A. and Vuori, E. (2008), 'An epidemic of fatal 3-methylfentalnyl poisoning in Estonia', *International Journal of Legal Medicine* 122, pp. 395–400.

Otiashvili, D., Zabransky, T., Kirtadze, I., et al. (2009), 'Why do the clients of Georgian needle exchange programs inject buprenorphine?' *European Addiction Research* 16 (1), pp. 1–8.

Partanen, T., Vikatmaa, P., Tukiainen, E., Lepantalo, M. and Vuola, J. (2009), 'Outcome after injections of crushed tablets in intravenous drug abusers in the Helsinki University Central Hospital', *European Journal of Vascular and Endovascular Surgery* 37, pp. 704–11.

Pavlenko, V. (2008), 'Peculiarities of stimulant use in Ukraine: the example of Donetsk region', 1st global conference on methamphetamine: Science, Strategy and Response, 15 September, Prague.

Perevoscikovs, J., Lucenko, I., Magone, S., et al. (2009), 'Community-wide outbreak of hepatitis A in Latvia in 2008: an update', *Eurosurveillance* 14 (3).

Pfeiffer-Gerschel, T., Kipke, I., Lang, P., et al. (2008), *2008 national report to the EMCDDA on the drug situation in Germany*, DBDD, Munich.

Pizzey, R. and Hunt, N. (2008), 'Distributing foil from needle and syringe programmes (NSPs) to promote transitions from heroin injecting to chasing: an evaluation', *Harm Reduction Journal* 5 (24). Available at http://www.harmreductionjournal.com/content/5/1/24.

Porter, J., Drucker, E., Hammond, J. and Lax, L. (1994), 'Crack smoking methods as risk factors for HIV infection', *International Conference on AIDS* 7–11 August, 10 (1), p. 391 (abstract no. PD0170).

Pozner, C., Levine, M. and Zane, R. (2005), 'The cardiovascular effects of cocaine', *Journal of Emergency Medicine* 29, pp. 173–8.

Prinzleve, M., Haasen, C., Zurhold, H., et al. (2004), 'Cocaine use in Europe — a multicentre study: patterns of use in different groups', *European Addiction Research* 10, pp. 147–55.

Rasmussen, D., and Benson, B. (1997), 'Reducing the harms of drug policy: an economic perspective', *Substance Use and Misuse* 3, pp. 49–68.

Rasmussen, D., Benson, B. and Sollars, D. (1993), 'Spatial competition in illicit drug markets: the consequences of increased drug law enforcement', *Review of Regional Studies*, 123, pp. 219–36.

Rehm, J., Gschwend, P., Steffen, T., et al. (2001), 'Feasibility, safety, and efficacy of injectable heroin prescription for refractory opioid addicts: a follow-up study', *Lancet*, 27 October, 358, pp. 1417–23.

Rhodes, T. (2002), 'The "risk environment": a framework for understanding and reducing drug-related harm', *International Journal of Drug Policy* 13, pp. 85–94.

Rhodes, T., Lowndes, C., Judd, A., et al. (2002), 'Explosive spread and high prevalence of HIV infection among injecting drug users in Togliatti City, Russia', *AIDS* 16, pp. F25–31.

Rhodes, T., Mikhailova, L., Sarang, A., et al. (2003), 'Situational factors influencing drug injecting, risk reduction and syringe exchange in Togliatti City, Russian Federation: a qualitative study of micro risk environment', *Social Science and Medicine* 57, pp. 39–54

Rhodes, T., Stoneman, A., Hope, V., Hunt, N. and Judd, A. (2006), 'Groin injecting in the context of crack cocaine and homelessness: from "risk boundary" to "acceptable risk"?' *International Journal of Drug Policy* 17, pp. 164–70.

Rhodes, T., Briggs, D., Kimber, J., Jones, S. and Holloway, G. (2007), 'Crack–heroin speedball injection and its implications for vein care: qualitative study', *Addiction* 102, pp. 1782–90.

Roux, P., Villes, V., Bry, D., et al. (2008), 'Buprenorphine sniffing as a response to inadequate care in substituted patients: results from the Subazur survey in south-eastern France', *Addictive Behaviors* 33, pp. 1625–9.

Sánchez-Niubò, A., Fortiana, J., Barrio, G., et al. (2009), 'Problematic heroin incidence trends in Spain', *Addiction* 104, pp. 248–55.

Seaman, S., Brettle, R. and Bied, S. (1998), 'Mortality from overdose among injecting drug users recently released from prison', *BMJ* 316, pp. 426–8.

Shaboltas, A., Toussova, O., Hoffman, I., et al. (2006), 'HIV prevalence, sociodemographic and behavioural correlates and recruitment methods among injection drug users in St. Petersburg, Russia', *Journal of Acquired Immune Deficiency Syndrome* 41, pp. 657–63.

Škařupová, K., Mravčík, V., and Orlíková, B. (2009), 'Hard gelatine capsules as a harm reduction drug delivery alternative to injecting' (in press).

Smith, J., Kacker, A. and Anand, V. (2002), 'Midline nasal and hard palate destruction in cocaine abusers and cocaine's role in rhinologic practice', *Ear, Nose and Throat Journal* 81, pp. 172–4, 176–7.

SIRUS (Norwegian Institute for Alcohol and Drug Research) (2008), *2008 national report to the EMCDDA on the drug situation in Norway*, SIRUS, Oslo.

Sozialdepartement der Stadt Zürich (2008), *Ein Ort wo man sein kann. Dir Zukunft der „Harm Reduction" am Beispiel der Kontakt- und Anlaufstellen der Stadt Zürich*, Edition Sozialpraxis Nr. 3, Zürich: Stadt Zürich.

Stakes (2008), *2008 national report to the EMCDDA on the drug situation in Finland*, Stakes, Helsinki.

Strang, J., Sheridan, J. and Barber, N. (1996), 'Prescribing injectable and oral methadone to opiate addicts: results from the 1995 national postal survey of community pharmacies in England and Wales', *BMJ* 3 August, 313, pp. 270–2.

Strang, J., Manning, V., Mayet, S., et al. (2008), 'Overdose training and take-home naloxone for opiate users: prospective cohort study of impact on knowledge and attitudes and subsequent management of overdoses', *Addiction* 103, pp. 1648–57.

Talu, A., Abel-Ollo, K., Vals, K. and Ahven, K. (2008), *2008 national report to the EMCDDA on the drug situation in Estonia*, National Institute for Health Development, Tallinn.

Talu, A., Rajaleid, K., Abel-Ollo, K., et al. (2010), 'HIV infection and risk behaviour of primary fentanyl and amphetamine injectors in Tallinn, Estonia: implications for intervention', *International Journal of Drug Policy* 21, pp. 56–63.

Topp, L., Day, C. and Degenhardt, L. (2003), 'Changes in patterns of drug injection concurrent with a sustained reduction in the availability of heroin in Australia', *Drug and Alcohol Dependence* 70, pp. 275–86.

Tortu, S., McMahon, J., Pouget, E. and Hamid, R. (2004), 'Sharing of noninjection drug-use implements as a risk factor for hepatitis C', *Substance Use and Misuse*, 39, pp. 211–24.

Tyndall, M., Currie, S., Spittal, P., et al. (2003), 'Intensive injection cocaine use as the primary risk factor in the Vancouver HIV-1 epidemic', *AIDS* 17, pp. 887–93.

Uusküla, A., Kals, M., Rajaleid, K., et al. (2008), 'High-prevalence and high-estimated incidence of HIV infection among new injecting drug users in Estonia: need for large scale prevention programs', *Journal of Public Health* 30, pp. 119–25.

Vallejo, R., de Leon-Casasola, O. and Benyamin, R. (2004), 'Opioid therapy and immuno-suppression: a review', *American Journal of Therapeutics* 11, pp. 354–65.

van Beek, I., Buckley, R., Stewart, M., MacDonald, M. and Kaldor J. (1994), 'Risk factors for hepatitis C virus infection among injecting drug users in Sydney', *Genitourin Med* 70, pp. 321–4.

van Beek, I., Dwyer, R. and Malcom, A. (2001), 'Cocaine injecting: the sharp end of drug-related harm', *Drug and Alcohol Review* 20, pp. 333–42.

Vicente, J., Giraudon, I., Matias, J., Hedrich, D. and Wiessing, L. (2009), 'Rebound of overdose mortality in the European Union 2003–2005: findings from the 2008 EMCDDA Annual Report', *Eurosurveillance* Edition, 14 (2). Available at http://www.eurosurveillance.org/ViewArticle.aspx?ArticleId=19088.

VWS (2008), *Tätigkeitsbereicht 2007*, ChEckiT!, Verein Wiener Sozialprojekte, Vienna. See ÖBIG (2008), 2008 national report to the EMCDDA on the drug situation in Austria, Österreichisches Bundesinstitut für Gesundheitswesen, Vienna, Table A20.

Williamson, A., Darke, S., Ross, J. and Teesson, M. (2006), 'The association between cocaine use and short-term outcomes for the treatment of heroin dependence: findings from the Australian Treatment Outcome Study (ATOS)', *Drug and Alcohol Review* 25, pp. 141–8.

Wood, E., Tyndall, M., Spittal, P., et al. (2002), 'Needle exchange and difficulty with needle access during an ongoing HIV epidemic', *International Journal of Drug Policy*, 13, pp. 95–102.

Zabransky, T. (2009), unpublished qualitative research on drug producers and police officers.

Zeziulin, O., Dumchev, K. and Schumacher, J. (2008), 'Injection stimulant use and HIV risk in Ukraine', 1st Global Conference On Methamphetamine: Science, Strategy And Response, 15 September, Prague.

Zule, W. and Bobashev, G. (2009), 'High dead-space syringes and the risk of HIV and HCV infection among injecting drug users', *Drug and Alcohol Dependence* 100, pp. 204–13.

Zule, W., Ticknor-Stellato, K., Desmond, D. and Vogtsberger, K. (1997), 'Evaluation of needle and syringe combinations', *Journal of Acquired Immune Deficiency Syndrome and Human Retrovirology* 14, pp. 294–5.

Zule, W., Desmond, D. and Neff, J. (2002), 'Syringe type and drug injector risk for HIV infection: a case study in Texas', *Social Science and Medicine* 55, pp. 1103–13.

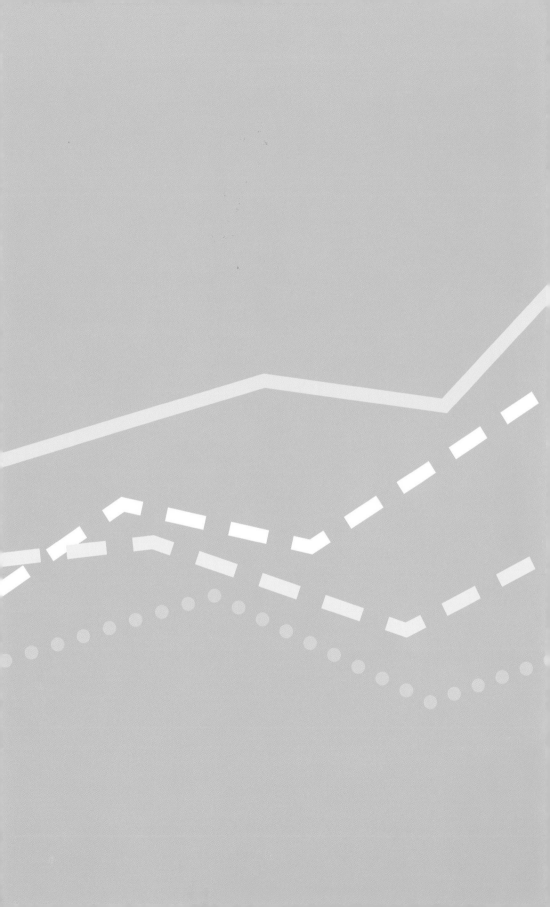

Conclusions

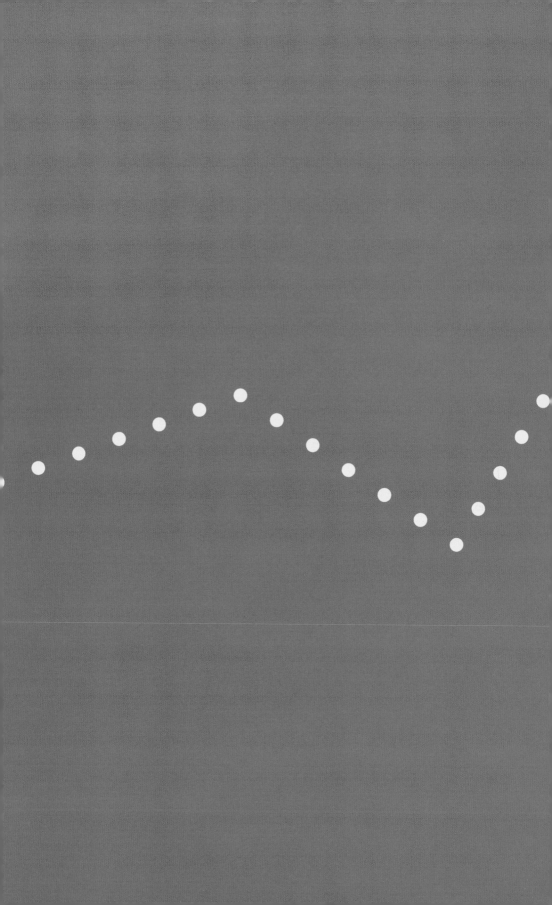

Chapter 16
Current and future perspectives on harm reduction in the European Union

Marina Davoli, Roland Simon and Paul Griffiths

The drift to evidence-based European drug policies

Over the last 20 years, whether as an overarching concept, or as shorthand for specific interventions, 'harm reduction' has changed the way we think about and respond to drug problems in Europe. Debates continue today about what sort of interventions legitimately fall under the heading of harm reduction, and what value they bring. However, measures that reduce harm, but do not specifically attempt to reduce drug use, are an important element in a drug strategy and harm reduction is now a largely uncontested component of European drug policy. Indeed, practice is ahead of political rhetoric in this respect, with governments sometimes being more cautious in their public pronouncements than they are in their actions.

How Europe got to today's pragmatic approach, where the balance is tipped to what can be *shown to work*, rather than what policymakers might *wish would work*, is addressed by many of the contributors to this monograph. It would be naive to suggest that modern drug policies are solely directed by a cold assessment of the scientific evidence for effectiveness. Many examples can be cited to demonstrate that this is not the case — for instance, the investment of large sums of money in anti-drug mass media campaigns where there is growing evidence that this approach is at best ineffective, and at worst counter-productive. Drug policies, like other social policies, are shaped by many factors, and Herring and colleagues' (2010) statement on alcohol is true for other substances as well: 'Evaluation and research findings are only one element in decisions to adapt or reject harm reduction as a legitimate goal for policy'.

Nonetheless, the development of harm reduction as a mainstream concept in Europe does demonstrate that over time, and when faced with a serious public health threat, evidence-based argument can result in the adoption of policy options that are initially viewed as controversial. It is beyond the scope of this chapter to discuss how the mainstreaming of harm reduction into drug policy was possible in the European Union (EU) and some other countries, whilst in other parts of both the developed and developing world harm reduction has remained largely outside of the mainstream. The diffusion of harm reduction in Europe was brought about initially by public health concerns related to HIV. It seems likely it has also been facilitated by structural factors, including a strong public health ethos, a culture of independence within the medical and health professions, activism and user involvement, and advocacy by affected individuals and communities. At the EU level, a growing political culture of sharing experiences of what works and moving towards common positions may have also played a part and, importantly, removed some of the anxiety felt by policymakers that they were moving alone into uncharted waters. It is interesting to note that many of the Member States joining the EU in 2004 very rapidly adopted relatively sophisticated drug policies that reflected Community norms, and in which harm reduction was a component. Arguably, a key factor contributing to these countries' avoidance of major HIV epidemics among their injecting populations is their rapid adoption of the European model in which HIV prevention was an integral element.

The question of definition

Interventions towards substance use and dependence have always been topics of discussion well beyond the public health arena. Ethical issues relating to the use of drugs have influenced the objectives and aims of interventions, both preventive and therapeutic. Indeed, the historical development of drug policy is often represented as an ongoing debate between a *moral position* in which drug use is portrayed as 'criminal' and 'deviant' and a *public health position* where drug users are seen as in need of treatment and help. Harm reduction gives clear primacy to a public health perspective in which the imperative is to reduce immediate harms, and the question of long-term abstinence from drug use is either unaddressed or left open. Moreover, many of those who advocate for a harm reduction approach also point out that the regulatory control system itself can contribute to harm, and some regard it as a major contributing factor. Furthermore, some, on both sides of the drugs debate, would equate harm reduction as running in close parallel to an anti-prohibitionist perspective. However, it is important to note that the mainstreaming of harm reduction within political policy debate at the European level has taken place overwhelmingly within a context of concern about the health of the public and has not be linked with the issue of drug prohibition.

From a European policy perspective, where Member States' domestic policies differ, the question of definition is an important one; or conversely, an important area for flexibility in interpretation. A fundamental position of current European drug policy is support for the international drug control conventions, and no European country would regard its policies as out of step with the leeway given to States to interpret their obligations in this respect. Harm reduction as mainstream in Europe is therefore viewed by policymakers as compatible with a balanced approach, which also includes support for vigorous supply reduction measures. This is not to say that policymakers have ignored the argument that harms can result from the drug control system. Recognition of this fact can be seen, for instance, in a shift in emphasis in which a distinction is now commonly made between those who traffic and trade in drugs, and those who consume them. It is reflected in policies that attempt to divert those with drug problems from the criminal justice system towards treatment or that introduce more lenient penalties for the personal use of drugs. These developments have, however, largely taken place within a policy debate on how the costs of drug control can be minimised and the benefits maximised. The reduction of harm is clearly part of this agenda, but this is usually implicit rather than explicit and harm reduction is most commonly discussed in the context of HIV risk reduction, not criminal justice policies. A strong argument can be made that the absence of an explicit common definition of what constitutes 'harm reduction' at the EU level has facilitated the mainstreaming of the concept against a background where there is considerable diversity in respect to national and local policies and actions. And when events have forced the adoption of a working definition the approach has usually been a relatively restricted one: for example, explicitly listing measures targeting HIV risk behaviour among drug injectors.

The question of evidence

The mantra for the European approach to drugs is for comprehensive, balanced and evidence-based policies. The importance given to evidence in this perspective can be contrasted with policies that are more ideologically driven. This raises two important questions. First, what constitutes sufficient evidence for policy formation? And second, to what extent are policies skewed towards the easily measurable, at the expense of the potentially most desirable?

It is probably fair to say that in many areas of drug policy the evidence base for supporting current approaches is often weak, and where evidence does exist it is rarely unequivocal. That said, the situation is considerably better than it once was and research and evaluation studies provide a growing base of evidence for informing policy decisions. It is understandable that policymakers will be more concerned with the quality and availability of evidence for politically controversial measures than they are for actions that have broad-based support. This is likely to be why harm reduction has come under greater scrutiny than many other areas of drug policy, although this is arguably changing in light of a more generic concern to fund only interventions that can be shown to be effective.

Appraisal of the available evidence for an intervention is a complex process requiring methodological rigour, particularly in conducting a comprehensive search of the literature, evaluating quality of primary studies and summarising the results (Higgins and Green, 2008). The credibility of this process depends on a rigorous approach to the evaluation exercise. The gold standard for the evaluation of medical research is the randomised control trial (RCT). This model is often applied to drug interventions, especially in the more medically orientated areas such as treatment. Interventions can be considered effective if there is evidence deriving from multiple well-conducted studies. In the last 15 years, considerable efforts have been made to ensure that all conducted RCTs are registered and their findings made accessible. This is not the case for most other types of research and comprehensively auditing and accessing the evidence base for other types of study design is consequently more difficult. The efforts made to improve the quality of reporting for RCTs has also to some extent resulted in an improvement in quality of the studies published in the scientific literature (Moher et al., 2001; Plint et al., 2006). Only recently have guidelines for reporting results of study designs other than RCTs also been published (von Elm et al., 2007).

For good reason, RCTs therefore represent a gold standard for research evidence as, when replicated and properly applied, they provide a robust evidence base for demonstrating with a high probability of certainty that a given intervention has resulted in a measurable effect. They do, however, have some obvious weaknesses that have important implications for their use in the drugs field. RCTs work best with simple study designs and where extraneous variables can easily be controlled for. This model fits well for testing the effectiveness of a new medicine where the condition to be treated is well described and the desired action of the drug can be easily measured. However, harm reduction interventions usually take place in real world settings, in which other interventions may also be taking place. Furthermore, confounding variables are difficult to control for, subject characteristics are often highly heterogeneous, and outcomes may be complex to interpret and difficult to measure. Practical, methodological and ethical challenges exist to developing convincing RCT study designs that are applicable to many areas of social policy evaluation. This is a particular problem for controversial social policy options as it may be in practice very difficult using other study designs to provide policymakers with the high level of certainty that properly conducted RCTs can provide. The number of RCT study designs in the harm reduction area is growing but remains limited. Not surprisingly RCTs are most commonly found in the treatment area, as this setting is most amenable to this kind of approach. In considering other areas, the evidence is largely drawn from more observational studies and ecological ones. Such studies provide a weaker evidence base for drawing conclusions and can be more challenging to interpret. These kind of studies are probably also at higher risk of publication bias, where there is a greater likelihood of getting positive rather than negative results published, although RCTs are not immune to this problem.

This monograph has provided the reader with a systematic review of the evidence regarding harm reduction among injecting opiate users. In other areas, the lack of studies makes a systematic appraisal more difficult but the contributions elaborate the evidence that exists. In order to consider future priorities for the European research agenda, we provide below an overview, using strict assessment criteria, of the current state of the art with respect to the evidence for effectiveness of harm reduction activities. The reader should note that lack of robust evidence means that the research conducted so far is not sufficient to make confident judgements, negative or positive, on the effectiveness of the intervention in question.

Harm reduction among injecting drug users

There is sufficient evidence to support the role of opioid substitution treatment (OST) in reducing HIV transmission, while the evidence in support of needle and syringe distribution programmes is more tentative, and the evidence that drug consumption reduces transmission is insufficient at present. All three interventions appear to reduce self-reported injecting risk behaviour. The evidence on the impact of drug consumption rooms and peer naloxone distribution in reducing overdose deaths at the community level remains insufficient, although the studies that have been conducted suggest the potential that these approaches may have and therefore both interventions remain important areas for further study. No strong evidence exists to support the concern that any of these interventions, when well managed, leads to increased harms for those using them, or encourages drug use in the wider community. However, a problem with the diversion of drugs from substitution treatment into the illicit market has been reported in some countries.

In terms of research priorities, methodologically robust primary studies on the impact of harm reduction interventions on the incidence of HIV and HCV are needed as are studies on what measures may reduce drug overdose deaths. In the EU, drug overdose now represents the major cause of avoidable morbidity associated with illegal drug use and therefore must be regarded as a priority area for the identification of effective interventions. In general, future studies of interventions designed to reduce drug-related infectious diseases would be wise to focus on primary biological outcomes rather than behavioural ones, as this is a key weakness in current evidence. Where possible, randomised designs should be employed and compare the impact of additional or increased intensity of interventions against current or low level of activity. A number of studies have suggested that the impact of interventions may be enhanced by, or even dependent upon, providing the target population with a package of different services. This implies the need to research how different interventions work together to provide benefit. Although this approach is analogous to some standard medical research questions — the provision of multi-drug therapy, for example — for interventions conducted in the real world settings, in which most harm reduction approaches are employed, such research questions pose real methodological challenges. More innovative approaches, including natural experiments, large-scale modelling and carefully evaluated case studies, may prove to be the way forward here.

Harm reduction policies for cocaine and other stimulants

There is now greater understanding of the mental and physical health consequences associated with the use of cocaine and other stimulants. However, to date, most harm reduction interventions have largely focused on risks related to infectious diseases transmission and assumptions are built largely on the evidence of HIV prevention among heroin injectors.

Although some studies have looked at crack cocaine users overall, there is little evidence from published studies on the effectiveness of harm reduction interventions among users of cocaine or other stimulants. This population is often considered a subset of a study, rather than the target population, and most research has exclusively focused on intravenous drug use. Interventions for crack users have been developed based on the assumption that providing material for safer crack smoking will reduce the risk of viral transmission, but these have not yet been systematically evaluated.

No convincing evaluations, and very limited service development, has targeted the majority of stimulant users who neither inject nor smoke their drugs. Some limited experimentation with pill testing initiatives has been conducted in some countries, but it has not been systematically evaluated, and recently the limited support for this kind of programme appears to be waning further.

'Safer dancing' programmes have looked at environmental risks such as fire safety and drinking water availability along with information-giving. Impact evaluations are not available in this area but as these measures are not viewed as particularly controversial and generally considered to represent sensible public health and safety measures, this may not be a priority as long as investment in researching more controversial measures is lacking.

In terms of research priorities, the extent of stimulant-related harm in Europe remains largely unmeasured. Around 400 deaths per year are thought to be associated with cocaine use but this may be an underestimate, as the extent to which cocaine use is an aggravating factor in deaths related to cardiovascular problems remains unknown. Treatment demands for stimulants are growing however, and some countries have long-established amphetamine injection populations that are probably not directly comparable to opioid injectors.

The pattern of polydrug use consumption, especially the co-use of alcohol, is also likely to be a major issue both for assessing the harm of different consumption patterns and for targeting interventions. Put simply, despite the growing importance of stimulant use with the European drug field, there is very little research evidence to permit an informed analysis of the effectiveness of harm reduction interventions and therefore even informed speculation on what approaches might prove successful currently remains difficult.

Harm reduction policies for cannabis

Despite a growing interest in, and evidence base for, harms attributed to cannabis use there is very limited evidence of effectiveness of the proposed harm reduction strategies in this area. There is not sufficient evidence that roadside drug-testing reduces mortality due to car crashes. Screening and brief interventions for excessive cannabis users have been proposed as adaptations of similar interventions for alcohol abuse, but no sufficient evidence is available yet on their effects. Vaporisers and other developing technology may reduce the risks associated with smoking cannabis products but the extent to which this is so remains unclear. The question also remains open on the extent to which vaporisers are likely to be viewed by consumers as acceptable alternatives to current modes, especially given the link between tobacco smoking and cannabis use that exists in Europe. There is therefore a wide range of important questions to be addressed by well-constructed primary research in this area. These include, but are not limited to: the extent to which roadside testing would reduce motor vehicle accident fatalities; whether informing cannabis users about related harms can reduce the actual levels of problems experienced; to what extent brief interventions can reduce harm; and how new technologies, or behavioral changes, reduce risks associated with smoking.

Harm reduction policies for tobacco

There is good evidence that public smoking bans and mandatory reduced ignition propensity standards for cigarettes reduce tobacco-related harms to non-smokers and improve health at the population level. There is no evidence that modified smoked tobacco products and cigarette-like devices substantially reduce harm, and limited evidence that pharmaceutical nicotine or low nitrosamine smokeless tobacco products might reduce tobacco-related harm in those who are unable or unwilling to quit but are willing to switch to such products. Nonetheless, given the high probability of health damage for those who continue to smoke there remains a considerable need for primary research into the extent to which innovative new products would be attractive to current smokers and to what extent they can reduce harm to users who are unable to quit. A parallel research question would be the extent to which 'safer smoking technologies', should they become available, would undermine smoking reduction policies at the population level. This is, however, an area in which multi-site RCTs to evaluate both benefits and risks of new products are clearly feasible. Studies in this area will need to identify biomarkers that are sensitive to short-term changes in smoking behaviour and are also predictive of long-term harm.

Alcohol harm reduction

There is sufficient evidence on the effectiveness for some outcome measures of a total ban on sales, minimum legal purchase age, government monopoly and restrictions of retail sales, alcohol taxes, lowered limits of blood alcohol concentration (BAC) for car drivers and low BAC limits for young drivers. There are several studies on public service messages and alcohol education in school but no evidence of effectiveness. There are too few studies in the areas of voluntary codes of bar practice, promoting alcohol-free activities, warning labels, college student education, designated drivers and ride services to allow comment on their effectiveness, although all these areas appear interesting topics for further research. In general there is a growing interest in interventions that can reduce the harm accruing from alcohol use, and across Europe alcohol problems are becoming an area of greater policy concern. As drugs and alcohol are often consumed together in recreational settings the challenge will be to develop research designs that are adequate to the complexities of assessing interventions targeting poly substance consumption patterns. Finally, in this area a clear need exists for a thorough systematic review to identify the key gaps in the current knowledge base and provide a better road map for setting future research priorities.

Pragmatism, policy and the evidence base

The value of taking a strict approach to assessing the quality of evidence concerning the impact of harm reduction interventions is that it allows policymakers to make decisions with greater certainty. The problem, however, is that this may set the bar too high, given that in the 'real world' there are practical, methodological and ethical reasons that mean that it may be extremely difficult or even impossible to generate such a high level of evidence. Moreover, if RCT designs are employed it may be necessary to control the parameters of the study so strictly that any findings may have limited applicability to the real world setting in which harm reduction interventions typically take place. This problem is not restricted to harm reduction but is common to many areas of social policy. Models are being developed that try to incorporate the available evidence to inform policy formation even if this has to be based on a lower level of certainty.

An interesting development in this field is the guidelines produced by the GRADE method group (Guyatt et al., 2008). This approach clearly opens the way towards considering other study designs in appraising the evidence. An example of this can be found in the recently published WHO guidelines for substitution treatment, which used non-randomised studies to evaluate the evidence supporting recommendations for the use of substitution treatment in reducing HIV infection and mortality (WHO, 2009).

In reality, policymakers are often faced with making choices in areas in which a high level of certainty is lacking and pragmatic choices are required. But how can pragmatic policy choice be supported? Evidence that interventions are not producing harm to those that receive them or to the wider community is likely to be important. As is evidence that they are reaching their intended recipients, who are appearing to benefit from well-constructed measures. If there is no evidence of harm, and some evidence of benefit, it can help to provide sufficient justification for pragmatic policy choices to be made, even when clear evidence of effectiveness is lacking.

This can be seen in the area of needle and syringe exchange where the evidence can still be regarded as tentative in respect of demonstrating that HIV transmission is reduced. However, numerous studies do show that reported risk behaviour is lowered and/or are suggestive that provision of syringe exchange can be associated with low, or reduced, rates of new HIV infections at the population level. Moreover, no strong evidence exists that this type of intervention delivers harm, although this concern has been repeatedly raised by those who were hostile to the development of this kind of service.

When faced with this evidence policymakers in Europe have made a pragmatic choice that there is sufficient data to include this sort of provision in a comprehensive package of services for drug injectors, even if it is still not possible to show conclusively that such services reduce by themselves rates of new infections. In practice needle and syringe programmes (NSPs) are usually not isolated services, but are typically implemented by agencies who offer a range of other services, operate in a variety of settings, and in the context of diverse epidemic and behavioral scenario. A multitude of mediating factors therefore have to be accounted for when assessing their impact, which complicate both the collection and interpretation of evidence.

Future perspectives: harm reduction and contemporary patterns of drug use in Europe

This monograph has provided a state-of-the-art reflection on the development of harm reduction services in Europe and considered what we know about their effectiveness. It has provided historical context and an analytical framework for understanding how harm reduction approaches have moved into the mainstream in Europe. It has also launched a discussion on the potential role for harm reduction in addressing the problems caused by the consumption of alcohol and tobacco. The EMCDDA's role is to monitor and report on drug use in Europe and the policies and responses Member States have developed to respond to the drug situation. It is from this perspective that we offer some concluding remarks on the future challenges that changing patterns of drug use will bring to the debate in Europe on how best to reduce the harm associated with drug consumption.

Drug policy at the European level is not only concerned with understanding the situation within the EU. An explicit element of the EU drug strategy and accompanying action plans is to enable the EU to have a strong and united voice in the international debate on drugs. This is important for many reasons, not least because the future drug problem faced by the EU will be influenced by the situation and policies of other countries. Drug problems transcend national boarders and are becoming increasingly global in nature. In this context, the situation in countries bordering the EU is clearly an important factor for consideration.

The issues for the diffusion of harm reduction practice look somewhat different when looking out from Europe rather than within. In many non-EU countries HIV epidemics among injectors appear to be a growing problem, the availability of services of all types is often limited, and considerable political and professional resistance can exist to introducing harm reduction approaches, even where the evidence base is robust. In international debates and in funding for development programmes, Europe has supported the role of harm reduction as an important part of a comprehensive HIV prevention strategy. This battle is far from won. Globally the problem of HIV infections acquired through drug injection remains a critically important public health issue and one in which Europe is likely to want to remain a strong advocate for evidence-based approaches.

Within the EU, preventing HIV infections related to drug injection remains an important objective for drug policies and there is a need to develop services and responses further. However, it no longer has the primacy it once had. Overall, the long-term trend appears to be for a stabilisation, or fall, in both levels of injecting, and opiate use, and despite some localised problems the assessment of the situation in respect to drug related HIV infections is generally a positive one (EMCDDA, 2009). Despite this, morbidity and mortality associated with drug injecting remains considerable. There is a need to develop treatment regimes that are attractive to those that are currently hard to treat. There is a need to develop effective approaches to HCV infection — which is found virtually universally at high prevalence among drug injectors across Europe. Finally, there is a pressing need to find effective measures to address opioid-associated drug overdose. This is now the major avoidable cause of morbidity amongst injectors. To date, in each of these areas some innovative harm reduction approaches have been developed, but the evidence base for informing policymakers remains inadequate.

At points throughout this monograph it has been argued that harm reduction interventions may sometimes be most effective when provided as part of a 'package' of care, rather than as a stand-alone approach. If this is the case, a challenge for the future will be to develop research and evaluation designs that are adequate to the task of exploring the impact of programmes delivered consequently, and across different levels of intensity. Methodologically this is no trivial task. Nonetheless, progress in this direction is required to gain a more holistic understanding of how interventions work in order to inform spending choices on what sort of programme mixes are likely to be most appropriate.

During the 1980s, and 1990s, the concept of problem drug use in Europe was virtually synonymous with opioid use and drug injection. It was recognised that some, mainly Nordic, countries had long-established amphetamine injecting populations, that smoking was becoming a common mode of administration among some heroin using groups, and that drugs like ecstasy were becoming more important on the recreational drug scene. However, the focus for discussions on drug problems remained very much on the chronic use of heroin usually by injection. The perspective today looks very different. Heroin and injecting problems remain with us, but policymakers are equally concerned by what can be seen as a broader, more complex and faster moving drug situation.

Today's concerns are as likely to focus on the widespread use of cocaine and other stimulants, the misuse of medicinal products, polydrug use including the use of licit substances or even intensive cannabis use, as they are to focus on heroin injecting. To some extent the harm reduction agenda has failed to keep pace with the political one in this respect. A challenge for the future growth of harm reduction services in Europe will be to develop intervention models that address the harms associated with a broader set of consumption patterns. This monograph helps to chart where developments are needed in these areas. Here, the boundaries between drug prevention, drug treatment and harm reduction become increasingly fluid. This can be seen at the service level, for example in brief interventions for cannabis users, and at the individual level, for example where practitioners develop client care plans that include prevention, treatment and harm reduction services simultaneously.

Finally, this monograph has concentrated on the topic of evidence and how it should be assessed. Yet it is important to remind ourselves that the absence of evidence does not necessarily justify the absence of action. As Fry (2010) argues in his discussion on the ethical aspects of harm reduction, 'values' have to be taken into account, especially when disputes and uncertainty about 'facts' exist. In this policy field, 'evidence' can be a precious commodity. The challenge for the research community is to provide policymakers with a higher degree of certainty that the policies and actions they pursue are more likely to reduce rather than augment harm.

References

EMCDDA (European Monitoring Centre for Drugs and Drug Addiction) (2009), *Annual report 2009: the state of the drugs problem in Europe*, Publications Office of the European Union, Luxembourg.

European Union (2008), 'EU drugs action plan for 2009–2012', 2008/C 326/09, *Official Journal of the European Union*, 20 December, C326/7–25.

Fry, C. (2010), 'Harm reduction: an "ethical" perspective', in Chapter 4, 'Perspectives on harm reduction: what experts have to say', in European Monitoring Centre for Drugs and Drug Addiction (EMCDDA), *Harm reduction: evidence, impacts and challenges*, Rhodes, T. and Hedrich, D. (eds), Scientific Monograph Series No. 10, Publications Office of the European Union, Luxembourg.

Guyatt, G. H., Oxman, A. D., Kunz, R., et al. for the GRADE Working Group (2008), 'Going from evidence to recommendations, *BMJ* 10 May, 336 (7652), pp. 1049–51.

Herring, R., Thom, B., Beccaria, F., Kolind, T. and Moskalewicz, J. (2010), 'Alcohol harm reduction in Europe', in European Monitoring Centre for Drugs and Drug Addiction (EMCDDA), *Harm reduction: evidence, impacts and challenges*, Rhodes, T. and Hedrich, D. (eds), Scientific Monograph Series No. 10, Publications Office of the European Union, Luxembourg.

Higgins, J. P. T. and Green, S. (eds) (2008), *Cochrane handbook for systematic reviews of interventions*, version 5.0.1 (updated September 2008), The Cochrane Collaboration. Available at www.cochrane-handbook.org.

Moher, D., Schulz, K. F. and Altman, D. G. (2001), 'The CONSORT statement: revised recommendations for improving the quality of reports of parallel-group randomised trials', *Lancet* 357 (9263), pp. 1191–4.

Plint, A. C., Moher, D., Morrison, A., et al. (2006), 'Does the CONSORT checklist improve the quality of reports of randomised controlled trials? A systematic review', *Medical Journal of Australia* 185 (5), pp. 263–7.

von Elm, E., Altman, D. G., Egger, M., Pocock, S. J., Gøtzsche, P. C. and Vandenbroucke, J. P. (2007), 'STROBE initiative: the strengthening the reporting of observational studies in epidemiology (STROBE) statement — guidelines for reporting observational studies', *Lancet* 20 October, 370 (9596), pp. 1453–7.

WHO (World Health Organization) (2009), *Guidelines for the psychosocially assisted pharmacological treatment of opioid dependence*, WHO, Geneva. Available at http://www.who.int/substance_abuse/publications/opioid_dependence_guidelines.pdf.

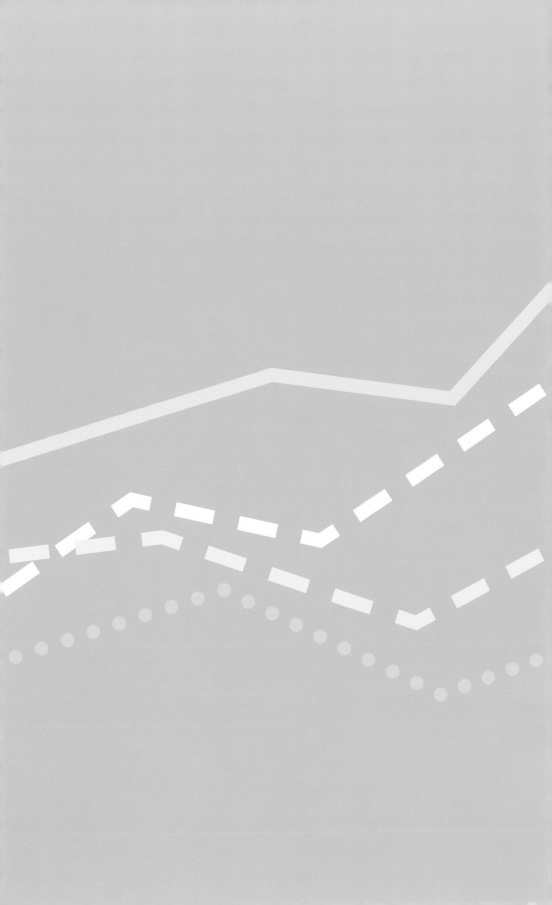

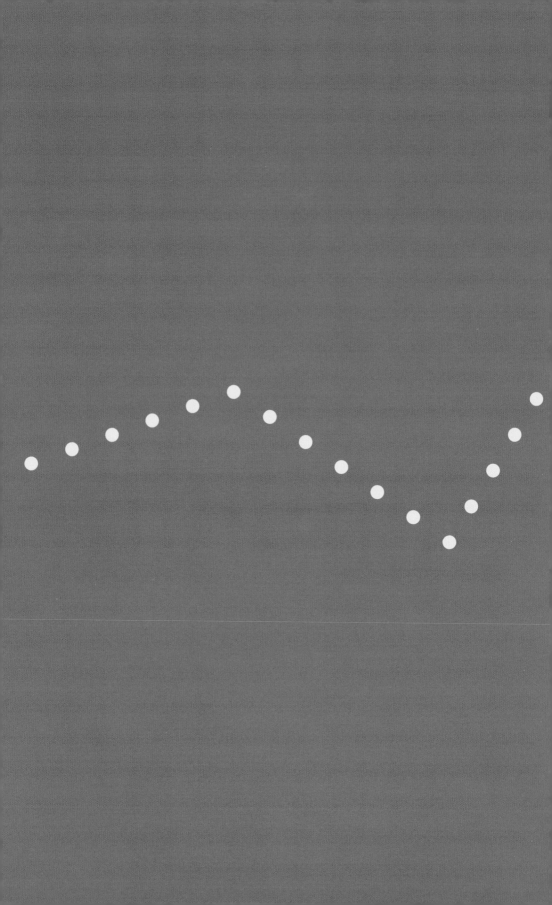

Contributors

Editors

Tim Rhodes
Professor of Public Health Sociology, and Director, Centre for Research on Drugs and Health Behaviour, London School of Hygiene and Tropical Medicine, University of London, UK

Dagmar Hedrich
Senior Scientific Analyst, Health and Social Responses, European Monitoring Centre for Drugs and Drug Addiction, Lisbon, Portugal

Authors

Eliot Albert
Drug user activist and researcher, London, UK
INPUD Membership Secretary

Rifat Atun
Professor of Evaluation, and Director of Strategy, Performance and Evaluation, Global Fund to Fight AIDS, Tuberculosis and Malaria, Geneva, Switzerland

Andrew Ball
Senior Strategy and Operations Advisor, Department of HIV/AIDS, World Health Organization, Geneva, Switzerland

Franca Beccaria
Researcher and Partner, Eclectica (research and communications agency), Turin, and Teacher Fellow, University of Turin, Italy

Peter Blanken
Senior Researcher, Parnassia Addiction Research Centre, The Hague, the Netherlands, and Central Committee Heroin Addiction Treatment (CCBH), Utrecht, Netherlands

Cinzia Brentari
European Institute of Social Services, University of Kent, UK

Jamie Bridge
Senior Coordinator: Events and Communications, International Harm Reduction Association, UK

Dick de Bruin
Director, Addiction Research Centre, Utrecht, Netherlands

Amador Calafat
President, European Institute of Studies on Prevention, Spain

Philip Coffin
Infectious Diseases Fellow, Division of Allergy and Infectious Diseases, University of Washington, USA

Catherine Cook
Senior Analyst: Public Health and Policy, International Harm Reduction Association, UK

Marina Davoli

Director of Clinical Epidemiology, Department of Epidemiology, ASL, Rome, Italy

Minke Dijkstra

Project Director, Addiction Research Centre, Utrecht, Netherlands

Françoise Dubois-Arber

Head, Unit for the Evaluation on Prevention Programmes, Institute of Social and Preventive Medicine (IUMSP), University Hospital Centre and University of Lausanne, Switzerland

Benedikt Fischer

Professor, Centre for Applied Research in Mental Health and Addictions (CARMHA), Faculty of Health Sciences, Simon Fraser University, Vancouver, and Centre for Addiction and Mental Health (CAMH), Toronto, Canada

Adam Fletcher

Lecturer, Centre for Research on Drugs and Health Behaviour, London School of Hygiene and Tropical Medicine, University of London, UK

Craig Fry

Murdoch Childrens Research Institute (Children's Bioethics Centre) and University of Melbourne (Centre for Applied Philosophy and Public Ethics), Australia

Coral Gartner

Post-doctoral Fellow, School of Population Health, University of Queensland, Australia

David Goldberg

Professor of Public Health, Health Protection Scotland, Glasgow, UK

Paul Griffiths

Scientific Coordinator and Head of Epidemiology, Crime and Markets Unit, European Monitoring Centre for Drugs and Drug Addiction, Lisbon, Portugal

Jean-Paul Grund

Senior Researcher, CVO — Research & Consultancy, Utrecht, Netherlands. Epidemiology Section, Department of Health, City of The Hague, the Netherlands

V. Anna Gyarmathy

Scientific Writer, European Monitoring Centre for Drugs and Drug Addiction, Lisbon, Portugal, and Adjunct Assistant Professor, Johns Hopkins Bloomberg School of Public Health, Baltimore, MD, USA

Wayne Hall

Professor of Public Health Policy and NHMRC Australia Fellow, School of Population Health, University of Queensland, Australia

Richard Hartnoll

Consultant, formerly Head of Department of Epidemiology, European Monitoring Centre for Drugs and Drug Addiction, Lisbon, Portugal

Dagmar Hedrich

Senior Scientific Analyst, Health and Social Responses, European Monitoring Centre for Drugs and Drug Addiction, Lisbon, Portugal

Rachel Herring
Senior Research Fellow, School of Health and Social Sciences, Middlesex University, UK

Matthew Hickman
Reader in Public Health, Department of Social Medicine, University of Bristol, UK

Neil Hunt
Director of Research, KCA; Honorary Senior Research Associate, University of Kent; Honorary Research Fellow, London School of Hygiene and Tropical Medicine, University of London, UK

Sharon Hutchinson
Senior Research Fellow, Department of Statistics and Modelling, University of Strathclyde, Glasgow, UK

Marie Jauffret-Roustide
Sociologist and Public Health Researcher, Centre for Research in Psychotropics, Health, Mental Health and Society, University of Paris-Descartes, Paris, and National Institute for Public Health Surveillance, Saint-Maurice, France

Michel Kazatchkine
Professor, and Executive Director, Global Fund to Fight AIDS, Tuberculosis and Malaria, Geneva, Switzerland

Thomas Kerr
Director, Urban Health Research Initiative, BC Centre for Excellence in HIV/AIDS
Assistant Professor, Dept. of Medicine, Division of AIDS, University of British Columbia, Vancouver, Canada

Jo Kimber
Research Fellow, Centre for Research on Drugs and Health Behaviour, London School of Hygiene and Tropical Medicine, University of London, UK
NHMRC Postdoctoral Fellow, National Centre in HIV Epidemiology and Clinical Research, University of New South Wales, Australia

Torsten Kolind
Associate Professor, Centre for Alcohol and Drug Research, Aarhus University, Denmark

Susanne MacGregor
Professor and Leverhulme Emeritus Fellow, London School of Hygiene and Tropical Medicine, University of London, UK

Ann McNeill
Professor of Health Policy and Promotion, UK Centre for Tobacco Control Studies, University of Nottingham, UK

Virginia Montañés Sánchez
Drug user activist and researcher, Institute of Women Studies, University of Granada, Granada; FAUDAS Technical Coordination, Spain; ENCOD Membership European Level

Jacek Moskalewicz
Head of Department of Studies on Alcoholism and Drug Dependence, Institute of Psychiatry and Neurology, Warsaw, Poland

Deborah Olszewski
Senior Scientific Analyst, European Monitoring Centre for Drugs and Drug Addiction, Lisbon, Portugal

Norah Palmateer
Epidemiologist, Health Protection Scotland, Glasgow, UK

Alessandro Pirona
Scientific Analyst, Health and Social Responses, European Monitoring Centre for Drugs and Drug Addiction, Lisbon, Portugal

Jürgen Rehm
Professor of Addictions, Technische Universität, Dresden, Germany and Centre for Addiction and Mental Health, Toronto, Canada

Tim Rhodes
Professor of Public Health Sociology, and Director, Centre for Research on Drugs and Health Behaviour, London School of Hygiene and Tropical Medicine, University of London, UK

Robin Room
Professor of Social Alcohol Research, School of Population Health, University of Melbourne, Australia and Centre for Social Research on Alcohol and Drugs, Stockholm University, Sweden

Roland Simon,
Deputy Scientific Coordinator and Head of Interventions, Law and Policies Unit, European Monitoring Centre for Drugs and Drug Addiction, Lisbon, Portugal

Mat Southwell
Project Manager, International Network of People who Use Drugs, Bath UK

Alex Stevens
Senior Lecturer in Criminology, School of Social Policy, Sociology and Social Research, University of Kent, UK

Gerry V. Stimson
Professor of Sociology, and Executive Director, International Harm Reduction Association, UK

Heino Stöver
Professor, University of Applied Sciences, Frankfurt, Germany

Betsy Thom
Professor of Health Policy, School of Health and Social Sciences, Middlesex University, UK

Peter Vickerman
Senior Lecturer in Mathematical Modelling, HIV Tools and Centre for Research on Drugs and Health Behaviour, London School of Hygiene and Tropical Medicine, University of London, UK

Marcus Whiting
ESRC Post-doctoral Research Fellow, Social Policy, University of Birmingham, UK

Tomas Zabransky
Centre for Addictology, Charles University, Prague, Czech Republic

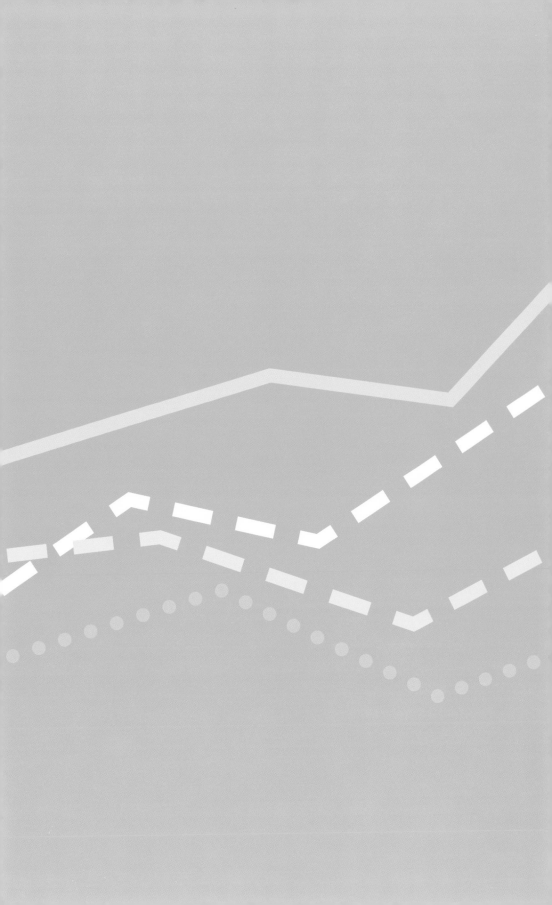

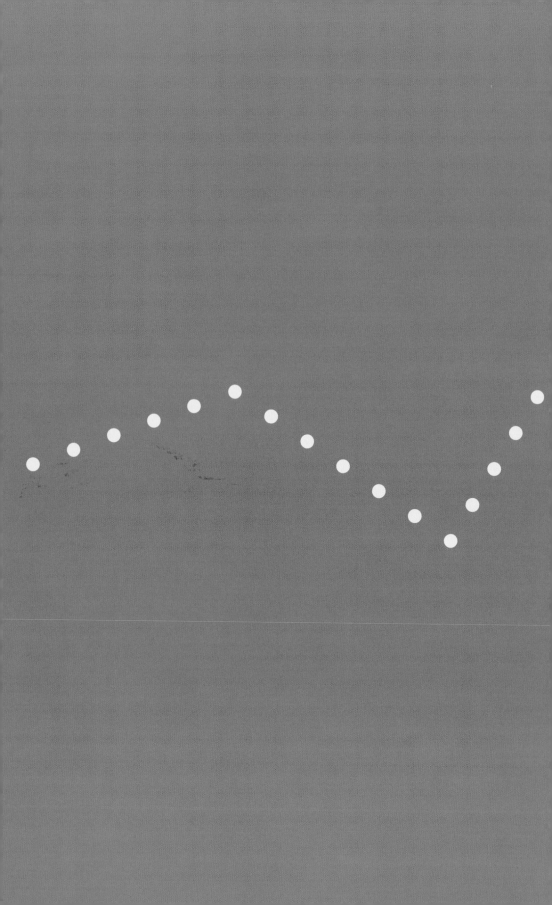

Abbreviations

AAC	Amsterdam Addiction Cohort
ACS	Amsterdam Cohort Study
ADHD	attention-deficit hyperactivity disorder
AIVL	Australian Injecting and Illicit Drug Users League
ASSIST	A Stop Smoking in Schools Trial
ASUD	Auto-support parmi les Usagers de Drogues
AUDIT	Alcohol Use Disorder Identification Test
BAC	blood alcohol concentration
BBN	Best Bar None
BBV	blood-borne virus
BMT	buprenorphine maintenance treatment
CASE	cannabis and smoking education
CBT	cognitive behaviour therapy
CE mark	Confirmatory European mark
CEEHRN	Central and Eastern European Harm Reduction Network
CM	contingency management
CND	Commission on Narcotic Drugs
COPD	chronic obstructive pulmonary disease
CREST	Cocaine Rapid Efficacy Screening Trial
CSC	Cannabis Social Club
CSC	Correctional Service of Canada
DCR	drug consumption room
DfID	Department for International Development (UK)
DPFU	Drug Policy Foundation — Users
DWI	driving while intoxicated
ECDP	European Cities on Drug Policy
EMCDDA	European Monitoring Centre for Drugs and Drug Addiction

ENCOD	European Coalition for Just and Effective Drug Policies
ENHPS	European Network of Health Promoting Schools
ESPAD	European School Survey Project on Alcohol and Other Drugs
EU	European Union
FAC	Spanish Federation of Cannabis Associations
FAUDAS	Spanish Nationwide Network of People Affected by Drugs and HIV
HBV	hepatitis B
HCV	hepatitis C
HDG	Horizontal Drugs Group
HIV	human immunodeficiency virus
HubCAPP	Hub of Commissioned Alcohol Projects and Policies
ICN	International Coalition of NGOs for Just and Effective Drug Policies
IDTS	Integrated Drug Treatment System
IDU	injecting drug user
IDUN	International Drug Users Network
IHRA	International Harm Reduction Association
INCB	International Narcotics Control Board
INPUD	International Network of People who Use Drugs
ISHN	International School Health Network
LMP	last month prevalence
LNSLT	low nitrosamine smokeless tobacco
LSD	Landelijk Steunpunt Druggebruikers
LTP	lifetime prevalence
LYP	last year prevalence
MDMA	3,4-methylenedioxy-N-methamphetamine (ecstasy)
MI	motivational interviewing
MMT	methadone maintenance treatment
MSIC	Medically Supervised Injecting Centre (Sydney)
NDUDA	National Drug Users Development Agency

NGO	non-government organisation
NIDA	National Institute on Drug Abuse
NIDU	non-injection drug use
NSP	needle and syringe programme
NTA	National Treatment Agency
OST	opioid substitution treatment
PIC	Pazienti Impazienti Cannabis (Cannabis Impatient Patients)
PITC	provider-initiated HIV testing and counselling
PLWHA	people living with HIV/AIDS
PN	pharmaceutical nicotin
PND	peer naloxone distribution
PNSP	prison needle and syringe exchange programme
POU	problem opioid user
QALYS	quality adjusted life years
RBS	responsible beverage service
RCT	randomised control trial
RIP	reduced ignition propensity
RIOTT	Randomised Injectable Opiate Treatment Trial
RJB	Rotterdam Junkie Union
SDM	syringe dispensing machine
SIF	supervised injection facility
SLT	smokeless tobacco
SR-IRB	self-reported injecting risk behaviour
SSTI	skin and soft tissue infection
STAD	Stockholm Prevents Alcohol and Drug Problems
STD	sexually transmitted disease
TASC	Tackling Alcohol Related Street Crime
TB	tuberculosis
THC	tetrahydrocannabinol

THR   tobacco harm reduction

TobReg   World Health Organization Study Group of Tobacco Product Regulation

UKCAPP   United Kingdom Community Alcohol Prevention Programme

UN   United Nations

UNAIDS   Joint United Nations Programme on HIV/AIDS

UNDCP   United Nations Office on Drugs and Crime Prevention

UNGASS   United Nations General Assembly Special Session

UNODC   United Nations Office on Drugs and Crime

VANDU   Vancouver Area Network of Drug Users

WHO   World Health Organization

YHLL   years of healthy life lost

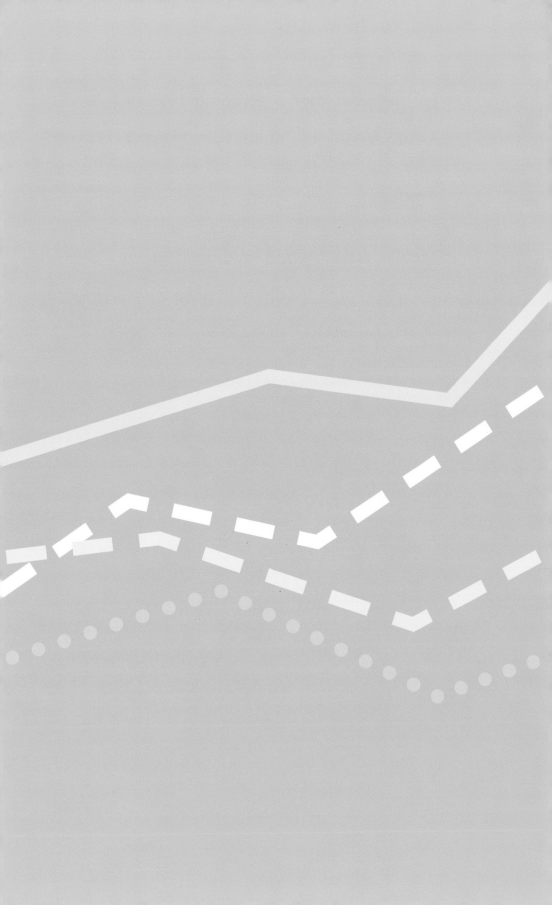

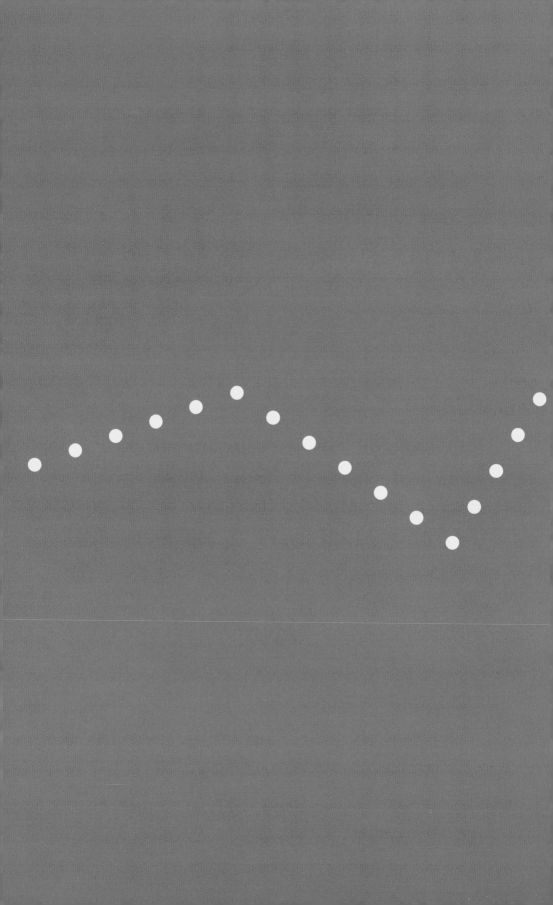

Further reading

EMCDDA publications and studies in the field of harm reduction

Monographs Series — http://www.emcdda.europa.eu/publications/monographs

Harm reduction: evidence, impact and challenges — Nº 10
Available in English — ISBN: 92-9168-419-9 (April 2010)

Hepatitis C and injecting drug use: impact, costs and policy options — N° 7
Available in English — ISBN: 92-9168-168-7 (December 2004)

Insights Series — http://www.emcdda.europa.eu/publications/insights

Injecting drug use, risk behaviour and qualitative research in the time of AIDS — N° 4
Available in English — ISBN: 92-9168-124-5 (June 2002)

Reviewing current practice in drug-substitution treatment in the European Union — N° 3
Available in English — ISBN: 92-9168-104-0 (November 2000)

Drugs in focus — http://www.emcdda.europa.eu/publications/drugs-in-focus

Cocaine use in Europe: implications for service delivery — Nº 17
Available in all EU languages — Catalogue number: TD-AD-07-003-EN-C (November 2007)

Overdose: a major cause of avoidable death among young people — N° 13
Available in all EU languages — Catalogue number: TD-AD-04-002-EN-C (January 2005)

Hepatitis C: a hidden epidemic — N° 11
Available in all EU languages — Catalogue number: TD-AD-03-005-EN-C (November 2003)

Drug injecting challenges public health policy — N° 4
Available in all EU languages — Catalogue number: TD-AD-02-004-EN-C (January 2002)

Other studies

European report on drug consumption rooms
Available in English – Only electronic – http://www.emcdda.europa.eu/themes/harm-reduction/consumption-rooms
(January 2004)

Guidelines for the evaluation of outreach work: a manual for outreach practitioners
Available in English – Only electronic – http://www.emcdda.europa.eu/publications/
manuals/outreach
(December 2001)

Annual report and Statistical bulletin

EMCDDA Annual report — http://www.emcdda.europa.eu/publications/annual-report
The state of the drugs problem in the EU – analysis and statistics

EMCDDA Statistical bulletin — http://www.emcdda.europa.eu/stats/home
Data tables and commentary

Web pages to related projects

Harm reduction: http://www.emcdda.europa.eu/themes/harm-reduction

Best practice portal: http://www.emcdda.europa.eu/themes/best-practice

Epidemiological key indicators: http://www.emcdda.europa.eu/themes/key-indicators
Deaths and mortality, Infectious diseases, Demand for treatment

European Monitoring Centre for Drugs and Drug Addiction

EMCDDA Scientific Monograph Series No 10

Luxembourg: Publications Office of the European Union

Harm reduction: evidence, impacts and challenges

2010 — 462 pp. — 16 x 24 cm

ISBN 978-92-9168-419-9

doi: 10.2810/29497

Price (excluding VAT) in Luxembourg: EUR 25